drawings paintings & sculptures

the contents

the foreword

With the approach of the Millennium, the Board of Nicholson and Bass decided to mark the event by producing a significant and prestigious publication. We seized the moment when the chance arose to collaborate with the Museums and Galleries of Northern Ireland (MAGNI) in a revision of their concise catalogue, which we offered to publish with colour illustrations. A book of such magnitude would not only emphasize our standing as the leading Fine Art colour printer in Ireland but also help to make the museums' collections more accessible to a wider audience than had previously been the case. We are deeply grateful to the many staff within MAGNI who were involved with the publication, in particular to Dr S B Kennedy, for his support of the project; Dr Eileen Black, who edited the catalogue; Mrs Patricia McLean and Michelle Brady, who dealt with copyright issues in the illustrated section and James Hanna, the catalogue's designer. We are also indebted to numerous business colleagues for their encouragement and assistance in the undertaking, notably to our long-term suppliers, the Robert Horne Paper Company, Robinson and Mornin, Bookbinders and Alphagraphic Inks. We trust that the book will create a greater awareness of the riches within the Museums and Galleries of Northern Ireland and help promote their collections throughout the world.

This catalogue is, in a sense, a double celebration. Not only is it a handsomely illustrated listing of the entire fine art collections of the Museums and Galleries of Northern Ireland, it is also the first major publication to appear since the amalgamation of the four museums - the Ulster Museum, the Ulster Folk and Transport Museum, the Ulster American Folk Park and Armagh County Museum - into a single organisation (MAGNI) in 1998. Its publication would not have been possible without the extremely generous sponsorship of Nicholson and Bass Ltd. On behalf of the Chairman and Board of Trustees of MAGNI I should like to express my sincere thanks to Messrs Nicholson and Bass for this. I am also grateful to the Friends of the Ulster Museum whose funding towards the cost of illustrations enabled the publisher to include many more images than would otherwise have been possible. Finally, I wish to record my thanks to the art division of the Ulster Museum and to the various other members of staff there who have helped to bring it to completion.

John Nicholson
Chairman,
Nicholson and Bass Ltd

Michael Houlihan
Chief Executive,
Museums and Galleries of Northern Ireland

This catalogue lists all the paintings, drawings, sculptures and relief works in the collections of the Museums and Galleries of Northern Ireland as of 31 December 1999. The first concise catalogue, which I compiled and edited, was published in 1986 without illustrations. This new edition, which includes 1,510 colour illustrations, is a thorough revision and updating of that volume. Of the illustrations, 1,199 are from the Ulster Museum's art collection and the remainder are from the museum's departments of Botany, Zoology and History, Armagh County Museum and the Ulster Folk and Transport Museum.

That the catalogue would not have happened but for Robert South of Nicholson and Bass is no exaggeration, for the suggestion was entirely his, dropped casually into a lunch-time conversation. Such generous sponsorship seldom occurs and to Robert and Messrs Nicholson and Bass I wish to express my sincere thanks. The project has involved colleagues from several departments within the museum. My particular thanks go firstly to Dr Eileen Black of the division of Fine and Applied Art for her assiduous revising and editing of the catalogue and for seeing it through to completion. Thanks, too, must go to Patricia McLean of the Marketing Department for her input to the illustrated section, especially as regards copyright matters and to her assistant, Michelle Brady. I am also grateful to the following for their time and effort: at the Ulster Museum, Martyn Anglesea (Art), Gillian O'Neill and Lyn Stinson (Conservation), Angela Ross (Zoology), Dr Vivienne Pollock (History); at Armagh County Museum, Catherine McCullough and Dr Greer Ramsay; and at the Ulster Folk and Transport Museum, Dr Jonathan Bell, Kenneth Anderson, Stephen Dennison, Clifford Harkness and Julie-Anne Tolerton. At the Ulster Museum I should also like to thank James Hanna who designed the catalogue; Bill Anderson-Porter, Bryan Rutledge and Michael McKeown who photographed the art works; and Marianne McKeown, who patiently typed and amended what became an extremely bulky text. The end result is a publication which will stand to the credit of the Museums and Galleries of Northern Ireland.

S. B. Kennedy
Head of Fine and Applied Art
Ulster Museum

The fine art collections of the Museums and Galleries of Northern Ireland have been built up since the late 1880s. Although Belfast had a museum from as early as 1831, namely that of the Belfast Natural History and Philosophical Society, it contained only antiquities and specimens relating to the natural sciences. There was no public art collection in the city until the late nineteenth century. However, towards the end of the century public opinion led to a demand for such a collection and so space for it was set aside on the top floor of the municipally owned Free Public Library (later the Central Reference Library) which opened, in Royal Avenue, in 1888. Thus began the municipal art collection.

The collection soon developed. Within a few months of its announcement, donations of paintings and sculptures were received and, at the suggestion of George Trobridge, headmaster of the School of Art, an application was made to the Department of Science and Art in London for a loan of art works from the South Kensington (now the Victoria and Albert) Museum. The loan, which was duly approved, placed the fledging museum and art gallery – it was known as a 'museum and art gallery' from the beginning – amongst other provincial museums entitled to receive loans from South Kensington, provided that the municipal authorities continued to make efforts to develop the collection.

This precondition spurred the committee to embark upon an active collecting strategy and equipped with £500 from Belfast Corporation and the promise of a similar amount from the Department of Science and Art, they purchased copies of antique

sculptures in Paris, Naples and elsewhere on the Continent during the winter of 1889-90. Thus, by the spring of 1890 the collection contained a variety of items, including the sculptures bought abroad, several portrait busts, oil portraits of local worthies, an historical seascape and watercolours of old Belfast. In April of that year a curator was appointed to look after the collection and in July the 'Belfast Museum and Art Gallery', situated in three rooms on the top floor of the library, was officially opened. Two of the rooms were devoted to the municipal collection whilst the third, and largest, contained the South Kensington loan, with representations of applied arts from Britain, Europe and the Orient. Also on display in this room were oil paintings by Thomas Gainsborough, Richard Wilson, Hyacinthe Rigaud and others, lent by the Earl of Kilmorey.

A year later, in 1891, Canon John Grainger, a local collector, donated a large number of natural science and antiquities specimens to the city Corporation, who built an annex to the library to house them. With this donation, what had been initially a museum of the fine and decorative arts, became instead a multi-disciplinary institution. In 1909 these scientific and antiquarian holdings were extended further when the Corporation assumed responsibility for the Belfast Natural History and Philosophical Society's collections. With this rapid growth of the municipal collections the Corporation decided to erect a purpose-built structure 'commensurate with the position of the City' to house them. After much delay, due mainly to the First World War, the new Museum and Art Gallery opened, in

1929, in a fine building situated on the Stranmillis Road. Known still as the Belfast Museum and Art Gallery, it continued as such until 1961, when it was transferred from Belfast Corporation to become a national institution, funded by government, and renamed the Ulster Museum. A large extension, which was opened in October 1972, was at the same time added to the 1929 building. With its numerous displays and lively educational and events programmes, the Ulster Museum became a vital part of Northern Ireland's cultural landscape. In 1998 it was amalgamated with the Ulster Folk and Transport Museum, Ulster American Folk Park and Armagh County Museum to form a single organisation, the Museums and Galleries of Northern Ireland (MAGNI).

The fine art collections of MAGNI, which continued to grow throughout the twentieth century, embrace a wide range of periods and schools. Paintings and sculptures by Irish artists, of which there is a representative holding dating from the late seventeenth century to the present, form one of the most important aspects of the collection. There is also a small, but notable, group of paintings by British masters of the eighteenth and nineteenth centuries, such as Sir Joshua Reynolds, Thomas Gainsborough, Sir Thomas Lawrence and J.M.W. Turner (Turner's **The Dawn of Christianity** is an important picture in the artist's oeuvre and, donated in 1913, was a significant gift to a collection still in its infancy). Of the forty or so Continental Old Masters, works by Dutch, Flemish and Italian painters ranging from the late fifteenth to the eighteenth centuries are to be found in almost equal numbers. The most noteworthy painting in this section is perhaps the monumental **St. Christopher Carrying the Christ Child,** by Jacob Jordaens. Major figures in British art of the twentieth century are also well represented, notably in the Lloyd Patterson

pictures which were acquired in the late 1920s and early 1930s. Thus, for example, Augustus John, Paul Nash, W.R. Sickert, Sir Stanley Spencer and Philip Wilson Steer are prominently seen as, from a later period, are Ben Nicholson, Graham Sutherland, Ivon Hitchens, Francis Bacon, Henry Moore, Barbara Hepworth, Sir Eduardo Paolozzi and many others. British, European and American art of the 1960s and 1970s also features prominently in the collection, with examples of many trends prevalent in those years - abstract expressionism, colour field painting (Morris Louis' **Golden Age** is the outstanding work), hard edge, op, pop, kinetic art and so on. Of more recent developments, Gilbert and George, John Keane and Mark Francis are all included.

The strength of the MAGNI collections lies not merely in their diversity but in the in-depth holdings of the work of many artists, including, for example, Alice Berger Hammerschlag, Basil Blackshaw, Paul Henry, Mainie Jellett, Sir John Lavery, Louis le Brocquy, F.E. McWilliam, Colin Middleton, Roderic O'Conor, William Scott and Kenneth Shoesmith. Other substantial groups of works within MAGNI's holdings are Belfast scenes and portraits by Frank McKelvey, in the Ulster Museum's History Division; paintings and drawings by William Conor, in the Ulster Folk and Transport Museum; and a collection of wildlife art in the Ulster Museum's Zoology department.

drawings paintings & sculptures
the notes on entries

Artists are arranged in alphabetical order. Successive works by each are listed numerically thereafter, in order of the catalogue numbers included at the beginning of each entry. The artist's nationality or school is given after his or her dates. Where possible, the title of the work is that used by the artist.

The date of a work is given when it is inscribed on a piece or is known from outside evidence. In some cases, an approximate date is given. Dimensions are in centimetres, height preceding width and preceding depth in the case of sculptures and reliefs. All works are two-dimensional unless otherwise stated.

A work noted as signed indicates that the artist has signed it in some form, either full name, initials or monogram, but does not indicate the presence or absence of other inscriptions.

Titles of works are given in bold. Other details included in titles and printed in regular case are supplied for purposes of information.

Francis Bacon 1909-92 **Head II (1949)** U436

Thomas Bate fl.c.1692 **Thomas, Lord Coningsby 1656-1729, Seated in a Romanticised Landscape, with a View of the North Prospect of Hampton Court, Herefordshire, in the Background (1692)** U1883

John Henry Fuseli 1741-1825 **Mrs. Fuseli in a Red Cap (1794)** U791

Thomas Gainsborough 1727-88 **Arthur, 1st Marquess of Donegall 1739-99** (c.1780) U35

drawings paintings & sculptures

the
ulster museum
fine art
collection

A

ABBOTT, John White 1763-1851 (English)

U734 **Near Rydal Hall (1791)** *(Illus.p.218)*
Watercolour, ink on paper 24 x 18.9
Signed, dated
Purchased 1953

U735 **Peamore Park, near Exeter (1793)**
(Illus.p.218)
Watercolour, ink on paper 18.1 x 22
Dated
Purchased 1955

ABLETT, William Albert 1877-1937 (English)

U4496 **Sir William Crawford 1840-1922 (1903)**
Oil on canvas 81.4 x 65.4
Donated by R. H. Crawford, 1943

ABSOLON, John 1815-95 (English)

U975 **Landscape with Distant River** (formerly
'Landscape') *(Illus.p.218)*
Watercolour, white on paper 35 x 48
Signed
Purchased 1955

ADAM, Joseph Denovan 1841-96 (Scottish)

U3 **Still Life (1888)** *(Illus.p.218)*
Oil on canvas 128.4 x 102.5
Donated by W. T. Braithwaite (per J.
Horner), 1906

ADAMS, John Clayton 1840-1906 (English)

U2 **The Cherry Orchard** *(Illus.p.218)*
Oil on canvas 61.5 x 91.1
Purchased 1890

AGHAJANIAN, Sophie b.1943 (Armenian,
works in Ireland)

U2514 **Interior**
Pencil on paper 54.6 x 75
Signed
Purchased 1978

AIZELIN, Eugène-Antoine 1821-1902 (French)
(after)

U1777 **Mignon**
Sculpture, bronze, ht. 78.7
Purchased 1893

ALBANI, Giovanni Battista 1616-61 (Italian)
(attributed to)

U199 **Group of Three Figures Carrying a
Statuette**
Oil on copper 15.7 x 20.3
Donated by W. T. Braithwaite (per J.
Horner), 1906

ALEXANDER, Herbert 1874-1946 (English)

U976 **The Ruined Castle of Grimaud**
(Illus.p.218)
Watercolour on paper 36.8 x 26.7
Signed
Donated by the artist, 1937

ALLAN, Robert Weir 1851-1942 (Scottish)

U1 **Waiting for the Tide** *(Illus.p.218)*
Oil on canvas 121.7 x 86.5
Bequeathed by Mrs. E. E. White, 1937

U605 **Safety Amidst Danger**
Oil on canvas 88 x 138.7
Signed
Acquired by exchange, 1919

ALLIN, William A. (?) 19th-20th century
(British?)

U2042 **Portrait of an Unknown Woman (1903?)**
Oil on canvas 79.8 x 65
Signed, dated indistinctly
Provenance unknown

ALLINGHAM, Helen 1848-1926 (English)

U977 **Feeding the Chickens (1878)**
(Illus.p.218)
Watercolour, white on paper 19.1 x 21.7
Signed, dated
Donated by Robert and Meta Dunlop,
1950

U4760 **Farmyard, Kent (c.1900)**
Watercolour on paper 16.7 x 20.2 (sight)
Bequeathed by Roberta and John Hewitt,
1987

ALLOM, Thomas 1804-72 (English)

U2113 **Stirling Bridge** *(Illus.p.218)*
Sepia on paper 10.2 x 14
Donated by J. H. Stirling, 1919

ALLORI, Cristofano 1577-1621 (Italian)

U26 **St. Francis in Prayer** *(Illus.p.219)*
Oil on copper 40 x 32
Donated by W. T. Braithwaite (per J.
Horner), 1906

ALLPORT, Henry C. fl.1808-23 (English)

U978 **Temple of the Sybil, Tivoli (1809)**
(formerly 'Classical Ruin, Tivoli')
(Illus.p.219)
Pencil, watercolour on card 16.6 x 23.7
Signed, dated
Provenance unknown

ANAUT, Felix b.1944 (Spanish)

U1944 **Figure in Movement (Catalan Series)
(1998)**
Oil, charcoal on paper 103.2 x 145.2
(sight)
Signed, dated
Donated by the artist, 1999

ANDERSON, William 1757-1837 (English)

U979 **Wapping** *(Illus.p.219)*
Watercolour, ink on paper 20.5 x 30.1
Purchased 1952

ANDREWS, Anna 19th century (Irish)

U2693 **Ballycraigy Waterfall (1851)**
Pencil, white on paper 38.1 x 27
Bequeathed by Mrs. Hannah Flanery,
1915

ANNESLEY, David b.1936 (English)

U960 **1968/8-2 (1968)**
Sculpture, painted aluminium and steel
217.2 x 199.4 x 60.9
Purchased 1969

ANNESLEY, Lady Mabel 1881-1959 (Irish)

U981 **Tully Cross** *(Illus.p.219)*
Watercolour, pencil on paper 27.8 x 38.5
Signed
Donated by the artist, 1939

U1263 **Table at a Window** *(Illus.p.219)*
Silverpoint on prepared board 35 x 27.2
Signed
Donated by the artist, 1939

APPEL, Karel Christian b.1921 (Dutch)

U515 **Portrait of César (1956)** *(Illus.p.219)*
Oil on canvas 185.5 x 120
Signed, dated
Purchased 1964

ARDIZZONE, Edward 1900-79 (English)

U982 **Arrival of American Troops in Northern
Ireland – Troops just Landed** *(Illus.p.219)*
Pencil, wash on paper 18.8 x 23.5
Signed
Donated by the War Artists' Advisory
Committee (per the Imperial War
Museum), 1946

U4700 **View on a Fortified Island (1941)**
Pencil, wash on paper 24.2 x 40.6
Donated by the War Artists' Advisory
Committee (per the Imperial War
Museum), 1946

ARMITAGE, Kenneth b.1916 (English)

U961 **Two Standing Women (1955)**
(Illus.p.219)
Sculpture, bronze 52.7 x 19.7 x 18.1
Signed
Purchased 1963

ARMSTRONG, Arthur Charlton b.1924 (Irish)

U231 **Bedroom at Ballylough (c.1956)**
(Illus.p.219)
Oil on canvas 45.7 x 66.3
Signed
Purchased 1957

ÁRPÁD, Romek 1883-1960 (Hungarian)

U232 **Brass and Glass** *(Illus.p.220)*
Oil on canvas 55 x 65.5
Signed
Purchased 1935

ASHFORD, William 1746-1824 (Irish)

U2295 **Landscape with Carriage and Horses
(c.1781)** *(Illus.p.220)*
Oil on canvas 72 x 89
Signed
Purchased 1975

ASTLEY, John 1724-87 (English)

U702 **The Molyneux Family of Castledillon,**

Co. Armagh (1758) *(Illus.p.220)*
Oil on canvas 240 x 313
Signed, dated
Permanent loan from the Department of
Health and Social Services (NI)

ATKINS, James 1799-1833 (Irish)

U215 **View of Ariccia, Albano**
Oil on canvas 46 x 60.5
Donated by Miss M. J. G. Hunter, 1939

U547 **Young Girl in a White Dress** *(Illus.p.220)*
Oil on board 22.7 x 18
Bequeathed by Miss H. M. McCleery,
1968

U711 **Girl with a Platter of Fruit** (after Titian)
(formerly 'Lavinia as Flora')
Oil on canvas 105 x 87
Purchased 1897

U2570 **George Hamilton, 3rd Marquess of
Donegall 1797-1883 (1824)** *(Illus.p.220)*
Oil on canvas 233.7 x 145.4
Signed, dated
Purchased 1980

ATKINS, Samuel fl.1787-1808 (English)

U736 **Sailing Ships** *(Illus.p.220)*
Watercolour, ink, pencil on paper 34.6 x
45.6
Signed
Bequeathed by Mrs. Hannah Flanery,
1915

ATKINSON, Barry Thompson b.c.1935 (Irish)

U247 **Harvest (1960)**
Oil on paper 51.7 x 63.7
Signed, dated
Provenance unknown

ATKINSON, John 1863-1924 (English)

U984 **Two Generations**
Watercolour, pencil, white on paper 17.1
x 23.5
Signed
Purchased 1928

AUSTIN, Robert Sargent 1895-1973 (English)

U4710 **Anson Wheel (1941)**
Charcoal, white on paper 63.5 x 48.3
Signed, dated
Donated by the War Artists' Advisory
Committee (per the Imperial War
Museum), 1946

AUSTIN, Samuel 1796-1834 (English)

U1636 **Church of St. Ouen, Rouen** *(Illus.p.220)*
Watercolour on paper 48.3 x 61.4
Signed
Bequeathed by Sir David Reid (per Lady
Reid), 1951

AYRES, Gillian b.1930 (English)

U434 **Untitled (1963)** *(Illus.p.220)*
Oil, charcoal on paper 52.2 x 76.2
Signed, dated
Purchased 1963

AYRTON, Eileen fl.1927-76 (Irish)

U1569 **Portrait of Miss May Morton**
Chalk on paper 51 x 45.7
Signed
Bequeathed by the sitter, 1957

U633 **Portrait of Cathleen Wright (Mrs.
Cathleen Boyd)** d.1994
Chalk on paper 49.5 x 41.9
Signed
Donated by J. Douglas Boyd, 1998

B

BACON, Francis 1909-92 (British)

U436 **Head II (1949)** *(Illus.p.xii)*
Oil on canvas 80 x 63.6
Donated by the Contemporary Art
Society, 1959

BAKER, Alfred Rawlings 1865-1939 (English,
worked in Ireland)

U1207 **Cornish Cliffs (1922)**
Watercolour, pencil on card 72.6 x 57.5
Signed, dated
Purchased 1922

U1921 **A St. Martin's Summer**
Oil on canvas 129.5 x 167.6
Purchased 1907; sold 1970

U1922 **Hay Harvest (1918)** *(Illus.p.220)*
Oil on canvas 50.9 x 75.9
Signed, dated
Donated by J. G. Crawford, 1918

BAKER, T. 19th century (British)

U2033 **Charles I** (after Van Dyck)
Oil on canvas 74.3 x 62.2
Bequeathed by H. Musgrave, 1922; sold
1970

BALFOUR, J. Lawson 1870-1966 (Australian,
worked in England)

U4509 **John Milliken (1895)**
Oil on canvas 114.5 x 91.2
Signed, dated
Donated by Mrs. G. A. Milliken, 1925

BALLAGH, Robert b.1943 (Irish)

U2258 **Cut-Out with a Dan Flavin (1974)**
Acrylic on board (with neon lights) 178.6
x 122.1
Purchased 1974

U2534 **Inside No. 3 (1979)** *(Illus.p.221)*
Acrylic on canvas 177.2 x 178.1
Purchased 1979

U4935 **Portrait of Dr. Liam McCormick 1916-96**
(Illus.p.221)
Oil on canvas 100.7 x 80.4 (sight)
Purchased 1992

BALLARD, Brian b.1943 (Irish)

U1681 **Light Strips (Purple) (1972)** *(Illus.p.221)*
Acrylic on canvas 91.5 x 101.6
Signed, dated

Purchased 1972

U2354 **Catch (1971)**
Acrylic on canvas 111.5 x 111.7
Signed, dated
Purchased 1975

U2507 **Portrait of Basil (1978)**
Oil on board 25.4 x 20.3
Signed, dated
Purchased 1978

U2508 **Self-Portrait (1978)**
Oil on board 25.4 x 20.3
Signed, dated
Purchased 1978

BANTING, John 1902-72 (English)

U1843 **Two Models (1935)** *(Illus.p.221)*
Gouache on paper 109.2 x 67.3
Signed
Purchased 1971

BARBER, Joseph 1757-1811 (English)

U985 **Landscape with Cottage** *(Illus.p.221)*
Watercolour, pencil on paper 19.6 x 25.6
Purchased 1936

BARBER, Rupert fl.1736-72 (Irish)

U1889 **Mrs. Anne Donnellan (1752)** *(Illus.p.221)*
Miniature in enamel 4.5 x 4.2 (oval)
Signed, dated
Purchased 1963

BARKER, Thomas of Bath 1769-1847 (English)

U4 **The Falls of Mawr**
Oil on canvas; measurements unknown
Donated by Sir Robert Anderson, 1907;
destroyed in Malone House fire, 1976

U795 **The Tinkers (c.1780-90)** *(Illus.p.221)*
Charcoal, chalk, wash on paper 22.8 x
27.8
Purchased 1953

BARNARD, Rev. William Henry 1767-1818
(Irish, worked in England)

U2304 **The Seven Churches, Glendalough
(1788)**
Ink, wash on paper 16.8 x 22.5
Dated
Purchased 1975

BARRALET, John James c.1747-1815 (Irish)

U2598 **View in Glenarm Deer Park** *(Illus.p.221)*
Sepia, pencil on paper 37.5 x 52
Purchased 1982

U2599 **Glenarm Harbour**
Ink, sepia on paper 37.5 x 52.7
Purchased 1982

U2600 **Glenarm River and Bridge, Looking
towards the Sea** *(Illus.p.221)*
Pencil, sepia on paper 37.2 x 49.8
Purchased 1982

U2601 **View in Home Park, Glenarm (1796)**
See under Barralet Pupil

U2602 **Marchioness of Antrim's Cottage,**

Glenarm Deer Park *(Illus.p.222)*
Pencil, sepia on paper 36.2 x 50.8
Purchased 1982

BARRALET, John James c.1747-1815 or **Pupil**

U2603 **North East View of Garron Point (1794)**
(Illus.p.222)
Pencil, sepia on paper 33.6 x 48.3
Dated
Purchased 1982
Formerly by Unknown

BARRALET Pupil

U2601 **View in Home Park, Glenarm (1796)**
(Illus.p.222)
Sepia on paper 31.3 x 50.2
Dated
Purchased 1982
Formerly by John James Barralet c.1747-
1815

U2604 **Presbyterian Meeting House, Glenarm**
(Illus.p.222)
Watercolour on paper 29.8 x 48.8
Purchased 1982
Formerly by Unknown

U2605 **Glenarm Church (1796)** *(Illus.p.222)*
Watercolour on paper 34.3 x 52.7
Dated
Purchased 1982
Formerly by Unknown

BARRE, William James 1830-67 (Irish)

U2705 **Design for Albert Memorial Clock,
Belfast** *(Illus.p.222)*
Watercolour, ink, white on paper 94.5 x
66
Donated by Lord Claude Hamilton, 1955

BARRET, George, Jnr. 1767-1842 (English)

U737 **Classical Landscape with Figures**
Watercolour, pencil on paper 31.9 x 43.2
Signed
Purchased 1939

U987 **Westminster from Vauxhall** *(Illus.p.222)*
Watercolour on paper 32 x 43.9
Purchased 1911

U1416 **Classical Landscape**
Watercolour, pencil on paper 24.4 x 30.9
Purchased 1964

BARRET, George, Snr. 1728/32-84 (Irish)

U986 **Going to Market**
Watercolour on paper 30.1 x 40.5
Purchased 1933

U2261 **Sunset and Ruins**
Oil on canvas 62.8 x 76.2
Donated by Mrs. Aileen Bodkin in
memory of her husband, Professor
Thomas Bodkin, 1974

U2418 **The Waterfall at Powerscourt** *(Illus.p.222)*
Oil on canvas 73 x 70
Purchased 1964

BARRIAS, Ernest 1841-1905 (French) (after)

U4853 **Palissy the Potter**
Sculpture, bronze, ht. 101.6
Signed
Purchased 1891

BARRIBAL, William H. fl.1919-38 (English)

U2553 **A 1920s Lady at a Party** *(Illus.p.222)*
Poster colour on board 34.9 x 43.2
Signed
Donated by Rowel Friers, 1947

BARRY, James 1741-1806 (Irish)

U14 **Venus Anadyomene (c.1772)** *(Illus.p.223)*
Oil on canvas 75 x 55
Donated by Mrs. Aileen Bodkin (per the
Friends of the National Collections of
Ireland) in memory of her husband,
Professor Thomas Bodkin, 1963

U988 **Head of a Young Boy** (formerly 'A Female
Head')
Pencil on paper 18.8 x 14.8
Purchased 1971

BARRY, Moyra 1886-1960 (Irish)

U590 **Rhododendrons (c.1934)**
Oil on canvas 45.5 x 48
Donated by the Thomas Haverty Trust,
1936

BARTLETT, William Henry 1809-54 (English)

U989 **Bridge over the Meuse near Namur**
Pencil, ink, sepia on paper 9.7 x 14.9
Purchased 1952

BARTLETT, William Henry 1858-1932 (English)

U4810 **The End of the Fair, Back to the Island
(1910)** *(Illus.p.223)*
Oil on canvas 35.6 x 55.8
Signed, dated
Purchased 1990

BARTON, Rose 1856-1929 (Irish)

U1570 **St. Patrick's Close, Dublin (1881)**
(Illus.p.223)
Watercolour, bodycolour on paper 52.1 x
35.2
Signed, dated
Bequeathed by Miss H. M. McCleery,
1968

BARYE, Antoine-Louis 1795-1875 (French)
(after)

U1779 **Peace**
Sculpture, bronze, ht. 49.5
Purchased 1891

U1780 **War**
Sculpture, bronze, ht. 49.5
Purchased 1891

BATE, Thomas fl.c.1692 (Irish)

U1883 **Thomas, Lord Coningsby 1656-1729,
Seated in a Romanticised Landscape,
with a View of the North Prospect of
Hampton Court, Herefordshire, in the
Background (1692)** *(Illus.p.xiii)*
Oil on canvas 78.8 x 88.9

Signed, dated
Purchased 1973

BATONI, Pompeo 1708-87 (Italian)

U5047 **James Stewart of Killymoon, Co. Tyrone
1741-1821 (1767)** *(Illus.p.223)*
Oil on canvas 137.2 x 99.1
Purchased with the aid of grants from the
Heritage Lottery Fund, the National Art
Collections Fund and the Esmé Mitchell
Trust, 1997

BATT, Rev. Narcissus George 1824-98 (Irish)

U3909 **Album of Fifty-five Drawings**
-3963 **(1879-82)**
Ink on paper 17.8 x 24.2
Donated by Mrs. A. L. Smyth, 1948
Titles and dates as given by the
artist

U3909 **Arched Rock, Lough Swilly**

U3910 **Rocks on Lough Swilly 1879**

U3911 **Middleham Chapel in Castle** (N. Yorks.)

U3912 **Bolton Castle, Yorkshire 1879**

U3913 **Middleham Castle** (N. Yorks.)

U3914 **Middleham Castle** (N. Yorks.)

U3915 **Coverham Abbey**

U3916 **Coverham Abbey 1879**

U3917 **Abbot's House, Jervaulx, Yorkshire 1879,
Sept. 3**

U3918 **Jervaulx Abbey Refectory 1879, Sept. 5**

U3919 **Chapter House, Jervaulx**

U3920 **Charlecote** (Warwicks.)

U3921 **Beaulieu Abbey April 23 1880** (Hants.)

U3922 **Newtownards** (Co. Down, Dominican
Friary Arcade)

U3923 **At Coverham Abbey** (Late Gothic
Doorway)

U3924 **Old House, Campden 1880** (Glos.)

U3925 **Grange at Broadway** (Worcs.)

U3926 **St. Nicholas, Caen 1881**

U3927 **St. Taurin, Evreux**

U3928 **Abbey aux Dames, Caen 1881** (St.
Trinite, W. End of Nave)

U3929 **N. Transept, St. Taurin, Evreux**

U3930 **Evreux Cathedral April 1881**

U3931 **Clock Tower, Evreux 1881**

U3932 **Abbaye aux Dames, Caen**
(Exterior from E.)

U3933 **Interior of St. George de Boscherville**

U3934 **St. George, Boscherville** (Facade)

U3935 **St. George de Boscherville, nr. Rouen**
(View from S.)

U3936 **Cathedral, Bayeux, Nave 1881**

U3937 Carew Castle. Fire Place 1881 (Pemb.)

U3938 Manorbier Castle (Pemb.)

U3939 Manorbier Castle, Aug. 19 1881 (Pemb.)

U3940 Pembroke Castle 1881

U3941 Pembroke Castle

U3942 Chapel in Tewkesbury Abbey (Glos.)

U3943 Abbot's House, Tewkesbury Sept. 1881 (Glos.)

U3944 Abbey Gate, Tewkesbury Sept. 2, 1881 (Glos.)

U3945 Abbey of Tewkesbury, N.E. (Glos.)

U3946 Leadenham Church, Lincolnshire (Exterior from S.)

U3947 Fiskerton Church, Lincoln Sept. 6, 1881 (Exterior from S.)

U3948 Fiskerton 1881 (View across Nave, with Font)

U3949 Tattersall Castle. Sept. 7, 1881 (Lincs.)

U3950 Tattersall Church and Castle Sept. 10, 1881 (Lincs.)

U3951 Somerton Castle nr. Lincoln Sept. 9, 1881

U3952 Kirkstead Abbey Sept. 7, 1881

U3953 Crypt of Somerton Castle

U3954 Organ Screen. Choir, Southwell Minster (Notts.)

U3955 Choir, Southwell

U3956 Southwell Palace Sept. 9, 1881

U3957 Thornbury Church and Castle (Glos.)

U3958 Hayles. Cloisters April 25, 1882 (Glos.)

U3959 Hayles Abbey from W.

U3960 Hayles Abbey from S. April 25, 1882

U3961 Hayles Abbey from N. April 25, 1882

U3962 Portugese Boats on the Douro. Regoa 1880

U3963 St. David's College and Palace (Pemb.)

U3964 Album of Fifty-six Drawings (1854--4019 62)
   Ink on paper 17.8 x 24.2
   Donated by Mrs. A. L. Smyth, 1948
   Titles and dates as given by the artist

U3964 Pilatus from Lucerne April 1854

U3965 Bellinzona 1854

U3966 Syra 1854

U3967 Smyrna May 27, 1854

U3968 Constantinople May 1854

U3969 Hagia Sophia

U3970 Graville Abbey

U3971 Malaga. 1859

U3972 Carisbrook, Wight (Castle Gateway)

U3973 Brading Ch. Wight. 1859

U3974 Rochester Castle, Kent (Interior of Keep)

U3975 Dorchester Abbey, Oxon. (Interior of E. End)

U3976 Dorchester Abbey, Oxon. (E. End with Tombs)

U3977 Dorchester Abbey, Oxon. (Exterior from N.E.)

U3978 Conway Castle (from N.)

U3979 Beaumaris Castle (Anglesey)

U3980 Stratford (upon Avon) Church (Warw., W. Front)

U3981 Chapel in Beaumaris Castle

U3982 Caernarvon Castle (Eagle Tower)

U3983 Penmon Priory, Anglesey

U3984 Huy. July 9, 1858

U3985 Arundel Castle (Sussex)

U3986 Vittoria Convent. Malaga 1859

U3987 St. Michael's Mount (Cornwall)

U3988 Malaga. 1859

U3989 Scarborough Castle from the Church

U3990 Scarborough Priory (Exterior from S.W.)

U3991 Bridlington Priory (Exterior from S.W.)

U3992 Byland Abbey. 1862 (W. Front)

U3993 Byland Abbey (W. Door)

U3994 Byland Abbey (E. End)

U3995 Rievaulx (Illus.p.223)

U3996 Rievaulx from the N.W.

U3997 Refectory at Rievaulx

U3998 Interior of Rievaulx Refectory

U3999 Rievaulx (from E.)

U4000 Malton Abbey (Yorks., W. Front)

U4001 Whitby Abbey W.

U4002 Whitby Abbey (from N.E.)

U4003 Whitby N.E. Aisle

U4004 Whitby Abbey N.

U4005 S.E. Whitby (Abbey)

U4006 Choir. Whitby

U4007 Mulgrave Castle (Yorks.)

U4008 Monmouth Castle

U4009 Fountain Court, Raglan Castle

U4010 Raglan Castle

U4011 Pulpit in the Refectory, Tintern. Pulpit in Refectory, Shrewsbury (Abbey)

U4012 Tintern Abbey (Crossing looking N.)

U4013 Chepstow Castle (Monm.)

U4014 Tintern N. (N. Transept from N.)

U4015 Chepstow Castle (Marten's Tower and Gatehouse)

U4016 Chepstow Castle (from Wye)

U4017 Shrewsbury Abbey. Nave

U4018 Abbey of Holy Cross, Shrewsbury (W. Tower)

U4019 St. Mary's, Shrewsbury (from S.)

U4020 Album of Seventy-three Drawings
-4092 (1846-85)
   Ink on paper 16.5 x 26
   Donated by Mrs. A. L. Smyth, 1948
   Titles and dates as given by the artist

U4020 Casale Rotondo Via Appia, or Tomb of Cottas. April 4, 1883

U4021 San Lorenzo (fuori i Mura) near Rome (Facade and Campanile)

U4022 Temple of Dioscuri in Forum. April 19

U4023 Temples of Antoninus and Romulus. April 5

U4024 Theatre of Marcellus. April 6

U4025 Temple of Minerva Medica

U4026 Porta Asinaria and Sta. Croce (in Gerusalemme)

U4027 Palace of the Caesars from the Forum. April 3

U4028 Tomb of Caecilia Metella from Circus of Romulus

U4029 The Alban Hills and Campagna from the Torre del Bove, via Appia. April 10

U4030 Sta. Cecilia in Trastevere April 13 (Facade and Campanile)

U4031 Aventine from Ponte Rotto. April 14 (Showing Sta. Sabina)

U4032 Temple of Saturn, Forum

U4033 Sta. Costanza and Sta. Agnese

U4034 S. Abbondio, Como (Interior)

U4035 Portico of Octavia. April 6

U4036 Tivoli (Town and Cascades)

U4037 Lerici March 1883

U4038 Abbey of Saint Abbondio, Como (Exterior)

U4039 Town Hall, Como

U4040 Lake of Lecco from Villa Serbelloni, Bellagio (with Colour Notes)

U4041 Lake of Como from Bellagio

U4042 St. Ives. June 1883 (Cornwall)

U4043 Kynance Rocks, Lizard

U4044 St. Ives Ch. Cornwall. 1883

U4045 Lelant Ch. Cornwall

U4046 Tresco Abbey, Scilly

U4047 St. Paul's near Penzance

U4048 Cromwell's Castle, Tresco, Scilly

U4049 High Town, St. Mary's Scilly. June 22, 1883

U4050 Rialton Grange, Bodwin Moor, near New Quay

U4051 St. Columb Minor, Cornwall (Church from S.)

U4052 St. Columb Major. June 25, 1883 (View across Nave, Looking S.)

U4053 St. Columb Major (Church from S.)

U4054 Lanherne (View across Nave, with Screen, Looking S.)

U4055 Lanherne Church (Exterior)

U4056 Lanherne

U4057 Restormel Castle

U4058 Fowey June 26

U4059 Pennard Castle, Gower (Glam.)

U4060 Lostwithiel Ch. 1883 (Cornwall. Spire)

U4061 Bishopstone. Gower (Church Tower. Glam.)

U4062 Pennard Castle, Gower

U4063 Penrice Castle, Gower

U4064 St. Michael's Mount, Cornwall

U4065 Tor. Oxwick Bay, Gower

U4066 Rossilly Ch. (Gower. Romanesque Arch)

U4067 Oystermouth Castle, 1883

U4068 Belfry of St. Peter's, Perugia, 1873

U4069 Fotheringay Tower (Leics.)

U4070 Huddingston Ch. in Worcester 1883 (Interior)

U4071 Tomb near Jerusalem now Called after its Discoverer, Bishop Barker, 1868

U4072 Tory Island, Aug. 21, 1885. S.W. Cliffs (Donegal)

U4073 Tory Island, Aug. 21, 1885 (Round Tower)

U4074 Tory Tower. Aug 21, 1885

U4075 VII Arches, Lough Swilly, July 1885 (Donegal)

U4076 Precinct Gate, Winchester

U4077 Trim Castle, Meath

U4078 Newtown Ch. near Trim

U4079 Killmallock Ch., Co. Limerick

U4080 Krishlawn na Kirka Hens Castle, Lough Corrib (Galway)

U4081 The Black Castle, Wicklow

U4082 Jarrow Ch. Durham (Exterior)

U4083 Finchale Priory, Durham. 1846

U4084 Bacharach on the Rhine 1858

U4085 Tangiers 1855

U4086 Gibraltar 1855

U4087 Beaumaris Castle (Anglesey)

U4088 Heroine and Boats at Malaga 1855

U4089 Blaydon, Somerset (Church Tower)

U4090 Kenilworth Priory Gate; verso, Chapel in Conisbough Castle 1887

U4091 Kenilworth Castle Gate

U4092 Criccieth Castle, Wales. Oct. 10, 1883

U4093 Album of Forty-eight Drawings
-4140 (1864-94)
Ink on paper 19 x 24.1
Donated by Mrs. A. L. Smyth, 1948
Titles and dates as given by the artist

U4093 Gate. Lehon Abbey, Dinan. 1864

U4094 Cathedral of Nantes, 1864 (Facade)

U4095 Fontevrault Abbey, Touraine, 1864 (E. End. Exterior)

U4096 La Tour d'Evrault — Abbey Kitchen, Fontevrault, Anjou, 1864

U4097 Porta Aurea, Spalato, April 12 1883 (Split)

U4098 Ludlow Castle (Shrops.)

U4099 St. Julian's Tours, 1864 (Interior)

U4100 Prebendal House, Tours. 1864

U4101 Swalcliffe Ch. nr. Banbury, Drawn 1853. Finished 1894 (Exterior from S.E.)

U4102 Remains of St. Martin's at Tours, 1863. Tour S. Martin. Tour Charlemagne

U4103 Beaulieu Abbey, Loches, Touraine

U4104 Chapel of Amboise Castle, 1864

U4105 At Amboise 1864

U4106 Chateau de Blois. N. Side 1864

U4107 St. Nicholas, Blois (Crossing)

U4108 Castle of Blois 1864

U4109 Harfleur Ch. (Spire)

U4110 Fontevrault Abbey, Touraine (Exterior from N.W.)

U4111 Refectory, Lehon Abbey, Dinant

U4112 Portal, Lehon Abbey, Dinant

U4113 Burley Priory, Suffolk (Coloured Crayon)

U4114 Dolmen near Saumur

U4115 Walsingham Priory, Norfolk

U4116 Haughmond Abbey, Chapter House (Shrops.)

U4117 Cirencester Church (Glos. from E.)

U4118 Kirkham Abbey Gate, Yorkshire

U4119 Gisburn Priory, Yorkshire

U4120 Hexham Abbey Choir before its Restoration

U4121 Small Church (Raphoe Cathedral, Co. Donegal?)

U4122 Selby Abbey, Yorkshire (W. Front before Oldrid Scott's Restoration)

U4123 One of the 7 Churches at Clonmacnoise, Nov. 1887 (Offaly)

U4124 Kenilworth Castle Signed

U4125 Chinan on the Vienne, Touraine

U4126 Entrance Priory now Deanery, Winchester

U4127 Portishead Ch. nr. Bristol (Exterior from N.E.)

U4128 Glastonbury Abbey (Som.)

U4129 St. Saviour's, Southwark, New Nave 1887 (Now Southwark Cathedral)

U4130 Hall of Vicars' College, Wells (Som.)

U4131 Vicars' College, Wells

U4132 Sketch of 'Low Window' and Sketch of Church Spire

U4133 Quinton Ch., Gloucestershire (Exterior from N.E.)

U4134 Chapel of the Holy Ghost nr. Basingstoke

U4135 Winchester College (Chapel and Tower)

U4136 Loches Castle, Touraine

U4137 Loches

U4138 Chateau de Langeais, Touraine

U4139 Langeais. Interior (Courtyard)

U4140 Winchelsea Church (Exterior from E.)

U4141 Album of Seventy-six Drawings
-4216 (1868-88)
Ink on paper 25.4 x 35.5
Donated by Mrs. A. L. Smyth, 1948
Titles and dates as given by the artist

U4141 Mont St. Michel?

U4142 Brecon Priory (Now Brecon Cathedral. Exterior from N.W.)

U4143 Tewkesbury Abbey (from E. with Sketch of Tracery)

U4144 Fountains Abbey N.E. (Choir and Huby's Tower)

U4145 Grosmount Castle, Herefordshire

U4146 Llanthony Abbey, S.W.

U4147 Llanthony Abbey, W.

U4148 Llanthony Abbey, N.E.

U4149 Llanthony Abbey, Nave

U4150 Brecon College

U4151 Brecon Castle

U4152 Goodrich Castle (Herefs.)

U4153 Goodrich Castle

U4154 Oak near Jedburgh

U4155 Caerphilly Castle

U4156 Caldicot Castle near Chepstow (Monm.)

U4157 Tintern Abbey (from S.W.)

U4158 Richmond Castle (N. Yorks.)

U4159 Easby Abbey (nr. Richmond); verso, Sketch of Whitby

U4160 Gate of Easby Abbey and Parish Church

U4161 Durham Castle (from Framwellgate Bridge)

U4162 Alnwick Castle (Northb.)

U4163 Dunstanburgh Castle (Northb.)

U4164 Dunstanburgh Castle, N.

U4165 Bamborough Castle from the North. 1870. Sept.

U4166 Prudhoe Castle

U4167 Lindisfarne Abbey. West

U4168 Bamborough. W. 1870 (Castle and Church)

U4169 Norham Castle Aug. 29 1870

U4170 Kelso Abbey, from the Tweed (Roxb.)

U4171 Norham Church (Northb.)

U4172 Jedburgh Abbey (Roxb.)

U4173 Hexham Choir (after Restoration of E. End)

U4174 Tynemouth Priory 1870

U4175 Tideswell Ch., Derbyshire. Sept. 11, 1874 (Exterior from S.E.)

U4176 Ludlow Castle, '76 (Shrops.)

U4177 Stokesay Castle 1876 (Shrops.)

U4178 Haddon Hall 1874 (Derbs.)

U4179 West Front, Tewkesbury (Glos.)

U4180 Chapter House, Cleeve Abbey (Som.)

U4181 Gateway of Cleeve Abbey from Interior

U4182 Gateway, Cleeve Abbey, Somerset, from Without

U4183 Launceston Castle, Cornwall

U4184 Loch Leven Castle

U4185 Neath Abbey Ch. (Glam.)

U4186 Charfield, near Bath (Church and Manor House)

U4187 Neath Abbey

U4188 Rhuddlan Castle, N. Wales

U4189 Cloisters, Valle Crucis (Llangollen)

U4190 Isola dei Pescatori, Lago Maggiore 1873

U4191 Abbey of San Zenone, Verona, May 9 1871 (Facade and Campanile)

U4192 Kilmallock, Co. Limerick (Friary)

U4193 Choir of Hore Abbey, Cashel (Tipperary)

U4194 Kilmallock (Friary, Co. Limerick)

U4195 Hore Abbey, N.W., and Rock of Cashel, Tipperary (View from S.W.)

U4196 Holy Cross Abbey, S. Transept (Tipperary)

U4197 Cloisters of Muckross Abbey, Killarney

U4198 Rock of Cashel from the Palace

U4199 Jerpoint Abbey. W. (Co. Kilkenny)

U4200 Jerpoint Abbey (from E.)

U4201 Jerpoint Church, Co. Kilkenny

U4202 Inniscattery Tower, Shannon

U4203 Inniscattery on the Shannon, Kilrush in Distance

U4204 Choir of Limerick Cathedral

U4205 Dunlecky Castle near Kilkea

U4206 Adare Castle (Co. Limerick)

U4207 Adare Church (Church of Ireland, formerly Dominican Church)

U4208 Adare Abbey, Cloisters (Franciscan Friary)

U4209 Saumur

U4210 Duomo, Arezzo (Exterior from S.E. minus Campanile)

U4211 Dominican Monastery, Perugia

U4212 Tintagel Castle, Cornwall. Sept. 1873

U4213 Temple at Kedes Naphtali. 1868

U4214 Rathaus, Lübeck. 1884

U4215 Conisborough Castle, May 1, 1888

U4216 Bolton Priory (Yorks.)

U4217 -4305 Album of Eighty-nine Drawings (1848-93)
Ink on paper 25.4 x 34.3
Donated by Mrs. A. L. Smyth, 1948
Titles and dates as given by the artist

U4217 Conway Castle May 1885 Omitting the Bridge

U4218 Abbey of Arbroath. July 29, 1889

U4219 Priory Church, St. Martin des Champs, Paris 1853 (now Musée des Arts et Metiers)

U4220 Mickleton Church, Gloucestershire (Exterior from S.E.)

U4221 Lamphey Court, Pembrokeshire

U4222 Crom Castle, Lough Erne

U4223 Pembroke Castle, the Gate Tower

U4224 Chapel in Conway Castle. May 8 1885

U4225 Pembroke Castle from the Creek

U4226 Thornbury Castle, Gloucestershire '64

U4227 Angevine Castle, Castellamare. March 17, 1883 (Naples)

U4228 Templars' Church, Luz, Pyrenees. 1875

U4229 Laon. N.E. 1874

U4230 Fortress of the Alhambra 1859

U4231 Abbey of St. Sernin, Valley of Argellez, Pyrenees. 1875

U4232 Bolton Priory, W. Craven (W. Front)

U4233 Jebel Mokattam near Cairo. 1868

U4234 Hattin Tabor in Galilee 1868 on Ascent to Saphel from Tiberias

U4235 Stanley St. Leonard, Gloucestershire. The First Pen and Ink Drawing (Church from N. E.)

U4236 Ruins of St. John Baptist's Church, Samaria. 1868

U4237 Old Mansion Called Plas Mawr, Conway, Wales, 1885 (Upper Courtyard)

U4238 Small Temple, Baalbek, 1868

U4239 Tewkesbury from the Mill, 11 March 1889

U4240 Carew Castle, Pembrokeshire

U4241 Vesuvius from Castel de Mare, March '93

U4242 Kidwelly Castle, S. Wales

U4243 Chapter House, Haughmond Abbey, Oct. 1889 (Shrops.)

U4244 Kidwelly Castle Chapel

U4245 Kidwelly Castle

U4246 Kidwelly Castle

U4247 Palace at St. David's (Pemb.)

U4248 Pavia (Bridge over Ticino)

U4249 Castle of Luz. Pyrenees. 1875

U4250 Abbey Church of Belem. 1875 (Portugal)

U4251 Barnard Castle, Durham. August 1, 1889

U4252 San Juan de Palmas, Seville, May 10, 1875

U4253 Haughmond Abbey, Oct. 3, 1885 (Shrops.)

U4254 Choir. Las Huelgas, Burgos. 1875

U4255 Santa Croce near Jerusalem. 1868

U4256 Conway Castle, May 1885 (from across the River, with Bridge)

U4257 Puerto del Sol, Toledo 1875

U4258 Stewkley Church, Sept. 19, 1889 (Bucks.)

U4259 Kidwelly Castle. Interior

U4260 Berkeley Castle '67 (Glos.)

U4261 The Hanging Rock. Lake Macneen, Fermanagh. May 27, 1885

U4262 Glendalough. Ruins of 7 Churches. Co Wicklow

U4263 Chipping Norton, Oxfordshire. '50 (Church from S.E.)

U4264 Killydonnel Abbey, East Window, Co. Donegal

U4265 Tower Arch. Rathmullan Priory

U4266 Choragic Monument of Lysicrates, Athens. Surrounding Ruins from an Old Drawing. 1893

U4267 Church with Round Tower Attached, Glendalough. (Called St. Kevin's Kitchen) 1865

U4268 Gate of the Agora, Athens. March 25 1893

U4269 Ruins of Episcopal Palace, St. David's (Pemb.)

U4270 Nave. Tewkesbury 1885

U4271 Encampment of Messrs. Batt and Musgrave in 1868 by the Barrada One Day from Damascus

U4272 Portico in the Agora, Athens. April 1893

U4273 Fiji Source of the Barada. Antile-hanoa. 1868

U4274 Jenim Ingannim, Palestine. Mt. Gilboa in Distance 1868

U4275 Mals, Tyrol

U4276 Fountain at Nazareth, 1868

U4277 Nr. Bruges, Jonell, '78

U4278 Golden Gate, Jerusalem, '68

U4279 Broughton Church, Sept. 1849 (Oxon. From S.E.)

U4280 Manor House at Buckland with its Ancient Hall or Chapel now Destroyed, 1870

U4281 Lynmouth and Lynton from the Beach, 1857 (N. Devon)

U4282 Hillborough from Harbour of Ilfracombe. 1857

U4283 Egyptian and Assyrian Rock Tablets near Beyrout. 1868. Ramases II. Sennacherib. On Banks of the Lycus – Nahr el Kelb. Dog River

U4284 Fecamp Abbey 1881 (from N.E. Normandy)

U4285 Monument in St. Margaret's, Leicester. Oct. 1884. John Penny, Bishop of Bangor and Carlisle, Abbot of Leicester (Yellow Wash)

U4286 Interior of Harlech Castle, Oct. 10, 1889 (Interior of Courtyard)

U4287 Castle of Banias, Palestine. 1868

U4288 Church Lench (Worcs. Church from S.E.)

U4289 Messina, Sicily, 1868

U4290 Manorbier Castle (Pemb.)

U4291 Hedon Ch. Yorkshire. June 30, 1887 (Exterior from N.)

U4292 Giralda, Seville, 1859

U4293 Ratisbon, June 16, '78 (Regensburg. Cathedral from Danube)

U4294 Erive Bridge, Connemara. 1848

U4295 Torcello near Venice, April 1893 (Campanile of Duomo)

U4296 Bolton Priory, N.E. 1869 (Yorks.)

U4297 St. Kenelm's Clent. July 1887 (Worcs. Tower and West Front)

U4298 Seville Cathedral, Spring of 1855 (behind the Organ)

U4299 St. John's, Kilkenny. May 23, 1885 (Interior of Lady Chapel)

U4300 Black Abbey, Kilkenny, Dominican Friary, 1885 (Exterior from S.E.)

U4301 W. St. Patrick's, Dublin, before its Restoration (W. Front with Minot's Tower)

U4302 Devenish, May 26, 1889 (St. Mary's Abbey, Cross and Round Tower)

U4303 Abbot's Salford Manor, 1890 (Warw.)

U4304 Agholt Church, Co. Wexford, near Clonegal. From a Photograph

U4305 Egglestone Abbey, Yorkshire 31 July 1889

U4306 **Album of Forty Drawings (1878-**
-4345 **83)**
       Ink on paper 33 x 24.1
       Donated by Mrs. A. L. Smyth, 1948
       Titles and dates as given by the artist

U4306 Creisker, S. Pol de Leon (Porch)

U4307 Creisker (Exterior from S.)

U4308 Creisker (Interior)

U4309 Creisker (Spire)

U4310 Well, St. Pol de Leon

U4311 Prebendal House, St. Pol

U4312 St. Pol. Cathedral. S.W.

U4313 Cathedral, St. Pol de Leon (W. Front)

U4314 Daoulas Abbey (W. Front)

U4315 Daoulas (Cloisters)

U4316 Deanery. Folgoët

U4317 Houses at Morleux

U4318 Le Folgoët (Exterior from S.E.)

U4319 Notre Dame de Grace – Cuim

U4320 Jubé. Folgoët

U4321 Chapel of the Khalis or Villa Viciosa, Cordoba Cathedral

U4322 Tomb at Burgos

U4323 St. Riquier

U4324 Sheriff Hutton (Castle)

U4325 Chapter House, Howden

U4326 Ferns (Co. Wexford. Castle)

U4327 Cathedral of Ratisbon, 1878 (Regensburg Cathedral. Apse from E.)

U4328 Compton Wynyates (Warw.)

U4329 Screen. St. David's Cathedral (Pemb.)

U4330 Remains of Macon Cathedral

U4331 Netley (Abbey, Hants.)

U4332 Compton Wynyates (Warw., Courtyard)

U4333 Compton Wynyates. S.

U4334 Stair. S. Sauveur, Caen. 1881

U4335 Paestum. Temple of Ceres

U4336 Temple of Neptune, Paestum

U4337 Bolton Priory. Choir. 1883 (Yorks.)

U4338 Kirkham Priory

U4339 Huddington. '83 (Timber-framed House) Signed

U4340 Sherborne Castle

U4341 Cloister, Kirkham Priory

U4342 St. Mary's, Beverley (E. Yorks. Interior)

U4343 Caughton Court (Warw. Courtyard)

U4344 Tower on Devenish Island (Co. Fermanagh)

U4345 Cross, Monasterboice, Co. Louth (the Tall Cross)

U4346 **Album of Forty Drawings (1842-**
-4385 **59)**
       Ink on paper 26.7 x 36.8
       Donated by Mrs. A. L. Smyth, 1948
       Titles and dates as given by the artist

U4346 Choir of St. Patrick's Cathedral Dublin, before its Restoration

U4347 Enniscorthy Castle (Co. Wexford)

U4348 Ferns Castle 1842 (Co. Wexford)

U4349 Ferns Abbey (Ruined Cathedral, Co. Wexford)

U4350 Carrickfergus Castle (Co. Antrim); Howth Church (Co. Dublin); Grey Abbey (Co. Down); Slane Abbey (Co. Meath)

U4351 St. Doulogh's Church (near Malahide, Co. Dublin)

U4352 Trim Castle, Co. Meath

U4353 Trim Castle, Co. Meath (on the Boyne)

U4354 St. John's Abbey, near Trim (on the

Boyne)

U4355 **St. Patrick's Cathedral, Dublin, Feb.1859** (W. Front and Minot's Tower)

U4356 **Christ Church Cathedral, Dublin before Restoration**

U4357 **Christ Church Cathedral, N.W., Dublin, before Restoration** (Exterior from N.W.)

U4358 **Lady Chapel, St. Audoen's Church, Dublin**

U4359 **Grey Abbey, Co. Down** (Choir from N.E.)

U4360 **Ruined Chapel at Malahide** (Co. Dublin)

U4361 **Bective Abbey, Co. Meath**

U4362 **Trim Abbey** (Yellow Steeple, Trim, Co. Meath)

U4363 **Trim Castle** (Co. Meath)

U4364 **Donaghmore, Co. Meath** (Church and Round Tower)

U4365 **Mellifont Abbey** (Baptistery and Chapel of St. Bernard, Co. Louth)

U4366 **Cong Abbey, Co. Galway**

U4367 **Downpatrick Cathedral. Interior of Choir and Exterior of East End**

U4368 **Burnshook Priory, Co. Mayo**

U4369 **Ballintubber Abbey, Co. Mayo** (Interior in Ruins)

U4370 **Murrisk Abbey, Co. Mayo. Achill in the Distance. Round Tower. Aghagower near Westport** (Co. Mayo)

U4371 **Ballintubber Abbey** (Co. Mayo)

U4372 **Kilconnell Abbey** (Co. Galway)

U4373 **Abbey Church, Clare, Galway** (Co. Galway)

U4374 **Seven Churches of Clonmacnoise on the Shannon** (Co. Offaly)

U4375 **St. Nicholas' Collegiate Church, Galway, July '46** (Exterior from S.W.)

U4376 **Abbey of Knockmoy, Co. Galway. Interior of Choir**

U4377 **Knockmoy Abbey** (Co. Galway)

U4378 **Tintern Abbey** (Co. Wexford. From N.E.)

U4379 **Dunbrody Abbey** (Co. Wexford. From S.E.)

U4380 **Ross Reilly** (Ross Erilly Friary, Co. Galway)

U4381 **Clonmines Church** (Co. Wexford. From S.E.)

U4382 **Interior of Chapel in the Tower of Ferns Castle, Sept. 1853** (Co. Wexford)

U4383 **Malahide Castle** (Co. Dublin)

U4384 **O'Rorke's Tower, Clonmacnoise; St. Bridget's Tower** (Kildare) (Teampul Finghin, Clonmacnoise); **Monasterboice;**

Magdalene Tower (Drogheda); **Dundrum** (Co. Down. Keep)

U4385 **Tintern Abbey** (Co. Wexford. From S.E.)

U4386 **Album of Fifteen Drawings (1868)**
-4400 Ink on paper 35.5 x 27.9
Donated by Mrs. A. L. Smyth, 1948
Titles and dates as given by the artist

U4386 **Mount Moriah from En Rogel or Fountain of Joab**

U4387 **Temple at Damascus** (Detail of Pediment)

U4388 **Nazareth from N.E. with Fountain of the Virgin**

U4389 **Sultan Barkook, Cairo** (Mosque)

U4390 **Baalbek** (Temple of Jupiter)

U4391 **Jerusalem from Road to Bethany**

U4392 **Rocktombs**

U4393 **Mount Ebal from Nablus**

U4394 **Columns at Samaria. April 1868**

U4395 **Gate of Banias**

U4396 **Rock of Banias**

U4397 **Nablus and Gerizim**

U4398 **Exedra, Baalbek**

U4399 **Banias**

U4400 **Tiberias. Easter 1868**

U4401 **Album of Eighty-one Drawings**
-4481 **(1868-84)**
Ink on paper 22.8 x 27.9
Donated by Mrs. A. L. Smyth, 1948
Titles and dates as given by the artist

U4401 **On the Freshwater Canal at Suez. With the English Camp. 1868**

U4402 **Castle of Sidon. 1868**

U4403 **Sarepta 1868**

U4404 **Cathedral of Tyre. 1868**

U4405 **Encampment at Nablus from the West. 1868**

U4406 **Pilgrims' Camp at Jericho. March 30, 1868**

U4407 **The Convent at Bethlehem. 1868**

U4408 **Tiberias from Site of the Ancient City. 1868**

U4409 **Tiberias from the Hot Springs, Easter Day 1868**

U4410 **Damascus. Hospital of Sultan Selim. 1868**

U4411 **Temple of Jupiter. Baalbek. Interior. 1868**

U4412 **Baalbek Trilithon. April 25 1868. The Stones are 64 Feet Long Each**

U4413 **Colonnade at Pompeiopolis, Cilicia. 1868**

U4414 **Beyrout, Lebanon. 1868**

U4415 **Castle of Tripoli (Syria) 1868**

U4416 **Rhodes from the Sea. 1868**

U4417 **Ruined Church at Porto Venere, Spezzia. 1876**

U4418 **Porto Venere near Spezzia, 1876**

U4419 **Mount Orgueil Castle, Jersey. 1877**

U4420 **Wimborne Minster 1879** (Crossing and Choir. Dorset)

U4421 **Isola Farnese (Citadel of Veii) 1878**

U4422 **Juno. Girgenti. 1876** (Doric Temple)

U4423 **Abbey. Taormina** (Sicily)

U4424 **Theatre at Taormina. 1876**

U4425 **Olympieum. Siracusa**

U4426 **Temple of Concord. Girgenti. N.E. March 21, 1876**

U4427 **Temple of Juno. S.E. Girgenti. 1876**

U4428 **Temple of Concord, Girgenti. S.E. March 21, 1876**

U4429 **Tomb of Theron. Girgenti. 1876**

U4430 **Temple of the Dioscuri, Girgenti. March 21, 1876**

U4431 **Girgenti. General View. 1876**

U4432 **Temple of Juno. Girgenti. 1876**

U4433 **Temple of Juno, Girgenti. 1876**

U4434 **St. John's, Syracuse. 1876**

U4435 **Cathedral of Syracuse. 1876**

U4436 **Roman Ruin at Baiae. 1876**

U4437 **Coast near Palermo. 1876**

U4438 **Sorrento. 1876**

U4439 **Tomb of Aruns. 1876. Albano**

U4440 **Stoneleigh Abbey** (Warw.)

U4441 **St. John's Hospital, Coventry. Sept. 16, 1876**

U4442 **Great Hall, Kenilworth Castle**

U4443 **Ruins of Selinus**

U4444 **Street of Tombs, Syracuse**

U4445 **Etna from Taormina**

U4446 **Heraeum. Girgenti. Interior facing S.W**

U4447 **Abbey of St. Martin nr. Palermo**

U4448 **Cefalu** (Cathedral from S.W. at some Distance)

U4449 **Untitled. Girgenti?**

U4450 **Lübeck. South Porch 1884. Marienkirche. 18 July; verso, Blaby Church near Leicester. 1884**

U4451 **St. Martin's, Leicester 1884** (Spire. Now Leicester Cathedral)

U4452 **St. Margaret's, Leicester. Oct. 1884** (Tower and South Porch)

U4453 **Salford Ch. Jan. 1885. Day of R. Ingram's Wedding** (Exterior from S.E.)

U4454 **St. Mary's Hall, Coventry. 188(4?)**

U4455 **St. Mary's, Leicester. 1884.** (Exterior from N.E.)

U4456 **All Saints, Stamford.1884. Lincs.** (Exterior from S.W.)

U4457 **Wenlock. Sept. 24, 1883. Shrops.** (Spire from N.W.)

U4458 **Wenlock Priory. West Front. 1883** (Shrops.)

U4459 **Wenlock Priory. S. 1883** (Shrops.)

U4460 **Old House at Wenlock. Aug 24, 1883**

U4461 **Harvington Hall 1883** (Near Chaddesley Corbett, Worcs.)

U4462 **Farm House, Quinton. Sep. 17, 1883** (Worcs.)

U4463 **Brailes Church 1883. Worcs.** (Exterior from S.W.)

U4464 **Tower on Walls of Nuremberg. 1884**

U4465 **Winderton Ch. Warwickshire. The Gift of Canon (Thornton?) 1883** (Exterior from S.E.)

U4466 **Compton Wynyates. 1883** (Warw.)

U4467 **Church. Nuremberg. 1884**

U4468 **Tower of Utrecht. June 1884** (Cathedral)

U4469 **Abbey of Laach. June 1884** (Maria Laach)

U4470 **Choir. Utrecht. June 24** (Cathedral)

U4471 **St. Marie Abbey Ch. Laach. June 26, 1884** (Maria Laach. Ext. from N.W.)

U4472 **Schloss Elz near the Mosel. June 27, 1884**

U4473 **Cochem on the Mosel. June 26, 1884**

U4474 **Walls and Bridge on Pegnitz, Nuremberg. 1884**

U4475 **Nassau House. Nuremberg. June 28, 1884**

U4476 **Frauenthor, Nuremberg. June 30, 1884**

U4477 **Choir Screen. Lübeck Cathedral. July 17, 1884**

U4478 **Castle of Lerici, near Spezia. 1883**

U4479 **St. Mary's, Stamford. Oct. 1, 1884** (Lines Exterior from S.); verso, **Watercolour of Fishing Boat**

U4480 **St. Leonard's Priory, Stamford, Oct. 1884** (Lincs. W. Front)

U4481 **Gate of Carmelites, Stamford. Oct. 1884**

BAWDEN, Edward 1903-89 (English)

U738 **Members of the Baluchi Regiment**

Digging in Gallabat
Watercolour, pencil on paper 40.4 x 53
Signed
Donated by the War Artists' Advisory Committee (per the Imperial War Museum), 1946

U1182 **Private Gul Sahir Khan, Royal Indian Army Service Corps** *(Illus.p.223)*
Pencil, ink, wash on paper 50 x 33
Signed
Donated by the War Artists' Advisory Committee (per the Imperial War Museum), 1946

BAXTER, Leslie O. 20th century (Irish)

U4761 **Mount Charles (1952)** *(Illus.p.223)*
Watercolour, pencil on paper 37.5 x 55 (sight)
Signed, dated
Bequeathed by Roberta and John Hewitt, 1987

BAYES, Walter 1869-1956 (English)

U990 **A French Hotel** *(Illus.p.223)*
Oil on paper 31 x 25.6
Signed
Purchased 1951

BAYNES, Keith Stuart 1887-1977 (English)

U677 **The Garden, Villa des Bois de St. Joseph (c.1932)** *(Illus.p.223)*
Oil on canvas 50.8 x 76.6
Signed
Purchased (Lloyd Patterson Collection) 1933

BEARD, Leonard b.1962 (English, lives in Spain)

U5044 **And (1996)**
Oil on canvas 240 x 179.7
Dated
Purchased 1997

BEAUMONT, Sir George Howland 1753-1827 (English) (attributed to)

U2117 **Dedham, Suffolk**
Pencil, watercolour on paper 14.9 x 21
Donated by J. H. Stirling, 1919

BEECHEY, Sir William 1753-1839 (English)

U696 **Portrait of a Woman (c.1785-95)** *(Illus.p.224)*
Oil on canvas 75 x 62.2
Purchased 1970

BELL, Larry b.1939 (American)

U2379 **Two-panel Glass Sculpture (1971-72)**
Glass, vacuum plated 213.3 x 121.8
Purchased 1976

BELL, Sandra b.1954 (Irish)

U5071 **Spirit of Duty Free (1997)** (Maquette)
Sculpture, bronze, ht. 33.5
Signed, dated
Donated by the Bell Gallery, 1998

BELL, Vanessa 1879-1961 (English)

U438 **Piazzetta Dei Cavalli Marini (1935)**
Oil on canvas 78.1 x 63.5
Signed, dated
Donated by the Contemporary Art Society, 1946

U440 **Flowers in a Ginger Jar (1931)** *(Illus.p.224)*
Oil on canvas 61.7 x 51.1
Signed, dated
Purchased (Lloyd Patterson Collection) 1933

BENGER, Berenger 1868-1935 (English)

U991 **Steyning, Sussex** *(Illus.p.224)*
Watercolour on paper 27.5 x 38.7
Signed
Donated by the artist's executors, 1935

BENNETT, William 1811-71 (English)

U2684 **Tantallon Castle**
Watercolour on paper 35.6 x 53.3
Bequeathed by Miss E. Taylor, 1983

BENNETT, William Mineard c.1778-1858 (English)

U1183 **Portrait of a Young Lady (1810)** *(Illus.p.224)*
Watercolour on paper 19.2 x 16.7
Signed, dated
Donated by J. St. Clair Boyd, 1947

BENTLEY, Charles 1805/6-54 (English)

U1184 **Carting Hay (1845)**
Pencil, watercolour, white on paper 34.2 x 65
Signed, dated
Purchased 1948

U1434 **Fishing Boats Entering Port** *(Illus.p.224)*
Watercolour on paper 33.6 x 49.5
Signed
Purchased 1935

BERCHEM, Nicolaes Claesz 1620-83 (Dutch)

U7 **Landscape with Figures and Animals** *(Illus.p.224)*
Oil on canvas 112.3 x 146.5
Purchased 1960

BERGER HAMMERSCHLAG, Alice 1917-69 (Austrian, worked in Ireland)

U300 **Calvary Old and New**
Oil on canvas 101.5 x 127
Signed
Purchased 1962

U302 **Merging Elements (1961)**
Oil on canvas 71.1 x 91.4
Signed
Purchased 1962

U699 **Point of Release No. 2 (1966)**
Oil on canvas 100.8 x 121.2
Signed, dated
Purchased 1970

U700 **Opposing Rhythms Subsiding (1967)**
Oil, acrylic on canvas 114 x 94

Signed, dated
Purchased 1970

U1162 **Yellow Drawing (1969)**
Felt pen, watercolour on paper 24.9 x 33.8
Purchased 1971

U5054 **Gathered Lightpoints (1968)**
Mixed media on canvas 37.6 x 37.6 (sight)
Bequeathed by Dr. Trudie Berger (per R. J. Brock), 1997

U5055 **Harvest Ode (1961)**
Oil, gouache on canvas on board 48 x 35.1
Bequeathed by Dr. Trudie Berger (per R. J. Brock), 1997

U5056 **Untitled**
Watercolour on board 28 x 28.7
Signed
Bequeathed by Dr. Trudie Berger (per R. J. Brock), 1997

U5057 **Untitled**
Oil on paper 38 x 15
Signed
Bequeathed by Dr. Trudie Berger (per R. J. Brock), 1997

U5058 **Untitled**
Oil on canvas 51 x 50.7
Bequeathed by Dr. Trudie Berger (per R. J. Brock), 1997

U5059 **Successive Phases (1963)**
Oil on canvas on board 44.3 x 60.3
Bequeathed by Dr. Trudie Berger (per R. J. Brock), 1997

U5060 **Untitled**
Oil on canvas 41 x 91.5
Signed
Bequeathed by Dr. Trudie Berger (per R. J. Brock), 1997

U5061 **Ode to a Night (1961)**
Oil, gouache on canvas on board 35.4 x 48
Bequeathed by Dr. Trudie Berger (per R. J. Brock), 1997

U5062 **Untitled**
Oil on canvas on board 71 x 83.6
Bequeathed by Dr. Trudie Berger (per R. J. Brock), 1997

U5063 **Untitled**
Oil on canvas 101 x 101.5
Signed
Bequeathed by Dr. Trudie Berger (per R. J. Brock), 1997

U5064 **Yeats's Hourglass (1961)**
Oil on canvas 91.3 x 91
Signed
Bequeathed by Dr. Trudie Berger (per R. J. Brock), 1997

U5065 **Untitled**
Oil on canvas 91 x 91
Bequeathed by Dr. Trudie Berger (per R. J. Brock), 1997

BERNEA, Horia b.1938 (Romanian)

U4819 **Steeple (1997)** *(Illus.p.224)*
Oil on canvas 140.5 x 110
Signed, dated
Purchased 1990

BERNSTEIN, Edward 20th century (American)

U2654 **Codrington Library (1979)** *(Illus.p.224)*
Pencil on paper 76.2 x 56.8
Signed, dated
Purchased 1982

BEUYS, Joseph 1921-86 (German)

U2306 **Untitled (1974)**
Chalk on blackboard 111.1 x 122
Donated by the artist, 1974

U2307 **Untitled (1974)**
Chalk on blackboard 111.1 x 122
Donated by the artist, 1974

U2308 **Untitled (1974)**
Chalk on blackboard 111.1 x 122
Donated by the artist, 1974

U2309 **Untitled (1974)**
Chalk on blackboard 111.1 x 122
Donated by the artist, 1974

BEVAN, Robert 1865-1925 (English)

U691 **The Yard Gate, Mydlow (c.1907)**
(Illus.p.224)
Oil on canvas 55.9 x 48.2
Purchased 1970

U739 **Tapster Water** *(Illus.p.225)*
Watercolour, charcoal on paper 34.6 x 43.3
Signed
Purchased 1954

BEVERLEY, A. W. 20th century (British)

U1394 **Park Place, Henley**
Watercolour, charcoal on paper 30 x 47.4
Signed
Purchased 1955

BEVERLEY, William Roxby 1824-89 (English)

U992 **Putney**
Pencil, watercolour on paper 21 x 45.5
Purchased 1952

BIJLERT, Jan van 1597/98-1671 (Dutch)

U229 **St. Matthew (c.late 1620s)** *(Illus.p.225)*
Oil on canvas 94.5 x 78.5
Signed
Purchased 1969

BILL, Max 1908-94 (Swiss)

U517 **Condensation towards Yellow (1965)**
(Illus.p.225)
Oil on canvas 112.6 x 113.5
Signed, dated
Purchased 1966

BINDON, Francis c.1690-1765 (Irish) (attributed to)

U105 **George Macartney 1671-1757 (c.1750)**

(Illus.p.225)
Oil on canvas 125.8 x 101
Purchased 1947
Formerly by Unknown

U111 **Colonel Henry O'Hara d.1745 (c.1725-35)**
Oil on canvas 76.1 x 63.5
Purchased 1965

U131 **George Macartney 1671-1757 (c.1750)**
Oil on canvas 72.5 x 62
Purchased 1947
Formerly by Unknown

BION, Cyril Walter 1889-1976 (English, worked in Ireland)

U252 **Himalayan Snowfield (c.1925)**
(Illus.p.225)
Oil on canvas 71.5 x 91.8
Purchased 1933

U1208 **Sunrise on the Chor**
Pencil, watercolour on card 55.3 x 77.5
Signed
Purchased 1933

BIRCH, Samuel John Lamorna 1869-1955 (English)

U437 **Tweed's Fair River, Melrose** *(Illus.p.225)*
Oil on canvas 63.5 x 90.3
Signed
Purchased 1924

BIRSS, Charles fl.1894-1925 (Scottish)

U1589 **A November Day**
Watercolour, bodycolour on paper 42.5 x 52.8
Signed
Donated by Miss P. Andrews, 1909

BISSILL, George William 1896-1973 (English)

U1927 **Avoca Bridge, Co. Wicklow (c.1932-33)**
(Illus.p.225)
Oil on canvas 47 x 67.4
Signed
Purchased (Lloyd Patterson Collection) 1933

BLACKSHAW, Basil b.1923 (Irish)

U238 **The Field (1953)** *(Illus.p.225)*
Oil on board 71.7 x 91.1
Signed, dated
Purchased 1955

U240 **Landscape (c.1963)**
Oil on canvas 51.4 x 76.9
Signed
Donated by Lewis Berger Ltd., 1963

U1185 **A Road** *(Illus.p.225)*
Charcoal, white on paper 38.5 x 56
Purchased 1963

U1878 **Nude (c.1972-73)**
Oil on panel 121.9 x 121.9
Signed
Purchased 1973

U2440 **Jennifer Johnston b.1930 (1973)**
Oil on canvas 61.3 x 60.9

Signed
Purchased 1977

U2573 **Portrait of John Hewitt 1907-87 (1956)**
Oil on canvas 61 x 50.5
Signed, dated
Donated by John Hewitt, 1980

U4762 **Roberta** (Portrait of Roberta Hewitt)
Crayon on paper 20 x 27 (sight)
Signed
Bequeathed by Roberta and John Hewitt,
1987

U4763 **Study for a Portrait of John Hewitt
(c.1956)**
Pencil on paper 25.2 x 19.7 (sight)
Signed
Bequeathed by Roberta and John Hewitt,
1987

U4764 **And Bay the Moon (c.1956)**
Crayon, ink on paper 14 x 19.5 (sight)
Signed
Bequeathed by Roberta and John Hewitt,
1987

U4765 **Portrait of John Hewitt 1907-87 (1984)**
Oil on board 25 x 30.6
Bequeathed by Roberta and John Hewitt,
1987

U4766 **Conversation in a Field (1952-53)**
(Illus.p.226)
Oil on board 33 x 27.5
Bequeathed by Roberta and John Hewitt,
1987

U4903 **Fighting Cock**
Oil on canvas 91.4 x 91.4
Signed
Donated by Ray Irwin, 1992

U4942 **The Barn (Blue II) (1991-92)**
(Illus.p.226)
Oil on canvas 50.8 x 61
Signed
Purchased 1992

BLAIR, Doris Violet fl.1940s-'80s (Irish)

U1395 **Preparing for Kit Inspection**
Watercolour, pencil on paper 28.2 x 39.4
Signed
Donated by the War Artists' Advisory
Committee (per the Imperial War
Museum), 1946

U1682 **Shattered Dwellings** *(Illus.p.226)*
Watercolour, pencil on paper 28.2 x 38.2
Signed
Purchased 1942

U3597 **The Arrival (1936)** *(Illus.p.226)*
Oil on canvas 104 x 123
Donated by the artist in memory of J.
Blair, 1984

U4701 **Policewoman of the ATS (c.1940-46)**
Watercolour on paper 38.1 x 28.6
Signed
Donated by the War Artists' Advisory
Committee (per the Imperial War
Museum), 1946

U4748 **Children Playing (1986)**
Acrylic on paper 50 x 72 (sight)

Signed, dated
Donated by the artist, 1989

BLAKESTON, Oswell 1907-85 (English)

U2428 **Untitled**
Watercolour on paper 36 x 23.5 (sight)
Signed
Donated by the artist, 1976

BLAND, John Humphrey 1828-1919 (Irish)

U15 **At Montreux (c.1906-7)** *(Illus.p.226)*
Oil on canvas 32.5 x 21.4
Signed
Donated by the artist, 1907

U16 **L'Hermitage Costabelle, Hyéres (c.1907)**
Oil on board 33 x 24.8
Signed
Donated by the artist, 1907

BLYTH, John 20th century (Scottish)

U4861 **Clokey Stained Glass Design No. 8463**
Watercolour, ink on paper 31.8 x 9.5
Donated by Harold Clokey, 1991

U4940 **Ascension with St. Simon and St. Patrick**
(Design for Stained Glass Window)
Watercolour, ink on paper 33.2 x 8
(Centre Light); 19.7 (Side Lights)
Donated by Harold Clokey, 1992

BOEHM, Sir Joseph Edgar 1834-90 (Hungarian,
worked in England)

U2704 **Queen Victoria 1819-1901 at a Spinning
Wheel (1869?)**
Sculpture, plaster, ht. 42.5, under glass
dome
Signed
Provenance unknown

U4838 **Queen Victoria 1819-1901**
Sculpture, marble bust, ht. 58.5
Signed
Donated by Lady Harland, 1888

BOMBERG, David 1890-1957 (English)

U441 **Self-Portrait (1932)**
Oil on board 59.6 x 49.4
Signed, dated
Purchased 1953

U4709 **Self-Portrait with Palette (1931)**
(Illus.p.226)
Oil on canvas 77 x 64.1
Donated by the Contemporary Art
Society, 1987

BONE, Sir Muirhead 1876-1953 (Scottish)

U741 **Alfriston, Sussex** *(Illus.p.226)*
Pencil on paper 19.8 x 27.8
Signed
Purchased 1952

BORTHWICK, M. A. fl.1851-53 (Scottish)

U1271 **Endymion (1853)**
Pencil on paper 29.7 x 22.2
Signed, dated
Provenance unknown

U1272 **Woman Spinning (1851)**

Pencil on paper 24.4 x 31.2
Signed, dated
Provenance unknown

U1273 **A Village Street**
Pencil on paper 19 x 25.9
Signed
Provenance unknown

BOTTOM, Robert D. b.1944 (English, works in
Ireland)

U5017 **At the Close of a Summer's Day, Fanad,
Co. Donegal (1995)**
Oil on board 76 x 92
Signed, dated
Purchased 1995

BOUCHER, Alfred 1850-1934 (French) (after)

U1781 **Labour** (Original at Hotel de Ville, Paris)
Sculpture, bronze, ht. 55.9
Purchased 1894

BOUGH, Samuel 1822-78 (Scottish)

U993 **The Tower of Said: Desert Landscape
with Figures** *(Illus.p.226)*
Pencil, watercolour, white on paper 14 x
21.6
Signed
Purchased 1964

BOURKE, Brian b.1936 (Irish)

U237 **Seated Woman (1965)**
Pencil, crayon on paper 80.5 x 56.5
Signed, dated
Purchased 1967

BOURKE, Michael J. (Micheál J. de Burca)
1913-85 (Irish)

U1226 **The Heckler (c.1935)** *(Illus.p.226)*
Charcoal, watercolour on paper 57.5 x
79.5
Signed
Donated by the Thomas Haverty Trust,
1941

BOWEN, Gretta 1880-1981 (Irish)

U2427 **A Night at Home (c.1951-56)**
Oil on panel 50.6 x 39.8
Signed
Purchased 1976

U4767 **Library (c.1953)** *(Illus.p.227)*
Oil on paper 25 x 35.4
Bequeathed by Roberta and John Hewitt,
1987

**BOYD and EVANS (Fionnuala Boyd, Leslie
Evans)** 20th century (British)

U2657 **Horizon (1982)** *(Illus.p.227)*
Pastel, oil on paper 125 x 308
Signed, dated
Purchased 1982

BOYD, Arthur b.1920 (Australian, works in
Britain)

U4739 **Landscape with Moose (1980)**
(Illus.p.227)
Oil on canvas 121.9 x 152.4

Donated by the Contemporary Art
Society, 1988

BOYD, Elizabeth Frances fl.1896-1935 (Scottish)

U608   **Venice, Rio della Croce** *(Illus.p.227)*
Oil on canvas 60.6 x 73.2
Signed
Donated by Miss M. Z. ffoliott, 1934

BOYLE, Alicia 1908-97 (Irish)

U242   **Potato Washers, Connemara (1949)**
(Illus.p.227)
Oil on muslin on board 50.8 x 60.1
Signed, dated
Purchased 1950

U245   **Bull in the Boreen**
Oil on canvas 55.9 x 46.3
Signed
Purchased 1959

U4768   **The Other Rose of Sharon (1946)**
Oil on board 35 x 25.4
Bequeathed by Roberta and John Hewitt,
1987

BOYLE, Mark b.1934 (British)

U683   **Street Corner Study: London Series
(1967-69)** *(Illus.p.227)*
Synthetic resin on wood frame 181.3 x
180.4
Purchased 1970

BOYS, Thomas Shotter 1803-74 (English)

U742   **The King's Palace, Brussels** *(Illus.p.227)*
Watercolour on paper 16.8 x 26.1
Signed
Purchased 1937

BRABAZON, Hercules Brabazon 1821-1906
(English)

U743   **View of Sousse, Tunisia** *(Illus.p.227)*
Watercolour, pencil on paper 24.9 x 34.8
Signed
Bequeathed by Dr. R. I. Best (per the
Friends of the National Collections of
Ireland), 1959

U744   **Grand Canal, Venice** *(Illus.p.227)*
Gouache, pencil on paper 16.5 x 23.4
Signed
Purchased 1952

BRADLEY, Martin b.1931 (English)

U236   **Inscription in a Garden (1957)**
Oil on board 60.9 x 122.3
Signed, dated
Donated anonymously, 1963

BRADY, Charles 1926-97 (Irish)

U2510   **Sweet Bag and Egg Box** *(Illus.p.228)*
Oil on canvas 60.5 x 61.4
Signed
Purchased 1978

BRAITHWAITE, Charles 1875-1941 (Irish)

U630   **The Village Street** *(Illus.p.228)*
Oil on canvas 31 x 38.4

Signed
Bequeathed by Mrs. W. A. M. Braithwaite,
1941

BRANDON, Jaques-Émile-Edouard 1831-97
(French)

U1576   **Drawing for Fresco in the Church of S.
Brigida in Piazza Farnese, Rome (1878)**
(Illus.p.228)
Chalk on paper 64 x 53.5
Signed, dated
Donated by J. H. Bland, 1908

BRANGWYN, Sir Frank William 1867-1956
(English)

U435   **The Drinkers (1912)** *(Illus.p.228)*
Oil on canvas 102.3 x 127.5
Signed, dated
Purchased 1928

BREAKEY, John b.1932 (Irish)

U1905   **Pentarhythms (1970)**
Sculpture, perspex 41.5 x 51 x 38
Purchased 1973

BRICARD, Xavier 19th-20th century (French)

U5   **Sous les Lauriers (1911)** *(Illus.p.228)*
Oil on canvas 180 x 139.5
Signed, dated
Purchased 1913

BRIDGFORD, Thomas 1812-78 (Irish)

U701   **The Deserter**
Oil on canvas 153 x 225
Signed
Purchased 1967

BRIDLE, Kathleen 1897-1989 (Irish)

U994   **Lough Erne from Rossfad (1945)**
(Illus.p.228)
Watercolour on paper 36.3 x 46.7
Signed, dated
Purchased 1951

BRIGHT, Henry 1810-73 (English)

U4675   **Orford Beach** *(Illus.p.228)*
Charcoal, crayon, bodycolour on paper
28 x 43.8
Signed
Bequeathed by Miss E. M. Colman (per
the National Art Collections Fund), 1949

BRITTON, Colin Richard 20th century (British)

U2519   **Whitby (1977)**
Pencil on paper 30 x 42
Signed, dated
Purchased 1979

BROADBENT, Arthur East b.1909 (Irish, worked
in England)

U4750   **Still Life**
Oil on canvas 50.6 x 60.8
Purchased 1988

BROCKHURST, Gerald Leslie 1890-1978
(English)

U2584   **Portrait of a Man (late 1920s)**
(Illus.p.228)
Pencil, wash on paper 45.7 x 32.4
Signed
Acquired by exchange (Lloyd Patterson
Collection), 1930

BROOKE, William Henry 1772-1860 (Irish)

U2325   **The Seven Castles of Clonmines from
Nelson's Bridge, Bannon, Co. Wexford
(1833)**
Ink, watercolour on paper 13.4 x 22.8
Signed, dated
Purchased 1975

U2326   **Castle of Clonmines: Abbey Church and
Tower (1833)**
Ink, watercolour on paper 22.8 x 14.3
Signed, dated
Purchased 1975

U2327   **Newtown Castle on the Far Moor (1833)**
Ink, watercolour on paper 14 x 22.9
Signed, dated
Purchased 1975

U2328   **Wellington Bridge over the Scar and the
Seven Castles of Clonmines (1833)**
(Illus.p.228)
Ink, watercolour on paper 14 x 22.8
Signed, dated
Purchased 1975

U4874   **Illustration to** *Fairy Tales of South West
Ireland*
Sepia, watercolour on paper 6.4 x 11.2
(sight)
Donated by Peter Brooke MP, 1991

U4875   **Illustration to** *Fairy Tales of South West
Ireland*
Sepia, watercolour on paper 6.4 x 11.2
(sight)
Donated by Peter Brooke MP, 1991

U4876   **Illustration to** *Fairy Tales of South West
Ireland*
Sepia, watercolour on paper 6.4 x 11.2
(sight)
Donated by Peter Brooke MP, 1991

BROWN, Deborah b.1927 (Irish)

U235   **Canvas, Paper and Paint (1961)**
Oil, paper on canvas 122 x 91.5
Signed, dated
Purchased 1962

U243   **The Fair Day (c.1951)** *(Illus.p.229)*
Oil on board 59.8 x 51.1.
Signed
Purchased 1951

U995   **Tempera on Paper (1961)**
Tempera on paper 37.4 x 27
Signed
Purchased 1962

U2298   **Glass Fibre Form (1974)** *(Illus.p.229)*
Sculpture, fibreglass 81.3 x 124.5 x 61
Purchased 1975

U4769   **Lucy Brown (1952)** *(Illus.p.229)*
Oil on board 31 x 23
Bequeathed by Roberta and John Hewitt,
1987

BRUCE-JOY, Albert 1842-1924 (Irish)

U1790 **Alexander Johns, JP (1892)**
Sculpture, marble bust, ht. 68.6
Signed, dated
Donated by the Presentation Committee,
1892

U1791 **Mary Anderson (Madame de Navarro as 'Galatea')**
Sculpture, plaster bust, ht. 79.4
Purchased 1891

BRUEGHEL, Jan I ('Velvet') 1568-1625
(Flemish) (after)

U17 **Landscape with Windmills** *(Illus.p.229)*
Oil on panel 18.4 x 28
Donated by W. T. Braithwaite (per J.
Horner), 1906

BRUEGHEL, Pieter II 1564-1638 (Flemish)
(after)

U12 **Spring (1633)** *(Illus.p.229)*
Oil on panel 42.8 x 58
Signed, dated
Donated by W. T. Braithwaite (per J.
Horner), 1906

U13 **Winter** *(Illus.p.229)*
Oil on panel 43.2 x 58
Donated by W. T. Braithwaite (per J.
Horner), 1906

BRUGES, School of, early 16th century (Flemish)

U1180 **Madonna and Child (The Carrickfergus Madonna)** *(Illus.p.229)*
Oil on panel 106.5 x 76.5
Purchased 1971

BRYSON, Alice M. fl.1925-40 d.c.1986 (Irish)

U4697 **The Edge of the Wood**
Watercolour on paper 26.7 x 36.8
Signed
Bequeathed by the artist (per White,
Brooks and Gilman), 1987

BUCK, Adam 1759-1833 (Irish)

U1179 **Annie Charlotte Hill Aged about Ten (1832)** *(Illus.p.229)*
Pencil, watercolour, white on paper 35.7
x 27
Signed, dated
Purchased 1971

BUNDY, Edgar 1862-1922 (English)

U4687 **The Last Ingredient: Three Huntsmen Sitting around a Punchbowl** *(Illus.p.229)*
Watercolour on paper 39 x 46.7
Signed
Bequeathed by Miss Averil Haslett, 1985

BURGESS, James Howard c.1810-90 (Irish)

U9 **Errigal Mountain (1870)**
Oil on canvas 50.8 x 80.6
Signed, dated
Donated by R. B. Dunwoody, 1964

U10 **Dundalk Bay**
Oil on canvas 50.8 x 61

Donated by R. B. Dunwoody, 1964

U202 **Belfast Lough from Sydenham**
Oil on canvas 71.3 x 91.2
Donated by J. St. Clair Boyd, 1947

U996 **Bolton Abbey, Yorkshire**
Pencil, white on paper 44.7 x 63.3
Signed
Purchased 1942

U997 **Bloody Bridge, Newcastle, Co. Down (1885)**
Pencil, watercolour, bodycolour on paper
25.5 x 36
Signed, dated
Purchased 1909

U998 **The Giant's Causeway** *(Illus.p.230)*
Charcoal, pencil, chalk on paper 53.8 x
67.8
Signed
Purchased 1909

U999 **Vale of Aber, near Bangor, North Wales (1871)** *(Illus.p.230)*
Pencil, watercolour, white on paper 30.6
x 42.4
Signed, dated
Purchased 1909

U1000 **Ranza Castle, Isle of Arran** (formerly 'Seascape with Cattle')
Watercolour, white on paper 21.2 x 39.7
Signed
Bequeathed by Sir R. Lloyd Patterson,
1919

U1001 **Cahan Abbey, with the O'Cahan Tomb, Dungiven, Co. Londonderry** *(Illus.p.230)*
(formerly 'Dungiven Church, Co.
Londonderry')
Pencil, watercolour, white on paper 35.5
x 26.3
Signed
Donated by W. T. Braithwaite (per J.
Horner), 1906

U1407 **Dundrennan Abbey, on the Solway Firth**
Pencil, white on paper 22 x 33
Signed
Provenance unknown

U1408 **Carrickfergus (1869)**
Pencil, watercolour, white on paper 32.8
x 44.1
Signed, dated
Provenance unknown

U2442 **Greencastle, Inishowen, Co. Donegal (1869)**
Watercolour on paper 49.6 x 73.6 (sight)
Signed, dated
Bequeathed by Miss E. Holland, 1951

U4693 **The Calder Fountain, Belfast (1859)**
Watercolour on paper 27 x 21
Signed
Purchased 1986

U4770 **The Gobbins, Islandmagee**
Pencil on paper 10.2 x 15.5 (sight)
(Vignette)
Signed
Bequeathed by Roberta and John Hewitt,
1987

BURKE, John b.1946 (Irish)

U1808 **Etsumi (1972)**
Sculpture, painted steel 61.5 x 125 x
48.2
Purchased 1973

BURLEIGH, Averil d.1949 (English)

U249 **Sand Dunes**
Tempera on board 46.4 x 49
Signed
Donated by Sir Joseph Duveen, 1928

BURN, Gerald Maurice 1862-1945 (English)

U8 **The Shipyard at Night (1910)**
Oil on canvas 92 x 122.2
Signed, dated
Donated by the artist, 1929

BURN, Rodney Joseph 1899-1985 (English)

U2679 **Sketch of an Imaginative Subject**
(formerly 'A Fanciful Subject')
(Illus.p.230)
Pencil, ink, sepia wash on paper 46.2 x
76.2
Provenance unknown

BURRA, Edward 1905-76 (English)

U745 **Dublin Street Scene No. 1 (1947-48)**
(Illus.p.230)
Pencil, watercolour on paper 66 x 101.6
Purchased 1970

BUTLER, Mildred Anne 1858-1941 (Irish)

U1002 **Springtime**
Pencil, watercolour, white on paper 12.7
x 17.8
Signed
Donated by Miss F. M. McTear, 1925

U1209 **A Sheltered Corner** *(Illus.p.230)*
Watercolour, white on board 52.5 x 71.2
Signed
Purchased 1910

U1635 **A Sunshine Holiday (1897)** *(Illus.p.230)*
Watercolour, bodycolour on paper 97.7 x
65.3
Signed, dated
Purchased 1914

BUTTNER, Werner b.1954 (German)

U4809 **Self-Portrait with Nun Dolls (1986)**
(Illus.p.230)
Oil on canvas 240 x 190
Purchased 1990

BYLERT, Jan van 1597/98-1671 (Dutch)
See under Bijlert

BYRON, B. 20th century (Haitian)

U2271 **Village Scene in Haiti (c.1960-63)**
Oil on board 122 x 60.7
Signed
Donated by H. Niblock, 1975

C

CAHILL, Richard Staunton c.1827-1904 (Irish)

U1414 **Cottage Interior (1884)**
Pencil, watercolour on paper 25 x 35.4
Signed, dated
Provenance unknown

CALDECOTT, Randolph 1846-86 (English)

U746 **An Awkward Predicament** *(Illus.p.230)*
Ink, watercolour, white on paper 14.8 x 19.9
Purchased 1952

CALLOW, William 1812-1908 (English)

U1003 **A Scene on the Rhine (1839)** (formerly 'Oberwesel on the Rhine, with the Castle of Schönburg') *(Illus.p.231)*
Pencil, watercolour, bodycolour on paper 32.7 x 48
Signed, dated
Purchased 1956

U1187 **Bellaggio, Lake Como, from Cadenabbia**
Pencil, watercolour on paper 21.4 x 33.2 (sight)
Signed
Purchased 1935

de CAMARGO, Sergio 1930-90 (Brazilian)

U532 **Relief No. 141 (1967)** *(Illus.p.231)*
Wood 114.7 x 85 x 10
Signed, dated
Purchased 1968

CAMERON, Sir David Young 1865-1945 (Scottish)

U747 **Hills of Angus** *(Illus.p.231)*
Watercolour, pencil on paper 27.6 x 37.5
Signed
Purchased 1932

CAMPBELL, Arthur M. d.1994 (Irish)

U1004 **Red Mill, Whitehouse (1948)** *(Illus.p.231)*
Pencil, watercolour on card 38.4 x 57.4
Signed
Purchased 1950

CAMPBELL, Cecilia Margaret 1791-1857 (Irish)

U748 **The Giant's Causeway** *(Illus.p.231)*
Watercolour on paper 19.6 x 27.6
Signed
Purchased 1952

U1227 **Landscape with Two Women by a Waterfall**
Pencil, watercolour on paper 18.9 x 29.6
Purchased 1967

CAMPBELL, Christopher 1908-72 (Irish)

U2425 **Self-Portrait: The Artist and his Sister (c.1930)** *(Illus.p.231)*
Oil on canvas 76.5 x 51
Purchased 1976

U2426 **Study for 'Self-Portrait: The Artist and his Sister' (1930)** (formerly 'Study for Male Figure in 2425') *(Illus.p.231)*
Charcoal on paper 52.1 x 36.8 (sight)
Signed, dated
Purchased 1976

U5006 **Ploughman (1930s)** *(Illus.p.231)*
Oil on canvas 69.8 x 89.8 (sight)
Signed
Purchased 1994

CAMPBELL, George 1917-79 (Irish)

U272 **Claddagh Duff, Connemara (c.1950-51)** *(Illus.p. 231)*
Oil on board 51.3 x 61.1
Signed
Donated by the Thomas Haverty Trust, 1957

U274 **Slack Day, Smithfield (c.1941-42)** *(Illus.p.232)*
Oil on canvas 55.9 x 73.1
Signed
Purchased 1944

U750 **Planting Potatoes**
Charcoal, crayon on paper 33 x 23
Donated by Z. Lewinter-Frankl, 1957

U1005 **Near Alicante, Andalusia (c.1951-52)** *(Illus.p.232)*
Gouache on board 37.9 x 53.8
Purchased 1952

U2334 **Gerard Dillon, Painter (1) (1968-69)**
Oil on board 31 x 30.1
Signed
Purchased 1975

U4771 **Hot Day, Alicante Way (c.1951)** *(Illus.p.)*
Watercolour on paper 14.7 x 16.2 (sight)
Bequeathed by Roberta and John Hewitt, 1987

CAMPBELL, John Henry 1757-1828 (Irish)

U751 **View near Kilcroney, Co. Wicklow**
Watercolour on paper 27 x 37.4
Signed
Purchased 1967

U752 **Lake of Killarney, Co. Kerry (1815)** *(Illus.p.232)*
Pencil, ink, watercolour on paper 38 x 48.3
Signed, dated
Purchased 1930

U1637 **Scene with Mountain in Background**
Watercolour on paper 13.5 x 17.2 (sight)
Signed
Donated by Miss F. M. McTear, 1926

U1638 **Scene with Bridge in Foreground**
Watercolour on paper 13.5 x 16.8 (sight)
Donated by Miss F. M. McTear, 1926

U2099 **View from Bray Head to Wicklow Head**
Watercolour on paper 22.2 x 29.8
Signed
Provenance unknown

U2100 **Cottage and Bridge**
Watercolour on paper 14.2 x 17.4
Provenance unknown

U2101 **Sugar Loaf Mountain, Co. Wicklow** *(Illus.p.232)*
Watercolour on paper 21.2 x 29.5
Provenance unknown

U2102 **Derrycunahy Cascade, Co. Kerry**
Watercolour on paper 20.9 x 30.5
Provenance unknown

U2103 **A Bridge and Cottage**
Watercolour on paper 13.2 x 17.7
Provenance unknown

U2104 **Rathgar Castle** (Dublin)
Watercolour on paper 15.8 x 19.6
Provenance unknown

U4671 **The Dodder near Dublin**
Watercolour on paper 44.5 x 33.6 (sight)
Purchased 1930

CAMPBELL, Lawrence 1911-68 (Irish)

U4846 **Head of Jack B. Yeats 1871-1957 (1944)** *(Illus.p.232)*
Sculpture, bronze, ht.46.5
Signed, dated
Purchased 1991

CANOVA, Antonio 1757-1822 (Italian) (after)

U1782 **Reconciliation of the Queens**
Now **Allegory of the Via Aemilia** by Unknown (Unknown Century and School)

U4847 **The Three Graces**
Sculpture, marble 81.2 x 45.7 x 25.4
Donated by R. A. Mitchell, 1926

CAREY, John 1861-1943 (Irish)

U1006 **Surprised (1890)** *(Illus.p.232)*
Pencil, watercolour on paper 39.7 x 27.4
Signed, dated
Bequeathed by Sir R. Lloyd Patterson, 1919

CAREY, Joseph William 1859-1937 (Irish)

U1007 **Dundrum, Co. Down (1924)** *(Illus.p.232)*
Pencil, watercolour on paper 34.2 x 53.1
Signed, dated
Donated by the artist, 1924

U1008 **Rothesay (1890)** *(Illus.p.232)*
Pencil, ink, watercolour, white on paper 37.8 x 55.9
Signed, dated
Bequeathed by Sir R. Lloyd Patterson, 1919

U1009 **Honfleur**
Pencil, watercolour on paper 35.5 x 26
Donated by members of the '1910' Sketching Club, 1937

U1188 **View in Scotland (1886)** (formerly 'Mountain Landscape') *(Illus.p.233)*
Pencil, watercolour, white on paper 27.8 x 39.5
Signed, dated
Bequeathed by Miss H. M. McCleery, 1968

U1189 **Old Houses, Howth (1887)** *(Illus.p.233)*
Pencil, watercolour, white on paper 25 x 35

Signed, dated
Bequeathed by Sir R. Lloyd Patterson,
1919

CARMICHAEL, John Wilson 1800-68 (English)

U754 **Whitby**
Pencil, wash, white on paper 12.7 x 20.4
Signed
Purchased 1952

CARO, Sir Anthony b.1924 (English)

U1430 **Rainy Day (1971)** *(Illus.p.233)*
Sculpture, welded steel 92 x 259 x 315
Purchased with the aid of a grant from
the Calouste Gulbenkian Foundation,
1971

CARR, Tom 1909-99 (Irish)

U259 **Making Coloured Parachutes (1944)**
Oil on canvas 76.5 x 63.8
Signed
Donated by the War Artists' Advisory
Committee (per the Imperial War
Museum), 1946

U260 **Children on the Front (1942)**
Oil on canvas 51.7 x 59.3
Signed
Donated by the Thomas Haverty Trust,
1942

U263 **Twilight, Moyadd (1952)** *(Illus.p.233)*
Oil on canvas 40.5 x 76.7
Signed
Purchased 1953

U1190 **Turfstacks (c.1950)**
Watercolour, bodycolour, ink on paper
58.4 X 45.6
Signed
Purchased 1962

U1888 **Mourne Foothills (c.1973)**
Watercolour on paper 36.5 x 57.2 (sight)
Purchased 1973

U2084 **Ormond Quay, Dublin (c.1939)**
(Illus.p.233)
Watercolour on paper 21.6 x 27.4 (sight)
Purchased 1974

U4746 **Self-Portrait with Vermeer Jug (c.1980)**
(Illus.p.233)
Oil on canvas 61 x 50.7
Signed, dated
Purchased 1988

CARSE, Alexander fl.1797-1838 (Scottish)
(attributed to)

U2674 **View of Edinburgh from Leith Mills**
(c.1820) *(Illus.p.233)*
Oil on canvas 95.5 x 149.8
Provenance unknown

CARVER, Richard d.1754 (Irish)

U132 **Landscape with Figures** *(Illus.p.233)*
Oil on canvas 101 x 131.5
Purchased 1968

CASEY, Comhghall b.1976 (Irish)

U5053 **Still Life**

Oil on canvas 55.8 x 66.3
Donated by the Thomas Haverty Trust,
1997

CATTERMOLE, Charles 1832-1900 (English)

U28 **Old Woman Knitting**
Oil on panel 17.8 x 25.1
Donated by W. T. Braithwaite (per J.
Horner), 1906

CAUER, Robert 1831-93 (German)

U1784 **Lord Kelvin 1824-1907 (1865)**
Sculpture, marble, ht.76.2
Signed, dated
Donated by Miss M. A. McKee, 1939

CAULFIELD, Patrick b.1936 (English)

U964 **Girl in a Doorway (1969)** *(Illus.p.233)*
Oil on canvas 274.3 x 182.9
Signed, dated
Purchased 1970

CERUTI, Giacomo 1698-1767 (Italian)

U19 **Boy with Vegetables** *(Illus.p.234)*
Oil on canvas 69.8 x 95.3
Purchased 1893

U20 **Boy with a Dog** *(Illus.p.234)*
Oil on canvas 71.1 x 96.5
Purchased 1893

CÉSAR b.1921 (French)

U969 **Une Place au Soleil (1960)** *(Illus.p.234)*
Sculpture, welded iron 56 x 38.5 x 42.8
Signed
Purchased 1965

CHALON, Alfred Edward 1780-1860 (English)

U1406 **A Reception** *(Illus.p.234)*
Watercolour, white on paper 14.9 x 10.8
Provenance unknown

CHALON, Henry Bernard 1770-1849 (English)

U2659 **The Curragh Sketchbook**
Pencil on paper 14 x 22.9, fifty pages,
half-bound
Donated by Mrs. Wilhelmina McAnally,
1953
Most of the following works are as titled
by the artist

1. Mr Padtesby / Baron Stockman / Sir
   Robt Gardner Bart. Black White and
   Raw Sienna / Asphaltum Indian Red
   and Blue / the Commencement
   Asphaltum / Black and Lake with
   Indian Red (Sketch of a Sunrise or
   Sunset over the Sea)

2. Olive Green Leaves / Pink Flowers

3. North East Side. The Cathedral of St
   Brigid Kildare, in Ireland. The Tower
   130 ft. in Height. / The Church of
   Kildare

4. Irish Girls

5. The Royal Stand / at the Curragh of /
   Kildare

6. The Curragh of Kildare in Ireland /
   Four Miles Post

7. The Curragh of Kildare in Ireland /
   Four Miles Post

8. The Road to Kildare / The Town of
   Kildare and the Curragh / The
   Rubbing House

9. Kildare / Hare Park / Rubbing
   House / The Curragh of Kildare /
   The Royal Stand

10. The Road to Kildare / Kildare / Red
    Hills /Straw Hill

11. Red Hills / The Gibbet Rath / The
    Curragh of Kildare

12. Hare Park / Kildare

13. The Road to Kildare / A Roman
    Catholic Chapel / The Friar's House

14. Road to Athy / Mrs Lee's Dairy /
    White Abbey

15. The Gate Belonging to White Abbey

16. Kildare's Chair

17. The Round Tower at Kildare in
    Ireland in Good Preservation at /
    Kildare it is a Hundred and Thirty
    Feet in Height, / Built of White
    Granite to about Twelve Feet above /
    the Ground, and the Rest of
    Common Blue Stone; / the Door is
    Fourteen Feet from the Foundation /
    A part of the Ruin of the Abbey / a
    Roman Catholic Chapel / the
    Pedestal of an Old Cross

18. The Ruins of St Bridget's Abbey /
    Kildare / Ireland

19. The Ruins of Jigginstown House,
    once a most Noble and Superb
    Edifice, / Built by the Unfortunate
    Earl of Strafford, and Intended as / a
    Country Residence for the Lord
    Lieutenant of Ireland, but / never
    Finished

20. The Ruins of the Old Church /
    Johnstown / Ireland

21. One Part of the Same Ruin of
    Johnstown's Church / Another view
    of the Same Church, Ireland

22. Newton House, Yorkshire

23. The Duke of Cleveland's Kennel at
    Newton House, / Yorkshire

24. The Duke of Cleveland's Kennel by
    Newton House Yorkshire

25. A River in a Valley

26. West View of the Iron Bridge,
    Sunderland

27. Part of North Shields towards Tyne
    Mouth

28. Tynemouth Castle. Sketch of a Dog

29. Mouth of the Tyne with the Harbour.

South Shields

30. **Tynemouth Castle** (the Ruins of Tynemouth Priory)

31. **Tynemouth Castle**

32. **Small Steamboats offshore**

33. **Two Sketches of Five-bar Gates**

34. **A Landscape with a Church Tower**

35. **A Dutch Barn**

36. **A Dog Carrying a Pheasant**

37. **A Dog Carrying a Pheasant, in a Landscape**

38. **A Dog Carrying a Pheasant**

39. **A Cottage and a Sketch of Bushes**

40. **Sir Tatton Syke's Covert**

41. **A Bridge**

42. **Thornton Hall** (Deer, Cattle, Horses and Sheep in a Park)

43. **Mr Hill's Eagle. Thornton, Yorksh.**

44. **Kerby Underdale**

45. **Repose Affection** (a Cat and Kitten asleep)

46. **Sketch of Farm Buildings**

47. **Sketches of a Farmhouse and some Farm Buildings**

48. **Studying Rufinus at St. Bees**

49. **Two Dogs Walking up Steps to a Doorway**

50. **Sheep by a Manger in a Park**

51. **A Dog Carrying a Pheasant**

CHANDRA, Avinash 1931-91 (Indian)

U1010 **Recollection of Belfast (1958)**
Ink, gouache on card 54.3 x 64.6
Signed, dated
Purchased 1958

CHARLEMONT, James Edward Geale Caulfield, 8th Viscount 1880-1949 (Irish)

U1572 **The Bell Tower, Chichester**
Pencil on paper 35.6 x 25.4
Signed
Donated by the artist, 1941

U1573 **Sherborne Minster, Dorset (1912)**
Pencil on paper 23.5 x 26.6
Signed, dated
Donated by the artist, 1941

CHARLES, James 1851-1906 (English)

U562 **The Goat Girl** (Illus.p.234)
Oil on canvas 46.4 x 68.8
Signed
Donated by Sir Hugh Lane, 1906

U587 **The Haystacks** (Illus.p.234)
Oil on canvas 61 x 48.2
Purchased 1923

CHAROUX, Siegfried 1896-1967 (Austrian, naturalised British)

U970 **The Friends (1951)**
Sculpture, bronze 63 x 26.5 x 16.5
Signed, dated
Purchased 1953

CHESTON, Charles Sidney 1882-1960 (English)

U1396 **River Barges** (Illus.p.234)
Pencil, watercolour on paper 21.2 x 29
Signed
Purchased 1954

CHINNERY, George 1774-1852 (English)

U1330 **Macao Harbour: Chinese River Scene (1839)**
Pencil on card 14.6 x 22
Signed, dated
Provenance unknown

CHIPP, Herbert fl.1877-98 (English)

U1687 **River Scene with Trees and Woman on Towpath (1878)** (Illus.p.234)
Pencil, watercolour on paper 26.2 x 51.5
Signed, dated
Purchased 1968

U1688 **Les Antelets, Sark, Channel Islands (1879)**
Watercolour on paper 16.4 x 30.7
Signed, dated
Purchased 1968

CHOWNE, Gerard 1875-1917 (English)

U1011 **A Park with a Pond** (formerly 'Landscape with Pond') (Illus.p.234)
Pencil, watercolour on paper 24.2 x 35.2
Donated by M. Salaman, 1944

CHRISTIE, Lorraine b.1967 (Irish)

U1949 **Floral Study**
Oil on canvas 27.9 x 35.5
Signed
Donated by Philip Solomon, 1999

CH'ÜAN, Chu 18th-19th century (?) (Chinese)

U346 **Riding Home with his Bag after a Night's Fowling**
See under Yü-Feng

CIPRIANI, Giovanni Battista 1727-85 (Italian)

U2110 **Seated Classical Female Figure** (Illus.p.235)
Ink, sepia on paper 25.3 x 35.2
Signed
Donated by J. H. Stirling, 1919

CLARKE, Carey 20th century (Irish)

U258 **Forestry Plantation, Winter** (Illus.p.235)
Oil on canvas 60.7 x 76.2
Signed
Donated by the Thomas Haverty Trust, 1966

CLARKE, Cyril 20th century (Irish)

U571 **Smithfield Market** (Illus.p.235)

Oil on canvas 50 x 65
Donated by J. Kavanagh, 1956

CLARKE, David 20th century (Irish)

U278 **Sevillana I (1949)** (Illus.p.235)
Gouache on board 66 x 47
Signed, dated
Donated by the Thomas Haverty Trust, 1950

CLARKE, Harry 1889-1931 (Irish)

U2644 **Cartoon for St. Hubert** (Illus.p.235)
Crayon, wash on paper 181 x 50
Purchased 1982

CLARKE, Margaret 1888-1961 (Irish)

U2645 **Portrait of Harry Clarke 1889-1931**
Oil on canvas 53 x 37.8
Signed
Purchased 1982

U4816 **Strindbergian (1927)**
Oil on canvas 127.5 x 102
Signed, dated
Purchased 1990

U5008 **Robin Redbreast** (Illus.p.235)
Oil on canvas 51 x 38.2
Signed
Purchased 1994

CLARKE-SMITH, Rosemary 20th century (British)

U709 **Dorothea Slate Quarry, Nantlle, North Wales (c.1968-69)** (Illus.p.235)
Ink, gouache on paper 77.2 x 55.3
Signed
Donated by R. A. Mitchell, 1969

CLARKSON, William H. fl.1893-1940 d.c.1944 (British)

U442 **Evening Star (c.1929)**
Oil on canvas 58.5 x 71.2
Signed
Donated by the Friends of the National Collections of Ireland, 1930

CLAUSEN, Sir George 1852-1944 (English)

U443 **Sunrise on the Road** (Illus.p.235)
Oil on canvas 51.3 x 61.4
Signed
Purchased 1947

U755 **Twilight** (Illus.p.235)
Gouache, watercolour on paper 24.3 x 29.4
Signed
Donated by the Contemporary Art Society, 1943

CLENNELL, Luke 1781-1840 (English)

U756 **Greenwich Park** (Illus.p.236)
Pencil, watercolour, white on paper 11.1 x 18.7
Purchased 1949

COCKRILL, Maurice b.1936 (British)

U2652 **Lawrence of Arabia's Brother (1979)**

(Illus.p.236)
Pastel on paper 73.6 x 54.6
Signed, dated
Purchased 1982

COHEN, Bernard b.1933 (English)

U527 **Knot (1962)** *(Illus.p.236)*
Oil on canvas 243.8 x 243.8
Signed, dated
Purchased 1965

COIGNET, Jules-Louis-Philippe 1798-1860
(French)

U1486 **Italian Landscape with Wagon**
Watercolour on paper 15.7 x 21.4
Signed
Donated by J. H. Bland, 1910

COLEMAN, Simon b.1916 (Irish)

U2078 **Interior with a Man at Breakfast Table
(1944)** *(Illus.p.236)*
Oil on canvas 50.8 x 40.6
Signed, dated
Bequeathed by Mrs. S. Allen Forbes, 1974

COLLIE, George Joseph 1904-75 (Irish)

U279 **Blighted Hopes (c.1933)** *(Illus.p.236)*
Oil on board 34 x 41.8
Signed
Donated by the Thomas Haverty Trust,
1936

COLLIER, Thomas 1840-91 (English)

U1012 **In Sussex**
Pencil, watercolour on paper 22.8 x 34.9
Signed
Purchased 1938

U1013 **Near Amberley, Sussex**
Watercolour on paper 24 x 35.5
Signed
Donated by Meta and Robert Dunlop,
1950

U1014 **The Path over the Moors** *(Illus.p.236)*
Pencil, watercolour on card 27.6 x 52.5
Signed
Purchased 1911

U1015 **Near Gomshall, Surrey**
Pencil, watercolour on paper 24.1 x 34.2
Signed
Donated by Meta and Robert Dunlop,
1950

COLLINS, Cecil 1908-89 (English)

U757 **Figure Seated in a Chair (1942)**
(Illus.p.236)
Ink, watercolour on paper 55.8 x 35
Signed, dated
Purchased 1970

COLLINS, Patrick 1910-94 (Irish)

U267 **Travelling Women (1957)** *(Illus.p.236)*
Oil on board 39.2 x 33.8
Signed
Donated by the Thomas Haverty Trust,
1960

U2660 **Fig Tree and Sun (1964)**
Oil on board 91.7 x 122.3
Signed, dated
Purchased 1983

COLLINS, William 1788-1847 (British)
(attributed to)

U96 **The Broom Seller**
Oil on board 56.4 x 46.6
Purchased 1954

CONDER, Charles Edward 1868-1909 (English)

U758 **In the Shadow of Pan (1905)** *(Illus.p.236)*
Watercolour on silk 45.5. x 84.8
Signed, dated
Purchased 1946

CONN, William H. 1895-1973 (Irish)

U1577 **Illustration to 'Willy Gilliland'**
(Illus.p.237)
Ink on paper 26.5 x 37.1
Signed
Purchased 1951

U1578 **Illustration to 'The Burial of King
Cormac'** *(Illus.p.237)*
Ink on paper 25.8 x 38
Signed
Purchased 1951

CONOR, William 1881-1968 (Irish)

U21 **R. V. Williams ('Richard Rowley') 1877-
1947**
Oil on canvas 86.7 x 69
Signed
Donated by J. S. Scott, 1935

U254 **The Jaunting Car (c.1933)** *(Illus.p.237)*
Oil on canvas 70.9 x 90.9
Signed
Donated by the Thomas Haverty Trust,
1936

U255 **The Melodeon Player**
Oil on canvas 90.2 x 69.8
Signed
Purchased 1922

U256 **Coortin' (c.1922)** *(Illus.p.237)*
Oil on canvas 75.6 x 50.2
Signed
Purchased 1922

U257 **The Painter's Mother (c.1919)**
Oil on canvas 74 x 60.5
Signed
Donated by the artist, 1957

U261 **Building an Air-raid Shelter (c.1940-41)**
Oil on board 58.5 x 47.9
Signed
Purchased 1941

U262 **Portrait of St. John Ervine 1883-1971
(1946)**
Oil on canvas 76 x 64
Signed
Donated by the sitter, 1965

U264 **Portrait of the Artist as a Young Man
(c.1920)**
Oil on board 54.9 x 37.9

Signed
Donated by the artist, 1957

U265 **The Warden**
Oil on canvas 50.8 x 40.6
Signed
Purchased 1941

U269 **The City Hall under Snow (c.1920s)**
(Illus.p.237)
Oil on canvas on board 42.9 x 53.3
Signed
Purchased 1957

U270 **The Latest News (1922)**
Oil on canvas 48.2 x 35.5
Signed, dated
Donated by Lady Cleaver, 1936

U289 **Christmas Card: Santa Claus Hanging
from a Lamp-post (1960)**
Ink, crayon on card 17 x 22
Signed, dated
Bequeathed by Mr. F. T. C. Lloyd, 1998

U875 **Recruiting Parade**
Crayon on paper 35.5 x 45.5
Signed
Purchased 1941

U876 **Men Working at a Shelter**
Crayon on paper 38 x 27.8
Signed
Purchased 1941

U877 **Children at the Building of a Shelter**
Crayon on paper 38.2 x 28
Signed
Purchased 1941

U878 **A Group of Evacuees**
Crayon on paper 38 x 27.7
Signed
Purchased 1941

U879 **The Signals**
Pencil, watercolour on paper 28.4 x 39.5
Signed
Purchased 1929

U880 **Study for Recruiting Parade: Bandsmen;
verso, Lola Montez**
Crayon, charcoal on paper 50.6 x 37.9
Signed
Purchased 1941

U881 **Shipyard Workers Crossing Queen's
Bridge (Study for 'Men of the Home
Front')**
Crayon on paper 38.2 x 27.9
Signed
Purchased 1941

U882 **A Sergeant of the ATS**
Crayon on paper 38.2 x 27.9
Signed
Purchased 1941

U883 **Ulster Rifleman's Wedding**
Crayon on paper 37 x 52.5 (sight)
Signed
Donated by the War Artists' Advisory
Committee (per the Imperial War
Museum), 1946

U884 **Evacuees at the Great Northern Railway
Station**

Crayon on paper 34 x 44.5 (sight)
Signed
Purchased 1941

U1016 **The Recruit (1914)**
Pencil, watercolour on paper 38.1 x 26.1
Signed, dated
Purchased 1915

U1168 **Fight and Endure (1914)**
Pencil, watercolour on paper 35 x 24.3
Signed, dated
Purchased 1915

U1169 **Ferry Boats, River Lagan**
Pencil, watercolour on paper 28.4 x 39
Signed
Purchased 1929

U1170 **Colin Glen, Belfast**
Pencil, watercolour on paper 39 x 28.5
Signed
Purchased 1930

U1171 **Men of Iron**
Pencil, crayon on paper 47.4 x 34
Signed
Purchased 1941

U1172 **Riveting**
Crayon on paper 45.5 x 35.5
Signed
Purchased 1941

U1173 **Evacuation of Children, Great Northern Railway Station, Belfast (1940s)**
Pencil, crayon on paper 34.5 x 46
Signed
Donated by the War Artists' Advisory Committee (per the Imperial War Museum), 1946

U1228 **The Lost Child** (Study)
Crayon on paper 86.8 x 57.8
Signed
Donated by the artist, 1922

U1229 **Off: The Ulster Division (1915)**
(Illus.p.237)
Charcoal, chalk on paper 55 x 37.3
Signed, dated
Donated by J. St. Clair Boyd, 1938

U1230 **Soldier on Point Duty**
Crayon on paper 51.7 x 38.2
Signed
Purchased 1941

U1231 **A Piper of the Irish Fusiliers**
Crayon on paper 53.3 x 36
Signed
Purchased 1941

U1232 **'Skins' on a Route March**
Crayon on paper 42.7 x 34.4 (sight)
Signed
Purchased 1941

U1233 **The Old Brigade**
Crayon on paper 50.9 x 33.6
Signed
Purchased 1941

U1234 **Lesson on a Bren Gun**
Crayon on paper 34.2 x 44 (sight)
Signed
Purchased 1941

U1235 **Grenade Throwing Practice**
Crayon on paper 45 x 34.3 (sight)
Signed
Purchased 1941

U1236 **Study for 'Grenade Throwing Practice'**
Crayon on paper 38.2 x 28.2
Signed
Purchased 1941

U1237 **FANYS crossing Donegall Place**
Crayon on paper 47.8 x 29 (sight)
Signed
Purchased 1941

U1238 **Soldier's Wedding;** verso, **Caroline Norton**
Crayon on paper 46 x 37.9
Signed
Purchased 1941

U1239 **Men of the Home Front** *(Illus.p.237)*
Crayon on paper 37.8 x 54.2
Signed
Purchased 1941

U1240 **Girls at Munitions**
Crayon on paper 39.5 x 29
Signed
Purchased 1941

U1241 **A Roof Spotter**
Crayon on paper 45.5 x 34.4
Signed
Purchased 1941

U1242 **Looking at Aeroplanes**
Crayon on paper 50.9 x 36.6
Signed
Purchased 1941

U1243 **Evacuee Children**
Crayon on paper 38.1 x 27.7
Signed
Purchased 1941

U1244 **Collecting Scrap Metal**
Crayon on paper 34.7 x 44.5 (sight)
Signed
Purchased 1941

U1245 **Thomas Carnduff 1886-1956**
Crayon on paper 38.3 x 28
Signed
Donated by the artist, 1947

U1246 **Passing the City Hall, Belfast, during a Recruiting March**
Crayon on paper 35 x 44.5 (sight)
Signed
Donated by the War Artists' Advisory Committee (per the Imperial War Museum), 1946

U1247 **A Tramway Depot, Belfast** (formerly 'A Training Depot, Belfast')
Crayon on paper 44 x 33.7 (sight)
Signed
Donated by the War Artists' Advisory Committee (per the Imperial War Museum), 1946

U1248 **Shipyard Workers Crossing Queen's Bridge (Men of the Home Front)**
Crayon on paper 34.5 x 46.8
Signed
Donated by the War Artists' Advisory

Committee (per the Imperial War Museum), 1946

U1249 **Lady Constance Malleson ('Colette O'Niel') 1895-1975;** verso, **Sketch of a Head**
Crayon on panel 88.7 x 67.9
Signed
Donated by the sitter, 1963

U1250 **The Riveter**
Chalk on paper 43.5 x 29.6
Signed
Provenance unknown

U1251 **Bugler, Ulster Division (1916)**
Charcoal, chalk on paper 55 x 37.9
Signed, dated
Purchased 1968

U1932 **Councillor James A. Doran, JP 1848-1934 (1930)**
Oil on canvas 76.2 x 62.8
Signed, dated
Donated by public subscription, 1931

U1934 **Ulster Past and Present (1931)** (Mural)
Oil on canvas 282.9 x 740.9
Signed, dated
Donated by Sir Robert Baird, 1932

U1935 **Variety Market**
Oil on canvas on board 46.4 x 36.2
Signed
Purchased 1957

U2108 **Two Uniformed Bandsmen and a Girl** (formerly 'Two Soldiers and a Girl')
Pencil, crayon on paper 30.2 x 22.9
Signed
Purchased 1956

U2322 **Weaving (Galway Bridge?)** *(Illus.p.237)*
Crayon on paper 45.1 x 30.2 (sight)
Signed
Donated by Mrs. Grace Leech, 1975

U2361 **Antirrinhums**
Pencil, watercolour on paper 38.7 x 28.6
Signed
Donated by Thomas Purdy, 1975

U2533 **Portrait of Leslie Montgomery ('Lynn Doyle') 1873-1961**
Crayon on paper 42.2 x 32.8 (sight)
Signed
Donated by Mrs. McCutcheon, 1980

U2651 **Samuel John Waddell 1878-1967**
Oil on canvas 45.6 x 35
Signed
Purchased 1982

U4670 **The Launch**
Crayon on paper 44.1 x 34.9 (sight)
Signed
Purchased 1941

U4740 **Return From Work (c.1931)**
Oil on canvas 105.4 x 80
Signed
Donated by Dr. Michael Smurfit in memory of his mother, Mrs. Ann Magee Smurfit and on behalf of the Jefferson Smurfit Foundation, 1988

U4772 **The Elder Sister (c.1920)**
Oil on board 60 x 50

Bequeathed by Roberta and John Hewitt, 1987

CONSTABLE, Jane Bennett b.1865 (Scottish)

U2685 **The Last Sheaves: October Harvest Sketch** *(Illus.p.237)*
Pastel on paper 43.2 x 78.7
Signed
Bequeathed by Miss E. Taylor, 1983

CONWAY, James 1891-1968 (Irish)

U277 **Sez You (1934)** *(Illus.p.238)*
Oil on canvas 69.7 x 49.7
Signed, dated
Donated by the Thomas Haverty Trust, 1936

COOGAN, Patric b.1935 (Irish)

U4724 **6.10 p.m.** *(Illus.p.238)*
Oil, acrylic on board 90.3 x 101.7
Signed
Purchased 1987

COOKE, Barrie b.1931 (Irish)

U253 **Current (1962-63)** *(Illus.p.238)*
Oil on canvas 126.7 x 126.8
Signed, dated
Purchased 1964

U2287 **Big Tench Lake (1972)** *(Illus. p.238)*
Oil on two canvases, 183.2 x 304.8 overall, with a perspex box 60.6 x 81.2 x 15.3
Signed, dated
Purchased 1974

U2666 **Recumbent Nude**
Oil on canvas 76 x 61
Purchased 1982

COOKE-COLLIS, Sylvia 1900-73 (Irish)

U1931 **Tinkers in the Nagle Mountains**
Oil on board 48.2 x 64.5
Donated by the Thomas Haverty Trust, 1950

COOLEY, Thomas 1795-1872 (Irish)

U1871 **Couple at a Games Table (1816)** *(Illus.p.238)*
Pencil, ink on paper 20 x 16.5
Signed, dated
Purchased 1973

COOPER, Thomas Sidney 1803-1902 (English)

U18 **Study of a Cow**
Oil on board 17 x 22.2
Bequeathed by Dr. R. I. Best (per the Friends of the National Collections of Ireland), 1959

COOPER, Winifred fl.1905-29 (British)

U1588 **Girl Using Pirn Winder or Swift (1918)** *(Illus.p.238)*
Charcoal on paper 36.8 x 26.5
Signed, dated
Donated by Paul Henry, 1937

COPNALL, Edward Bainbridge 1903-73 (English)

U1857 **Mother and Child (1930)** *(Illus.p.238)*
Sculpture, Portland stone 102.5 x 99 x 49.6
Signed, dated
Donated by the Friends of the National Collections of Ireland, 1940

CORKERY, Daniel 1878-1964 (Irish)

U760 **Frankfield, Cork** *(Illus.p.238)*
Watercolour on paper 20.1 x 27.6
Provenance unknown

U4722 **An Open Landscape**
Watercolour on board 18.8 x 27
Provenance unknown

CORRY, Emily D. 1873-1942 (Irish)

U275 **Elderberries** *(Illus.p.238)*
Oil on canvas 50.8 x 76.2
Signed
Donated by J. W. Corry, 1943

U1017 **Long Shadows, Torquay Woods**
Pencil, watercolour on paper 38.1 x 26.7
Signed
Donated by J. W. Corry, 1943

COTA, Frane 1898-1951 (Yugoslavian)

U1783 **Zlatko Neumann 1902-69 (1929)** (formerly 'Head of a Young Man')
Sculpture, bronze head, ht. 39.4
Signed
Purchased 1931

COTMAN, John Sell 1782-1842 (English)

U761 **Harlech Castle (c.1803-4)** *(Illus.p.239)*
Pencil, watercolour on paper 34.4 x 43.9
Purchased 1935

COULTER, Laurence b.1937 (American)

U4976 **Professor Anne Crookshank b.1927 (1994)** *(Illus.p.239)*
Oil on board 122 x 91.1
Signed
Purchased 1994

COX, David 1783-1859 (English)

U762 **The Snowstorm** *(Illus.p.239)*
Pencil, charcoal, watercolour on paper 37.5 x 54.7
Signed
Purchased 1954

U763 **Near Bettws-y-Coed** *(Illus.p.239)*
Watercolour on paper 49.7 x 74
Signed
Purchased 1937

U764 **Landscape with Figure and Cattle**
Watercolour on paper 16 x 22.7
Signed
Purchased 1912

U765 **Scarborough**
Pencil, watercolour on paper 29.7 x 45.4
Purchased 1923

U4666 **Mountain Landscape**
Watercolour, charcoal on paper 26 x 17.8

Purchased 1924

COX, David, Jnr. 1809-85 (English) (attributed to)

U766 **Landscape with Shed (1843)**
Pencil, watercolour, white on paper 32 x 45.5
Signed, dated
Purchased 1950

COZENS, John Robert 1752-97 (English)

U767 **Capo di Bove** (Tomb of Caecilia Metella, Appian Way, Rome) *(Illus.p.239)*
Pencil, watercolour on paper 31.2 x 28.1
Purchased 1938

CRABTREE, Jack b.1938 (English)

U4707 **Portrait of Brian Friel b.1929 (1986-87)** *(Illus.p.239)*
Oil on canvas 167.5 x 168.2
Signed, dated
Purchased 1987

U4734 **Study for 'Portrait of Brian Friel' (1987)**
Watercolour, gouache on paper 74.5 x 54.5 (sight)
Signed, dated
Donated by the artist, 1988

U4969 **Patterson's Spade Mill, Templepatrick** *(Illus.p.239)*
Oil on canvas, four paintings in one frame, each 86 x 86; 172.7 x 172.7 overall
Purchased 1993

CRACE, John Diblee 1838-after 1914 (English)

U2480 **Lough Cutra Castle, Co. Galway (1891)**
Pencil, watercolour on paper 12.7 x 17.8
Dated
Purchased 1978

CRAFT, Percy Robert 1856-1934 (English)

U612 **An Impression of Damascus**
Pastel on paper 50.4 x 75.8
Signed
Donated by H. B. Craft, 1935

CRAIG, James Humbert 1877-1944 (Irish)

U268 **A Good Catch, Co. Donegal (1943-44)**
Oil on canvas 49.6 x 59.7
Donated by Mrs. A. S. Craig, 1945

U271 **The Kerry Coast (c.1928)** *(Illus.p.239)*
Oil on canvas 61.7 x 76.8
Signed
Donated by the artist, 1930

U276 **Turf Bog, Connemara (c.1920-40)**
Oil on canvas 50.8 x 61
Signed
Acquired by exchange from Mrs. A. S. Craig, 1945

U280 **A Summer Day on the Thames (c.1930)**
Oil on board 26.4 x 29.5
Signed
Purchased 1931

U577 **Grey Day, Cushendun**
Oil on canvas 38.2 x 50.9

Signed
Purchased 1945

U4773 **Drumfresky, Cushendun**
Oil on board 25.7 x 35.7
Bequeathed by Roberta and John Hewitt,
1987

CRAIG-MARTIN, Michael b.1941 (British)

U2567a **Untitled Wall Drawing (1979)** (Original
Drawing for U2567)
Tape on acetate on paper 41.6 x 59
Signed, dated
Purchased 1980

U2567 **Untitled Wall Drawing (1979)**
Chartpak tape on gallery wall, size
variable (from projected image)
Purchased 1980

CRANE, Walter 1845-1915 (English)

U1274 **A Pastoral (1872)** *(Illus.p.239)*
Bodycolour on paper 49.4 x 68.5
Signed, dated
Purchased 1952

CRAWFORD, Ebenezer 1830-74 (Irish)

U1275 **Sketch for 'An Incident of the Great
Plague of London, 1665' (1872)**
(Illus.p.240)
Pencil, sepia, white on paper 14.6 x 12
Donated by B. McCoy, 1909

CRAWLEY, Thomas A. 20th century (Irish)

U1018 **The Shelter Warden (1942)**
Pencil, watercolour on paper 29.8 x 46.8
Signed, dated
Purchased 1943

CREGAN, Martin 1788-1870 (Irish)

U731 **Francis Johnston 1760-1829, his Wife
and Two Nephews (c.1827)** *(Illus.p.240)*
Oil on canvas 97.7 x 80.3
Purchased 1971

CRETI, Donato 1671-1749 (Italian)

U24 **Pastoral Landscape with Figures**
(Illus.p.240)
Oil on copper 58 x 76.5
Purchased 1963

CRISTALL, Joshua 1767-1847 (English)

U1019 **A Stick Gatherer near Hastings (1807)**
(Illus.p.240)
Pencil, watercolour on paper 21.7 x 12.1
Signed, dated
Purchased 1952

CRONE, David b.1937 (Irish)

U651 **Rocks and Vegetation (1964)**
Oil on canvas 76 x 102
Purchased 1965

U4721 **Figures in the City (1985)**
Gouache, chalk on paper 98 x 112
Purchased 1986

U4890 **By Railings (1991)** *(Illus.p.240)*

Oil on canvas 140 x 275
Purchased 1991

CROSS, Dorothy b.1956 (Irish)

U5002 **Passion Bed (1990)** *(Illus.p.240)*
Sculpture, wire and sand-blasted wine
glasses 154.5 x 169 x 52
Purchased 1994

CROWLEY, Nicholas Joseph 1819-57 (Irish)

U22 **Self-Portrait (c.1854)**
Oil on canvas 91.5 x 73.5
Donated by J. F. Johnson, 1896

U643 **John Ward 1777-1836 (c.1836)**
(Illus.p.240)
Oil on canvas 71 x 59
Purchased 1938

CROZIER, William b.1930 (Scottish)

U749 **Still Life** *(Illus.p.240)*
Oil on canvas 107.2 x 113.7
Signed
Purchased 1999

CRUICKSHANK, William fl.1866-79 (English)

U4510 **Still Life with Dead Hare and Grouse**
(Illus.p.240)
Miniature, watercolour on ivory 9.4 x
13.6
Signed
Donated by Meta and Robert Dunlop,
1950

U4511 **Bird's Nest and Lilac** *(Illus.p.241)*
Miniature, watercolour on ivory 12.5 x
10 (sight) (oval)
Signed
Donated by Meta and Robert Dunlop,
1950

CRUMPLIN, Colin b.1946 (British)

U2531 **Homage à Queneau (1971-75)**
Pencil on paper, ten works, each 30.5 x
30.5
Donated by the Contemporary Art
Society, 1980

CULLEN, Michael b.1946 (Irish)

U4979 **Mexican Video Banditti and the
Prosciutto Hunters** *(Illus.p.241)*
Oil, wax on linen 203 x 203
Purchased 1994

CUTHBERTSON, William A. fl.1920-46
(English)

U2681 **On the Beach** *(Illus.p.241)*
Oil on canvas on board 24.1 x 33
Signed
Bequeathed by Miss E. Taylor, 1983

D

DADD, Frank 1851-1929 (English)

U1541 **Book Illustration**
Ink on paper 14.9 x 9.9 (sight)

Signed
Purchased 1928

U1815 **Book Illustration**
Ink on paper 14.9 x 9.9 (sight)
Signed
Purchased 1928

U1958 **Book Illustration**
Ink on paper 14.9 x 9.9 (sight)
Signed
Purchased 1928

DAINTREY, Adrian Maurice 1902-88 (English)

U445 **Philip Wilson Steer 1860-1942 (1933)**
Oil on canvas 76.2 x 63.7
Signed, dated
Donated by the Contemporary Art
Society, 1944

DANBY, Francis 1793-1861 (Irish)

U769 **The Folly, Blaise Castle, near Bristol**
(Illus.p.241)
Pencil, watercolour on paper 19.2 x 26.9
Purchased 1911

U2095 **Ringsend from Beggar's Bush, Co.
Dublin** *(Illus.p.241)*
Watercolour on paper 20.8 x 30.5
Signed
Provenance unknown

U2096 **Mill near Beggar's Bush, Co. Dublin**
(Illus.p.241)
Watercolour on paper 21 x 27.9
Signed
Provenance unknown

U2097 **Castle Archdale on Lough Erne, Co.
Fermanagh** *(Illus.p.241)*
Watercolour on paper 22.2 x 30.5
Signed
Provenance unknown

U2098 **Dunleary from the South** *(Illus.p.241)*
Watercolour on paper 22.8 x 30.5
Signed
Provenance unknown

DANCE, George 1741-1825 (English)

U2460 **William Dickson 1745-1804, Bishop of
Down and Connor (1794)** *(Illus.p.241)*
Pencil, wash on paper 25.8 x 19.4
Signed, dated
Purchased 1978

DAVIDSON, Charles 1824-1902 (English)

U770 **Newcastle, Co. Down** *(Illus.p.242)*
Pencil, watercolour on paper 19.7 x 46.7
Signed
Purchased 1952

DAVIDSON, Lilian Lucy 1879-1954 (Irish)

U609 **Low Tide, Wicklow (c.1934)** *(Illus.p.242)*
Oil on canvas 73 x 92
Signed
Donated by the Thomas Haverty Trust,
1936

DAVIE, Alan b.1920 (Scottish)

U535 **Imp of Clubs (1957)** *(Illus.p.242)*

                                     ULSTER MUSEUM, FINE ART COLLECTION

Oil on canvas 213 x 172.7
Signed, dated
Purchased 1963

DAVIES, Anthony b.1947 (English)

U4815 **Old Couple at Home (1990)** *(Illus.p.242)*
Watercolour on white paper 78.1 x 112
Purchased 1990

DAVIES, John b.1946 (English)

U2413 **Man with Ring (1975)** *(Illus.p.242)*
Sculpture, fibreglass, cloth, mixed media
186 x 57 x 53.5; base 195.7 x 167.9 x 4.4
Purchased 1976

DAWSON, Robert (Bobby) d.1991 (Irish)

U4904 **Head in Equilibrium (1940)**
Oil on paper 31.7 x 31.7
Signed
Donated by Miss Marjorie Walsh, 1992

DAYES, Edward 1763-1804 (English)

U1020 **Dunfermline Abbey, Fife, Scotland**
(Illus.p.242)
Pencil, watercolour on paper 29.1 x 23.4
Signed
Purchased 1937

DEALY, Janie M. (Lady Lewis) fl.1881 d.1939
(English)

U1021 **Children on the Beach** (Four Book
Illustrations)
Each ink, watercolour on paper 7.5 x 8.3
(sight)
Signed
Purchased 1928

DE BURCA, Micheál J. 1913-85
See under Michael J. Bourke

DE CRESPIGNY, Rose fl.1891-1929 (Irish)

U1022 **Charing Cross Bridge, London**
(Illus.p.242)
Watercolour on paper 28.7 x 38.8
Signed
Bequeathed by H. Musgrave, 1922

DE FRANCIA, Peter b.1921 (British)

U4776 **Figure Drawing (1962)** *(Illus.p.242)*
Pencil on paper 35.5 x 25.5
Signed, dated
Bequeathed by Roberta and John Hewitt,
1987

DELAMOTTE, William 1775-1863 (English)

U771 **Ghent (1818)** *(Illus.p.242)*
Pencil, watercolour on paper 11.9 x 18.6
Signed, dated
Purchased 1952

DELANEY, Edward b.1932 (Irish)

U1758 **Cathedral No. 1 (1965)** *(Illus.p.243)*
Sculpture, bronze 85.7 x 15.9 x 11.7
Purchased 1965

DELAPLANCHE, Eugène 1836-91 (French)
(after)

U1785 **Maternal Education**
Sculpture, bronze, ht. 62.2
Purchased 1892

DELEN, Dirck van 1605-71 (Dutch)

U32 **Interior of a Renaissance Church (1652)**
(Illus.p.243)
Oil on panel 59 x 81
Signed, dated
Bequeathed by W. T. Braithwaite (per J.
Horner), 1906

DELLA PORTA, Fra Guglielmo d.1577 (Italian)
(after)
See under Porta

DENNY, Robyn b.1930 (English)

U536 **Remember (1966-67)**
Oil on canvas 243.8 x 198.1
Purchased 1969

DEVIS, Anthony 1729-1816 (English)

U772 **Olivares and La Brisca** *(Illus.p.243)*
Pencil, watercolour on paper 36 x 52.2
Purchased 1948

U2432 **Dublin Bay**
Pencil, wash, watercolour on paper 35 x
47.7
Purchased 1977

DEVIS, Arthur 1711-87 (English)

U2312 **Richard Boyle, 2nd Earl of Shannon
1727-1807 (1748)** *(Illus.p.243)*
Oil on canvas 61 x 40.5
Signed, dated
Purchased 1975

DE WINT, Peter 1784-1849 (English)

U773 **Landscape with Cottage** *(Illus.p.243)*
Watercolour on paper 22.1 x 33.9
Purchased 1926

U774 **An Upland Village** *(Illus.p.243)*
Watercolour on paper 61.2 x 44.3
Purchased 1948

DICKEY, E.M. O'Rorke 1894-1977 (Irish)

U282 **San Vito Romano (1923)** *(Illus.p.243)*
Oil on canvas 82.1 x 101.9
Signed, dated
Purchased 1924

U4902 **Budleigh Salterton from Jubilee Park
(1925-26)** *(Illus.p.243)*
Oil on canvas 101.6 x 76.2
Purchased 1992

DICKSON, Rodney b.1956 (Irish)

U1175 **Sketch Book for 'The Hurricane'**
(Seventy-eight Leaves)
Charcoal on paper 30.2 x 21.5
Donated by the artist, 1998

U1220 **Sketch Book for 'The Hurricane'**
(Seventy-three Leaves)
Charcoal on paper 30.2 x 21.5

Donated by the artist, 1998

U5070 **The Hurricane (Portrait of Alex Higgins)
b.1949 (1992)**
Oil on canvas 260 x 300
Donated by the artist, 1998

DIGHTON, Robert 1752-1814 (English)

U2530 **Mr. William Irwin (1798)** *(Illus.p.243)*
Watercolour on paper 24.4 x 17.2
Signed, dated
Purchased 1979

DILLON, Gerard 1916-71 (Irish)

U283 **Yellow Bungalow (1954)** *(Illus.p.244)*
Oil on canvas 76.8 x 81.2
Signed
Donated by the Thomas Haverty Trust,
1956

U287 **Medical Students (c.1949)** *(Illus.p.244)*
Oil on canvas 46 x 56.4
Signed
Donated by the Thomas Haverty Trust,
1951

U288 **The Yellow Field** *(Illus.p.244)*
Ink, crayon on paper 24 x 35 (sight)
Signed
Purchased 1957

U1879 **Puck**
Gouache, crayon on paper 41.9 x 30.5
Donated by W. A. Seaby, 1973

U4899 **Circus Acrobats**
Oil on canvas 58.4 x 41.9
Signed
Donated by J. A. H. Allen, 1992

U4900 **Glenoe Village, Co. Antrim**
Oil on board 40.6 x 30.5
Signed
Donated by J. A. H. Allen, 1992

U4901 **Children Playing on Lagan**
Oil on canvas on cardboard 33.6 x 43.8
Signed
Donated by J. A. H. Allen, 1992

U4974 **Self-contained Flat** *(Illus.p.244)*
Oil on hardboard 121.5 x 183.2
Signed
Purchased 1993

DIXON, James 1887-1970 (Irish)

U284 **British Minesweepers at Work between
Tory Island and the Mainland (1965)**
(Illus.p.244)
Oil on paper on board 56.1 x 75.9
Signed, dated
Donated by Derek Hill, 1965

U726 **Mr. William Rogers Plowing (sic) in
Dixon Farm Tory Island: The First
Tractor that ever Came to Tory Island
(1967)**
Oil on paper on board 57.2 x 76
Signed, dated
Purchased 1971

DIXON, John d.1970 (Irish)

U733 **Tory Island** *(Illus.p.244)*

Oil on paper 54.8 x 75
Purchased 1967

DIXON, Samuel fl.1748-69 (Irish)

U2329 **The Red-legged Partridge from Barbary**
(Illus.p.244)
Bodycolour on embossed paper 25.3 x
20.3
Purchased 1975

U2330 **The Peacock Pheasant from China**
(Illus.p.244)
Bodycolour on embossed paper 23.8 x
18.2
Purchased 1975

DOKOUPIL, Jiri Georg b.1954
(Czechoslovakian)

U4694 **Untitled (1982)** *(Illus.p.244)*
Oil on canvas 250 x 158
Donated by the Contemporary Irish Art
Society, 1986

DOMINGUEZ, Goyo b.1960 (Spanish)

U5043 **Bodegon Bellini (1996)** *(Illus.p.245)*
Acrylic on board 81 x 100
Signed, dated
Donated by the artist, 1996

DONAGH, Rita b.1939 (English)

U2509 **'...morning workers pass...'** *(Illus.p.245)*
Oil, newspaper on canvas 140 x 200
Purchased 1978

DONALD, Adam Tannochie 1911-91 (Scottish)

U4842 **Small Farm, Donegal** *(Illus.p.245)*
Pencil, watercolour on paper 26.7 x 36.8
(sight)
Signed
Donated by Ruth Donald, 1991

U4843 **Building a Haystack**
Charcoal on paper 25.4 x 36.8
Signed
Donated by Ruth Donald, 1991

U4844 **Drawings for Abstract Compositions**
Pencil, gouache on paper 25.4 x 38.1
Donated by Ruth Donald, 1991

DONALDSON, Antony b.1939 (English)

U958 **Iris (1968)** *(Illus.p.245)*
Sculpture, painted metal, fibreglass, wood
186.1 x 188.5 x 60
Purchased 1969

DONNELLY, Micky b.1952 (Irish)

U4945 **Connolly's Chair (1992)** *(Illus.p.245)*
Oil, mixed media on canvas 152 x 152
Purchased 1992

DOUGLAS, Harry R. 1862-1934 (Irish)

U33 **Isaac W. Ward 1834-1916**
('Belfastiensis') (c.1895-1905)
(Illus.p.245)
Oil on canvas 58.5 x 47.8
Signed
Purchased 1917

U219 **Robert Barklie, FCS, MRIA 1837-1910**
(1895)
Oil on canvas 91.6 x 71.2
Signed, dated
Donated by Mr. F. Barklie and Mrs. I.
Barklie, c.1951

U569 **Lady M. A. Henderson 1861-1942**
(c.1898)
Oil on canvas 117 x 91.5
Signed
Donated by Mrs. M. Haughton, 1967

U682 **Portrait of a Man**
Oil on canvas 51.4 x 41
Signed
Purchased 1969

U1936 **James Alexander Henderson 1823-83**
Oil on cardboard 38 x 30.6
Signed
Donated by Sir Trevor Henderson, 1928

U2459 **Portrait of an Unknown Man (1924)**
Oil on canvas 142.5 x 111.7
Signed, dated
Provenance unknown
Formerly by Unknown, Art dept. U4490

U4492 **Jonathan Phenix, JP 1845-97**
Oil on canvas 126.5 x 88.3
Signed
Donated by Portrait Committee, 1898

U4506 **Sir William Turner 1872-1937**
Oil on canvas 52 x 47.5
Provenance unknown

DOUGLAS, Jessie fl.1893-1928 (Irish)

U1023 **Cherry Ripe** *(Illus.p.245)*
Watercolour on paper 32 x 26
Provenance unknown

DOWNSHIRE, Evelyn, Marchioness of d.1942
(Irish)

U285 **Mountain Scene, Co. Down**
Oil on canvas 50.7 x 61.1
Donated by the Downshire Estate, 1944

DOYLE, Richard 1824-83 (British)

U1024 **Girl Reading** (Book Illustration)
(Illus.p.245)
Ink, watercolour on paper 22.7 x 16.5
Signed
Purchased 1952

DOYLE, Richard or **Charles Altimont DOYLE**
1832-93

U1025 **Fairy Ploughing** (formerly 'Fantasy')
(Illus.p.245)
Ink, watercolour on paper 18.5 x 31.8
Purchased 1951

DREW, Pamela 1910-89 (Irish)

U1939 **Tanker 'British Explorer', Basin Trials**
(1950)
Oil on board 36.8 x 53.3
Signed, dated
Purchased 1953

DRUMMOND, Malcolm 1880-1945 (English)

U2077 **Landscape with Trees (c.1925)**
(Illus.p.246)
Oil on canvas 51.2 x 34.9
Purchased 1974

U2080 **Landscape with Trees (c.1925)** (Study
for U2077)
Pencil, sepia on paper 30.5 x 21.5
Purchased 1974

DRURY, Susanna fl.1733-70 (Irish)

U1652 **East Prospect of the Giant's Causeway**
(c.1739) *(Illus.p.246)*
Gouache on vellum 34 x 67.8
Signed
Purchased 1971

U1653 **West Prospect of the Giant's Causeway**
(c.1739) *(Illus.p.246)*
Gouache on vellum 34.1 x 66.6
Purchased 1971

DUBUFFET, Jean 1901-85 (French)

U524 **Femme et Bébé (1956)** *(Illus.p.246)*
Oil on canvas 100.6 x 81.6
Signed, dated
Purchased 1965

DUFEU, Edouard-Jacques 1840-1900 (French)

U657 **Still Life** *(Illus.p.246)*
Oil on panel 32.9 x 41.1
Signed
Donated by Dr. R. H. Hunter, 1941

DUFFY, Rita b.1959 (Irish)

U4698 **Dr. D. B. McNeill b.1911 (1987)**
Oil on board 122 x 88.6
Signed, dated
Purchased 1987

U4984 **Nuptial Grooming (1994)** *(Illus.p.246)*
Oil on canvas 122.2 x 122.2
Signed
Purchased 1994

DULAC, Edmund 1882-1953 (French, worked in
England)

U2066 **Caricature of George Moore 1852-1933**
Pencil on paper 31.5 x 22.3
Purchased 1974

DU MAURIER, George 1834-96 (French,
naturalised British)

U1595 **'Valour in the Field'** *(Illus.p.246)*
Pencil, ink on paper 35.5 x 25.4
Signed
Donated by the National Art Collections
Fund, 1935

U1596 **'The Art of Conversation'**
Pencil, ink on paper 35.6 x 25.7
Signed
Donated by the National Art Collections
Fund, 1935

U1597 **'Unlucky Compliment' (1892)**
Pencil, ink on paper 25.5 x 20.8
Signed
Donated by the National Art Collections
Fund, 1935

U1598 'L'axong d'Albiong'
Pencil, ink on paper 25 x 25.7
Signed
Donated by the National Art Collections
Fund, 1935

U1599 'English as She is Sometimes Spoke'
Pencil, ink on paper 25.3 x 17.4
Signed
Donated by the National Art Collections
Fund, 1935

DUNCAN, Edward 1803-82 (English)
Fifty-two works, each with a studio stamp

U1496 Windmill Study, near Paris
Pencil on paper 21.6 x 34.2
Donated by J. F. Johnson, 1896

U1497 At Strasbourg (1835)
Pencil, ink, sepia on paper 26.2 x 35.6
Dated
Donated by J. F. Johnson, 1896

U1498 Market Place, Boulogne
Pencil, ink, sepia on paper 23.3 x 32.4
Donated by J. F. Johnson, 1896

U1499 The Happy Valley: near Marquise, France
Pencil on paper 18.5 x 26.3
Donated by J. F. Johnson, 1896

U1500 Notre Dame, Paris
Pencil on paper 22.9 x 34.8
Donated by J. F. Johnson, 1896

U1501 On the Seine, Paris
Pencil, white on paper 19.6 x 33.9
Donated by J. F. Johnson, 1896

U1502 Near Boulogne, France
Pencil on paper 24.2 x 35.2
Donated by J. F. Johnson, 1896

U1503 Metz, Lorraine, Rue des Tanneurs
Pencil on paper 16.9 x 21.6
Signed
Donated by J. F. Johnson, 1896

U1504 Strasbourg (1839)
Pencil, white, sepia on paper 23.5 x 34.3
Dated
Donated by J. F. Johnson, 1896

U1505 Near Boulogne
Pencil, watercolour on paper 26.3 x 36.8
Donated by J. F. Johnson, 1896

U1506 Entrance to Boulogne from the East Road
Pencil, sepia on paper 24.6 x 34.5 (sight)
Donated by J. F. Johnson, 1896

U1507 On the Seine, Paris
Pencil on paper 20 x 34.7
Donated by J. F. Johnson, 1896

U1508 A Frenchwoman, Right Profile
Pencil on paper 29 x 18.2
Donated by J. F. Johnson, 1896

U1509 Two Studies of a Peasant Woman
(Illus.p.246)
Pencil, watercolour on paper 20 x 27
Signed
Donated by J. F. Johnson, 1896

U1510 Welsh Girl on a Donkey
Pencil, watercolour on paper 22.4 x 19.3

Donated by J. F. Johnson, 1896

U1511 Scottish Peasants: Seated Girl and
Standing Young Man (1876)
Pencil, watercolour on paper 19.4 x 18.2
Dated
Donated by J. F. Johnson, 1896

U1512 Young Scottish Peasant
Pencil on paper 17.5 x 9.5
Donated by J. F. Johnson, 1896

U1513 Man in Smock
Pencil on paper 18.7 x 11
Signed
Donated by J. F. Johnson, 1896

U1514 Man in Shooting Attire
Pencil on paper 16 x 7.8
Donated by J. F. Johnson, 1896

U1515 Fisherman with Basket
Pencil on paper 16 x 13.6
Signed
Donated by J. F. Johnson, 1896

U1516 Man Sitting on a Bank
Pencil on paper 18 x 11.8
Signed
Donated by J. F. Johnson, 1896

U1517 Peasant Girl Seated on a Rock
Pencil, watercolour on paper 16.2 x 13.4
Donated by J. F. Johnson, 1896

U1518 Girl Seated on Ground
Pencil, watercolour on paper 19.6 x 15.3
Donated by J. F. Johnson, 1896

U1519 Barefoot Peasant Woman
Pencil, watercolour on paper 21.9 x 15.8
(sight)
Donated by J. F. Johnson, 1896

U1520 Girl with Basket
Pencil, watercolour on paper 26 x 16.3
Donated by J. F. Johnson, 1896

U1521 Girl Seated amongst Hay
Pencil, watercolour on paper 20 x 21.4
Donated by J. F. Johnson, 1896

U1522 Boy Carrying Bundle
Pencil, watercolour on paper 19.7 x 13.4
Donated by J. F. Johnson, 1896

U1523 Scottish Soldier Wearing Kilt
Pencil on paper 24 x 14.6
Donated by J. F. Johnson, 1896

U1524 Standing Woman with Clasped Hands
Pencil on paper 25.1 x 14.8
Donated by J. F. Johnson, 1896

U1525 Study of a Boy Full Face
Pencil, watercolour on paper 14.7 x 6.9
Donated by J. F. Johnson, 1896

U1526 Study of a Boy in Profile
Pencil, watercolour on paper 14.3 x 7.5
Donated by J. F. Johnson, 1896

U1527 Woman Shielding Eyes
Pencil, watercolour on paper 17.4 x 10
Donated by J. F. Johnson, 1896

U1528 Woman Carrying Baskets
Pencil, watercolour on paper 19.7 x 12
Donated by J. F. Johnson, 1896

U1529 Three Groups of French (?) Peasants
Pencil, watercolour, ink on paper 9.4 x
20.7
Donated by J. F. Johnson, 1896

U1530 A Soldier, a Group of Sailors and a
Woman
Pencil, watercolour, ink, sepia on paper
8.6 x 16.1
Donated by J. F. Johnson, 1896

U1531 Group of Seven French (?) Peasants
Pencil, watercolour, ink, sepia on paper
10.8 x 19.7
Donated by J. F. Johnson, 1896

U1532 Peasant Woman at a Pump
Pencil, ink on paper 8.6 x 12.4
Donated by J. F. Johnson, 1896

U1533 Two Women with Shrimp Nets
Pencil, ink on paper 8 x 11.3
Donated by J. F. Johnson, 1896

U1534 Two Studies of a Woman and a Donkey
Pencil, ink on paper 11.2 x 9.1
Donated by J. F. Johnson, 1896

U1535 Three Studies of Women
Pencil, ink on paper 12.7 x 14.3
Donated by J. F. Johnson, 1896

U1536 Five Women Laundering Clothes
Pencil, ink on paper 11.8 x 25.8
Donated by J. F. Johnson, 1896

U1547 Man with Fishing Rod
Pencil on paper 10.6 x 7.5
Donated by J. F. Johnson, 1896

U1548 Man Digging
Pencil on paper 13.6 x 8.9
Donated by J. F. Johnson, 1896

U1549 Man with Stick and Lantern
Pencil on paper 15.4 x 9.9
Donated by J. F. Johnson, 1896

U1550 Man Leaning on a Wall
Pencil on paper 11.9 x 8.1
Donated by J. F. Johnson, 1896

U1551 Woman with Basket on her Back
Pencil, ink on paper 13.1 x 8.2
Donated by J. F. Johnson, 1896

U1552 Studies of Horses and Wagon
Pencil, ink on paper 6.4 x 23.9
Donated by J. F. Johnson, 1896

U1553 Two Horse-drawn Wagons and Study of a
Horse (formerly 'Two Horse-drawn
Wagons')
Pencil, ink on paper 9.8 x 29.9
Donated by J. F. Johnson, 1896

U1554 Three Horses Carrying Baggage
Pencil, watercolour on paper 8 x 14.5
Donated by J. F. Johnson, 1896

U1555 Man with Pitchfork
Pencil, watercolour, bodycolour on paper
7 x 7.2
Donated by J. F. Johnson, 1896

U1556 Haycart with Two Figures
Pencil, watercolour on paper 6.2 x 10.9
Donated by J. F. Johnson, 1896

U1557 Carthorse and Two Figures
Pencil, watercolour, ink on paper 7.6 x 14.4
Donated by J. F. Johnson, 1896

DUNLOP, Ronald Ossory 1894-1973 (British)

U446 Buildings at Walberswick *(Illus.p.246)*
Oil on canvas 63.8 x 76.9
Signed
Purchased (Lloyd Patterson Collection) 1932

U447 Portrait of the Artist
Oil on canvas 56.2 x 46
Signed
Donated by Z. Lewinter-Frankl, 1944

U448 R. V. Williams ('Richard Rowley') 1877-1947
Oil on canvas 51.2 x 40.9
Donated by Capt. A. Williams, 1958

U449 Portrait of a Woman
Oil on canvas 41.2 x 30.9
Signed
Donated by T. Johnston (per the National Art Collections Fund), 1957

DUNLUCE, Alexander McDonnell, Viscount b.1935 (Irish)

U2443 Old Coast Guards' Look-out, Garron Tower
Oil on canvas on board 26.3 x 31.5
Signed
Purchased 1977

DU PAN, Barthélémy 1712-63 (Swiss)

U129 Augusta of Saxe-Gotha, Princess of Wales 1719-72 (c.1745) *(Illus.p.247)*
Oil on canvas 187.4 x 118.8
Purchased 1959

U130 Frederick, Prince of Wales 1707-51 (c.1745) *(Illus.p.247)*
Oil on canvas 187 x 118.7
Purchased 1959

E

EDOUART, Augustin Amant Constant Fidèle 1789-1861 (French)

U4877 The Family of Robert James Tennent (1839)
Series of cut-out silhouettes on paper 42.4 x 58
Signed, dated
Provenance unknown

U4878 The Domestic Servants of Robert James Tennent (1839)
Series of cut-out silhouettes on paper 31.8 x 47
Signed, dated
Provenance unknown

EDRIDGE, Henry 1769-1821 (English)

U1558 Paris: Notre Dame and Ile de la Cité *(Illus.p.247)*
Pencil on paper 19.5 x 28.3

Purchased 1911

U1559 Hotel de Ville, Paris (1817)
Pencil on paper 20.1 x 28.2
Dated
Purchased 1911

EDWARDS, Handel b.1923 (Welsh)

U2522 The Miner's Kitchen (1973) *(Illus.p.247)*
Sculpture, Honduras mahogany relief 91.5 x 152.4 x 20.3
Purchased 1979

EDWARDS, Mary Ellen (Mrs. Freer, thereafter Mrs. Staples) 1839-c.1908 (British)

U1026 Carol Singing (1885) (Book Illustration)
Pencil, watercolour, white on paper 21.8 x 13.7
Signed, dated
Purchased 1928

U1027 Feeding the Lamb (Book Illustration)
Ink, watercolour, white on paper 24.7 x 13.1
Signed
Purchased 1928

U1028 Two Girls Reading a Bible in Church (1885) (Book Illustration) (formerly 'Two Children Reading')
Pencil, watercolour, white on paper 21.5 x 14
Signed, dated
Purchased 1928

U1029 Girl with a Doll
Ink, watercolour, white on paper 17.9 x 12.7 (sight)
Signed
Purchased 1928

U1030 He Was Six, She Was Four (Book Illustration)
Ink, watercolour on paper 12 x 9.8 (sight)
Signed
Purchased 1928

U1031 Girl with Kittens (Book Illustration)
Ink, watercolour, white on paper 17.9 x 12.7 (sight)
Signed
Purchased 1928

U1032 Mother with Two Children (Book Illustration)
Ink on paper 19 x 14 (sight)
Signed
Purchased 1928

U1033 Girl Surrounded by Birds and Butterflies (Book Illustration)
Ink on paper 19 x 14 (sight)
Signed
Purchased 1928

U1034 Girl Collecting Eggs from a Chicken-coop (Book Illustration) (formerly 'Girl with Hen and Chickens')
Ink on paper 19 x 14 (sight)
Signed
Purchased 1928

U1035 Young Girl with Kitten (Book Illustration) *(Illus.p.247)*
Ink on paper 19 x 14 (sight)

Signed
Purchased 1928

EDWARDS, Peter b.1955 (English)

U4825 Portrait of Michael Longley b.1939 (1989-90) *(Illus.p.247)*
Oil on canvas 231.1 x 166.3
Purchased 1990

EGAN, Felim b.1952 (Irish)

U2523 Line Composition - Blue (1979) *(Illus.p.247)*
Acrylic on canvas 147.5 x 147.5
Signed, dated
Purchased 1979

U2606 Score (1981) *(Illus. Cover)*
Acrylic, neon light on canvas 160 x 160
Purchased 1982

U4743 Apollo (1984)
Mixed media on paper 70 x 101
Signed, dated
Donated by the Contemporary Irish Art Society, 1998

EGESTORFF, Paul d.1995 (German, worked in Ireland)

U4818 Fusion (1948) *(Illus.p.247)*
Oil on canvas 91 x 77
Signed
Purchased 1990

ELCOCK, Charles 1834-1910 (English, worked in Ireland)

U1036 St. MacDara's Oratory, Roundstone (1895)
Sepia, watercolour on paper 19 x 25.9
Signed, dated
Provenance unknown

EMMET, Jane Erin 1873-1957 (American)

U307 The Sierra Nevadas, Granada (c.1921) *(Illus.p.247)*
Oil on canvas on board 44.8 x 51.8
Signed
Bequeathed by Dr. R. I. Best (per the Friends of the National Collections of Ireland), 1959

ENOKURA, Koji b.1942 (Japanese)

U4682 Untitled (1979) *(Illus.p.248)*
Oil on canvas 250 x 750
Signed
Donated by Illa Kodicek (per the Contemporary Irish Art Society), 1985

EPSTEIN, Sir Jacob 1880-1959 (American, worked in England)

U948 Crouching Nude *(Illus.p.248)*
Charcoal on paper 43.8 x 34.2
Signed
Purchased 1959

U966 Ahmed (1932) (Doris Ahmed) *(Illus.p.248)*
Sculpture, bronze bust, ht. 49.5
Donated by the Friends of the National Collections of Ireland, 1956

U5011 Head of Joan Greenwood 1921-87
Sculpture, bronze, ht. 46
Bequeathed by Miss H. F. Campbell,
1995

EUN-MO, Chung b. 1946 (Korean)

U4936 Villa Amnissos Projection - Red (1990)
(Illus.p.248)
Oil on canvas 150 x 150
Purchased 1992

EURICH, Richard E. 1903-92 (English)

U596 Boats at Lyme Regis (1937) *(Illus.p.248)*
Oil on canvas 50.6 x 60.9
Signed, dated
Purchased (Lloyd Patterson Collection)
1938

EVANS, David b.1934 (Irish)

**U4956 Ulster Museum from Botanic Gardens
(1992)**
Watercolour on paper 45 x 63.5
Signed, dated
Donated by the Thomas Haverty Trust,
1992

**U4957 Interior of Art Galleries, Ulster Museum
(1992)** *(Illus.p.248)*
Watercolour on paper 45.5 x 63.5
Signed, dated
Donated by the Thomas Haverty Trust,
1992

EVANS, Garth b.1934 (English)

U2532 Frill No. 49 (1972)
Sculpture, metal 82.5 x 125 x 137
Donated by the Contemporary Art
Society, 1979

EWALD, Clara d.c.1949 (German, worked in
Belfast)

U297 Mrs. Glen Hamilton (1946) *(Illus.p.248)*
Oil on canvas 50.7 x 38.5
Signed, dated
Provenance unknown

U1661 Portrait of a Soldier (1941)
Oil on canvas 55.5 x 45.5
Signed, dated
Provenance unknown

U1662 Portrait of a Man (1940)
Oil on canvas 55.5 x 45.6
Signed, dated
Provenance unknown

F

FAIRWEATHER, Ian 1891-1974 (Scottish)

U450 Chinese Tea Garden, Peking
Oil on board 63.9 x 81
Donated by the Contemporary Art
Society, 1942

FANCOURT, E. fl.c.1820 (English)

U225 Rev. Joseph Wolff 1795-1862 (c.1827)
Oil on canvas 76 x 63.2

Donated by R. A. Mullan (per K.
Darwin), 1967

FANTIN-LATOUR, Henri 1836-1904 (French)

U128 The Wedding Feast at Cana (1867)
(after Veronese) *(Illus.p.248)*
Oil on canvas 169.9 x 250
Purchased 1892

FARQUHARSON, David 1839-1907 (Scottish)

U601 Spring in the Trossachs (1890-91)
(Illus.p.248)
Oil on canvas 82 x 127.4
Signed, dated
Purchased 1910

FARRELL, Micheal 1940-2000 (Irish)

U521 Study Monochrome (1967) *(Illus.p.249)*
Acrylic on canvas 131.8 x 211.1
Signed, dated
Purchased 1967

U723 Pressé Series with Cream (1970)
(Illus.p.249)
Acrylic on canvas 122.4 x 122
Signed, dated
Purchased 1970

FEDDEN, A. Romilly 1875-1939 (English)

U2575 The Fun of the Fair (1908) *(Illus.p.249)*
Watercolour on paper 30 x 66
Signed, dated
Provenance unknown

FEITO, Luis b.1929 (Spanish)

U290 Cuadro No. 281 (1961) *(Illus.p.249)*
Oil on canvas 100.2 x 79.9
Signed, dated
Purchased 1963

FERGUSON, Shaun b.1963 (Irish)

U4840 Shepherd's Farm 3 *(Illus.p.249)*
Oil on canvas 71.1 x 147.3
Purchased 1991

FERGUSSON, John Duncan 1874-1961
(Scottish)

U451 The Liberty Men (1916) *(Illus.p.249)*
Oil on canvas 71.1 x 76
Signed, dated
Purchased 1949

FERRAN, Brian b.1940 (Irish)

U2332 Pat (1971)
Oil on paper on board 69.8 x 49.9
Signed, dated
Purchased 1975

U2333 Conchobor (1971) *(Illus.p.249)*
Oil on paper on board 50.2 x 66.4
Signed, dated
Purchased 1975

FIELDING, Anthony Vandyke Copley 1787-
1855 (English)

U775 Bay Scene - Sunset (1819) *(Illus.p.249)*
Watercolour on paper 29.8 x 40.7

Signed, dated
Purchased 1948

U776 Seascape, Storm off Dover (?) (formerly
'Seascape') *(Illus.p.249)*
Watercolour on paper 26.5 x 37.8
Signed
Donated by Meta and Robert Dunlop,
1950

U777 A Lakeside
Watercolour, bodycolour on paper 25 x
36.8
Purchased 1934

U885 Near Malden, Surrey
Watercolour on paper 12.2 x 20.4
Signed
Purchased 1912

U2419 River Scene (1806)
Watercolour on paper 21.3 x 27.8
Signed, dated
Donated by R. V. Williams ('Richard
Rowley'), 1930

U4665 View of Ventimiglia
Pencil, watercolour on paper 15.9 x 22.9
Bequeathed by Sir David Reid (per Lady
Reid), 1951

FIRTH, William A. fl.1889-1911 (Irish)

U1405 Seascape (1911); verso, Seascape Sketch
Watercolour on paper 17.1 x 24.6
Signed, dated
Provenance unknown

U1686 Landscape with Trees on Skyline (1911)
Watercolour on paper 13.9 x 18.8
Signed, dated
Donated by J. S. Stendall, 1966

FISHER, Jonathan d.1809 (Irish)

**U59 A View of the Canal between the Lakes
of Killarney (c.1770)**
Oil on canvas 50.8 x 63.5
Purchased 1962

**U659 View of the Ferry and Castle of Narrow
Water (c.1771)** *(Illus.p.250)*
Oil on canvas 80.6 x 127
Purchased 1969

FISHER, William Mark 1841-1923 (American,
worked in England)

U453 Landscape with Sheep (c.1881-87)
(Illus.p.250)
Oil on canvas 35.9 x 50.9
Signed, dated indistinctly
Purchased 1911

U778 Corner of the Lake *(Illus.p.250)*
Watercolour, pencil, gouache on paper
24.3 x 35.4
Signed
Purchased 1913

FITZPATRICK, A. 19th century (English)

U2874 Somebody Coming
Oil on canvas 28.5 x 28
Donated by W. T. Braithwaite (per J.
Horner), 1906

FLANAGAN, Barry b.1941 (British)

U2555 **New Metal Piece (1978)** *(Illus.p.250)*
Sculpture, mild steel 218 x 456 x 216
Purchased 1979

FLANAGAN, Philip b.1960 (Irish)

U4897 **Dave 'Boy' McAuley b.1961 (1991)**
Sculpture, bronze head, ht. 35
Signed, dated
Purchased 1992

FLANAGAN, Terence Philip b.1929 (Irish)

U293 **Autumn Lough (1961)** (formerly 'Winter Lough')
Oil on board 29.7 x 62.6
Signed
Purchased 1962

U549 **Gortahork (2) (1967)** *(Illus.p.250)*
Oil, acrylic on board 92.2 x 118.9
Signed
Purchased 1969

U1404 **Bog Landscape (1961)**
Crayon on paper 27.8 x 37.8
Signed, dated
Provenance unknown

U2252 **Landscape with Five Trees (1961)**
Charcoal, crayon on paper 27.8 x 37.8
Signed, dated
Provenance unknown

U2363 **Poppies and a Sepia Drawing (c.1975)**
Pencil, watercolour on paper 55.2 x 76.5
Signed
Purchased 1975

U2655 **Twilight on a Bog (1982)**
Watercolour on paper 53 x 73.7 (sight)
Signed
Purchased 1982

U4758 **John D. Stewart d.1988 (c.1970)**
Watercolour on paper 100 x 77.5
Signed
Purchased 1989

U4774 **View from Saint Mary's (1968)**
Gouache on paper 24.5 x 34.5 (sight)
Signed, dated
Bequeathed by Roberta and John Hewitt, 1987

U4775 **Green Landscape (1957)**
Oil on board 28 x 39.4
Signed, dated
Bequeathed by Roberta and John Hewitt, 1987

U5041 **Weir on the Blackwater River, Co. Cork (1993)** *(Illus.p.250)*
Oil on canvas 121.9 x 91.5
Signed, dated
Purchased 1996

FLANNAGAN, John B.1898-1942 (American)

U4954 **Kitten on its Back (c.1932-33)**
Sculpture, stone 9.8 x 15 x 25
Purchased 1991

U4958 **The Rag Doll**
Sculpture, bronze, ht. 52.7
Purchased 1993

FLAXMAN, John 1755-1826 (English)

U779 **Swedenborgian Subject (?)** *(Illus.p.250)*
Ink, wash on paper 35 x 48.8
Donated by Mrs. E. M. Wheeler, 1922

FLAXMAN, John 1755-1826 (English) (after)

U780 **Illustration for Aeschylus' 'Prometheus Bound'**
Ink on paper 17.1 x 24.7
Purchased 1962

FLINT, Sir William Russell 1880-1969 (English)

U781 **A Neglected Domain** *(Illus.p.250)*
Watercolour on paper 50.7 x 68
Signed
Purchased 1949

FLINTOFF, Thomas c.1809-91 (English, worked in Australia)

U1941 **Gordon Augustus Thomson 1799-1886 (1885)** *(Illus.p.250)*
Oil on canvas 92.3 x 71.3
Signed, dated
Donated by the sitter, 1885

FOLEY, John Henry 1818-74 (Irish)

U1788 **Helen Faucit (Lady Martin)**
Sculpture, plaster relief 80.7 x 99 x 7.6
Donated by the National Museum of Ireland, 1914

FORD, Henry Justice 1860-1941 (English)

U40 **Island off Sark (1893)**
Oil on board 17.9 x 25.3
Signed, dated
Donated by Mrs. Walter Ford, 1963

FORRESTER, James 1730-76 (Irish) (attributed to)

U1037 **The Falls of Powerscourt** *(Illus.p.251)*
Ink, wash, pencil, chalk on paper 39.3 x 26.5
Purchased 1971

FORT, Jean-Antoine-Siméon 1793-1861 (French)

U1038 **Swiss Scene (1829)** *(Illus.p.251)*
Ink, sepia wash on paper 17 x 24
Signed, dated
Donated by J. H. Bland, 1928

FOSTER, Myles Birket 1825-99 (English)

U782 **Bringing Daddy's Dinner** *(Illus.p.251)*
Watercolour, white on paper 18.1 x 13.2
Signed
Donated by Lady Cleaver, 1936

U783 **Lyme Regis from the Charmouth Road** (Vignette) (formerly 'Lyme Regis') *(Illus.p.251)*
Pencil, watercolour, white on paper 19.8 x 24
Signed
Donated by Lady Cleaver, 1936

U784 **Falls of the Tummel** (Vignette)
Watercolour on paper 16.5 x 19.2
Signed

Donated by Lady Cleaver, 1936

U1191 **A Pedlar** *(Illus.p.251)*
Watercolour, white on paper 44.4 x 67.8
Signed
Donated by Lady Cleaver, 1936

U1560 **The Haymakers** *(Illus.p.251)*
Watercolour, bodycolour on paper 53.3 x 82.1
Signed
Donated by Lady Cleaver, 1936

U1639 **Going to Market** *(Illus.p.251)*
Watercolour, bodycolour on paper 29.5 x 74
Signed
Donated by Lady Cleaver, 1936

U4512 **Trout Fishing**
Watercolour on paper 13.6 x 18.7 (sight)
Signed
Donated by Lady Cleaver, 1936

U4513 **Cattle Crossing a Bridge** *(Illus.p.251)*
Watercolour on paper 27.9 x 40 (sight)
Signed
Donated by Lady Cleaver, 1936

U4514 **Oranges and Lemons - Mediterranean** *(Illus.p.251)*
Watercolour on paper 30.2 x 44.8 (sight)
Signed
Donated by Lady Cleaver, 1936

U4672 **Interesting News**
Watercolour, bodycolour on paper 19.8 x 27.8 (sight)
Signed
Donated by Meta and Robert Dunlop, 1950

FOY, William 1791-c.1859 (Irish)

U1658 **James Greer (1859)**
Oil on canvas 76.7 x 64.2
Donated by Lt. Col. P. B. Fleming, 1964

FRANCIS, Mark b.1962 (Irish)

U5036 **Negative (4) (1994)** *(Illus.p.252)*
Oil on canvas 180 x 180
Donated by the Contemporary Art Society, 1996

FRANCIS, Sam 1923-94 (American)

U553 **Grey Space (1950-51)** *(Illus.p.252)*
Oil on canvas 115.8 x 81
Signed
Purchased 1969

FRANKENTHALER, Helen b.1928 (American)

U534 **Sands (1964)** *(Illus.p.252)*
Acrylic on canvas 196.2 x 198.4
Signed, dated
Purchased 1965

FRAPIÉ 19th century (French)

U2072 **Unknown Lady** (after Joseph Karl Stieler 1781-1858)
Miniature, watercolour on ivory 8.6 x 6.7 (oval)
Signed

Donated by W. Kinning Crone, 1947

FRAZER, Hugh fl.1813-61 (Irish)

U543   **View of Cavehill from the Lagan**
Oil on canvas 34.9 x 48
Bequeathed by Miss H. M. McCleery,
1968

U568   **River Lagan with Barge**
Oil on panel 30.6 x 41
Bequeathed by Miss H. M. McCleery,
1968

FRENCH, Percy 1854-1920 (Irish)

U1039   **On the Donegal Coast**
Watercolour on paper 16.8 x 25
Signed
Donated by Meta and Robert Dunlop,
1950

U1192   **Landscape near Falcarragh, Co. Donegal**
(Illus.p.252)
Watercolour, bodycolour on paper 18 x
25
Signed
Bequeathed by Miss H. M. McCleery,
1968

U1193   **Coast Scene (1910)**
Watercolour on paper 24 x 35 (sight)
Signed, dated
Bequeathed by Miss H. M. McCleery,
1968

U2596   **A Devon Stream**
Watercolour on board 26.7 x 31.4
Signed
Donated by the Misses Ettie and Joan
French, 1981

FRIERS, Rowel Boyd 1920-98 (Irish)

U292   **The Poachers (1946)** *(Illus.p.252)*
Oil on canvas 50.9 x 76.5
Signed, dated
Donated by the Thomas Haverty Trust,
1950

U1264   **RUA Exhibition of 'Livid' Irish Art
(1958)**
Pencil, ink on paper 21.7 x 28.5
Signed
Provenance unknown

U1276   **Courtney and Son;** verso, **Dog Study**
Ink on paper 22.3 x 17.4
Donated by the artist (per Ian Friers),
1946

U1277   **Stalin and another Head;** verso, **Dog
Studies**
Pencil on paper 22.5 x 17.1
Donated by the artist (per Ian Friers),
1946

U1278   **A Russian and a Redskin;** verso, **Dancing
Couple**
Ink, watercolour on paper 22.4 x 17.2
Donated by the artist (per Ian Friers),
1946

U1279   **Himmler, Hitler and Hess;** verso, **Cow's
Head and Hens**
Pencil, ink, watercolour on paper 22.3 x
17.1

Donated by the artist (per Ian Friers),
1946

U1280   **J. Langtry Lynas 1879-1956 (?);** verso,
'Le Saboteur'
Ink, watercolour on paper 25.8 x 19.8
Donated by the artist (per Ian Friers),
1946

U1281   **Caricatures of Six Belfast Artists**
(formerly 'Sketches of Local Artists');
verso, **A Mexican Peasant**
Ink, watercolour, pencil on paper 25.8 x
20
Donated by the artist (per Ian Friers),
1946

U1282   **Caricatures of Theo. J. Gracey 1895-
1959;** verso, **A US Serviceman and his
Girl**
Pencil, ink on paper 25.8 x 19.8
Donated by the artist (per Ian Friers),
1946

U1283   **R. Taylor Carson b.1919;** verso, **A Fairy**
Pencil, ink, watercolour on paper 16.6 x
14.3
Signed
Donated by the artist (per Ian Friers),
1946

U1284   **B. P. Doherty;** verso, **A Painter in Overalls**
Pencil, ink, watercolour on paper 22.5 x
17.3
Donated by the artist (per Ian Friers),
1946

U1285   **Theo Gracey 1895-1959;** verso, **Tulips
and a Bee**
Pencil on paper 22.3 x 17.2
Donated by the artist (per Ian Friers),
1946

U1286   **Theo Gracey 1895-1959;** verso, **A
Farmyard**
Pencil, ink on paper 22.5 x 17.2
Donated by the artist (per Ian Friers),
1946

U1287   **Frank McKelvey 1895-1974**
Pencil on paper 22.7 x 17.8
Donated by the artist (per Ian Friers),
1946

U1288   **Frank McKelvey 1895-1974**
Pencil on paper 12.4 x 8.8
Donated by the artist (per Ian Friers),
1946

U1289   **US Personnel** (Cartoon Sketches)
Pencil, ink on paper 22.7 x 17.2
Donated by the artist (per Ian Friers),
1946

U1290   **Studies of Four Black American
Servicemen**
Pencil, ink on paper 22.8 x 17.8
Donated by the artist (per Ian Friers),
1946

U1291   **Two US Sailors;** verso, **Sketch of a Head**
Pencil, brush, ink on paper 22.5 x 16.2
Donated by the artist (per Ian Friers),
1946

U1292   **'Old and New';** verso, **'I Am E. K. Dalton'**
(Cartoon)

Ink, watercolour on paper 22.3 x 17.3
Donated by the artist (per Ian Friers),
1946

U1293   **'The Boot on the Other Foot';** verso, **A
US Officer** (Cartoon)
Ink on paper 22.8 x 16.3
Donated by the artist (per Ian Friers),
1946

U1579   **From a Cartoonist's Sketchbook: Three
Groups of American Servicemen (1943-
44)**
Ink on paper 22.8 x 16.5
Dated
Donated by the artist (per Ian Friers),
1946

U1580   **From a Cartoonist's Sketchbook:
American Soldier Talking to a Woman
and Two American Civilians (1943-44)**
Ink on paper 22.8 x 16.5
Dated
Donated by the artist (per Ian Friers),
1946

U4817   **The Botany Lesson (1990)**
Pencil, watercolour on paper 73.6 x
104.1 (sight)
Signed, dated
Purchased 1990

U4936   **The Old Masters (1992)**
Pencil on paper 78 x 105.5 (sight)
Signed, dated
Purchased 1992

FRIPP, George Arthur 1813-96 (English)

U1040   **Raby Castle, Co. Durham** (formerly 'A
Castle Gateway') *(Illus.p.252)*
Watercolour, pencil on paper 13.6 x 21.6
Signed
Purchased 1934

FRITH 19th century (British)

U4925   **Richard Blunt (1833)**
Silhouette, ink, gold on paper 26.7 x 19
(sight)
Signed
Donated by Miss Ileene Chesney, 1980

U4926   **Mrs. Richard Blunt (1833)**
Silhouette, ink, gold on paper 26.7 x 19
(sight)
Signed
Donated by Miss Ileene Chesney, 1980

FRITH, William Powell 1819-1909 (English)

U631   **Sterne and the French Innkeeper's
Daughter** *(Illus.p.252)*
Oil on canvas 36 x 27.3
Signed
Purchased 1896

FROMUTH, Charles Henry b.1866 (American)

U1041   **Gold Sail, Blue Nets No. 2, Concarneau
(1921)**
Chalk on paper 30.6 x 27.9
Signed, dated
Donated by Miss G. M. Kyle, 1938

FROST, Sir Terry b.1915 (English)

U520 **Mars Orange and Black (1961)**
(Illus.p.252)
Oil on canvas 122.8 x 122.4
Signed, dated
Purchased 1962

FRY, Roger Eliot 1866-1934 (English)

U452 **Valley of the Rhone (1930)** *(Illus.p.252)*
Oil on canvas 54.4 x 65.3
Signed, dated
Purchased (Lloyd Patterson Collection)
1930

FRY, William Arthur 1865-1936 (English, worked in Ireland)

U1252 **Howd's Hole, Ardglass** *(Illus.p.253)*
Pencil, watercolour on paper 53 x 36.6
Signed
Purchased 1919

FULTON, David 1848-1930 (Scottish)

U37 **An Autumn Morning** *(Illus.p.253)*
Oil on canvas 51.1 x 61.3
Signed
Donated by Mrs. A. Thompson and Miss
L. Stevenson, 1935

FUSELI, John Henry (Johann Heinrich Füssli)
1741-1825 (Swiss, worked in England)

U785 **Pylades and Orestes Escaping from
Tauris with Iphigenia (c.1810-20)**
(Euripides' 'Iphigenia in Tauris')
(Illus.p.253)
Pencil, ink, watercolour on paper 26.1 x
18.2
Donated by J. F. Johnson, 1896

U786 **Two Courtesans at a Window; verso,
Threequarter-length Figure and a Head
(both of Mrs. Fuseli) (1790)** *(Illus.p.253)*
Ink, wash, watercolour, white on paper
22.2 x 17.8
Dated
Donated by J. F. Johnson, 1896

U787 **Studies of Three Courtesans with
Extravagant Hairstyles (1807)**
(Illus.p.253)
Pencil, watercolour, bodycolour on paper
22.1 x 18.1
Dated
Donated by J. F. Johnson, 1896

U788 **Woman at a Dressing Table (1792)**
(Illus.p.253)
Pencil, ink, watercolour on paper 22.2 x
17.6
Donated by J. F. Johnson, 1896

U789 **Seated Woman with Finger on Mouth
(c.1796-99)** (Study for 'Il Penseroso')
(Illus.p.253)
Pencil, watercolour on paper 22.9 x 18.4
Donated by J. F. Johnson, 1896

U790 **Mrs. Fuseli in a Large Hat; verso, Mrs.
Fuseli in a Hat (c.1792-95)** *(Illus.p.253)*
Ink, watercolour, bodycolour on paper
20.6 x 18.3
Donated by J. F. Johnson, 1896

U791 **Mrs. Fuseli in a Red Cap; verso, Pencil**

Sketches of Women (1794) *(Illus.p.xiv)*
Pencil, watercolour, bodycolour on paper
34.3 x 21.3
Dated
Donated by J. F. Johnson, 1896

U792 **Two Women with Fans Walking in a
Garden; verso, Four Pencil Sketches of
Women (1795)** *(Illus.p.253)*
Pencil, watercolour, bodycolour on paper
38.1 x 24.5
Dated
Donated by J. F. Johnson, 1896

U793 **Milton when a Boy, Instructed by his
Mother (c.1796-98)** *(Illus.p.254)*
Pencil, ink, watercolour on paper 43 x
30.4
Donated by J. F. Johnson, 1896

U794 **Study after a Roman Portrait Bust of a
Lady (1810)** *(Illus.p.254)*
Pencil, wash on paper 30.8 x 19.3
Dated
Donated by J. F. Johnson, 1896

G

GABRIEL, G. L. b.1958 (German)

U4896 **S-Bahnhof Friedrichstrasse (1991)**
(Illus.p.254)
Mixed media (mainly oil) on canvas 220
x 220
Signed, dated
Purchased 1991

GAINSBOROUGH, Thomas 1727-88 (English)

U35 **Arthur, 1st Marquess of Donegall 1739-
99 (c.1780)** *(Illus.p.xv)*
Oil on canvas 232.4 x 152.4
Purchased with the aid of a grant from
the National Art Collections Fund, 1967

U5067 **Miss Theodosia Magill 1744-1817,
afterwards Countess of Clanwilliam
(1765)** *(Illus.p.254)*
Oil on canvas 127 x 102
Signed, dated
Purchased with the aid of grants from the
Heritage Lottery Fund, the National Art
Collections Fund (with a contribution
from the Wolfson Foundation) and the
Esmé Mitchell Trust, 1998

GALLAGHER, Frederick O'Neill 19th-20th
century (Irish)

U2574 **A View on the Seine (1915)** *(Illus.p.254)*
Oil on canvas 46 x 60.8
Signed, dated
Purchased 1980

GAMBIER, Léon 20th century (French)

U458 **Port de Dieppe (1948)** *(Illus.p.254)*
Oil on canvas 60.2 x 81
Signed, dated
Purchased 1951

GARSTIN, Norman 1847-1926 (Irish)

U2586 **King's Bench Walk**

Oil on panel 15 x 13
Signed
Donated by the Contemporary Art
Society, 1980

U2587 **Arabs, Tangier (1885)** *(Illus.p.254)*
Oil on panel 23 x 13
Signed, dated
Donated by the Contemporary Art
Society, 1980

U2588 **At the Fair** *(Illus.p.254)*
Oil on panel 12.5 x 15
Donated by the Contemporary Art
Society, 1980

U2589 **Roundabout, Diest** *(Illus.p.254)*
Oil on panel 20.7 x 26.6
Signed
Donated by the Contemporary Art
Society, 1980

GARVEY, Edmund d.1808 (Irish)

U1181 **A View of Kilkenny** *(Illus.p.255)*
Oil on canvas 91.4 x 152.3
Purchased 1971

GASTINEAU, Henry 1791-1876 (English)

U1042 **Voreppe - on the Road to the Grande
Chartreuse** *(Illus.p.255)*
Pencil, watercolour on paper 39 x 28.6
Purchased 1937

U1822 **Glenarm, Co. Antrim (1859)** *(Illus.p.255)*
Watercolour on paper 77.5 x 133
Signed, dated
Donated by Miss I. Sawbridge (per the
National Art Collections Fund), 1938

GAUDIER-BRZESKA, Henri 1891-1915 (French,
worked in England)

U796 **Study of a Nude Woman**
Ink on paper 38 x 25.2
Purchased 1970

U974 **Masque Ornementale (1912)**
(Illus.p.255)
Sculpture, bronze 70 x 68 x 21 (cast from
plaster original, 1969-70)
Signed, dated
Purchased 1970

GEDDES, Wilhelmina 1888-1955 (Irish)

U1397 **Portrait of Rosamond Praeger 1867-1954**
(Illus.p.255)
Pencil on paper 23.4 x 13.8
Donated by Miss E. M. Geddes, 1960

U4831 **Moses (c.1929)** (Cartoon for Stained
Glass Window)
Charcoal on paper on plywood, approx.
203.2 x 63.5, arched top
Signed
Provenance unknown

U4832 **Christ Blessing Little Children (c.1929)**
(Cartoon for Stained Glass Window)
Charcoal on paper on plywood, approx.
203.2 x 63.5, arched top
Provenance unknown

U4833 **Pilgrim's Progress (c.1929)** (Cartoon for
Stained Glass Window)

Charcoal on paper on plywood, approx.
63.5 x 63.5, segmental top
Signed
Provenance unknown

U4834 Christ Blessing His Disciples (c.1929)
(Cartoon for Stained Glass Window)
Charcoal on paper on plywood, approx.
63.5 x 63.5, segmental top
Provenance unknown

GEORGE, Sir Ernest 1839-1922 (English)

U1043 Rotterdam (1879) *(Illus.p.255)*
Pencil, watercolour on paper 36.5 x 26.4
Signed, dated
Purchased 1937

GERTLER, Mark 1892-1939 (British)

U456 Sleeping Nude (1928) *(Illus.p.255)*
Oil on canvas 75.5 x 101
Signed, dated
Bequeathed by Thomas Balston (per the
National Art Collections Fund), 1968

U457 The Mandoline (1931)
Oil on canvas 92.1 x 71.5
Signed, dated
Purchased (Lloyd Patterson Collection)
1932

GETHIN, Percy 1874-1916 (Irish)

U4695 A Sonata of Daicellos (1907)
Oil on canvas 91.5 x 71.1
Signed, dated
Purchased 1986

GILBERT and GEORGE b.1943, b.1942 (British)

U2668 To the Fallen (1982)
Photopiece on paper 302 x 303
Signed, dated
Purchased 1982

GILBERT, Hubert Donald McGeoch 1900-61
(English)

U1761 George Russell ('AE') 1867-1935 (1933)
Sculpture, bronze bust, ht. 54
Signed, dated
Purchased 1957

GILBERT, Sir John 1817-97 (English)

U1640 Don Quixote and Rosinante *(Illus.p.255)*
Watercolour, bodycolour on paper 36.5 x
48.1
Purchased 1956

GILBERT, Stephen b.1910 (British)

U4751 Untitled (1950) *(Illus.p.255)*
Oil on canvas 80.5 x 65.5
Signed, dated
Purchased 1989

GILMER, Arthur 1882-1929 (Irish)

U1331 Cottages (1926)
Pencil, chalk on paper 15.5 x 23.9
Dated
Provenance unknown

U1332 An Irish Clachan (1927)

Charcoal, chalk on paper 15.6 x 24.3
Dated
Provenance unknown

U1333 Irish Landscape
Charcoal, watercolour, white on paper
15.9 x 24
Provenance unknown

U1334 An Irish Coast Scene
Pencil, watercolour, white on paper 16.5
x 23.8
Provenance unknown

U1335 An Irish Village
Charcoal, watercolour, white on paper
15.4 x 23.8
Provenance unknown

U1336 Irish Cottages
Charcoal, watercolour, white on paper
15.9 x 23.8
Provenance unknown

U1337 Seascape with Cliffs (1926)
Charcoal, watercolour, white on paper
15.5 x 24
Signed, dated
Provenance unknown

U1338 Looking across a Lough
Charcoal, watercolour, white on paper
15.7 x 24
Provenance unknown

U1339 Irish Landscape
Pencil, watercolour, white on paper 15.7
x 23.5
Provenance unknown

U1340 Bay with Headland
Watercolour, white on paper 15.5 x 24
Provenance unknown

U1341 Peat Stacks *(Illus.p.256)*
Charcoal, watercolour, white on paper
15.9 x 24
Provenance unknown

U1342 Irish Seascape
Charcoal, watercolour, white on paper
15.6 x 23.7
Provenance unknown

U1343 Seascape towards a Distant Point
Charcoal, watercolour, white on paper
15.4 x 24
Provenance unknown

U1344 An Irish Hillside
Charcoal, watercolour, white on paper
15.9 x 23.5
Provenance unknown

U1345 Kiel Island (?) (1926)
Pencil, watercolour, white on paper 15.6
x 23.6
Dated
Provenance unknown

U1346 Coastal View with Trees
Pencil, watercolour, bodycolour on paper
15.9 x 23.4
Provenance unknown

U1347 Kiel Island (1927)
Pencil, watercolour, white on paper 15.9
x 24.1

Dated
Provenance unknown

U1348 An Irish Landscape with Cottages
Pencil, watercolour, bodycolour on paper
13.3 x 24.5
Provenance unknown

U1349 Scene across a Peat Bog
Charcoal, watercolour, white on paper
16.2 x 24
Provenance unknown

U1350 Cruaghann from Pollaft (?) Bog (1927)
Charcoal, watercolour, white on paper
15.9 x 24
Dated
Provenance unknown

U1351 Landscape with Lough
Charcoal, watercolour, white on paper
15.8 x 23.6
Provenance unknown

U1352 Headland with Lighthouse
Pencil, watercolour, white on paper 15.6
x 24
Provenance unknown

U1353 Irish Landscape
Charcoal, watercolour, white on paper
15.3 x 24.1
Provenance unknown

U1354 Donegal, Looking towards Tory Island
Charcoal, watercolour, white on paper
15.9 x 24
Provenance unknown

U1355 Harbour Entrance
Pencil, watercolour, white on paper 16 x
23.9
Provenance unknown

U1356 Peat Stacks below a Mountain (1929)
Charcoal, watercolour, white on paper
15.5 x 23.9
Dated
Provenance unknown

U1357 Campan Bog (1926)
Charcoal, watercolour, white on paper
15.1 x 24.1
Dated
Provenance unknown

U1358 Cottages (1926)
Charcoal, white on paper 16 x 23.8
Dated
Provenance unknown

U1359 Sandy Bay
Pencil, watercolour, white on paper 15.9
x 23.8
Provenance unknown

U1360 Coastal View with Harbour
Pencil, ink, watercolour, white on paper
15.5 x 23.6
Provenance unknown

U1361 Rocky Island
Pencil, ink, watercolour on paper 15.5 x
23.8
Provenance unknown

U1362 Rocky Island
Pencil, ink on paper 15.7 x 23.9

Provenance unknown

U1375 **Tenement Housing**
Charcoal, chalk on paper 24 x 16
Provenance unknown

U1376 **Street Scene**
Charcoal, chalk on paper 15.6 x 24.2
Provenance unknown

U1377 **A Church Tower (St. Michan?)**
Charcoal, chalk on paper 15 x 23.9
Provenance unknown

U1378 **Whitefriars Street (?)**
Charcoal, chalk on paper 16 x 24.1
Provenance unknown

U1379 **Winetavern Street**
Charcoal, chalk on paper 16 x 23.9
Provenance unknown

U1380 **Looking towards the City Hall**
Charcoal, chalk on paper 24.3 x 15.9
Provenance unknown

U1381 **St. Patrick's**
Charcoal, chalk on paper 24.2 x 16.1
Provenance unknown

U1382 **Off Moote Street**
Charcoal, chalk, watercolour on paper
15.9 x 23.5
Provenance unknown

U1383 **Flemish Houses**
Charcoal, chalk on paper 15.9 x 24
Provenance unknown

U1384 **Group of Town Houses**
Charcoal, chalk, watercolour, bodycolour
on paper 15.6 x 24.2
Provenance unknown

U1385 **House behind a High Wall**
Charcoal on paper 24.2 x 15.9
Provenance unknown

U1386 **Dutch-style Houses**
Charcoal, chalk on paper 23.7 x 15.5
Provenance unknown

U1387 **Castle Arch, Ship Street Gate**
Charcoal, chalk on paper 16 x 24.1
Provenance unknown

U1388 **At the Castle, Little Ship Street**
Charcoal on paper 15.8 x 24.3
Provenance unknown

U1389 **A High House Seen over Roof Tops**
Charcoal, chalk on paper 24.3 x 13.8
Provenance unknown

U1390 **Haymarket, Smithfield**
Charcoal, chalk on paper 15.9 x 23.9
Provenance unknown

U1391 **A Town Lane**
Charcoal, chalk on paper 15.6 x 24
Provenance unknown

U1392 **Near Coombe**
Charcoal, chalk on paper 16 x 23.8
Provenance unknown

U1393 **Church Tower over the Backs of Houses
(St. Michan)**
Charcoal, chalk, crayon on paper 15.4 x

23.7
Provenance unknown

GILPIN, Sawrey 1733-1807 (English)

U1641 **Landscape with Cattle, Donkeys and
Horses (1799)** *(Illus.p.256)*
Watercolour on paper 36.5 x 53.8
Signed, dated
Donated by J. St. Clair Boyd, 1934

GILPIN, Rev. William 1724-1804 (English)

U1642 **Mountain Landscape with Bridge**
(Illus.p.256)
Ink, wash on paper 26.5 x 36.6
Purchased 1914

GINGLES, Graham b.1943 (Irish)

U2597 **Christmas '79 (1979)**
Pencil, ink, watercolour, crayon on paper
40.7 x 55.8
Signed, dated
Purchased 1982

GINNER, Charles 1878-1952 (British)

U455 **Clarendon Dock, Belfast (1921)**
(Illus.p.256)
Oil on canvas 106.9 x 83
Signed
Purchased 1924

U797 **Hampstead Study**
Crayon on paper 30 x 23.3
Donated by the National Art Collections
Fund, 1946

U798 **Storm over Clearbury Ring** *(Illus.p.256)*
Ink, watercolour, bodycolour on paper
28.2 x 38
Signed
Donated by the National Art Collections
Fund, 1946

GLENAVY, Lady Beatrice 1883-1968 (Irish)

U2529 **Enigma (c.1930s)** *(Illus.p.256)*
Oil on canvas 43.8 x 36
Signed
Purchased 1979

GLOAG, Isobel Lilian 1865-1917 (English)

U1044 **One of London's Citizens** *(Illus.p.256)*
Pencil, watercolour on card 59.9 x 49.3
Signed
Donated by J. T. Godfrey, 1932

GLOVER, John 1767-1849 (English) (attributed
to)

U1045 **Endsleigh Cottage, Devon (1819?)**
Pencil, watercolour on paper 37 x 50.8
Purchased 1937

GOODWIN, Albert 1845-1932 (English)

U799 **Lincoln Cathedral** *(Illus.p.256)*
Ink, watercolour, bodycolour on paper
19.9 x 28.6
Signed
Purchased 1952

GOODWIN, Edward fl.1801-15 (English)

U1643 **Kenilworth Castle (1814)** *(Illus.p.256)*
Watercolour on paper 42.5 x 67.3
Signed, dated
Bequeathed by Sir David Reid (per Lady
Reid), 1951

GORDON, W. R. 1872-1955 (Irish)

U1046 **Clady Bridge, Glendun** *(Illus.p.257)*
Pencil, watercolour on paper 31.2 x 44.7
(sight)
Signed
Purchased 1947

U1047 **Showers, Bog Meadows**
Pencil, watercolour on paper 25 x 34.4
Signed
Purchased 1955

U4663 **Downpatrick**
Watercolour on paper 51.4 x 36.2 (sight)
Purchased 1931

GORDON, W. R. and John Frederick HUNTER
1893-1951 (both Irish)

U1945 **The Bronze Age in Ulster (1934)**
Oil on three canvases, 287.4 x 1221.3
overall
Signed, dated
Donated by the Thomas Haverty Trust,
1934

GORE, Spencer Frederick 1878-1914 (English)

U459 **Applehayes (c.1909-10)** *(Illus.p.257)*
Oil on canvas 51.1 x 61.1
Signed
Purchased (Lloyd Patterson Collection)
1929

GORMAN, Richard b.1946 (Irish)

U4807 **Lifetenant (1989-90)** *(Illus.p.257)*
Oil on canvas 190 x 170
Purchased 1990

GOULD, David 1872-1952 (Scottish, worked in
Ireland)

U39 **Sketch Near Lisburn (c.1915)**
(Illus.p.257)
Oil on board 25.4 x 30.5
Purchased 1915

U1048 **Spring Sunshine (1938)**
Pencil, watercolour on paper 37.5 x 55.5
(sight)
Signed, dated
Purchased 1938

GRAEVENITZ, Gerhard von 1934-83 (German)

U2450 **Kinetic Object with Quadrangle on
Crossing Lines (1977)**
Motorised kinetic work with aluminium
rods on board 120 x 120 x 9.7
Purchased 1977

GRAFFIN, Daniel b.1938 (French)

U5050 **Cellular Curve (1981)**
Polyester taffeta, no fixed dimensions
Purchased 1987

GRAHAM, Carol b.1951 (Irish)

U2506 **Light Falls Within (1978)** *(Illus.p.257)*
Oil, acrylic on canvas on board 64.8 x
74.9
Signed, dated
Purchased 1978

U4749 **Portrait of James Galway b.1939 (1988)**
(Illus.p.257)
Oil on canvas 121.9 x 152.4
Signed, dated
Commissioned 1988

U4968 **Mary Robinson, President of the
Republic of Ireland b.1944 (1993)**
Pencil on paper 153 x 124.5
Signed, dated
Purchased 1993

GRANT, Duncan 1885-1978 (British)

U454 **Interior (1918)** *(Illus.p.257)*
Oil on canvas 163 x 174.8
Purchased (Lloyd Patterson Collection)
1929

GRANT, Hugh b.c.1865/67-d.c.1947 (Irish)

U1586 **Lavery's at the Back of the Wood,
Soldierstown (1903)** *(Illus.p.257)*
Pastel on card 40.7 x 32
Signed, dated
Donated by Sir John Lavery, 1931

GREEN, Anthony b.1939 (English)

U1842 **Mr. and Mrs. Stanley Joscelyne: The
Second Marriage (1972)** *(Illus.p.257)*
Oil on board 213.4 x 213.4
Signed, dated
Purchased 1972

U4944 **Madeleine Joscelyne with her Son
(1987) (Fifth Working Drawing)**
Pencil, watercolour, oil pastel on paper
110 x 113
Signed, dated
Purchased with the aid of a grant from
the National Art Collections Fund, 1993

GREEN, Benjamin Richard 1808-76 (English)

U1049 **Tintern Abbey** *(Illus.p.258)*
Pencil, watercolour, white on paper 25.6
x 20.1
Signed
Donated by Meta and Robert Dunlop,
1950

GREENAWAY, Kate 1846-1901 (English)

U1194 **Girl Spinning while a Fairy Appears
Riding on a Dove**
Ink on paper 14.8 x 11.7
Signed
Purchased 1928

U1195 **Girl Seated on Sea Shore Watched by a
Bearded Man**
Ink on paper 14.8 x 11.4
Signed
Purchased 1928

U1196 **Two Young Ladies at a Garden Gate**
Ink on paper 15 x 11.2

Purchased 1928

U1197 **A Little Boy with Toys and a Dove**
Ink on paper 15 x 11.2
Signed
Purchased 1928

U1198 **A Young Man and Two Girls by a
Window**
Ink on paper 15.5 x 11.5
Signed
Purchased 1928

U1199 **Making a Laurel Wreath**
Ink on paper 15.1 x 11.7
Signed
Purchased 1928

GREENHILL, John 1644-76 (British) (attributed
to)

U673 **James II when Duke of York 1633-1701**
Oil on canvas 125.7 x 101.6
Purchased 1959

GREGORY, Christine 1880-1962 (English)

U1789 **The Circle of Spring (1921)** *(Illus.p.258)*
Sculpture, bronze 41.9 x 35.5 x 35.5
Signed, dated
Purchased 1928

GREY, Charles 1808-92 (Scottish, worked in
Ireland)

U30 **Captain Alexander Chesney 1755-1843
(1841)** *(Illus.p.258)*
Oil on canvas 76.5 x 63.5
Signed, dated
Donated by Miss Kathleen Chesney, 1962

U2517 **Portrait of an Unknown Man (1842)**
Chalk on paper 38 x 31 (sight)
Signed, dated
Donated by Miss Frances McTear, 1926

GRIFFITH, Moses 1747-1819

U4800 **Kenilworth Castle** *(Illus.p.258)*
Watercolour on paper 21 x 34
Signed, dated
Bequeathed by Roberta and John Hewitt,
1987

GRIJN, Erik Adriaan van der b.1941 (Dutch,
works in Ireland)

U2441 **Hard Shoulder (1974)**
Oil on three canvases, 152.6 x 320.2
overall
Signed, dated
Purchased 1977

GRIMM, Samuel Hieronymus 1733-94 (Swiss,
worked in England)

U1644 **St. Paul's Cathedral from St. George's
Fields (1770)** *(Illus.p.258)*
Ink, watercolour on paper 28.9 x 36.3
Signed, dated
Purchased 1935

GROSE, Francis 1731-91 (English)

U949 **Rochester Castle (1768)** *(Illus.p.258)*
Ink, wash, watercolour on paper 29.3 x

47.5
Dated
Purchased 1935

GROSS, Anthony 1905-84 (English)

U801 **Red Cock and Black Hen** *(Illus.p.258)*
Ink, watercolour on paper 37.9 x 55.6
Signed
Purchased 1954

GRÜDER, Julius 1824-90 (German) (attributed
to)

U2266 **William Thompson 1805-52 (1859)**
Oil on canvas 92.1 x 78.1
Bequeathed by Miss E. F. Thompson,
1915

U2267 **William Thompson 1805-52**
Oil on canvas 92.1 x 78.1
Provenance unknown

GÜLICH, John Percival 1864-98 (British)

U1873 **On the Quay, Belfast (1889)** *(Illus.p.258)*
Ink on board 24.5 x 34.8
Signed, dated
Purchased 1932

GUNN, Sir Herbert James 1893-1964 (Scottish)

U2225 **Field-Marshal The Viscount Montgomery
of Alamein and Hindhead, GCB,DSO
1887-1976 (1944)** *(Illus. p.258)*
Oil on canvas 91.3 x 71.1
Signed, dated
Donated by Lady Montgomery, 1946

GUTHRIE, William d.1924 (Irish)

U4503 **James Guthrie d.1878 (1892)**
Oil on canvas 67 x 51.1
Signed, dated
Donated by the artist, 1896

H

HAAG, Carl 1820-1915 (German)

U1050 **Ruins of the Palace of Diocletian, Split
(1855)** *(Illus.p.259)*
Ink, watercolour, bodycolour on paper
50.8 x 35.6
Signed, dated
Purchased 1913

U1398 **Rocks on a Hill Overhanging the Rhine
(1852)** *(Illus.p.259)*
Watercolour on card 35.4 x 50.6
Signed, dated
Purchased 1955

HAENSBERGEN, Johan van 1642-1705 (Dutch)

U53 **Portrait of a Gentleman (c.1690)**
(Illus.p.259)
Oil on canvas 46 x 37
Purchased 1953

HAGEN, Willem van der fl.1700-40 (Dutch,
worked in Ireland)

U43 **Landing of King William of Glorious**

Dame Barbara Hepworth 1903-75 **Curved Form (Delphi) (1955)** U965

Jan van der Heyden 1637-1712 **A View of the Palace of the Dukes of Brabant, Brussels (poss. 1660s)** U644

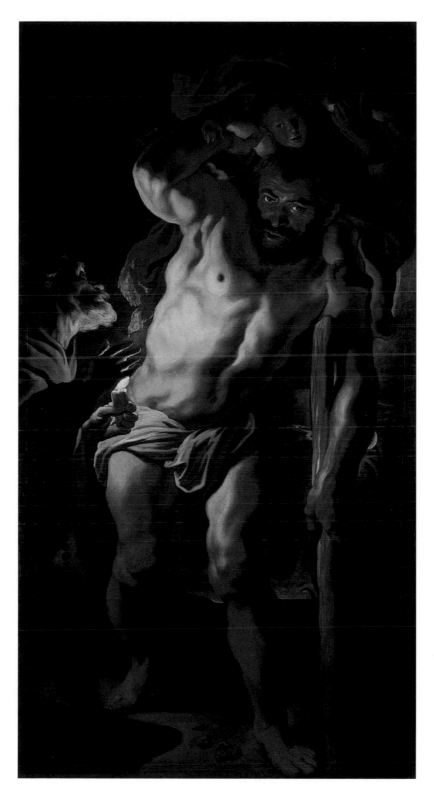

Jacob Jordaens 1593-1678 **St. Christopher Carrying the Christ Child (c. 1625-30)** U133

Sir John Lavery 1856-1941 **Under the Cherry Tree (1884)** U67

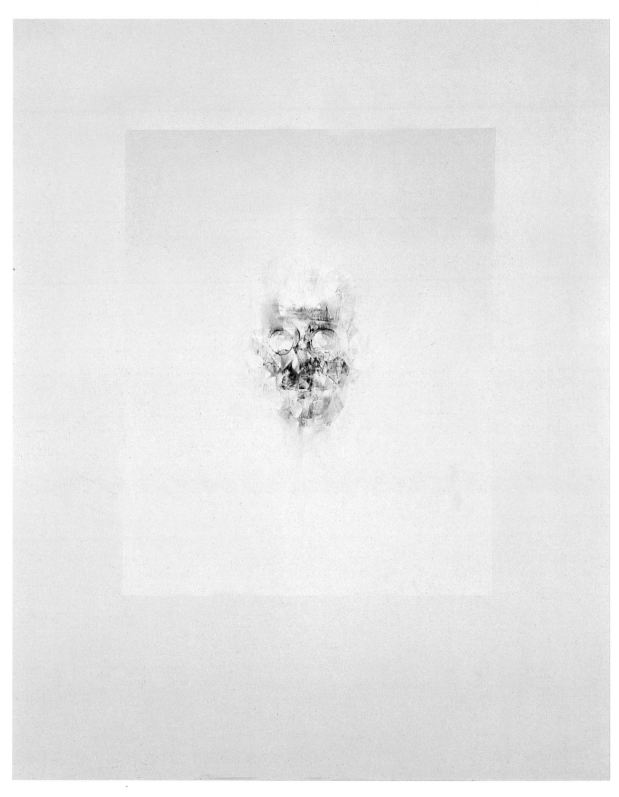

Louis le Brocquy b. 1916 **Image of James Joyce (1977)** U2528

Morris Louis 1912-62 **Golden Age (1958)** U526

F. E. McWilliam 1909-92 **Man and Wife (1948)** U967

Isamu Noguchi 1904-88 **Black Sun (1967)** U980

Memory at Carrickfergus, 1690 (c.1728)
(Illus.p.259)
Oil on canvas 183 x 131.5
Purchased 1967

HAGHE, Louis 1806-85 (Belgian)

U1210 **A Church Interior (1868)** *(Illus.p.259)*
Pencil, watercolour, bodycolour, gum on
paper 45.5 x 56.3
Signed, dated
Purchased 1912

HAHN, Friedemann b.1949 (German)

U4895 **Kopf mit Hut und welken Blumen
(1989)** *(Illus.p.259)*
Oil on canvas 209 x 174
Purchased 1992

HALL, Adrian b.1943 (English)

U2465 **Sculptogram: Number Thirty (1976)**
Colour photograph on paper 76.8 x 51.3
Signed, dated
Purchased 1978

U2466 **Sculptogram: Number Twenty-seven
(1976)**
Colour photograph on paper 51.4 x 76.7
Signed, dated
Purchased 1978

U2467 **Sculptogram: Number Twenty-nine
(1976)**
Colour photograph on paper 51.3 x 76.5
Signed, dated
Purchased 1978

U4744 **Double Portrait: Gordon Lambert and
David Hendriks (1979-80)**
Photographs, mixed media on paper
on board, two panels, each 82.5 x 58.3;
82.5 x 116.6 overall
Signed, dated
Donated by Gordon Lambert, 1988

HALL, Clifford 1904-73 (English)

U463 **Place du Tertre, Paris (1934)** *(Illus.p.259)*
Oil on canvas 61 x 45.7
Signed, dated
Donated by Dr. R. H. Hunter, 1941

HALL, Kenneth 1913-46 (British)

U4977 **Trafalgar Square IV - October 8th 1937**
(Illus.p.259)
Oil on canvas 76 x 101.5
Purchased 1994

HAMILTON, Eva Henrietta 1880-1959 (Irish)

U315 **Tobar Pádraig, Co. Mayo (1925)**
(Illus.p.259)
Oil on board 21.2 x 25
Bequeathed by Dr. R. I. Best (per the
Friends of the National Collections
of Ireland), 1959

HAMILTON, Hugh Douglas 1739-1808 (Irish)

U48 **James Moore O'Donnell 1770-1806
(c.1795-96)** *(Illus.p.260)*
Oil on canvas 76.2 x 63.3
Donated by Sir Francis and Lady Stronge

(per the Rt. Hon. Sir James
Stronge), 1925

U51 **Colonel Hugh O'Donnell d.1799
(c.1795-96)**
Oil on canvas 76.2 x 63.3
Donated by Sir Francis and Lady Stronge
(per the Rt. Hon. Sir James
Stronge), 1925

U4975 **Lord Edward Fitzgerald 1763-98
(c.1798)** *(Illus.p.260)*
Oil on canvas 71.1 x 55.9
Purchased 1994

HAMILTON, Letitia Marion 1880-1964 (Irish)

U312 **Irish Market Scene (c.1923)**
Oil, gouache on panel 30.2 x 42
Signed
Bequeathed by Dr. R. I. Best (per the
Friends of the National Collections of
Ireland), 1959

U314 **Fiesole Hill, Florence (c.1930s)**
Oil on board 17.7 x 22.9
Bequeathed by Dr. R. I. Best (per the
Friends of the National Collections of
Ireland), 1959

U586 **Donkeys (c.1930-32)** *(Illus.p.260)*
Oil on board 55.9 x 66
Signed
Donated by the Thomas Haverty Trust,
1936

U4933 **The Twelve Pins, Connemara**
Oil on canvas 51 x 60.6
Bequeathed by M. Kennedy, 1992

HAMILTON, Richard b.1922 (English)

U2571 **Bronze by Gold (1948)** *(Illus.p.260)*
Pencil, watercolour on paper 56.7 x 38.7
(sight)
Signed
Purchased 1980

HANLON, Rev. Jack Paul 1913-68 (Irish)

U306 **The Grey Hat** *(Illus.p.260)*
Oil on canvas 61 x 51.3
Donated by the Thomas Haverty Trust,
1960

U555 **Flowers**
Oil on canvas 61.1 x 50.5
Bequeathed by the artist's estate, 1968

U556 **Still Life with Figure**
Oil on canvas 50.7 x 76.2
Bequeathed by the artist's estate, 1968

U557 **Sunbathing**
Oil on canvas 54.4 x 81.6
Bequeathed by the artist's estate, 1968

U1223 **The Flowershop** *(Illus.p.260)*
Watercolour on paper 28.6 x 38.7
Signed
Bequeathed by the artist's estate, 1968

U1224 **The Palm Tree**
Pencil, watercolour on paper 32.3 x 46.5
Signed
Bequeathed by the artist's estate, 1968

U1225 **Chimney Sweep (1965)** *(Illus.p.260)*
Pencil, watercolour on paper 58 x 78.8
Signed, dated
Bequeathed by the artist's estate, 1968

HARDING, James Duffield 1797-1863 (English)

U1051 **An Eastern Landscape (1834)**
(Illus.p.260)
Pencil, ink, watercolour on paper 22.5 x
33.4
Signed, dated
Purchased 1929

HARDING, Morris 1874-1964 (English, worked
in Ireland)

U2223 **Angel (1909)**
Sculpture, plaster 55.2 x 14.3 x 14.9
Signed, dated
Purchased 1960

HARDWICK, Philip 1792-1870 (English)

U1052 **A Country Road** (formerly 'English
Landscape')
Ink, watercolour on paper 14.5 x 18.5
Purchased 1927

U1053 **A London Street** (formerly 'Street
Scene') *(Illus.p.260)*
Pencil, ink, watercolour on paper 18.8 x
14
Purchased 1927

HARDY, James, Jnr. 1832-89 (English)

U41 **The Ballad (1861)** *(Illus.p.261)*
Oil on panel 18.6 x 24.6
Signed, dated
Donated by W. T. Braithwaite (per J.
Horner), 1906

HARDY, Thomas Bush 1842-97 (English)

U4673 **Boulogne (1877)** *(Illus.p.261)*
Watercolour on paper 31.8 x 49.5 (sight)
Signed, dated
Purchased 1949

HARMAR, Fairlie, Viscountess Harberton 1876-
1945 (English)

U462 **L'Aveyron (c.1932)** *(Illus.p.261)*
Oil on canvas 63.2 x 75.8
Signed
Purchased (Lloyd Patterson Collection)
1932

HARPER, Charles b.1943 (Irish)

U2416 **Imminence (1975)**
Acrylic, pencil on paper 62 x 72.5 (sight)
Signed, dated
Purchased 1976

HARRISON, Colin b.1939 (English)

U2083 **Albert and William Bogle (c.1974)**
Pencil, acrylic, sellotape on paper 45.8 x
63.5 (sight)
Purchased 1974

U2294 **A and the Dog (1974)** *(Illus.p.261)*
Acrylic on board 56.9 x 46.8
Purchased 1974

U2364　**William Bogle with Memento of Arnold (c.1975)**
Oil, pencil on canvas on board 50.9 x 61
Purchased 1975

HARRISON, Sarah Cecilia 1863-1941 (Irish)

U46　**Rt. Rev. Monsignor James O'Laverty 1826-1906 (1906)**
Oil on canvas 91.5 x 71.1
Signed, dated
Donated by the artist, 1915

U49　**Henry Joy McCracken 1767-98 (1926)**
(Illus.p.261)
Oil on canvas 63.5 x 56.2
Signed, dated
Donated by the artist, 1927

U1950　**Robert Lloyd Praeger, DSc 1865-1953 (1931)**
Oil on canvas 80.1 x 65.5
Signed, dated
Donated by the artist, 1932

U2275　**Portrait of a Lady**
Oil on canvas 76.7 x 63.8
Signed
Donated by Mrs. Walter Ford, 1963

HARTLAND, Henry Albert 1840-93 (Irish)

U802　**A Country Lane** *(Illus.p.261)*
Watercolour, white on paper 20 x 28.7
Signed
Purchased 1970

U2479　**Carriganass Castle, Co. Cork** *(Illus.p.261)*
Watercolour on paper 63.5 x 97
Purchased 1978

HASSALL, John 1868-1948 (English)

U1294　**'The Whole Town's Talking'** *(Illus.p.261)*
Ink, watercolour, white on paper 66.3 x 51.5
Signed
Donated by Rowel Friers, 1947

U1295　**Head of a Man in a Bowler Hat**
(Caricature)
Ink, watercolour, white on card 26.7 x 20.5
Signed
Donated by Rowel Friers, 1947

HAUGHTON, Benjamin 1865-1924 (English)

U310　**Winter in a Devon Valley** *(Illus.p.261)*
Oil on canvas 35.6 x 45.8
Signed
Donated by Miss B. M. B. Haughton, 1937

U1951　**Frosty Morning**
Oil on panel 25.7 x 20.3
Signed
Donated by Mrs. J. Haughton, 1937

HAUGHTON, Wilfred J. 1921-99 (Irish)

U303　**First Snow in Norfolk (1960-61)**
(Illus.p.262)
Oil on canvas 63.4 x 75.8
Signed

Donated by the artist, 1961

HAVERTY, Joseph Patrick 1794-1864 (Irish) (after)

U1895　**Daniel O'Connell 1775-1847**
Miniature, watercolour on ivory 10.5 x 8
Provenance unknown

HAWKSETT, Samuel 1801-59 (Irish)

U34　**Portrait of a Man (c.1830s)**
Now **Dr. James Forsythe 1756-1849 (c.1815-20)** by Unknown, 19th century (Irish)

U209　**David McTear 1756-1840 (c.1836)**
Oil on canvas 129.8 x 101.6
Donated by Miss F. Riddell and Miss E. McTear, 1920

U221　**Portrait of a Young Man (c.1820-30)**
Oil on canvas 85.2 x 66.6
Donated by Miss Margaret Dobbs, 1951

U585　**Robert Langtry d.1859 (c.1843)**
(Illus.p.262)
Oil on canvas 131.5 x 101.2
Donated by Professor Dill, 1890

U2458　**Joseph Stevenson 1764-1837 (c.1837)**
Oil on canvas 128.7 x 101.5
Provenance unknown

HAWTHORNE, Elwin b.1905 (English)

U666　**Halbut Street**
Oil on board 41.6 x 55.8
Signed
Provenance unknown

HAYES, Claude 1852-1922 (Irish, worked in England)

U1561　**A Windmill in Sussex** *(Illus.p.262)*
Pencil, watercolour on paper 49.4 x 74.9
Signed
Purchased 1930

U1562　**Across the Common**
Watercolour on paper 54.8 x 75.4
Signed
Purchased 1911

HAYES, Edwin 1819-1904 (English, worked in Ireland)

U544　**Fishing Boats, Holland**
Oil on panel 30.8 x 45.5
Bequeathed by Miss H. M. McCleery, 1968

U546　**Dutch Shipping Scene**
Oil on canvas 30.5 x 50.9
Signed
Bequeathed by Miss H. M. McCleery, 1968

U634　**Morning after the Storm off Yarmouth**
(Illus.p.262)
Oil on canvas 41 x 61
Bequeathed by H. Musgrave, 1922

U4674　**Towing a Vessel into Harbour**
Watercolour, gum, scraping on paper 40.6 x 61 (sight)
Signed

Provenance unknown

HAYNES-WILLIAMS, John 1836-1908 (English)

U1952　**Sir Otto Jaffé, JP 1846-1929**
Oil on canvas 126.8 x 97
Transferred from City Hall, Belfast, 1922

U1953　**Sir Robert Lloyd Patterson, JP, DL, FLS 1836-1906 (1897)** *(Illus.p.262)*
Oil on canvas 128 x 87.1
Signed, dated
Bequeathed by the sitter, 1906

HEARNE, Thomas 1744-1817 (English)

U803　**Caister Castle, Norfolk** *(Illus.p.262)*
Pencil, sepia wash on paper 19.3 x 25
Signed
Purchased 1952

HEDEGAARD, Peter b.1939 (Danish, works in England)

U1887　**Green and Orange to Blue (1973)**
Watercolour on paper 76.2 x 55.9
Signed, dated
Purchased 1973

HEERSCHOP, Hendrik 1620-72 (Flemish)

U11　**The Alchemist's Shop** *(Illus.p.262)*
Oil on canvas 60.8 x 55
Donated by W. T. Braithwaite (per J. Horner), 1906

HENDERSON, Brian b.1950 (Irish)

U4756　**Brilliant Crack NYC (1987)** *(Illus.p.262)*
Acrylic on canvas 269.2 x 411.5
Purchased 1989

HENNELL, Thomas 1903-45 (English)

U1054　**Loading into Barn, Kilpeck, Herefordshire** *(Illus.p.262)*
Charcoal, ink, watercolour on paper 48.5 x 31.8
Signed
Purchased 1951

U1055　**US Skipton Camp, Reykjavik, Iceland (1943)**
Pencil, ink, watercolour on paper 32 x 48.5
Signed, dated
Donated by the War Artists' Advisory Committee (per the Imperial War Museum), 1946

U4702　**US Sailors Packing Mail, Rejkjavik (1943)**
Watercolour on paper 31.1 x 47
Signed, dated
Donated by the War Artists' Advisory Committee (per the Imperial War Museum), 1946

HENNESSY, Patrick 1915-81 (Irish)

U4973　**The Old Tree (c.1970-71)** *(Illus.p.263)*
Oil on canvas 63.2 x 88.5
Signed
Purchased 1993

HENNESSY, William John 1839-1917 (Irish-

American)

U4708 **Fête Day in a Cider Orchard, Normandy
(1878)** *(Illus.p.263)*
Oil on canvas 99 x 178
Signed, dated
Purchased 1987

HENRI, Robert 1863-1929 (American, worked in
Ireland)

U4889 **Achill Island, Co. Mayo (1913)**
(Illus.p.263)
Oil on board 32.2 x 40.5
Signed, dated
Purchased 1991

HENRY, Emily Grace 1868-1953 (Irish)

U294 **Paul Henry 1876-1958 (c.1898-1900)**
(Illus.p.263)
Oil on canvas 45 x 40
Donated by Mrs. Creed Meredith, 1954

U295 **Professor Robert Mitchell Henry 1873-
1950** *(Illus.p.263)*
Oil on canvas on board 44.6 x 36.4
Donated by Mrs. Creed Meredith, 1954

U296 **Landscape with Three Cottages (prob.
1910-19)**
Oil on board 33.2 x 42.1
Signed
Bequeathed by Miss Emily S.
Montgomery, 1961

U664 **The Easy Chair**
Oil on canvas on board 46.5 x 37.9
Signed
Donated by Lady Mabel Annesley, 1934

U2435 **Liscannor (c.1945-53)**
Oil on panel 14.2 x 18.1
Signed
Bequeathed by J. N. Bryson (per L.
Bryson), 1977

HENRY, Olive 1902-89 (Irish)

U1056 **Road Block, Belfast (1940)** *(Illus.p.263)*
Oil on paper 38 x 30.5
Signed
Purchased 1944

U1436 **Boats in a Harbour (1957)**
Watercolour on paper 26.5 x 36.5 (sight)
Signed, dated
Donated by Jack Kerr in memory of
Nancy Ferguson, 1999

U4859 **Stained Glass Design No. 6369**
Watercolour, ink on paper 40.5 x 18.8
(sight)
Purchased 1991

U4860 **Stained Glass Design No. 6649**
Watercolour, ink on paper 40.5 x 23.8
(sight)
Purchased 1991

U5013 **Clokey Design No. 7001**
Watercolour on paper 56 x 29.5
Donated by Mrs. Audrey Rebbeck, 1995

U5014 **Stained Glass Cartoon**
Watercolour on paper 128 x 76
Donated by Mrs. Audrey Rebbeck, 1995

HENRY, Paul 1876-1958 (Irish)

U301 **Dawn, Killary Harbour (1921)**
(Illus.p.263)
Oil on canvas 69.1 x 83.3
Signed
Purchased 1923

U311 **Leenane (1913)** *(Illus.p.263)*
Oil on board 34 x 41.2
Signed, dated
Bequeathed by Dr. R. I. Best (per the
Friends of the National Collections
of Ireland), 1959

U2081 **My Friend Michael Mangan (1910-12)**
(Illus.p.263)
Oil on board 15.7 x 10.9
Signed
Purchased 1974

U2085 **Storm over the Bog (c.1910-14)**
Charcoal on paper 51 x 73
Purchased 1974

U2086 **Water Meadows (1907)** *(Illus.p.264)*
Charcoal, white on paper 34 x 46.5
Purchased 1974

U2362 **Professor Robert Mitchell Henry 1873-
1950 (c.1932-33)**
Charcoal on paper 45 x 41.9 (sight)
Purchased 1975

U2434 **Keel, Achill (c.1910-19) (formerly
'Untitled')**
Oil on canvas on board 21.7 x 31.3
Signed
Bequeathed by J. N. Bryson (per L.
Bryson), 1977

U4931 **Wicklow Landscape**
Oil on canvas board 34.2 x 39.5
Signed
Bequeathed by M. Kennedy, 1992

U4953 **A Prayer for the Departed (1910-12)**
Oil on canvas 40.5 x 35.4
Signed
Purchased 1993

U4960 **Arthur O'Gorman Lalor (1916)**
(Illus.p.264)
Charcoal on paper 38 x 35
Purchased 1993

U4972 **The Potato Digger (1912-15)**
(Illus.p.264)
Oil on canvas 35.2 x 46
Purchased 1993

U4999 **The Blacksmith (1910-13)** *(Illus.p.264)*
Oil on panel 15.6 x 12.8
Donated by Mervyn Solomon, 1994

U5000 **My Host and Hostess (1910-13)**
Oil on panel 15.3 x 12.4 (sight)
Donated by Mervyn Solomon, 1994

U5001 **A Man of the Hills (1910-13)**
Oil on panel 15 x 12 (sight)
Donated by Mervyn Solomon, 1994

HEPWORTH, Dame Barbara 1903-75 (English)

U965 **Curved Form (Delphi) (1955)**
(Illus.p.33)

Sculpture, wood, white paint, string
106.7 x 78.7 x 81.3
Purchased with the aid of a grant from
the Calouste Gulbenkian Foundation,
1967

HERKOMER, Sir Hubert von 1849-1914
(English)

U1057 **An Old Bavarian Peasant Woman**
(Illus.p.264)
Watercolour on paper 47.1 x 32
Signed
Donated by Meta and Robert Dunlop,
1950

HERMAN, Josef 1911-2000 (Polish, naturalised
British)

U4685 **Eventide**
Oil on canvas 51 x 66
Signed
Donated by Mr. and Mrs. Philip Solomon,
1985

HERMANN, H. J. 19th century (German?)

U1438 **Wooded Ravine with Waterwheel (1887)**
Watercolour on paper 30 x 22.3
Donated by W. T. Braithwaite (per J.
Horner), 1906

HERON, Hilary 1923-77 (Irish)

U1765 **A Stone in the Hand 1 (1961-63)**
Sculpture, brass, stone, ht. 106.7
Purchased 1963

HERON, Patrick 1920-99 (English)

U2369 **Ceruleum and Scarlet in Ultramarine
with Emerald and Violet Edges, 1970**
(Illus.p.264)
Gouache on paper 59 x 79.2
Donated by the Contemporary Art
Society, 1975

HERRING, John Frederick, Snr. 1795-1865
(English) (attributed to)

U567 **Farmyard Scene** *(Illus.p.264)*
Oil on canvas 63.8 x 77
Signed
Donated by Mr. Williamson, 1966

HEWLETT, Francis b.1930 (English)

U2264 **Travelling Light (1973)**
Sculpture, ceramic 97.5 x 105 x 75
Signed, dated
Purchased 1973

HEYDEN, Jan van der 1637-1712 (Dutch)

U644 **A View of the Palace of the Dukes of
Brabant, Brussels (poss. 1660s)**
(Illus.p.34)
Oil on panel 45.7 x 56.6
Signed
Accepted in lieu of inheritance tax from
the estate of Nicholas Phillips by HM
Government and allocated to the
National Museums and Galleries of
Northern Ireland, 1998

HICKEY, Patrick b.1927 (Irish)

U305   **Landscape, Ireland (1950s)** *(Illus.p.264)*
Oil on canvas 76.2 x 92
Donated by the Thomas Haverty Trust,
1960

HICKS, George Elgar 1824-1914 (English)

U1712   **Winged Male Nude with Helmet (1846)**
Ink on card 47 x 35.7
Signed, dated
Provenance unknown

U1713   **Mailed Knights at a Battle**
Ink on card 35 x 51.3
Provenance unknown

U1714   **King on Horseback with Three Attackers**
Ink on card 35.5 x 51.3
Provenance unknown

U1715   **Head of a Young Lady**
Chalk on paper 39.2 x 28.5
Provenance unknown

U1716   **Head of a Girl**
Chalk on paper 35.2 x 30
Provenance unknown

U1717   **Miss Harrison (1883)**
Chalk on paper 35.5 x 27
Signed, dated
Provenance unknown

U1718   **The Hon. Winifred Sturt (1882)**
(Illus.p.264)
Chalk on paper 41.5 x 33.5
Signed, dated
Provenance unknown

U1719   **Two Young Ladies**
Chalk on paper 38.6 x 31
Signed
Provenance unknown

U1720   **Head of a Young Child**
Chalk on paper 46.4 x 33.8
Provenance unknown

U1721   **Head of a Woman**
Chalk on paper 43.7 x 34
Provenance unknown

U1722   **Head of a Girl**
Chalk on paper 43.8 x 33.5
Provenance unknown

U1723   **Bubbs Gilbert (?) aged Three (1888)**
Chalk on paper 45 x 34.5
Provenance unknown

U1724   **Head of a Little Girl**
Chalk on paper 39 x 31.5
Provenance unknown

U1725   **Head of a Woman**
Chalk on paper 39.8 x 31.4
Provenance unknown

U1726   **Head of a Young Child**
Chalk on paper 27.5 x 33
Provenance unknown

U1727   **Head and Left Arm of a Baby**
Chalk on paper 25 x 31.5
Provenance unknown

U1728   **Averil Vivian, aged Five**
Chalk on paper 38 x 31.5
Provenance unknown

U1729   **Head of a Child**
Chalk on paper 37.3 x 27.9
Provenance unknown

U1730   **Noel (1875)** (Head of a Boy)
Chalk on paper 34 x 33
Provenance unknown

U1731   **Head of a Girl**
Chalk on paper 39.5 x 35.5
Provenance unknown

U1732   **Study for 'The Last Shilling' (1852)**
(formerly 'Man Wearing an Overcoat')
(Illus.p.265)
Pencil on paper 17 x 10.8
Signed, dated
Provenance unknown

U1733   **Flower Seller (1852)** (formerly 'Woman
with Basket of Flowers') *(Illus.p.265)*
Pencil on paper 17.7 x 11.8
Signed, dated
Provenance unknown

U1734   **Woman Carrying a Child across
Stepping Stones**
Pencil, white on paper 29 x 20
Provenance unknown

U1735   **Two Men Resting on a Grassy Bank**
Pencil, white on paper 26 x 36.6
Provenance unknown

U1736   **Workman with Pickaxe**
Pencil on paper 9 x 5
Provenance unknown

U1737   **Fisherman with Creel**
Pencil on paper 10.2 x 4.9
Provenance unknown

U1738   **Workman with Hands in his Pockets**
Pencil on paper 9 x 5.1
Provenance unknown

U1739   **Standing Woman with Shawl**
Pencil on paper 10.7 x 5
Provenance unknown

U1740   **Workman and a Woman**
Pencil on paper 21.2 x 11.1
Signed
Provenance unknown

U1741   **A Gnarled Tree Trunk**
Oil on paper 32.4 x 26.5
Provenance unknown

U1742   **Academy Study (Adam and Eve?)**
Chalk on paper 56.5 x 38.6
Provenance unknown

U1743   **Academy Study (Satan?)**
Chalk on paper 53.5 x 41
Provenance unknown

U1744   **Female Nude Study**
Chalk on paper 56.5 x 38.8
Provenance unknown

U1745   **Seated Female Nude**
Chalk, sanguine on paper 38.5 x 28
Provenance unknown

U1746   **Head of a Tiger**
Charcoal on paper 12.5 x 15.8
Catalogued erroneously; is by Morris
Harding 1874-1964 and has been
removed to the collections of the
departments of Botany and Zoology

U1747   **Female Nude**
Chalk on paper 32.3 x 25
Provenance unknown

U1748   **Female Nude Kneeling** *(Illus.p.265)*
Chalk, sanguine on paper 56.2 x 25.7
Provenance unknown

U1749   **Male Nude Study**
Chalk, sanguine on paper 50.5 x 31.5
Provenance unknown

HIGHMORE, Joseph 1692-1780 (English)
(attributed to)

U50   **Portrait of a Boy (c.1740)** *(Illus.p.265)*
Oil on canvas 77.5 x 64
Purchased 1943

HILL, Derek 1916-2000 (English, worked in
Ireland)

U299   **Tory Island from Tor More (1958-59)**
(Illus.p.265)
Oil on canvas 71.3 x 122.3
Purchased 1961

U4981   **Sir John Heygate 1903-76 (c.1960-65)**
Oil on canvas 50.3 x 40.3
Purchased 1994

HILL, James John 1811-82 (English)

U42   **The Gleaners** *(Illus.p.265)*
Oil on board 25.2 x 22.7
Signed
Donated by J. F. Johnson, 1896

HILL, Thomas 1829-1908 (English)

U45   **Giant Redwood (1896)**
Oil on canvas 222.7 x 76.9
Signed, dated
Provenance unknown

HILLS, Robert 1769-1844 (English)

U1058   **Deer in a Highland Glen** *(Illus.p.265)*
Pencil, watercolour on paper 26.5 x 19.9
Purchased 1952

HILLS, Robert 1769-1844 (after)

U1161   **Mule Train**
Pencil, watercolour on paper 33.3 x 48.8
Donated by J. St. Clair Boyd, 1954
Formerly by Unknown

HILTON, Roger 1911-75 (English)

U545   **January 1962 (1962)** *(Illus.p.265)*
Oil on canvas 113.8 x 126.9
Signed, dated
Purchased 1962

HITCHENS, Sydney Ivon 1893-1979 (English)

U461   **Flower Painting (1933)**
Oil on canvas 61.1 x 56
Signed, dated

Donated by the Contemporary Art
Society, 1957

U551 **Spring in Autumn (1967)** *(Illus.p.265)*
Oil on canvas 58.8 x 155.2
Signed, dated
Purchased 1969

HOARE, William, of Bath 1707-92 (after)

U1865 **Alexander Pope 1688-1744** *(Illus.p.266)*
Ink on paper 18.8 x 11.5
Donated by C. H. Crawford, 1973

HODGE, Francis Edwin 1883-1949 (English)

U298 **Unfinished Sketch of Sir William Orpen
1878-1931 (1929-31)**
Oil on canvas 91.6 x 71.2
Signed, dated
Donated by Mrs. Howard Fish, 1952

HODSON, William fl.1885-89 (Irish)

U1059 **Town and Castle of Carrickfergus
(1886)** *(Illus.p.266)*
Pencil, watercolour, white on paper 32.7
x 43
Signed, dated
Donated by J. Stelfox, 1907

HOLDEN, Donald b.1931 (American)

U4982 **Dusk at Gull Pond V (1994)**
Watercolour on paper 18.5 x 27.3 (sight)
Signed, dated
Donated by the artist in memory of
Samuel Carr, 1994

HOLLAND, James 1800-70 (English)

U804 **A Venetian Canal** *(Illus.p.266)*
Pencil, watercolour on paper 33.8 x 49.1
Purchased 1939

U4725 **A Venetian Canal (1860)**
Pencil, watercolour on paper 29 x 34
(sight)
Signed, dated
Purchased 1948

HOLLYWOOD, William b.1923 (English,
worked in Ireland)

U5046 **MacArt's Fort (1951)** *(Illus.p.266)*
Oil on canvas 63.5 x 91.4
Signed, dated
Donated by the Friends of the National
Collections of Ireland, 1997

HOLMES, Sir Charles John 1868-1936 (English)

U304 **Grenfell Crag (1919)**
Oil on canvas 46 x 81.5
Signed, dated
Purchased 1944

U1060 **The Lune near Tebay (1934)**
Chalk, watercolour on paper 17.8 x 25.6
Signed, dated
Donated by the National Art Collections
Fund, 1946

HOME, Robert 1752-1834 (English, worked in
Ireland)

U23 **Captain Waddell Cunningham 1730-97
(c.1786)** *(Illus.p.266)*
Oil on canvas 61 x 50.5
Purchased 1932

HONE, Evie 1894-1955 (Irish)

U308 **Ruin at Ardmore (c.1946)** *(Illus.p.266)*
Oil on panel 46.3 x 55.2
Signed
Donated by the Friends of the National
Collections of Ireland, 1958

U805 **Composition (prob. c.1920-33)**
(Illus.p.266)
Gouache on card 29.5 x 42
Signed
Purchased 1965

U4965 **Ardmore, Co. Waterford**
Gouache on paper 24 x 37
Bequeathed by Mary Kate Donnellan,
1993

HONE, Horace 1756 1825 (Irish)

U1885 **Portrait of Major Holt Waring c.1722-
1806 (1796)** *(Illus.p.266)*
Pencil, watercolour, bodycolour on paper
11.1 x 9
Signed, dated
Purchased 1973

HONE, Nathaniel 1718-84 (Irish)

U228 **A Boy Deliberating on his Drawing
(c.1769)** *(Illus.p.266)*
Oil on canvas 63.5 x 76
Purchased 1969

U1890 **Unknown Man (1757)**
Miniature in enamel 3.2 x 2.7 (oval)
Signed, dated
Purchased 1962

HONE, Nathaniel 1831-1917 (Irish)

U54 **Cows under Trees**
Oil on board 18.5 x 25.8 (sight)
Purchased 1925

U55 **Bundoran Sands: Stormy Day**
Oil on board 17.9 x 26.6
Purchased 1925

U56 **Park, St. Doulough's**
Oil on board 20.5 x 25.5
Purchased 1925

U565 **Landscape with Cattle** *(Illus.p.267)*
Oil on canvas 33.2 x 45.7
Signed
Bequeathed by Dr. R. I. Best (per the
Friends of the National Collections of
Ireland), 1959

U886 **Pastures with Cows**
Watercolour on paper 12.5 x 21.8
Stamped with monogram
Purchased 1925

U887 **On the Nile** *(Illus.p.267)*
Watercolour on paper 11.9 x 19.2
Stamped with monogram
Purchased 1925

U888 **Coast with Green Shore**
Watercolour on paper 11.4 x 16

Stamped with monogram
Purchased 1925

U889 **Two Horses and a Cart** (Study)
Watercolour on paper 10.8 x 14
Stamped with monogram
Purchased 1925

U890 **Sea and Distant Mountains**
Watercolour on paper 11.9 x 19.4
Stamped with monogram
Purchased 1925

U891 **Sandy Bay with Rocky Foreground**
Watercolour on paper 12.4 x 17.3
Stamped with monogram
Purchased 1925

HOOKE, Richard 1820-1908 (Irish)

U44 **William Herdman 1777-1855**
Oil on canvas 91.5 x 70.5
Donated by R. E. Herdman, 1931

U1960 **Dr. James Patterson 1810-69 (c.1860)**
Oil on card 28 x 25.3
Donated by T. O. Millar, 1927

U1961 **John Rowan 1787-1858 (c.1830s)**
Oil on canvas 127 x 99
Donated by the Rowan family (per J.
Malone), 1922

U1962 **Dr. T. Henry Purdon**
Oil; no further details
Donated by Mrs. Purdon, 1899; destroyed
1945

U1963 **William Rowan**
Oil on canvas 76.5 x 63.5
Donated by the Rowan family (per J.
Malone), 1922

U2341 **George Benn 1801-82** *(Illus.p.267)*
Oil on canvas 92.3 x 71.9
Donated by Miss H. Benn, 1891

U2343 **Edward Jones Smith**
Oil on a photograph on board 21.8 x
18.2
Donated by Mrs. J. Galt Smith, 1922

U2583 **James MacAdam 1801-61**
Oil on canvas 73.9 x 58.5
Donated by the Belfast Natural History
and Philosophical Society, 1910

HOUTHUESEN, Albert 1903-79 (Dutch,
naturalised British)

U2585 **Wheels, Maes Gwyn Farm (1934)**
(Illus.p.267)
Oil on canvas 86.4 x 111.5
Signed, dated
Donated by Miss E. McKee (per the
artist's widow), 1981

HOWARD, Ken b.1932 (English)

U5005 **Ulster Crucifixion (1978)** (Triptych with
Predella) *(Illus.p.267)*
Oil on canvas, centre 116.2 x 89.2 (sight);
sides, each 119.2 x 43 (sight); predella
19.5 x 89.2 (sight)
Purchased with the aid of a grant from
the National Art Collections Fund, 1995

HOYLAND, John b.1934 (English)

U720 **3:8:68 (1968)** *(Illus.p.267)*
Acrylic on canvas 198.4 x 366.4
Purchased 1970

HUBBARD, Eric Hesketh 1892-1957 (English)

U579 **Dunluce Castle** *(Illus.p.267)*
Oil on canvas 64.1 x 76.6
Signed
Purchased 1945

HUBERT, Jean-Baptiste-Louis 1801-after 1865 (French)

U1061 **Figure by a River (1829)**
Pencil, sepia on paper 26.9 x 20.9
Signed, dated
Donated by J. H. Bland, 1910

U1062 **View in Switzerland (1827)**
Pencil, sepia on paper 20.4 x 27.5
Signed, dated
Donated by J. H. Bland, 1910

U1063 **Swiss View, Figures by a River (1830)**
Pencil, sepia on paper 23.1 x 32
Signed, dated
Donated by J. H. Bland, 1910

U1064 **View in Switzerland (1829)**
Pencil, sepia on paper 21.5 x 30.3
Signed, dated
Donated by J. H. Bland, 1910

U1065 **Cattle by a Stream** *(Illus.p.267)*
Pencil, sepia on paper 41.3 x 34.4
Donated by J. H. Bland, 1910

U1066 **Two Fishermen (1830)**
Pencil, sepia wash on paper 25.8 x 31.3
Signed, dated
Donated by J. H. Bland, 1910

U1067 **Figures by a Pond (1832)**
Pencil, sepia on paper 26.5 x 36.2
Signed, dated
Donated by J. H. Bland, 1910

U1068 **Trees and a Water Spout (1829)**
(Illus.p.267)
Pencil, sepia on paper 26.1 x 19.3
Signed, dated
Donated by J. H. Bland, 1910

U1475 **Bridge and Cottage (1832)**
(Switzerland?)
Pencil on paper 24.5 x 32.4
Signed, dated
Donated by J. H. Bland, 1910

U1476 **Rock Face and Cave in a Wood**
Pencil, sepia on paper 25.4 x 23.6
Donated by J. H. Bland, 1910

U1477 **Mountains and Farm by a Stream**
(Switzerland?)
Pencil, sepia on paper 19.7 x 30.4
Donated by J. H. Bland, 1910

U1478 **A Two-arched Stone Bridge**
Pencil, watercolour on paper 21.5 x 28.3
Donated by J. H. Bland, 1910

U1479 **Canal with Timbered Buildings**
Pencil, watercolour on paper 31.3 x 24.7
Donated by J. H. Bland, 1910

U1480 **An Italian Villa (?)**
Pencil, watercolour on paper 13 x 26.3
Donated by J. H. Bland, 1910

U1481 **River with Wooden Footbridge**
Pencil, watercolour on paper 20.8 x 27.5
Donated by J. H. Bland, 1910

U1482 **Mountains, River and a Man with a Stick**
Pencil, watercolour on paper 17.5 x 27.2
Donated by J. H. Bland, 1910

U1483 **Harbour Scene with a Hulk**
Pencil, watercolour on paper 18.5 x 25.8
Donated by J. H. Bland, 1910

U1484 **A Stream between Two Houses** (Italy?)
Pencil, watercolour on paper 23 x 30.2
Donated by J. H. Bland, 1910

U1872 **Trees by a Stream**
Pencil on paper 34.6 x 26.9
Signed
Donated by J. H. Bland, 1910

HUBERT, Jean-Baptiste-Louis 1801-after 1865 (French) (attributed to)

U1485 **Mountainous Landscape with Farm Buildings**
Pencil, watercolour on paper 25.5 x 36.4
Donated by J. H. Bland, 1910

U1684 **Gabled Buildings by Water**
Watercolour on paper 23 x 31.7
Donated by J. H. Bland, 1910

HUGHES, David Gordon b.1957 (Irish)

U1954 **Flowers**
Oil on canvas 59.8 x 59.8
Signed
Donated by Philip Solomon, 1999

HUGHES, John 1865-1941 (Irish)

U2415 **Thérèse (1896)** *(Illus.p.268)*
Sculpture, bronze 8.6 x 56.5 x 10 (cast in 1927)
Signed, dated
Purchased 1976

HULL, Frederick W. 1867-1953 (Irish)

U313 **Winter above Ligoniel** *(Illus.p.268)*
Oil on panel 35.7 x 45.8
Signed
Purchased 1949

U578 **The White Rocks, Portrush (c.1913-14)**
(Illus.p.268)
Oil on canvas 56.1 x 76.7
Signed
Purchased 1914

HUNT, Cecil Arthur 1873-1965 (English)

U1069 **Evening at Valoscura, San Rafael, California** *(Illus.p.268)*
Pencil, watercolour on paper 28.5 x 39.5
Signed
Bequeathed by Sir David Reid (per Lady Reid), 1951

U1211 **Gibraltar** *(Illus.p.268)*
Pencil, watercolour, bodycolour on paper 53 x 77.5

Signed
Bequeathed by Sir David Reid (per Lady Reid), 1951

HUNT, Walter 1861-1941 (English)

U602 **The Twins (1904)**
Oil on canvas 102.5 x 168
Signed, dated
Purchased 1911; destroyed in Malone House fire, 1976

HUNT, William Henry 1790-1864 (English)

U806 **The Link Boy** *(Illus.p.339)*
Now by Unknown, 19th century
(Unknown School)

HUNTER, George Leslie 1877-1931 (Scottish)

U4777 **Fishing Village** *(Illus.p.268)*
Oil on panel 15 x 29.5
Bequeathed by Roberta and John Hewitt, 1987

U4778 **Ceres, Fife: Church and Village**
(Illus.p.268)
Gouache on paper 42.5 x 48.5
Bequeathed by Roberta and John Hewitt, 1987

HUNTER, John Frederick 1893-1951 (Irish)

U309 **Still Life and Figures** *(Illus.p.268)*
Oil on panel 50.4 x 61
Signed
Purchased 1951

HUNTER, John Frederick and **W. R. GORDON** 1872-1955 (both Irish)

U1945 **The Bronze Age in Ulster (1934)**
Oil on three canvases, 287.4 x 1221.3 overall
Signed, dated
Donated by the Thomas Haverty Trust, 1934

HUNTER, Mercy 1910-89 (Irish)

U1683 **Friar's Bush Graveyard, Belfast (1953)**
(Illus.p.268)
Pencil on paper 73.6 x 53.3 (sight)
Signed, dated
Purchased 1953

HUNTER, Robert fl.1752-1803 (Irish)

U47 **Simon Harcourt, 1st Earl Harcourt 1714-77 (1772-75)** *(Illus.p.269)*
Oil on canvas 76.7 x 64
Donated by B. McCoy, 1892

HURTADO, Fabio 20th century (Spanish)

U728 **Three Seated Women and a Dog**
(Illus.p.269)
Oil on canvas 114.5 x 162.5
Signed, dated
Donated by Philip Solomon, 1998

HUSSEY, Philip 1713-83 (Irish)

U1664 **The Family of Thomas Bateson, Esq. 1705-91 (1762)** *(Illus.p.281)*
Now attributed to Strickland Lowry

1737-c. 85

HUXLEY, Paul b.1938 (English)

U2676 **Spanish Cubism (1978)** *(Illus.p.269)*
Acrylic on canvas 203 x 203
Signed, dated
Donated by the Contemporary Art
Society, 1983

I

IBBETSON, Julius Caesar 1759-1817 (English)

U38   **View of Beeston Castle, Cheshire**
(Illus.p.269)
Oil on canvas 46.5 x 57
Purchased 1958

U58   **Scene in the Lake District (1817?)**
Oil on canvas 46.5 x 57
Signed, dated indistinctly
Purchased 1958

INCE, Joseph Murray 1806-59 (English)

U1070 **Off Calshot Castle (1848)** *(Illus.p.269)*
Ink, watercolour on paper 20.5 x 34.4
Signed, dated
Purchased 1954

INDONI, Filippo fl.1883-89 (Italian)

U1071 **Italian Girl Spinning with Distaff**
(Illus.p.269)
Pencil, watercolour on paper 55.1 x 37.7
Signed
Bequeathed by Sir R. Lloyd Patterson,
1919

INLANDER, Henry 1925-83 (British)

U465   **The Creation of Eve**
Oil on canvas 137.2 x 137.5
Signed
Donated by the Contemporary Art
Society, 1962

INNES, James Dixon 1887-1914 (Welsh)

U464   **Olives at Collioure (1911)** *(Illus.p.269)*
Oil on canvas 30.8 x 40.9
Signed, dated
Purchased (Lloyd Patterson Collection)
1929

IRWIN, Mrs. Maud fl.1912-40 (Irish?)

U1072 **Snowscape, Belfast (1939)** (formerly
'Winter Afternoon')
Pencil, watercolour on card 53.8 x 38
Signed, dated
Donated by G. Irwin (per M. Harding),
1946

ITEN, Hans 1874-1930 (Swiss, worked in
Ireland)

U316   **Old Lime Kiln, Port-na-Blagh**
Oil on canvas 76.3 x 101.8
Signed
Purchased 1931

U317   **Small Holding in Switzerland**

(Illus.p.269)
Oil on canvas 49.7 x 68
Signed
Donated by Dr. R. H. Hunter, 1941

U318   **Les Capucines** *(Illus.p.269)*
Oil on canvas on board 40.6 x 50.3
Signed
Purchased 1921

U319   **Surge of the Sea, Ardglass** *(Illus.p.270)*
Oil on board 26.9 x 34.8
Signed
Donated by Meta and Robert Dunlop,
1950

U320   **Heath with Trees in Background**
Oil on panel 15.4 x 21.4
Signed
Purchased 1931

U321   **Five Trees by a River**
Oil on canvas on panel 15.3 x 24.7
Signed
Purchased 1931

U322   **Meadow with Trees by a River**
Oil on board 15.3 x 21.8
Signed
Purchased 1931

U548   **Her Little Holding** *(Illus.p.270)*
Oil on board 26.8 x 34.8
Signed
Bequeathed by Miss H. M. McCleery,
1968

U576   **Farmlands, Donegal (c.1929-30)**
Oil on canvas 76.2 x 101.1
Signed
Purchased 1931

U580   **St. John's Point, Killough**
Oil on panel 15.2 x 21.6
Signed
Purchased 1931

U581   **Study from Nature**
Oil on board 15.3 x 21.6
Signed
Purchased 1931

U588   **Spring Flowers** *(Illus.p.270)*
Oil on canvas 45.7 x 35.5
Signed
Donated by Meta and Robert Dunlop,
1950

U632   **Autumn** *(Illus.p.270)*
Oil on canvas 58.5 x 50.2
Signed
Provenance unknown

U635   **Still Life with Oysters** *(Illus.p.270)*
Oil on canvas 64 x 80.5
Purchased 1904

U652   **Landscape**
Oil on board 15.5 x 21.6
Signed
Purchased 1931

U1590 **Study for 'Old Lime Kiln, Port-na-Blagh'**
(U316)
Ink over pencil on canvas 45.3 x 60.2
Donated by Mrs. Hans Iten, 1931

U1965 **Tulips and Violets**
Oil on paper on board 40.6 x 33
Signed
Donated by Stephen Gilbert (executor of
Forrest Reid), 1955

U2282 **Trees, Ploughed Field and Hills**
Oil on board 15.4 x 21.3
Signed
Purchased 1931

U2349 **Horseshoe Flower Bed in Ormeau Park,
Belfast (c.1910)**
Oil on panel 31.7 x 38
Donated by Mrs. C. M. D. Morrison, 1975

J

JACKSON, Anthony Thomas fl.c.1850-after
1908 (Irish)
Titles and dates as given by the artist

U4539 **Montataire Ch[urch] near Creil. Arch in
Nave. 28 Augt. 1861**
Pencil on paper 20.8 x 17.8
Signed
Donated by the artist, 1906

U4540 **Montataire. Cap[ital] in Nave. 28 Augt.
1861**
Pencil on paper 35.5 x 21.6
Signed
Donated by the artist, 1906

U4541 **S. Aisle, St. Etienne Beauvais. 30 Angles
(Exterior Buttress)**
Pencil on paper 14.6 x 10.5
Signed
Donated by the artist, 1906

U4542 **Beauvais Cathedral. Various Sketches. 30
Augt. '61**
Pencil on paper 25.3 x 35.6
Signed
Donated by the artist, 1906

U4543 **Chamant 2 Sept. '61. Near Senlis**
Pencil on paper 25.3 x 17.8
Signed
Donated by the artist, 1906

U4544 **Néry. 2 Sept. '61**
Pencil on paper 25.3 x 17.8
Signed
Donated by the artist, 1906

U4545 **Soissons Cathedral S. Transept Sept. 4
'61**
Pencil on paper 25.3 x 17.8
Signed
Donated by the artist, 1906

U4546 **St. Jean de Vignes, Soissons. S. Tower of
Abbey. Sept. 5 '61**
Pencil on paper 25.3 x 17.8
Signed
Donated by the artist, 1906

U4547 **Laon Cathedral. 7 Sept. '61**
Pencil on paper 25.3 x 15.5
Signed
Donated by the artist, 1906

U4548 **N.W. Tower Top, Laon Cathedral. 7 Sept.
'61**

Pencil on paper 25.3 x 15.5
Signed
Donated by the artist, 1906

U4549 **Main Pillar of Apse, S.E. S. Leu**
Pencil on paper 10.5 x 17.8
Signed
Donated by the artist, 1906

U4550 **Top of Buttress W. Porch, Seen through Central Arch. Noyon Cathedral. Sept. 11/'61**
Pencil on paper 25.3 x 15.5
Signed
Donated by the artist, 1906

U4551 **Chapel, S. Aisle of Choir, Notre Dame, Noyon. Sept. 11/'61**
Pencil on paper 25.3 x 15.5
Signed
Donated by the artist, 1906

U4552 **N.W. Door Notre Dame, Paris. N.W. Door, Notre Dame, Paris** (Two Capitals)
Pencil on paper 13 x 22.2
Signed
Donated by the artist, 1906

U4553 **Archbishop Peckham's Tomb, Canterbury Cathedral Sept. 14/'61**
Pencil on paper 23.3 x 17.8
Signed
Donated by the artist, 1906

U4554 **Queen Eleanor's Cross, near Northampton. Sept. 18/'61**
Pencil on paper 35.5 x 23.3
Signed
Donated by the artist, 1906

U4555 **Wollaston Church Steeple from East. Sept. 19/'61. Near Earl's Barton**
Pencil on paper 23.3 x 10.8
Signed
Donated by the artist, 1906

U4556 **Stanwick Steeple, Northamptonshire. Sept. 21/'61**
Pencil on paper 23.3 x 10.8
Signed
Donated by the artist, 1906

U4557 **Raunds Steeple. 180 ft. High. Sept. 23/'61**
Pencil on paper 35.5 x 23.3
Signed
Donated by the artist, 1906

U4558 **Geddington Cross. Sept. 24/'61. Northamptonshire**
Pencil on paper 23.2 x 10.8
Signed
Donated by the artist, 1906

U4559 **Crowland West Door Arch Moulding. Scale 1 1/2 to 1 Foot**
Pencil on paper 23.5 x 16.5
Signed
Donated by the artist, 1906

U4560 **Crowland** (West Door of Abbey)
Pencil on paper 23.3 x 10.8
Signed
Donated by the artist, 1906

U4561 **Warmington Steeple from S.E. Sept. 27/'61**

Pencil on paper 23.3 x 10.8
Signed
Donated by the artist, 1906

U4562 **Heckington** (Heckington Church, Lincs. Plan on Back is not Heckington)
Pencil on paper 23.3 x 29.8
Signed
Donated by the artist, 1906

U4563 **Angel Choir N. Side, Lincoln Cathedral. 1st Oct. '61**
Pencil on paper 35.6 x 23.3
Signed
Donated by the artist, 1906

U4564 **St. Mary's, Stamford. Oct. 2/'61**
Pencil on paper 23.3 x 10.8
Signed
Donated by the artist, 1906

U4565 **Ludlow Castle, Ludlow – Hereford. 19/6/'63**
Pencil on paper 14 x 21.6
Signed
Donated by the artist, 1906

U4566 **Welsh Chapel, Ely Place, Holborn** (Window Tracery, St. Ethelburga's, Ely Place)
Pencil on paper 22.9 x 14
Signed
Donated by the artist, 1906

U4567 **Eardisley – Hereford. 25 June 1863** (Font)
Pencil on paper 29 x 25.5
Signed
Donated by the artist, 1906

U4568 **Font, Eardisley, Hereford. Subject Continued 25 June 1863** (Carvings round Bowl of Font)
Pencil on paper 35.5 x 6.6
Donated by the artist, 1906

U4569 **Rome. 21/4/'64** (Forum, Temple of Saturn and Temple of Vespasian)
Pencil on paper 23.3 x 35.6
Signed
Donated by the artist, 1906

U4570 **Piazza Bocca della Verita, Rome. 25 Apl. '64** (Shows the Temples and Sta Maria in Cosmedin Surrounded by Buildings)
Pencil on paper 24.1 x 36.9
Signed
Donated by the artist, 1906

U4571 **S. Paolo Fuori le Mura. 29 Apl. Rome** (Cloister)
Pencil, wash on paper 14 x 22.8
Signed
Donated by the artist, 1906

U4572 **Staircase, Braschi Palace. See Notebook for Balluster. 2 May 1864**
Pencil on paper 17.8 x 12.8
Signed
Donated by the artist, 1906

U4573 **Ponte Sant Angelo and San Pietro**
Pencil on paper 14 x 22.9
Signed
Donated by the artist, 1906

U4574 **St. Jno Lateran** (Cloister of St. John

Lateran)
Pencil on paper 23.3 x 10.8
Signed
Donated by the artist, 1906

U4575 **Genazzano 11 May '64**
Pencil on paper 16.5 x 12.8
Signed
Donated by the artist, 1906

U4576 **Genazzano 11 May 1864**
Pencil on paper 16.5 x 14
Signed
Donated by the artist, 1906

U4577 **Drawing of Gothic Window Opening, Measured. Probably Genazzano**
Pencil on paper 19.1 x 14
Signed
Donated by the artist, 1906

U4578 **Fountain - Viterbo 23 May 1864**
Pencil on paper 19.7 x 14
Signed
Donated by the artist, 1906

U4579 **S. Maria - Toscanella. 25 May '62** (Study of Wheel Window)
Pencil on paper 35.6 x 23.3
Signed
Donated by the artist, 1906

U4580 **W. Door, S. Maria, Toscanella. 25 May '62** (Measured Drawings)
Pencil on paper 35.6 x 23.3
Signed
Donated by the artist, 1906

U4581 **Windows in Town Hall - Orvieto - 30 May '64. Corbels, Town Hall. Antiqu. Orvieto 30 May 1864. String in House near Cathedral. Semi-C Arch Mould in Street opposite to Cathedral**
Pencil on paper 22.8 x 14
Signed
Donated by the artist, 1906

U4582 **Pope's Palace - Orvieto – 30 May '64. Label; Arch and Cusp; String; Quatrefoil; Arch in Cusp; String** (Studies of Windows)
Pencil on paper 22.8 x 14
Signed
Donated by the artist, 1906

U4583 **West Front, Orvieto Cath.**
Pencil on paper 30.5 x 23.3
Signed
Donated by the artist, 1906

U4584 **N. Pier of Chancel, S. Fortunatus, Todi. 1st June '64. Nail Head. Caps. to Sqr. Piers of Chapels. Groin Rib Corbel N. Transept**
Pencil on paper 22.8 x 14
Donated by the artist, 1906

U4585 **Todi, Town Hall. 1 June '64**
Pencil on paper 14 x 22.8
Signed
Donated by the artist, 1906

U4586 **West Doorway, St. Francesco, Assisi. 6 June '64**
Pencil on paper 28.5 x 24.1
Signed

Donated by the artist, 1906

U4587 **Perugia. 8 June '64** (Government House)
Pencil on paper 23.3 x 35.6
Signed
Donated by the artist, 1906

U4588 **Upper Windows of Government House, Perugia, 9 June '64**
Pencil on paper 22.8 x 14
Signed
Donated by the artist, 1906

U4589 **Lower Windows of Government House, Perugia, 9 June '64**
Pencil on paper 22.8 x 14
Signed
Donated by the artist, 1906

U4590 **Top of Govmt. House, Perugia. 9 June '64**
Pencil on paper 22.8 x 14
Signed
Donated by the artist, 1906

U4591 **S. Agatha, Perugia. 10 June '64** (Doorway)
Pencil on paper 22.8 x 14
Signed
Donated by the artist, 1906

U4592 **In Arezzo Cathedral** (Tomb of Bishop, Measured Sketch)
Pencil on paper 22.8 x 14
Signed
Donated by the artist, 1906

U4593 **Baptistery, Siena Cath. 16 June 1864** (Detailed Elevation of Exterior)
Pencil on paper 23.3 x 21.6
Signed
Donated by the artist, 1906

U4594 **Baptistery, Siena Cathedral. Base of East Front. 16 June '64** (Measured Sketch of Moulding)
Pencil on paper 22.8 x 14
Signed
Donated by the artist, 1906

U4595 **Baptistery, Siena Cathedral. 17 June '64** (Measured Sketch of Buttress)
Pencil on paper 14 x 22.8
Signed
Donated by the artist, 1906

U4596 **Siena. 17 June '64**
Pencil on paper 22.8 x 14
Signed
Donated by the artist, 1906

U4597 **Door Bolt, Town Hall, Siena. 18 June '64**
Pencil on paper 14 x 22.8
Signed
Donated by the artist, 1906

U4598 **Cornice Table, Siena. 20 June '64. Red Brick and Terracotta**
Pencil on paper 22.8 x 14
Donated by the artist, 1906

U4599 **Palazzo Tolomei Siena. 20 June '64**
Pencil on paper 22.8 x 14
Signed
Donated by the artist, 1906

U4600 **Torch Holder at Column, Piazza**

Postierla Siena. 20 June '64
Pencil on paper 21.6 x 13.4
Signed
Donated by the artist, 1906

U4601 **At S. M. Novella, Florence. 22 June '64** (Measured Sketch of Pierced Wall of Cemetery on East Side of Sta Maria Novella)
Pencil on paper 8 x 8
Signed
Donated by the artist, 1906

U4602 **S. Maria Novella, Florence** (Sketch of Campanile); **Garden Wall, Siena. 20 June '64** (Measured Sketch and Details Of Sta Maria Novella Cemetery Wall)
Pencil on paper 19.8 x 13.4
Donated by the artist, 1906

U4603 **Convento di Badia, Florence. 23 June '64** (Campanile of the Badia)
Pencil on paper 22.8 x 14
Signed
Donated by the artist, 1906

U4604 **Screen in Sacristy, S. Croce, Florence. 24 June '64** (Iron Grille, Measured Sketch)
Pencil on paper 22.4 x 14
Signed
Donated by the artist, 1906

U4605 **Altar. S. Fortunatus, Todi. 30 June '64. Door Head in N. Transept**
Pencil on paper 14 x 22.8
Signed
Donated by the artist, 1906

U4606 **Chiesa della Spina — Pisa — 12 July '64** (East Facade with Details Of Mouldings)
Pencil on paper 17.8 x 24.2
Signed
Donated by the artist, 1906

U4607 **[Sta Maria] Della Spina, Pisa. 14 July '64** (View from South West)
Pencil on paper 24.8 x 29.2
Signed
Donated by the artist, 1906

U4608 **Baptistery Column, Pisa. Architrave W. Door. Cath. Pisa. 11 July '64**
Pencil on paper 22.8 x 14
Signed
Donated by the artist, 1906

U4609 **S. Catarina, Pisa. 15 July '64** (Facade)
Pencil on paper 23.3 x 23.3
Signed
Donated by the artist, 1906

U4610 **[Sta Maria] della Spina - Pisa. 15 July '64** (Measured Sketch of Window); **S. Paolo - Pisa. 15 July '64** (Facade)
Pencil on paper 35.6 x 23.3
Signed
Donated by the artist, 1906

U4611 **S. Maria della Rosa – Lucca – 18 July '64** (Sketch Plan, Longitudinal and Transverse Sections, Measured)
Pencil on paper 35.6 x 23.3
Signed
Donated by the artist, 1906

U4612 **Santa Maria della Rosa, Lucca, 18 July**

'64 N. Elevation (Measured)
Pencil on paper 17.1 x 26
Signed
Donated by the artist, 1906

U4613 **Cathdl. S. Martin, Lucca, 18 July '64** (W. Facade and Campanile Cut off by Top of Paper)
Pencil on paper 27.9 x 24.1
Signed
Donated by the artist, 1906

U4614 **S. Julia – Lucca. 19 July 1864** (Elevation of Facade and Details of Jambs and Mouldings) **Fresco. M.D. and Child, S. Julia and another Saint** (in Lunette over Door)
Pencil on paper 30.5 x 23.3
Signed
Donated by the artist, 1906

U4615 **Palazzo Giunigi – Lucca. 19 July '64** (View of Corner from Street, with Top of Tower)
Pencil on paper 35.6 x 23.3
Signed
Donated by the artist, 1906

U4616 **S. Cristofano – Lucca, 20 July 1864** (Detached Study of Upper Part of Facade with Wheel Window and Door Recess and Mouldings)
Pencil on paper 35.6 x 23.3
Signed
Donated by the artist, 1906

U4617 **S. Frediano, Lucca. 20 July '64** (Apse and Campanile)
Pencil on paper 35.6 x 23.3
Signed
Donated by the artist, 1906

U4618 **Cathedral – Pistoia. 22 July '64** (Pistoia Cathedral and Campanile from North West, Showing Large 17th century Clock on North Face of Campanile, since Removed)
Pencil on paper 35.6 x 23.3
Signed
Donated by the artist, 1906

U4619 **Altarpiece, Pistoia Cathedral**
Pencil on paper 12.8 x 16.5
Signed
Donated by the artist, 1906

U4620 **Pulpit by Giovanni Pisano, S. Andrea, Pistoia. 23 July '64**
Pencil on paper 35.6 x 23.3
Signed
Donated by the artist, 1906

U4621 **From Pulpit in S. Bartolomeo [in Pantano] Pistoia, 25 July '64** (Seated Figure Supporting Column)
Pencil on paper 22 x 12.8
Donated by the artist, 1906

U4622 **From Pulpit, S. Bartolomeo [in Pantano] Pistoia [Lion Base] 25 July '64**
Pencil on paper 12.7 x 22.7
Signed
Donated by the artist, 1906

U4623 **W. Door. S. Pietro, Pistoia. 25 July '64** (Detached Measured Sketch of

Tympanum on Facade)
Pencil on paper 35.6 x 23.3
Signed
Donated by the artist, 1906

U4624 1st Floor Windows, Palazzo della
Communita, Pistoia. 25 July
Pencil on paper 17.8 x 12.8
Signed
Donated by the artist, 1906

U4625 Upper Windows, Palazzo della
Communita, Pistoia. 25 July
Pencil on paper 17.8 x 12.8
Signed
Donated by the artist, 1906

U4626 Half Destroyed Palace near Baptistery -
Pistoia. 25 July '64
Pencil on paper 17.8 x 12.8
Signed
Donated by the artist, 1906

U4627 S. Paolo - Pistoia. Pilaster Caps. Wall
Base between Pilasters. 25 July '64
Pencil on paper 22.2 x 13.4
Signed
Donated by the artist, 1906

U4628 E[ast] W[indow], S. Domenico - Prato.
26 July
Pencil on paper 20.3 x 12.8
Signed
Donated by the artist, 1906

U4629 [Tomb of] Rolandino Passageri 1200. In
Piazzo S. Domenico Bologna. 29 July '64
Pencil on paper 21.6 x 14
Signed
Donated by the artist, 1906

U4630 At Corner of Street, Bologna. Brick
Painted. 29 July '64 (Study of Arcading)
Pencil on paper 21.6 x 14
Signed
Donated by the artist, 1906

U4631 San Petronio - Bologna - 30 July '64
(Interior of Nave)
Pencil on paper 35.6 x 23.3
Signed
Donated by the artist, 1906

U4632 Angle Window, S. Petronio - Bologna
30 July '64
Pencil on paper 19.8 x 12.8
Signed
Donated by the artist, 1906

U4633 Egidio Foscarari Monument, Piazza S.
Domenico, Bologna. 30 July
Pencil on paper 21 x 15.2
Signed
Donated by the artist, 1906

U4634 Arcade, Bologna, July '64
Pencil on paper 14 x 21
Signed
Donated by the artist, 1906

U4635 Cloisters S. Stefano - Bologna - 2
Augt. '64
Pencil on paper 23.3 x 17.8
Signed
Donated by the artist, 1906

U4636 S. Apollinare, Ravenna. 4 Augt. '64

(Campanile)
Pencil on paper 35.2 x 23.3
Signed
Donated by the artist, 1906

U4637 S. Vitale, Ravenna. 4 Augt. '64 (Interior)
Pencil on paper 35.2 x 23.3
Signed
Donated by the artist, 1906

U4638 S. Giovanni Battista. 6 Augt. Ravenna.
1864 (Campanile)
Pencil on paper 24.1 x 17.8
Signed
Donated by the artist, 1906

U4639 Entrance to Yard, S. Giovanni
Evangelista, Ravenna. 6 Augt.
Pencil on paper 23.3 x 17.8
Signed
Donated by the artist, 1906

U4640 S[anta] M[aria] Porto Fuori - Ravenna.
8 Aug. '64 (Interior)
Pencil on paper 23.3 x 17.8
Signed
Donated by the artist, 1906

U4641 Wall on S. Side of S. Maria in Porto
Fuori, Ravenna. Aug. 8/'64
Pencil on paper 23.6 x 35.6
Signed
Donated by the artist, 1906

U4642 Cathedral, Ferrara, 11 Aug. '64 (Facade)
Pencil on paper 23.3 x 27.9
Signed
Donated by the artist, 1906

U4643 S. Antonio - Padua. 13 Aug. '64 (The
Santo from North West with Restoration
Work on North Dome)
Pencil on paper 35.6 x 23.3
Signed
Donated by the artist, 1906

U4644 S. Lucia Theatre, Padua. 15 Aug. '64. S.
Antonio E. View. Padua 15 Aug. 1864
Pencil on paper 35.6 x 23.3
Donated by the artist, 1906

U4645 Palazzo Contarini, Venice. 26 Aug. '64
(View of Back of Palace with Staircase
and Line of Washing)
Pencil on paper 35.6 x 23.3
Signed
Donated by the artist, 1906

U4646 Palazzo Faccariori, Canal della Fava. 26
Aug. '64
Pencil on paper 23.3 x 17.8
Signed
Donated by the artist, 1906

U4647 S. Gregorio – Grand Canal – Venice.
27 Aug. '64
Pencil on paper 23.3 x 17.8
Signed
Donated by the artist, 1906

U4648 Ponte del Paradiso - Venice. 29 Aug. '64
Doorway Abbazia S[anta] M[aria]
Misericordia, Venice. 30 Augt. 1864
Pencil on paper 23.3 x 35.6
Signed
Donated by the artist, 1906

U4649 Palazzo Priuli a S. Severo, Venice. 31
Aug. '64. Broletto Brescia - 12 Sept. '64
Pencil on paper 23.3 x 35.6
Signed
Donated by the artist, 1906

U4650 Cathedral - Murano - 1st Sept. '64
(Apse)
Pencil on paper 23.3 x 35.6
Signed
Donated by the artist, 1906

U4651 Giovanni Scaligero. 5 Sept. '64 (Tomb at
S. Maria Antiqua, Verona)
Pencil on paper 17.8 x 23.3
Signed
Donated by the artist, 1906

U4652 Secondo Mastino della Scala, Verona.
Sculptured by Magister Pierino, 1351. 5
Sept. '64 (Tomb at S. Maria Antiqua)
Pencil on paper 35.5 x 23.3
Signed
Donated by the artist, 1906

U4653 Campanile, S. Andrea - Mantua. 9 Sept.
'64
Pencil on paper 35.6 x 23.3
Signed
Donated by the artist, 1906

U4654 At West End, S. Francesco, Mantua. 9
Sept. '64 (Wheel Window)
Pencil on paper 19.1 x 22.8
Signed
Donated by the artist, 1906

U4655 N. Door. S. Maria Maggiore, Bergamo, 15
Sept. '64
Pencil on paper 35.6 x 23.3
Signed
Donated by the artist, 1906

U4656 Broletto - Bergamo. 15 Sept. '64
Pencil on paper 17.8 x 23.3
Signed
Donated by the artist, 1906

U4657 [Tomb of] Guillielme Delongis, 1318.
S.M. Maggiore - Bergamo 16 Sept. '64
(Measured)
Pencil on paper 23.3 x 17.8
Signed
Donated by the artist, 1906

U4658 S. Tommaso near Almeno, 8 Miles W. of
Bergamo. 17 Sept. '64 (Sketch Plan and
Section, Measured)
Pencil on paper 22.2 x 35.6
Signed
Donated by the artist, 1906

U4659 S. Gotardo, Campanile near Duomo,
Milan. 23 Sept. '64
Pencil on paper 35.6 x 23.3
Signed
Donated by the artist, 1906

U4660 Chamber of Commerce, Milan, 24 Sept.
'64 (Facade)
Pencil on paper 17.8 x 23.3
Signed
Donated by the artist, 1906

U4661 Broletto, Monza. 26 Sept. '64
Pencil on paper 23.5 x 33.6
Signed

Donated by the artist, 1906

U4735 Baptistery, Pisa
Pencil on paper 35.5 x 23.3
Signed
Donated by the artist, 1906

**U4736 W. Door. S. Francesco, Bologna. 1st Augt.
'64**
Pencil on paper 23.3 x 17.8
Signed, dated
Donated by the artist, 1906

**U4737 [Tomb of] Prince Castelbarco. Verona. 6
Sept. '64 (Sta Anastasia)**
Pencil on paper 23.3 x 17.8
Signed
Donated by the artist, 1906

**U4738 Torre delle Palatta da Contrada della
Pace. Brescia. 14 Sept. '64**
Pencil on paper 35.5 x 23.3
Signed
Donated by the artist, 1906

JAMIESON, Robert Kirkland 1881-1950
(Scottish)

U466 The Pool *(Illus.p.270)*
Oil on canvas 63.6 x 76.6
Signed
Purchased 1933

JANSEN, Willem Georg Frederik 1871-1949
(Dutch)

U563 Cattle Entering the Stall *(Illus.p.270)*
Oil on canvas 40.5 x 50.4
Signed
Bequeathed by Mrs. E. Monteagle
Browne, 1928

JEANNIN, Georges 1841-1925 (French)

U600 Roses *(Illus.p.270)*
Oil on canvas 59.5 x 73.2
Signed
Purchased 1909

U2311 Still Life
Oil on canvas 81.2 x 100
Signed
Donated by Mrs. Hans Iten, 1931

JEFFREY, James Hunter 1874-after 1932 (Irish)

U1073 Brown's Bay, Islandmagee (1932)
(Illus.p.270)
Watercolour on paper 28 x 39.1
Signed, dated
Donated by Miss M. E. Burns, 1963

JELLETT, Mainie 1897-1944 (Irish)

U324 Composition (c.1932)
Oil on canvas 91.6 x 71.2
Signed
Purchased 1962

U325 Painting (1938)
Oil on canvas 76 x 64.6
Signed, dated
Donated by the Thomas Haverty Trust,
1941

U326 Composition (c.1932-35)
Oil on canvas 91.1 x 71.1

Purchased 1962

U2293 Seated Female Nude (1921-22)
(Illus.p.271)
Oil on canvas 56.3 x 46.2
Purchased 1975

U2296 Abstract (1922) *(Illus.p.271)*
Oil on canvas 91.9 x 72
Signed, dated
Purchased 1975

U2384 Seated Nude (1914-15) *(Illus.p.271)*
Oil on canvas 91.3 x 61.2
Signed
Purchased 1976

U2385 Still Life (1914-16)
Oil on canvas 33.7 x 33.9
Purchased 1976

U2710 Sketch Book with Eighty-three Drawings
(mostly Life Drawings)
Brush, ink on paper 55 x 44
Purchased 1980

U2711 Life Study, Female Nude
Ink on paper 44 x 33.1
Purchased 1980

U2712 Female Nude Kneeling
Ink on paper 41.9 x 33.1
Purchased 1980

U2713 Female Nude from Side
Ink on paper 42.5 x 33.2
Purchased 1980

U2714 Female Nude from Back
Ink on paper 41.5 x 33.1
Purchased 1980

U2715 Female Nude from Back, Kneeling
Ink on paper 41.6 x 33.1
Purchased 1980

U2716 Three Studies for Compositions
Pencil on paper 26.8 x 21
Purchased 1980

U2717 Sixteen Studies for Compositions
Pencil on paper 26.6 x 21
Purchased 1980

U2718 Seven Cards of Colour Studies
Gouache on card, the largest 37 x 23.8
Purchased 1980

U2719 Two Studies for Compositions
Pencil on paper, each 26.1 x 20
Purchased 1980

U2720 Three Studies for Compositions
Pencil on paper, each 26.1 x 20
Purchased 1980

U2721 Six Studies for Compositions
Pencil on paper, each 26.8 x 20.9
Purchased 1980

U2722 Ten Studies for Compositions
Pencil on paper, each 26.8 x 20.9
Purchased 1980

U2723 Two Studies for Compositions
Pencil on paper, each 26.6 x 20.9
Purchased 1980

U2724 Five Studies for a Madonna and Child

with Angels
Pencil on paper, each 26.8 x 20.9
Purchased 1980

U2725 Four Studies for Compositions
Pencil on paper, the largest 28 x 22.1
Purchased 1980

U2726 Eight Studies for a Virgin and Child
Pencil on paper, each 26.6 x 20.7
Purchased 1980

U2727 Two Studies for Compositions
Pencil on paper, each 26.2 x 20
Purchased 1980

U2728 Three Studies for Compositions
Pencil on paper, each 26.2 x 20.1
Purchased 1980

U2729 Five Studies for Compositions
Pencil on paper, each 26.8 x 21
Purchased 1980

U2730 Six Studies for Compositions
Pencil on paper, each 26.9 x 20.9
Purchased 1980

U2731 Five Studies for a Madonna and Child
Pencil on paper, each 27 x 20.9
Purchased 1980

U2732 Two Studies for Compositions
Pencil on paper, each 26.9 x 21
Purchased 1980

U2733 Two Studies for Compositions
Pencil on paper, each 26.8 x 20.8
Purchased 1980

**U2734 Twelve Studies for a Madonna and
Angels**
Pencil on paper, each 20.9 x 27
Purchased 1980

U2735 Study for a Composition
Pencil on paper, 19 x 44.6
Purchased 1980

U2736 Study for a Composition
Pencil on paper, 37.9 x 24
Purchased 1980

U2737 Study for a Composition
Pencil on paper,
38 x 25.2
Purchased 1980

U2738 Study for a Composition
Pencil, ink, wash on paper 24.8 x 37.2
Purchased 1980

U2739 Study for a Composition
Ink on paper 39 x 24.2
Purchased 1980

U2740 Study for a Composition
Watercolour, wash on paper 37.9 x 25
Purchased 1980

U2741 Study for a Composition
Ink on paper 37.9 x 26.9
Purchased 1980

U2742 Three Studies for a Composition
Pencil on paper each 27 x 20.8
Purchased 1980

U2743 Study for a Still Life Composition

Pencil on paper 37.4 x 63.3
Purchased 1980

U2744 **Study for a Figure Composition**
Pencil on paper 14.7 x 44.7
Purchased 1980

U2745 **Horses**
Pencil on paper 25.6 x 43.1
Purchased 1980

U2746 **Study of Haymakers**
Pencil on paper 23 x 25
Purchased 1980

U2747 **Two Studies: Spinning and People at
Work**
Pencil on paper 24.8 x 62.1
Purchased 1980

U2748 **Study for a Composition**
Pencil on paper 21.5 x 29.8
Purchased 1980

U2749 **Study for a Composition** (Broadcasting?)
Pencil on paper 25.3 x 37.9
Purchased 1980

U2750 **Study for a Composition** (Broadcasting?)
Pencil on paper 25 x 38
Purchased 1980

U2751 **Two Men in a Curragh**
Pencil on paper 50.5 x 37.7
Purchased 1980

U2752 **Study for a Composition**
Pencil on paper 43.5 x 31
Purchased 1980

U2753 **Three Studies for a Composition**
Pencil on paper 25.5 x 20.2
Purchased 1980

U2754 **Study for a Composition**
Pencil on paper 20.6 x 26.8
Purchased 1980

U2755 **Study for a Composition**
Pencil on paper 26.8 x 21
Purchased 1980

U2756 **Study for a Composition**
Pencil on paper 26.7 x 20.5
Purchased 1980

U2757 **Two Studies for Figure Compositions
with Horses**
Pencil on paper 20 x 32.5
Purchased 1980

U2758 **Study for a Madonna and Child**
Pencil on paper 37.8 x 25
Purchased 1980

U2759 **Study for a Composition**
Pencil on paper 37.8 x 28
Purchased 1980

U2760 **Study for 'Western Procession' (1943-44)**
Pencil on paper 27.5 x 37.8
Purchased 1980

U2761 **Oceanic Composition**
Pencil on paper 18.5 x 24.5
Purchased 1980

U2762 **Two Studies for a Street Scene with
Figures**

Pencil on paper 25.2 x 22.5
Purchased 1980

U2763 **Path with Trees**
Gouache on paper 21.2 x 25.2
Purchased 1980

U2764 **Study of a Tree**
Pencil on paper 28.5 x 19.3
Purchased 1980

U2765 **Study of Horses**
Pencil on paper 22.8 x 29.5
Purchased 1980

U2766 **Study of Horses**
Pencil on paper 19.5 x 35.5
Purchased 1980

U2767 **Study of Horses**
Ink, wash on paper 18.2 x 42.5
Purchased 1980

U2768 **Study of Horses**
Pencil on paper 19.5 x 30
Purchased 1980

U2769 **Study of Horses**
Ink, wash on paper 29.5 x 25.2
Purchased 1980

U2770 **Figures in a Street**
Pencil on paper 34 x 18
Purchased 1980

U2771 **Houses on an Estuary**
Watercolour on paper 37.8 x 26
Purchased 1980

U2772 **Study for a Composition**
Pencil on card 12.1 x 14.2
Purchased 1980

U2773 **Three Studies for a Composition**
Pencil on paper 37.7 x 25.2
Purchased 1980

U2774 **Two Studies for a Wood Nymph**
Pencil on paper 37.8 x 25.5
Purchased 1980

U2775 **Two Studies for a Still Life**
Pencil on paper 26.8 x 20.8
Purchased 1980

U2776 **A Saint Giving Benediction**
Pencil on paper 25 x 20.6
Purchased 1980

U2777 **Two Studies for 'Ave Maria'**
Pencil on paper 26.8 x 20.7
Purchased 1980

U2778 **Ave Maria**
Gouache on card 30.3 x 23.2
Purchased 1980

U2779 **Woman at a High Desk**
Pencil on paper 28.8 x 22.5
Purchased 1980

U2780 **Study for Christ Carrying the Cross**
Pencil on paper 31.5 x 25.6
Purchased 1980

U2781 **Study for a Pietà with Saints**
Pencil on paper 37.9 x 32.1 (irregular)
Purchased 1980

U2782 **Head Studies**
Pencil on paper 30 x 22.5
Purchased 1980

U2783 **Study of a Seated Female Nude**
Pencil on paper 26.8 x 21
Purchased 1980

U2784 **Study for a Composition**
Pencil on paper 25.7 x 19.5
Purchased 1980

U2785 **Study for a Design**
Pencil on paper 12 x 25.2
Purchased 1980

U2786 **Study of a Seated Woman**
Pencil on paper 27 x 21
Purchased 1980

U2787 **Two Studies for a Landscape with
Figures**
Pencil on paper 27 x 21
Purchased 1980

U2788 **Study for a Landscape with a Donkey**
Pencil on paper 25.2 x 36
Purchased 1980

U2789 **Study for a House and Gardens**
Pencil on paper 27 x 21
Purchased 1980

U2790 **Study for a Composition**
Ink, wash on paper 20.2 x 32.9
Purchased 1980

U2791 **Study of a Seated Woman**
Pencil on paper 27 x 21
Purchased 1980

U2792 **Study of a Girl Writing**
Pencil on paper 25.4 x 20.3
Purchased 1980

U2793 **Head of a Girl**
Pencil on paper 26.3 x 20.1
Purchased 1980

U2794 **Study of a Horse**
Pencil on paper 12 x 12.4 (irregular)
Purchased 1980

U2795 **Study for a Landscape**
Pencil on paper 27 x 21
Purchased 1980

U2796 **Study in a Graveyard**
Gouache on paper 28.7 x 22.5
Purchased 1980

U2797 **Study of Trees**
Pencil on paper 25.8 x 23.2
Purchased 1980

U2798 **Study for a Composition**
Pencil on paper 26.7 x 19.4
Purchased 1980

U2799 **Study for a Composition**
Pencil on paper 27 x 21.1
Purchased 1980

U2800 **Three Studies of Horses Grazing**
Pencil on paper, each 27.5 x 38
Purchased 1980

U2801 **Six Studies for a Composition**
Pencil on paper 20.2 x 33

Purchased 1980

U2802 **Drawing of Curraghs on the Shore**
Pencil on paper 40.2 x 49
Purchased 1980

U2803 **Two Studies for a Landscape by the Sea**
Pencil on paper, each 38 x 51.5
Purchased 1980

U2804 **Study for a Composition**
Pencil on paper 45.7 x 25.5
Purchased 1980

U2805 **Study for a Composition of Figures by the Sea**
Pencil on paper 29.2 x 37.2
Purchased 1980

U2806 **Study for a Landscape Composition**
Pencil on paper 38.2 x 50.3
Purchased 1980

U2807 **Study for a Landscape Composition**
Pencil on paper 31.2 x 50.5
Purchased 1980

U2808 **Study for a Landscape Composition**
Pencil on paper 25.3 x 39
Purchased 1980

U2809 **Study for a Landscape Composition**
Pencil on paper 50.7 x 45
Purchased 1980

U2810 **Two Studies for a Figure Composition**
Pencil on paper 44 x 55.4
Purchased 1980

U2811 **Study for a Composition**
Pencil on paper 50.7 x 35.6
Purchased 1980

U2812 **Study for a Landscape with Goats**
Pencil on paper 40.9 x 49.6
Purchased 1980

U2813 **Three Studies for a Composition**
Pencil on paper, each 26 x 20.1
Purchased 1980

U2814 **Six Studies for a Composition**
Pencil on paper, each 26.9 x 20.7
Purchased 1980

U2815 **Study for a Composition**
Pencil on paper 20.9 x 27
Purchased 1980

U2816 **Study for a Composition**
Pencil on paper 26.7 x 20.8
Purchased 1980

U2817 **Two Studies for a Composition**
Pencil on paper 20.9 x 27
Purchased 1980

U2818 **Study for a Composition**
Pencil on paper 26.3 x 20.8
Purchased 1980

U2819 **Two Studies for an Assumption**
Pencil on paper, each 25.3 x 19
Purchased 1980

U2820 **Study for an Assumption**
Pencil on paper 36 x 25.1 (irregular)
Purchased 1980

U2821 **Study for a Composition**
Pencil on paper 20.9 x 26.7
Purchased 1980

U2822 **Study for a Composition**
Pencil on paper 50.4 x 38.2
Purchased 1980

U2823 **Study for a Pietà (1940)**
Pencil on paper 26 x 19.7
Dated
Purchased 1980

U2824 **Study for a Pietà (1940)**
Pencil on paper 33.5 x 50.4 (irregular)
Dated
Purchased 1980

U2825 **Study for a Composition**
Pencil on paper 38 x 50.4 (irregular)
Purchased 1980

U2826 **Study for a Composition**
Pencil on paper 29.6 x 39.4
Purchased 1980

U2827 **Five Studies for a Repeating Pattern Design**
Pencil, charcoal, ink on paper, each 56 x 44.5
Purchased 1980

U2828 **Design for a Carpet Square**
Gouache on paper 50.6 x 41.6
Purchased 1980

U2829 **Two Studies for a Repeating Pattern Design**
Pencil, ink on paper, each 44.2 x 55.9
Purchased 1980

U2830 **Design for a Repeating Pattern**
Gouache on paper 86.3 x 56
Purchased 1980

U2831 **Design for a Repeating Pattern**
Charcoal, pencil on paper 44.1 x 56
Purchased 1980

U2832 **Design for a Repeating Pattern**
Charcoal on paper 44.5 x 56
Purchased 1980

U2833 **Design for a Repeating Pattern**
Gouache on board 55.9 x 35
Signed
Purchased 1980

U2834 **Design for a Repeating Pattern**
Gouache on board 53.9 x 25.2
Signed
Purchased 1980

U2835 **Composition (1938)**
Gouache on paper 25.5 x 61.1
Signed, dated
Purchased 1980

U2836 **Allegorical Scene**
Oil on canvas 51.2 x 82.6
Purchased 1980

U2837 **Standing Female Nude**
Oil on canvas 60.3 x 45
Purchased 1980

U2838 **Head of a Woman**
Oil on canvas 46 x 40.7
Purchased 1980

U2839 **Tulips**
Oil on canvas 49.5 x 33
Purchased 1980

U2840 **Composition Based on Fra Angelico's 'Coronation of the Virgin'**
Gouache on paper 50.5 x 31.9
Purchased 1980

U2841 **Study for U2840**
Pencil on paper 64 x 48.5
Purchased 1980

U2842 **Study for U2840**
Pencil on paper 63.2 x 50.6
Purchased 1980

U2843 **Study for U2840**
Pencil on paper 39 x 39.6
Purchased 1980

U2844 **Study for a Composition with Three Figures**
Pencil on paper 45.5 x 37.6
Purchased 1980

U2845 **Head of a Girl (1929)**
Pencil on paper 30.5 x 22.5
Signed, dated
Purchased 1980

U2846 **Seated Female Nude; verso, Other Drawings**
Pencil on paper 35.5 x 25.4
Purchased 1980

U2847 **Communion of Hands (1939)**
Gouache on board 56 x 44.5
Signed, dated
Purchased 1980

U2848 **Two Studies for U2847**
Wash on paper, each 50.5 x 45.5
Purchased 1980

U2849 **Study for U2847**
Pencil on paper 52 x 45
Purchased 1980

U2850 **Reclining Female Nude**
Ink on paper 44 x 55.7
Purchased 1980

U2851 **Four Life Drawings**
Ink on paper, each 41.5 x 33
Purchased 1980

U2852 **Male Life Study**
Ink on paper 41.5 x 33
Purchased 1980

U2853 **Abstract Composition**
Pencil on paper 49 x 34.5 (irregular)
Purchased 1980

U2854 **Study for a Composition of a Madonna**
Pencil on paper 50.1 x 31
Purchased 1980

U2855 **Study for a Figure Composition**
Pencil on paper 50.2 x 38
Purchased 1980

U2856 **Study for an Abstract Composition**
Pencil on paper 40 x 49
Purchased 1980

U2857 **Study for an Abstract Composition**
Pencil on paper 44 x 56

Purchased 1980

U2858 **Two Studies for a Three Figure Composition**
Pencil on paper, each 43.5 x 56
Purchased 1980

U2859 **Study for an Abstract Composition**
Pencil on paper 55.6 x 44.2
Purchased 1980

U2860 **Study for an Abstract Composition**
Crayon on paper 56 x 44
Purchased 1980

U2861 **Study for an Abstract Composition**
Pencil on paper 56 x 44.3
Purchased 1980

U2862 **Study for an Abstract Composition**
Pencil on paper 55.8 x 44.5
Purchased 1980

U2863 **Five Sketches for Abstract Compositions**
Pencil on paper, the largest 25.5 x 15.5
Purchased 1980

U2864 **Study for an Abstract Composition**
Pencil on paper 36.8 x 25
Purchased 1980

U2865 **Study for an Abstract Composition**
Pencil on paper 28.6 x 44
Purchased 1980

U2866 **Study for an Abstract Composition**
Pencil on paper 26 x 50
Purchased 1980

U2867 **Study for an Abstract Composition**
Pencil on paper 51.2 x 38
Purchased 1980

U2868 **Study for an Abstract Composition**
Pencil on paper 39.5 x 50.5
Purchased 1980

U2869 **Study for a Figure Composition**
Pencil on paper 54.6 x 37.6
Purchased 1980

U2870 **Study for a Madonna and Child**
Pencil on paper 44.4 x 27.8
Purchased 1980

U2871 **Angular Abstract Composition**
Pencil on paper 50.2 x 35.6
Purchased 1980

U2872 **Study for an Abstract Composition**
Pencil on paper 55.8 x 37.8
Purchased 1980

U2873 **Study for an Abstract Composition**
Pencil on paper 54.5 x 37.8
Purchased 1980

U4662 **Two Studies for Compositions**
Pencil on paper, the larger 21.7 x 30.5
Purchased 1980

JENKINS, Paul b.1923 (American)

U528 **Phenomena Borne by Red (1963)**
(Illus.p.271)
Acrylic on canvas 116 x 89.1
Signed, dated
Purchased 1963

U552 **Glade (1958)**
Acrylic on canvas 130.2 x 96.7
Signed, dated
Donated by Mr. and Mrs. Clement Greenberg (per the American Federation of Arts), 1969

JENNENS and BETTRIDGE 1816-64 (English)

U2082 **View of Londonderry (1848)**
Oil on panel 40.5 x 79.7 (oval)
Signed, dated
Purchased 1974

JOHANSSON, Janeric 20th century (Swedish)

U2653 **Struggle for Power (1981)** (Diptych)
(Illus.p.271)
Pencil on paper, each sheet 83.8 x 59.7
Signed, dated
Purchased 1982

JOHN, Augustus 1878-1961 (Welsh)

U323 **Vivien (c.1929)** *(Illus.p.271)*
Oil on canvas 72.3 x 51.8
Signed
Purchased (Lloyd Patterson Collection) 1929

U327 **The Red Feather (c.1911)** *(Illus.p.271)*
Oil on board 40.2 x 32.4
Signed
Purchased (Lloyd Patterson Collection) 1929

JOHN, Gwen 1876-1939 (Welsh)

U2075 **Cat** *(Illus.p.271)*
Ink, wash, white on paper 21.2 x 16.7 (sight)
Donated by S. A. Forbes, 1974

JOHNSON, Nevill 1911-99 (English)

U2476 **Summer Solstice (1978)** *(Illus.p.271)*
Acrylic, ballpen on paper on canvas 80.2 x 92
Signed, dated
Purchased 1978

JOHNSTON, Roy b.1936 (Irish)

U1633 **Over View (1971)**
Acrylic on canvas 270.1 x 210
Signed
Purchased 1971

U4684 **Study for a Painting (1984)**
Charcoal, acrylic on paper 132.4 x 99
Signed, dated
Purchased 1985

U4699 **Permutation and Shift (1980)**
Acrylic on two canvases, 191.5 x 192 overall
Signed, dated
Donated by the artist, 1987

JONES, Allen b.1937 (English)

U554 **Automatic Shift (1969)** *(Illus.p.272)*
Acrylic on two canvases, 183.5 x 91.7 overall
Signed, dated
Purchased 1969

JONES, David 1895-1974 (English)

U807 **Seascape: Caldy Island (1927)**
(Illus.p.272)
Pencil, watercolour on paper 39.5 x 57.3
Signed, dated
Donated by the Contemporary Art Society, 1935

JONES, Kent b.1949 (American)

U2646 **Cheetah (1981)** *(Illus.p.272)*
Acrylic on canvas 102 x 153
Signed, dated
Purchased 1982

U2647 **Cheetah (1981)** (Study for U2646)
Pencil, gouache on paper 41.9 x 29.5
Donated by the artist, 1982

JONES, Sir Thomas Alfred c.1823-93 (Irish)

U1663 **Portrait of an Unknown Man**
Oil on canvas 76.4 x 63.3
Signed
Donated by Philip Johnston and Sons Ltd., 1964
Formerly by Unknown

U1966 **George Kennedy Smith 1812-86 (c.1880)**
Oil on canvas 127.5 x 102
Donated by Mrs. J. Galt Smith, 1922

JONZEN, Basil b.1916 (British)

U1212 **West African Still Life (1943)**
(Illus.p.272)
Gouache on paper 48 x 62.5
Signed, dated
Donated by the Contemporary Art Society, 1944

JORDAENS, Jacob 1593-1678 (Flemish)

U133 **St. Christopher Carrying the Christ Child (c.1625-30)** *(Illus.p.35)*
Oil on canvas 313 x 162
Purchased with the aid of a grant from the National Art Collections Fund, 1966

K

K., H. [H. K.] 19th century (French or German)

U2073 **Lola Montez 1818-61** (after Joseph Karl Stieler 1781-1858)
Formerly 'Portrait of a Woman' by Unknown
Miniature, watercolour on ivory 8.6 x 6.5 (oval)
Donated by W. Kinning Crone, 1947

KANE, George McDowell 1889-1954 (Irish)

U1567 **Portrait of Hans Iten 1874-1930 (1913)**
(Illus.p.272 and Cover)
Charcoal on paper 46.4 x 31.5
Signed, dated
Donated by Dr. R. H. Hunter, 1935

U1792 **John Whaley 1880s-1950 (1912)**
Sculpture, plaster bust, ht. 53.3
Signed, dated
Bequeathed by the sitter (per Miss P.

Mollan), 1951

U2220　**Portrait of Forrest Reid 1875-1947 (1915)** *(Illus.p.272)*
Charcoal on paper 47.8 x 29.6
Signed, dated
Donated by Stephen Gilbert (executor of Forrest Reid), 1955

U2447　**Dr. T. J. A. Connolly (1950)**
Pencil on paper 25.8 x 17.8
Signed, dated
Bequeathed by the sitter, 1977

U4677　**John Whaley 1880s-1950 (1912)**
Sculpture, bronze bust, ht. 53.3
(cast in 1951 from U1792 above)
Signed, dated

KANTOR, Maxim b.1957 (Russian)

U4983　**Two Versions of History (1993)** *(Illus.p.272)*
Oil on canvas 270 x 240
Signed
Purchased 1994

KAUFMANN, Angelica 1741-1807 (Swiss) (attributed to)

U1200　**A Reclining Girl Reading**
Charcoal on paper 22.6 x 34.4
Donated by J. H. Stirling, 1919

KAVANAGH, Joseph Malachy 1856-1918 (Irish)

U2381　**Gipsy Encampment on the Curragh** *(Illus.p.272)*
Oil on canvas 71.5 x 91.6
Signed
Purchased 1976

KEANE, John b.1954 (English)

U5068　**The Other Cheek? (1989)** *(Illus.p.272)*
Oil, mixed media on canvas 244 x 274
Signed, dated
Purchased 1998

KEATING, Séan 1889-1977 (Irish)

U589　**Slan Leat a Athair/Goodbye, Father (1935)** *(Illus.p.273)*
Oil on canvas 175.9 x 175
Signed
Donated by the Thomas Haverty Trust, 1941

KEIR, Harry 1902-77 (Irish)

U340　**The Bagpiper (1959)**
Oil on board 32.7 x 46
Signed, dated
Donated by J. B. Francey, 1961

U341　**Tam O'Shanter (1959)**
Oil on board 30.4 x 45.8
Signed, dated
Donated by J. B. Francey, 1961

KELLY, Frances fl.1930s (Irish)

U329　**Looking into the Garden (c.1938)**
Oil on canvas 90.2 x 72.4
Donated by the Thomas Haverty Trust, 1941

U330　**The Window Table (c.1936)**
Oil on canvas 65.3 x 81.9
Donated by the Thomas Haverty Trust, 1941

U4711　**Portrait of Frank O'Connor 1903-66**
Oil on canvas 81 x 57
Signed
Purchased 1987

KELLY, John F. b.1921 (Irish)

U4978　**Still Life (1992)**
Oil on canvas 30.4 x 40.5
Signed, dated
Donated by the Thomas Haverty Trust, 1993

KERNOFF, Harry 1900-74 (Irish)

U331　**The Connoisseur (1959)**
Oil on board 50.1 x 38.4
Signed, dated
Donated by the Thomas Haverty Trust, 1966

U1074　**Boon Companions (1934)** *(Illus.p.273)*
Pencil, watercolour on paper 25.5 x 32.4
Signed, dated
Donated by Hon. Mr. Justice Creed Meredith, 1935

U4811　**Bend in the Road near Richmond, Surrey (1947)** *(Illus.p.273)*
Oil on board 66 x 96.8
Signed, dated
Purchased 1990

KIDD, Richard b.1952 (English)

U2579　**Northumber (1980)** *(Illus.p.273)*
Acrylic, graphite on canvas 226 x 213.5 (irregular)
Signed, dated
Purchased 1980

U4939　**Polar Cathedral (1991)** *(Illus.p.273)*
Oil on canvas 158.7 x 179
Donated by the Contemporary Art Society, 1992

KINDNESS, John b.1951 (Irish)

U5038　**Belfast Frescoes (1994)**
Gesso on slate (series of twenty), each 30.5 x 61
Purchased 1995

KING, Brian b.1942 (Irish)

U954　**Zig (1969)** *(Illus.p.273)*
Sculpture, painted plywood, perspex 152.5 x 152.5 x 152.5
Purchased 1970

U1904　**Red Shift (1969)**
Sculpture, painted wood, plastic 38.1 x 88.8 x 38
Signed, dated
Purchased 1973

KING, Cecil 1921-86 (Irish)

U973　**Interstice**
Pastel on paper 51 x 38 (sight)
Signed

Purchased 1971

U2297　**Easter (1974)** *(Illus.p.273)*
Acrylic on canvas 228.5 x 142
Purchased 1975

KING, Phillip b.1934 (English)

U952　**Through (1965)** *(Illus.p.273)*
Sculpture, painted fibreglass 216.5 x 311 x 319.5
Purchased 1967

U2359　**Ascona (1972)** *(Illus.p.273)*
Sculpture, painted steel 231.1 x 457.2 x 457.2
Purchased 1975

KING, Yeend 1855-1924 (English)

U656　**Stick Gatherers** *(Illus.p.274)*
Oil on canvas 101.5 x 76
Signed
Purchased 1909

KINNAIRD, Elizabeth b.1897 d.c.1980 (Irish)

U4837　**Profile Study of an Old Man**
Chalk on paper 45.7 x 30.5
Donated by Robert P. Smyth, 1991

KIRK, Thomas 1781-1845 (Irish)

U1167　**Towneley Patten Filgate 1753-1828 (1828)**
Sculpture, marble bust, ht. 69.9
Signed, dated
Purchased 1959

KNELLER, Sir Godfrey 1646/49-1723 (German, worked in England) (attributed to)

U583　**William III 1650-1702** *(Illus.p.274)*
Oil on canvas 219 x 147
Purchased 1893

U584　**Mary II 1662-94** *(Illus.p.274)*
Oil on canvas 218.4 x 146
Purchased 1893

KNELLER, Sir Godfrey 1646/49-1723 (German, worked in England) (after)

U2338　**William III 1650-1702**
Oil on canvas 72.5 x 62
Bequeathed by Mrs. G. Hadden, 1933

KNIGHT, John Prescott 1803-81 (English)

U4501　**William Sharman Crawford, MP 1781-1861 (c.1843)** *(Illus.p.274)*
Oil on canvas 91.9 x 71
Purchased 1947

KNOWLES, Margaret fl.1880s-1933 (Irish)

U1539　**Head of a Girl (1881)**
Chalk on paper 47.6 x 35.1
Signed, dated
Donated by the Misses Stewart, 1958

U1968　**William James Knowles, FRSAI, MRIA 1832-1927 (1922)**
Oil on canvas 102.1 x 76.4
Signed, dated
Donated by Miss Stewart, 1957

U2424   **William James Knowles, FRSAI, MRIA 1832-1927 (1911)**
Oil on canvas 91.5 x 71.1
Signed, dated
Donated by Hilda and Margaret Knowles, 1933

KNOX, Kyle 20th century (Irish)

U5039   **Landscape near Paris**
Oil on canvas 63 x 80
Donated by Mrs. H. M. Ireland, 1996

KOMZA, Marek 20th century (Polish)

U184   **House (1977)** *(Illus.p.274)*
Pencil on paper 28.3 x 36.5
Signed, dated
Purchased 1977

KONODY, Pauline Evelyn fl.1926-36 (English)

U1075   **Summer Mist** *(Illus.p.274)*
Watercolour on board 37.5 x 53.2
Signed
Purchased 1927

KYLE, Georgina Moutray 1865-1950 (Irish)

U332   **A Market in France (c.1929)**
Oil on canvas 35.3 x 61.1
Signed
Bequeathed by the artist, 1950

U333   **The Coming Storm, Volendam, Holland**
Oil on canvas on panel 60.9 x 45.8
Provenance unknown

U334   **Gleams of Sunshine, Belfast Harbour (c.1938)**
Oil on canvas on cardboard 60.9 x 41.1
Signed
Bequeathed by the artist, 1950

U335   **Beauty and the Beasts**
Oil on canvas on panel 44.3 x 49.8
Signed
Bequeathed by the artist, 1950

U336   **At the Market at Belfast (c.1928)**
Oil on canvas on panel 38.5 x 48.7
Signed
Bequeathed by the artist, 1950

U337   **La Marché dans la Rue, Concarneau (c.1925)** *(Illus.p.274)*
Oil on board 38.4 x 45.9
Signed
Bequeathed by the artist, 1950

U338   **The Incoming Tide (c.1937)** *(Illus.p.274)*
Oil on canvas on panel 35.1 x 46.4
Donated by the artist, 1939

U339   **A Busy Day in Smithfield, Belfast**
Oil on canvas on board 49.1 x 45.2
Signed
Purchased 1927

U342   **The Lifting of the Fog at the Gasworks, Belfast (c.1926)** *(Illus.p.274)*
Oil on canvas 55.1 x 73.5
Signed
Bequeathed by the artist, 1950

U1969   **Friday at the Belfast Market**
Oil on canvas on board 45.7 x 53.3

Bequeathed by the artist, 1950

U1970   **The Market, Concarneau**
Oil on canvas 55.9 x 40.6
Purchased 1927

U1971   **My Dear Little Lady**
Oil on canvas on board 73.7 x 53.6
Signed
Bequeathed by the artist, 1950

L

LAMB, Charles 1893-1964 (Irish)

U345   **A Lough Neagh Fisherman (1920)** *(Illus.p.275)*
Oil on canvas 76 x 50.8
Signed, dated
Purchased 1922

U347   **On Achill Island (c.1938)**
Oil on canvas 51.2 x 61.2
Signed
Donated by the Thomas Haverty Trust, 1941

U5018   **Leenane** *(Illus.p.275)*
Oil on canvas 45.5 x 56
Signed
Donated by the Diver family in memory of their parents, Charles and Mary Diver, 1995

LAMB, Henry 1883-1960 (British)

U467   **David Garnett 1892-1981 (1930)**
Oil on canvas 76.2 x 63.8
Signed, dated
Purchased (Lloyd Patterson Collection) 1933

U1537   **Men on a Park Bench (1903)** *(Illus.p.275)*
Pencil, charcoal, sanguine on paper 23.8 x 38
Signed, dated
Purchased 1952

LAMBERT, Gene b.1952 (Irish)

U4898   **Still Life No. 4 (1991)** *(Illus.p.275)*
Oil on canvas on board 86.3 x 80
Purchased 1991

LAME, Biagio dalle (called Pupini) d. after 1575 (Italian) (attributed to)

U753   **Marriage of the Virgin** *(Illus.p.275)*
Ink, wash, white on paper 25.4 x 19.8
Signed
Donated by J. H. Stirling, 1919

LAMONT, Elish 1816-70 (Irish)

U1891   **Miss O'Hara of Ballymena** *(Illus.p.)*
Miniature, watercolour on ivory 10.8 x 8.2
Purchased 1927

LANCASTER, Mark b.1938 (English)

U1174   **Cambridge Standard (1969)** *(Illus.p.)*
Liquitex on canvas 172.7 x 172.7
Signed, dated
Purchased 1971

LANFRANCO, Giovanni 1582-1647 (Italian) (after)

U197   **Glorification of the Virgin** (Fresco in Dome of S. Andrea della Valle, Rome) *(Illus.p.)*
Oil on canvas 53.3 x 73.7
Donated by J. F. Johnson, 1896

U1689   **Glorification of the Virgin** (Fresco in Dome of S. Andrea della Valle, Rome)
Ink on paper, two sheets, 19.8 x 26.5 and 17.5 x 25.1
Donated by J. F. Johnson, 1896

LANYON, Peter 1918-64 (English)

U2355   **Rosewall (1960)** *(Illus.p.275)*
Oil on canvas 182.9 x 152.4
Signed, dated
Purchased 1975

LASZLO, Philip Alexius de 1869-1937 (Hungarian)

U65   **Evelyn, Marchioness of Downshire d.1942 (1919)**
Oil on canvas 91.3 x 60.9
Signed, dated
Donated by the trustees of the Downshire Estate, 1944

U639   **Priscilla, Countess Annesley d.1941 (1915)** *(Illus.p.276)*
Oil on board 91.4 x 71.1
Signed
Bequeathed by the executors of H. Armitage Moore, 1960

LATHAM, James 1696-1747 (Irish)

U2513   **Captain Charles Janvre de la Bouchetière d.c.1743 (c.1730-35)** *(Illus.p.276)*
Oil on canvas 126 x 97
Purchased 1978

LATHAM, John b.1921 (British)

U538   **Observer 4 (1959)** *(Illus.p.276)*
Mixed media on canvas on board 153 x 183.3 x 25
Signed, dated
Donated by the Marquess of Dufferin and Ava and the Kasmin Gallery, 1969

LAURI, Filippo 1623-94 (Italian)

U85   **Pan and Diana** *(Illus.p.276)*
Oil on canvas 61.5 x 74.9
Purchased 1968

LAVERY, Sir John 1856-1941 (Irish)

U60   **The Bridge at Grès (1901)** *(Illus.p.276)*
Oil on canvas 89.1 x 148.3
Donated by the artist, 1929

U61   **Most Rev. Charles Frederick D'Arcy, MA, DD 1859-1938, Archbishop of Armagh and Primate of All Ireland (1928)**
Oil on canvas 102.1 x 76.3
Signed, dated
Donated by the artist, 1929

U62   **Joseph MacRory, DD 1861-1945,**

Archiepiscopus Armachanus Totius Hiberniae Primus (1928)
Oil on canvas 102.2 x 76.5
Signed, dated
Donated by the artist, 1929

U63 **Joseph Devlin, MP 1871-1934 (1928)**
Oil on canvas 102.1 x 76.7
Signed, dated
Donated by the artist, 1929

U64 **His Eminence Cardinal Logue 1840-1924 (1920)** *(Illus.p.276)*
Oil on canvas 79.1 x 64.1
Signed, dated
Donated by the artist, 1929

U66 **The Red Hammock (1936)** *(Illus.p.276)*
Oil on canvas 168.8 x 198.4
Signed, dated
Donated by the artist, 1929

U67 **Under the Cherry Tree (1884)**
(Illus.p.36)
Oil on canvas 150.8 x 150.4
Signed, dated
Donated by the artist, 1929

U68 **The Green Coat (1926)** *(Illus.p.276)*
Oil on canvas 198.4 x 107.8
Signed, dated
Donated by the artist, 1929

U69 **Priscilla, Countess Annesley d.1941 (1910)**
Oil on canvas 127.2 x 102.4
Signed, dated
Bequeathed by C. J. E. Armitage Moore, 1961

U70 **The Lady in Black (Mrs. Trevor) (c.1908)**
Oil on canvas 189.5 x 92.3
Signed, dated
Purchased 1913

U71 **Daylight Raid from my Studio Window, 7 July 1917** *(Illus.p.276)*
Oil on canvas 141.5 x 89.9
Signed, dated
Donated by the artist, 1929

U72 **The Mother (1909)** *(Illus.p.277)*
Oil on canvas 104 x 129.1
Signed, dated
Donated by the artist, 1929

U73 **Anne Moira and the Hon. Mrs. Forbes-Sempill (1923)**
Oil on canvas 100.6 x 91.4
Signed, dated
Donated by the artist, 1929

U74 **Sir Edward Mervyn Archdale, PC, DL 1853-1943 (1928)**
Oil on canvas 76.8 x 64.2
Signed, dated
Donated by the artist, 1929

U75 **The Rt. Hon. Hugh O'Neill, PC, First Speaker of the House of Commons, Northern Ireland (1922)**
Oil on canvas 76.3 x 63.6
Signed, dated
Donated by the artist, 1929

U76 **Sir Joseph Davison d.1948 (1928)**
Oil on board 76.1 x 63.7

Signed, dated
Donated by the artist, 1929

U77 **The Twelfth of July in Portadown (1928)**
(Illus.p.277)
Oil on board 63.8 x 76.4
Signed, dated
Donated by the artist, 1929

U78 **The Walls of Marakesh (1920)**
(Illus.p.277)
Oil on canvas 51 x 76.4
Signed, dated
Donated by the artist, 1929

U79 **Phyllis Dare (c.1910-20)**
Oil on panel 76.5 x 50.2
Purchased 1954

U80 **Eileen, Her First Communion (1901)**
Oil on board 25.2 x 20.8
Signed, dated
Donated by the artist, 1929

U81 **Alice (1919)**
Oil on board 35.4 x 25.4
Donated by the artist, 1929

U82 **The Weighing Room, Hurst Park (1924)**
(Illus.p.277)
Oil on canvas 51.1 x 61.2
Signed, dated
Donated by the artist, 1929

U343 **Eileen in Primrose Yellow (1926)**
Oil on canvas 183.6 x 91.8
Signed, dated
Donated by the artist, 1929

U570 **The Amazon (1911)**
Oil on canvas 275.2 x 306.3
Signed, dated
Donated by the artist, 1929

U593 **Florida in Winter (1927)**
Oil on canvas 76.2 x 63.5
Signed, dated
Donated by the artist, 1929

U594 **Twilight, Lake of Geneva (1924)**
Oil on board 61.5 x 51.5
Signed, dated
Donated by the artist, 1929

U615 **Second Study for the King, the Queen, the Prince of Wales, the Princess Mary, Buckingham Palace (1913)** *(Illus.p.277)*
Oil on canvas 76.1 x 63.4
Signed, dated
Donated by the artist, 1919

U616 **Self-Portrait (1928)**
Oil on canvas 107.6 x 77
Signed, dated
Donated by the artist, 1929

U617 **Rt. Hon. The Viscount Craigavon 1871-1940, First Prime Minister of Northern Ireland (1923)**
Oil on canvas 91.5 x 71.1
Donated by the artist, 1929

U620 **Tangier Bay - Sunshine (1920)**
(Illus.p.277)
Oil on canvas 63.5 x 76.1
Signed, dated
Donated by the artist, 1929

U621 **Tangier Bay - Rain (1910)**
Oil on canvas 63.6 x 76.4
Signed, dated
Donated by the artist, 1929

U622 **Switzerland in Winter (The Monk) (1913)**
Oil on canvas 76.2 x 63.5
Signed, dated
Donated by the artist, 1929

U623 **Spring, the Garden, Villa Sylvia (1921)**
Oil on canvas 63.5 x 76.2
Signed, dated
Donated by the artist, 1929

U624 **The Greyhound (Sir Reginald Lister and Eileen Lavery. The Last British Minister, the Drawing Room, British Legation, Tangier) (1910)** *(Illus.p.277)*
Oil on canvas 63.6 x 77.1
Signed, dated
Donated by the artist, 1929

U636 **The Most Hon. the Marquess of Dufferin and Ava 1875-1930, First Speaker of the Senate, Northern Ireland**
Oil on canvas 76.2 x 63.5
Signed
Donated by the artist, 1929

U637 **Rt. Rev. Dr. Charles T. P. Grierson 1857-1935, Bishop of Down and Dromore (1928)**
Oil on canvas 76.2 x 63.5
Signed, dated
Donated by the artist, 1929

U638 **The Marquess of Londonderry, KG 1878-1949, Chancellor of The Queen's University of Belfast (c.1924)**
Oil on canvas 101.6 x 76.2
Signed
Donated by the artist, 1929

U641 **Lord Carson, PC 1854-1935 (1922)**
Oil on canvas 91.4 x 71.1
Signed, dated
Donated by the artist, 1929

U1631 **Edith Joseph (1907)**
Oil on canvas 75 x 62
Signed, dated
Bequeathed by C. M. S. Nissim, 1971

LAWRENCE, Eileen b.1946 (Scottish)

U2456 **A Quiet Place, Still / With Centuries Lying / Deep underfoot. / Only the Birds, Fearful / For their Hidden Nests, / Disturb the Silence (1976)**
Watercolour, pencil, collage on paper, four vertical scrolls, each 213 x 50.8
Purchased 1978

LAWRENCE, Sir Thomas 1769-1830 (English)

U83 **Harriet Anne, Countess of Belfast 1799-1860 (c. 1822-23)** *(Illus.p.277)*
Oil on canvas 208.2 x 143.5
Purchased with the aid of a grant from the National Art Collections Fund, 1958

U4964 **Amelia Anne, Dowager Marchioness of Londonderry d.1829 (c.1825)**
(Illus.p.277)

Chalk on paper 30.2 x 24
Purchased 1993

LAWSON, George Anderson 1832-1904
(Scottish)

U4850   **Robert Burns 1759-96 (1891)**
Sculpture, bronze statuette, ht. 96.5
Signed, dated
Donated by Burns' admirers in Belfast,
1893

LEADER, Benjamin Williams 1831-1923
(English)

U119   **Evening on a Surrey Common (1911)**
(*Illus.p.278*)
Oil on canvas 65.1 x 101
Signed, dated
Purchased 1911

LEAR, Edward 1812-88 (English)

U808   **Corfu: The Citadel from near the Village
of Ascension (1856)** (*Illus.p.278*)
Watercolour, white on paper 17.6 x 25.4
Signed, dated
Purchased 1953

U809   **Malta (1866)** (*Illus.p.278*)
Watercolour, pencil, ink, white on paper
24.8 x 35.5
Dated
Donated by R. P. Smyth, 1969

U810   **Oxen and Cart**
Pencil, wash on paper 15.8 x 30.5
Purchased 1952

LE BROCQUY, Louis b.1916 (Irish)

U234   **Girl in White (1941)** (*Illus.p.278*)
Oil on canvas on board 122.2 x 47.8
Signed, dated
Donated by the Thomas Haverty Trust,
1945

U239   **Variety Rehearsal at the Olympia (1942)**
(*Illus.p.278*)
Oil on board 52.9 x 65.6
Signed, dated
Donated by the Thomas Haverty Trust,
1945

U241   **Tired Child (1954)** (*Illus.p.278*)
Oil on canvas 61.2 x 51
Signed, dated
Donated by the Thomas Haverty Trust,
1960

U246   **Recumbent Nude (1958)** (*Illus.p. 278*)
Oil on canvas 61 x 76.5
Signed, dated
Purchased 1959

U811   **Skilful Boy (1947)**
Pencil, ink, watercolour on paper 12.2 x
15.2
Signed, dated
Donated by the Contemporary Art
Society, 1964

U812   **Study (1963)**
Watercolour on paper 39.4 x 32
Signed, dated
Purchased 1965

U2386   **Study towards an Image of W. B. Yeats
(1975)** (*Illus.p.278*)
Watercolour on paper 21.9 x 17.8 (sight)
Signed, dated
Purchased 1976

U2528   **Image of James Joyce (1977)** (*Illus.p.37*)
Oil on canvas 146 x 113.7
Signed, dated
Purchased 1979

LEECH, John 1817-64 (English)

U1319   **Head of a Girl** (*Illus.p.278*)
Ink, crayon on paper 23.4 x 20.1
Donated by Mrs. J. Worthington, 1951

LEECH, William John 1881-1968 (Irish)

U344   **Railway Embankment** (*Illus.p.279*)
Oil on canvas 60.2 x 73.2
Signed
Donated by Mr. and Mrs. Z. Lewinter-
Frankl, 1954

U892   **Sunflowers** (*Illus.p.279*)
Pencil, watercolour on paper 51.1 x 35.6
Signed
Bequeathed by Dr. R. I. Best (per the
Friends of the National Collections of
Ireland), 1959

U1163   **Self-Portrait**
Oil on canvas 53.5 x 46
Signed
Purchased 1971

U2709   **Aloes (c.1920s)** (*Illus.p.279*)
Oil on canvas 181 x 148.3
Signed
Purchased with the aid of a grant from
the National Heritage Memorial Fund,
1984

U4747   **May (c.1920-25)** (The Artist's Wife)
Sculpture, bronze, ht. 47.5 (including
base)
Signed
Purchased 1989

LEE-HANKEY, William 1869-1952 (English)

U1213   **The Confession** (*Illus.p.279*)
Pencil, watercolour, bodycolour, gum on
paper 61.7 x 50
Signed
Purchased 1909

LEGROS, Alphonse 1837-1911 (French, worked
in England)

U1568   **Head of a Monk** (*Illus.p.279*)
Sanguine on paper 34.8 x 24
Bequeathed by Miss S. R. Praeger, 1954

LEIGH, Roger b.1925 (English)

U1755   **Flatsider (1969)**
Sculpture, painted wood 137.2 x 137.2 x
66
Donated by Messrs. John Player and Sons,
1971

LEITCH, William Leighton 1804-83 (Scottish)

U1076   **Baptistery, S. Marco, Venice** (*Illus.p.279*)

Watercolour on paper 27.8 x 22
Signed
Purchased 1952

LENNON, Ciarán b.1947 (Irish)

U4959   **Scotoma II/H (1992-93)** (*Illus.p.279*)
Oil on canvas 243.8 x 365.6
Purchased 1993

U4961   **1-11-92 Oil Bar (1992)**
Oil bar on paper 57 x 114
Signed, dated
Donated by the artist, 1993

LE PARC, Julio b.1928 (Argentinian)

U955   **Continuel-Lumière Cylindre (1962-66)**
Kinetic work in wood, aluminium,
electric light, motor 169 x 122 x 35
Signed, dated
Purchased 1968

LË PHÖ b.1907 (Vietnamese)

U4733   **Maternity** (*Illus.p.279*)
Watercolour, gouache on paper faced
with silk 63.6 x 50.5
Signed
Donated by Miss Monica Murphy, 1988

LE SIDANER, Henri Eugène Augustin 1862-
1939 (French)

U164   **Le Gouter au Jardin (1903)** (*Illus.p.279*)
Oil on canvas 72.8 x 87.2
Signed
Donated by Miss Penelope Andrews and
Miss Helen M. Brett (on behalf of
subscribers), 1906

LESLIE, Charles Robert 1794-1859 (English)

U646   **Don Quixote**
Oil on board, diameter 12 (circular)
Bequeathed by H. Musgrave, 1922

U647   **Sancho**
Oil on board, diameter 12 (circular)
Bequeathed by H. Musgrave, 1922

LESSORE, Thérèse 1884-1945 (British)

U468   **Flute and Harp**
Oil on canvas 61.2 x 51.1
Donated by the Sickert Trust (per Mrs. L.
Powell), 1947

U813   **Circus Audience**
Ink, wash on paper 38 x 28.7
Signed
Donated by the Sickert Trust (per Mrs. L.
Powell), 1947

U893   **Sleeping Girl** (*Illus.p.280*)
Pencil, watercolour on paper 32.6 x 26.1
Donated by the Sickert Trust (per Mrs. L.
Powell), 1947

LEVENTIS, Michael b.1944 (British)

U4745   **Critic in Artist's Studio (David Sylvester)
(1988)** (*Illus.p.280*)
Oil, acrylic with letraset on canvas 120 x
100.5
Signed, dated

Purchased 1988

LEWIS, Alfred Neville 1895-1972 (South African, worked in England)

U469 **Basuto Boy (c.1928-29)**
Oil on panel 28.6 x 25.9
Signed
Purchased (Lloyd Patterson Collection)
1929

LEWIS, John fl.1740-69 (Irish)

U4752 **Portrait of an Unknown Man (1748)**
(Illus.p.280)
Oil on canvas 74.8 x 25.8
Signed, dated
Purchased 1989

LEWIS, Percy Wyndham 1882-1957 (English)

U814 **Seated Woman (1922)** *(Illus.p.280)*
Pencil, watercolour on paper 46 x 34.1
Signed, dated
Purchased 1959

LHOTE, André 1885-1962 (French)

U1903 **Femme dans sa Cuisine (1935-40)**
(Illus.p.280)
Oil on canvas 61 x 38.1
Signed
Donated by the Friends of the National
Collections of Ireland, 1973

LIBUTZ, L. or D. 20th century (Eastern European?)

U1937 **Street Scene**
Oil on board 61 x 46.1
Provenance unknown

LILLEY, Herbert 1886-1970 (Irish)

U1077 **Quai St. Pierre, Bruges (1914)**
Watercolour, pencil on paper 27 x 36.5
Signed, dated
Purchased 1915

LINDSAY, Mrs. Ruth fl.1880-87 (British)

U1078 **Wallflowers (1885)**
Pencil, watercolour on paper 24.5 x 17.2
Signed, dated
Donated by Miss F. M. McTear, 1925

LINNELL, John 1792-1882 (English)

U88 **Captain Holland Lecky 1794-1854
(1838-45)** *(Illus.p.280)*
Oil on panel 38.1 x 31
Signed, dated
Purchased 1962

U815 **Portrait of a Gentleman** (Study)
(Illus.p.280)
Pencil, chalk, watercolour on paper 49 x
33.1
Purchased 1918

U816 **Landscape with Sheep (1861)**
(Illus.p.280)
Pencil, watercolour, bodycolour on paper
18.1 x 31.1
Signed, dated
Purchased 1937

U1266 **The Gleaners**
Watercolour, white on paper 38.5 x 51
Purchased 1929

LINTON, William 1791-1876 (British)
(attributed to)

U1884 **Sunset in Italy**
Oil on canvas 83.8 x 104.2
Donated by Miss J. Lee, 1973

LIPPI, Lorenzo 1606-65 (Italian)

U36 **An Allegory of Fortune** *(Illus.p.280)*
Oil on canvas 76.2 x 63.2
Purchased 1963

LLEWELLYN, Sir William (1860-1941) (English)

U2067 **Field-Marshal Sir George Stuart White,
VC, OM 1835-1912 (1893)**
Oil on canvas 153 x 92.2
Signed, dated
Donated by the Hon. Lady Napier, 1974

LOCKHART, William Ewart 1846-1900 (Scottish)

U1972 **Sir James Porter Corry, Bt., MP 1826-91
(1892)**
Oil on canvas 184.2 x 140.5
Signed, dated
Donated by the Presentation Committee,
1892

LOGAN, Lewis fl.1950s (Irish)

U817 **The Cornfield (1955-56)** *(Illus.p.281)*
Gouache on paper 28.1 x 38.2
Signed, dated
Purchased 1957

LOMBARD, Alfred 19th-20th century (French)

U592 **Le Village de Clans** *(Illus.p.281)*
Oil on canvas 81.2 x 66
Donated by the Hon. Mr. Justice Creed
Meredith, 1930

LONGHI, Luca 1507-80 (Italian) (attributed to)

U2286 **The Holy Family with Saints (c.1530)**
(Illus.p.281)
Oil on panel 78.3 x 58.6
Donated by J. F. Johnson, 1896
Formerly by Unknown

LOUIS, Morris 1912-62 (American)

U526 **Golden Age (1958)** *(Illus.p.38)*
Acrylic on canvas 230 x 378
Purchased 1968

LOVER, Samuel 1797-1868 (Irish)

U1079 **Master Henry Lover** *(Illus.p.281)*
Pencil, watercolour on paper 21.3 x 15.7
Signed
Purchased 1909

LOWRY, Laurence Stephen 1887-1976 (English)

U355 **Street Scene (1947)** *(Illus.p.281)*
Oil on canvas 51.2 x 41.2
Signed, dated
Purchased 1954

LOWRY, Strickland 1737-c.85 (English, worked in Ireland)

U84 **Portrait of a Lurgan Volunteer (1780)**
(Illus.p.281)
Oil on canvas 92.5 x 72.5
Dated
Purchased 1967

U712 **Portrait of a Lady (c.1780)** *(Illus.p.281)*
Oil on canvas 92.7 x 72.4
Purchased 1967

LOWRY, Strickland 1737-c.85 (attributed to)

U206 **Stewart Banks 1725-1802 (c.1760-65)**
Oil on canvas 76.5 x 62.9
Donated by J. Ellison-Macartney, 1963
Formerly by Unknown

U222 **Mrs. Banks or Mrs. Catherine Macartney
(c.1760-65)**
Oil on canvas 76.8 x 63.3
Donated by J. Ellison-Macartney, 1963
Formerly by Unknown

U1664 **The Family of Thomas Bateson, Esq.
1705-91 (1762)** *(Illus.p.281)*
Oil on canvas 163.7 x 264
Purchased 1971
Formerly attributed to Philip Hussey
1713-83

LUCEBERT b.1924 (Dutch)

U518 **Die Verschwörer (1962)** *(Illus.p.281)*
Oil on canvas 89.8 x 130.6
Signed, dated
Purchased 1965

LUCKX, Frans Joseph 1802-49 (Belgian)

U87 **Two Figures at a Window (1847)**
(Illus.p.282)
Oil on panel 24.8 x 20.8
Signed, dated
Bequeathed by W. T. Braithwaite (per J.
Horner), 1906

LUKE, John 1906-75 (Irish)

U348 **Dr. Alexander Irvine 1863-1941 (1938)**
(Illus.p.282)
Tempera on board 55.3 x 42.6
Signed, dated
Purchased 1939

U352 **The Fox (1937)** *(Illus.p.282)*
Oil, tempera on panel 38 x 54
Signed, dated
Donated by the Thomas Haverty Trust,
1941

U1433 **Baby** (Study for 'The Rehearsal')
Pencil on paper 15.5 x 13.3
Purchased 1950

U1906 **Sketch for Mural in Belfast City Hall
(1951)**
Pencil on paper 39 diameter (sight)
(semi-circular)
Signed, dated
Donated by the artist, 1952

U1907 **Sketch for Mural in Belfast City Hall
(1951)** *(Illus.p.282)*
Bodycolour on paper 39 diameter (sight)

(semi-circular)
Signed, dated
Donated by the artist, 1952

U1908 **Four Nude Studies for the Woman in
'The Rehearsal'**
Pencil on paper 28.9 x 12.6
Purchased 1950

U1909 **Three Studies for the Woman in 'The
Rehearsal'**
Pencil on paper 28.8 x 12.7
Purchased 1950

U1910 **Drawing of the Woman in 'The
Rehearsal'**
Pencil on paper 54.6 x 23.7
Purchased 1950

U1911 **Four Composition Sketches for 'The
Rehearsal' (1948)**
Pencil on paper 13.6 x 18.8, 12.3 x 18.8,
10.4 x 16.8, 10.4 x 16
Signed, dated
Purchased 1950

U1912 **Composition Drawing for 'The
Rehearsal'**
Pencil on paper 38.2 x 55.8
Purchased 1950

U1913 **Squared Composition Drawing for 'The
Rehearsal'**
Pencil on paper 38.3 x 55.8
Purchased 1950

U1914 **Tracing Composition for 'The Rehearsal'**
Pencil on paper 37.8 x 55.6
Purchased 1950

U1915 **Study of a Horse for 'The Rehearsal'**
Pencil on paper 29.4 x 31.7
Purchased 1950

U1916 **Drawing of a Baby for 'The Rehearsal'**
Pencil on paper 27.7 x 17
Purchased 1950

U1917 **The Rehearsal (1950)** (Monochrome)
Tempera on board 60.6 x 103.7
Signed, dated
Purchased 1950

U1918 **The Rehearsal (1950)** *(Illus.p.282)*
Oil, tempera on canvas on board 60.6 x
103.7
Signed, dated
Purchased 1950

U1919 **The Three Dancers (1945)** *(Illus.p.282)*
Oil, tempera on canvas on board 30.7 x
43
Signed, dated
Purchased 1945

U2022 **Baby** (Study for 'The Rehearsal')
Pencil on paper 15.2 x 12.6
Purchased 1950

U2026 **Harlequin** (Study for 'The Rehearsal')
Pencil on paper 19.8 x 37.7
Purchased 1950

U2027 **Girl** (Study for 'The Rehearsal')
Pencil on paper 35.7 x 35.7
Purchased 1950

U2031 **Woman** (Study for 'The Rehearsal')

Pencil on paper 25.4 x 43.2
Purchased 1950

U2035 **Girl** (Study for 'The Rehearsal')
Pencil on paper 23.9 x 35.7
Purchased 1950

U2036 **Horse** (Study for 'The Rehearsal')
Pencil on paper 31.9 x 29.5
Purchased 1950

U2118 **Seraph (c.1940)**
Sculpture, Bathstone head 21.5 x 19.1 x
23.3
Donated by the artist, 1946

U2119 **Head of a Woman in Profile (c.1939-40)**
(Illus.p.282)
Sculpture, Yorkstone relief 40 x 32.5 x
6.5
Donated by the artist, 1946

U2331 **Self-Portrait (c.1927-28)**
Oil on canvas on board 49.9 x 36.4
Purchased 1975

U2524 **Seated Nude** *(Illus.p.282)*
Oil on canvas 44 x 21
Purchased 1979

U2525 **The Tipster (1928)** *(Illus.p.282)*
Oil on canvas 56 x 40
Signed
Purchased 1979

U2526 **Self-Portrait** *(Illus.p.283)*
Pencil on paper 30.2 x 25 (sight)
Signed
Purchased 1979

U2527 **The Harbour** *(Illus.p.283)*
Pencil on paper 41.4 x 29.6 (sight)
Purchased 1979

U4754 **In the Mournes (1936)**
Tempera on board 53.6 x 65.1
Signed, dated
Bequeathed by Mrs. Moya Woodside,
1989

U4779 **The Lustre Jug (1934)**
Oil on board 39 x 30
Signed
Bequeathed by Roberta and John Hewitt,
1987

U4780 **Sketch of John Hewitt 1907-87 (1932)**
Ink on paper 21 x 16
Bequeathed by Roberta and John Hewitt,
1987

U4781 **The Road to the West (1944)**
(Illus.p.283)
Oil, tempera on board 37 x 63
Signed, dated
Bequeathed by Roberta and John Hewitt,
1987

U4782 **Portrait of Roberta (1935)**
Crayon on paper 51 x 48
Bequeathed by Roberta and John Hewitt,
1987

LUNDBERG, Gustaf 1695-1786 (Swedish)

U86 **George, 1st Earl Macartney 1737-1806**
(Illus.p.283)
Pastel on paper on canvas 66.5 x 51.5

Purchased 1947

LUTTERELL, Edward fl.c.1673-d. after 1723
(Irish)

U1432 **Jan Lutma (1703)** (after Rembrandt)
(Illus.p.283)
Pastel on paper on card 25.5 x 20.6
Signed, dated
Purchased 1971

LYNAS, John Langtry 1879-1956 (Irish)

U350 **Wellington Place from the City Hall
Grounds** *(Illus.p.283)*
Oil on panel 34.5 x 36.8
Purchased 1949

U351 **My Son Rodin (1925)** *(Illus.p.283)*
Oil on panel 41.7 x 30.4
Signed, dated
Purchased 1950

U353 **My Mother (1909)**
Oil on canvas 33.2 x 27.7
Signed, dated
Purchased 1949

U354 **Self-Portrait**
Oil on board 31.4 x 25.1
Purchased 1949

U1080 **Self-Portrait (1936)**
Pencil, watercolour on paper 28.1 x 22.8
Signed, dated
Donated by W. Moore, 1947

U1296 **Study for 'The Creation of Man' (1934)**
Crayon on paper 23.3 x 18.2
Signed, dated
Donated by the artist, 1949

U1297 **Study of a Seated Nude**
Crayon on paper 25.1 x 19.5
Donated by the artist, 1949

U1298 **Study of a Seated Woman**
Crayon on paper 26.1 x 19.8
Donated by the artist, 1949

U1299 **Study of a Kneeling Nude**
Crayon on paper 26.1 x 19.8
Donated by the artist, 1949

U1300 **Sketch: Seated Woman**
Crayon on paper 26.1 x 19.8
Donated by the artist, 1949

U1301 **Study of a Woman**
Crayon on paper 26.1 x 19.8
Donated by the artist, 1949

U1302 **Sketch: Standing Nude**
Crayon on paper 26.1 x 19.8
Donated by the artist, 1949

U1303 **Study of a Nude**
Crayon on paper 26.1 x 19.8
Donated by the artist, 1949

U1304 **Sketch: Standing Female Nude**
Crayon on paper 26.1 x 19.8
Donated by the artist, 1949

U1305 **Study of a Woman**
Crayon on paper 26.1 x 19.8
Donated by the artist, 1949

U1306 **Study of a Nude Woman**

Crayon on paper 26.1 x 19.8
Donated by the artist, 1949

U1307 **Study of a Nude Woman**
Crayon on paper 26.1 x 19.8
Donated by the artist, 1949

U1308 **Study for 'They Gave All' (1932)**
Crayon on paper 26.1 x 19.8
Signed, dated
Donated by the artist, 1949

U1309 **Study of a Female Nude**
Crayon on paper 26.1 x 19.8
Donated by the artist, 1949

U1310 **Study of a Female Nude**
Crayon on paper 26.1 x 19.8
Donated by the artist, 1949

U1311 **Studies for 'Temple de Profundis' (1932)**
Crayon on paper 26.1 x 19.8
Signed, dated
Donated by the artist, 1949

U1312 **Study for Door, 'Temple de Profundis' (1932)**
Crayon on paper 26.1 x 19.8
Signed, dated
Donated by the artist, 1949

U1313 **Studies of Crouching Men**
Crayon on paper 26.1 x 19.8
Donated by the artist, 1949

U1314 **Study for 'They Gave All'**
Crayon on paper 26.1 x 19.8
Signed
Donated by the artist, 1949

U1315 **Study for 'They Gave All' (1932)**
Crayon on paper 26.1 x 19.8
Signed, dated
Donated by the artist, 1949

U1316 **Sketch: Foot and Arms**
Crayon on paper 26.1 x 19.7
Donated by the artist, 1949

U1317 **Sketch: Female Nude with Raised Arm**
Crayon on paper 26.1 x 19.7
Donated by the artist, 1949

U1318 **Sketch: the Artist and his Heroes**
Pencil on paper 20.5 x 26.1
Donated by the artist, 1949

U1370 **Study for 'They Gave All' (1932)**
Crayon on paper 26.1 x 19.9
Signed, dated
Donated by the artist, 1949

U1371 **Two Seated Women: Study for 'They Gave All' (1932)**
Crayon on paper 19.9 x 25.1
Signed, dated
Donated by the artist, 1949

U1372 **Study of a Crowd**
Crayon on paper 16.9 x 27.2
Donated by the artist, 1949

U1373 **Study for 'They Gave All' (1932)**
Crayon on paper 26.1 x 19.8
Signed, dated
Donated by the artist, 1949

U1374 **Study: Angels on Pillars**

Crayon on paper 26.2 x 19.8
Donated by the artist, 1949

U1542 **Dante Rossetti Lynas (1924)** *(Illus.p.283)*
Pastel on card 33 x 27.9 (sight)
Signed, dated
Donated by the artist, 1924

U1630 **Self-Portrait (1924)** *(Illus.p.283)*
Pastel on card 36.2 x 28.6 (sight)
Signed, dated
Donated by the artist, 1924

U3033 **Self-Portrait**
Oil on board 56 x 39.5
Signed
Donated by Peter Woodard, 1996

U3034 **Christ Revealing Himself before Sin**
Watercolour on card 35.5 x 25.5
Donated by Peter Woodard, 1996

LYNN, Samuel Ferres 1836-76 (Irish)

U1794 **Unknown Man (1871)**
Sculpture, marble bust, ht.73.7
Signed, dated
Provenance unknown

U1795 **Rev. Dr. Henry Cooke 1788-1868**
Sculpture, plaster statuette, ht.81.3
Donated by Sir Thomas Drew, 1907

U1796 **Lord Farnham, 7th Baron 1799-1868 (1869)**
Sculpture, plaster statuette, ht.81.3
Signed, dated
Donated by Sir Thomas Drew, 1907

U1797 **John Lytle, JP**
Sculpture, plaster bust, ht.78 (cast by Joseph Holland fl.1861-90)
Signed, dated
Donated by D. B. Lytle, JP; year unknown

U1798 **James Heron**
Sculpture, plaster bust, ht. 75
Donated by W. C. Heron, 1893

LYNN, William Henry 1829-1915 (Irish)

U1081 **Design for Old Conna Hill, Bray, Co. Wicklow**
Ink, watercolour on paper 36.7 x 52.5
Donated by Miss E. M. Cooper, 1916

U1082 **Britannia Tubular Bridge over Menai Straits** *(Illus.p.284)*
Pencil, watercolour on paper 24 x 34
Donated by Miss E. M. Cooper, 1916

U1083 **Waterfoot, Co. Antrim**
Pencil, watercolour on paper 17.6 x 25.3
Donated by Miss E. M. Cooper, 1916

U1084 **Kenbane Head, Ballycastle**
Pencil, watercolour on paper 37.2 x 49
Donated by Miss E. M. Cooper, 1916

U1085 **Design for Glasslough House, Co. Monaghan** (Castle Leslie)
Pencil, ink, watercolour, white on paper 36.7 x 52.5
Donated by Miss E. M. Cooper, 1916

U1864 **Design for St. Andrew's Church, Dublin (1860)** *(Illus.p.284)*
Ink, watercolour, bodycolour on paper

54.4 x 74
Signed, dated
Donated by Miss E. M. Cooper, 1916

U2370 **Design for Unitarian Church, St. Stephen's Green, Dublin (1862)** *(Illus.p.284)*
Ink, watercolour, bodycolour on paper 61.3 x 45.1
Donated by Miss E. M. Cooper, 1916

U2371 **Design for Guild Hall and Public Offices, Plymouth: General View of Proposed Buildings (1869)**
Ink, watercolour on paper 58.7 x 87
Donated by Miss E. M. Cooper, 1916

U2372 **Design for Proposed Town Hall, Gateshead**
Ink, watercolour on paper 48.9 x 73
Donated by Miss E. M. Cooper, 1916

U2373 **A Competition Drawing: Proposed Carlisle Bridge, Dublin (1862)**
Ink, watercolour on paper 60 x 99.4
Signed
Donated by Miss E. M. Cooper, 1916

U2473 **A Competition Drawing: Proposed Carlisle Bridge, Dublin (1862)**
Ink, watercolour on paper 59 x 97 (sight)
Signed
Donated by Miss E. M. Cooper, 1916

U4732 **Design for Parliament Buildings of New South Wales, Sydney (1861)**
Watercolour on paper 70 x 113.3
Signed, dated
Donated by Miss E. M. Cooper, 1916

U4855 **Design for a Town Hall**
Pencil on paper 48.9 x 63.5 (sight)
Donated by Miss E. M. Cooper, 1916

U4856 **Clarke Halls, Paisley (1876)**
Pencil on paper 45.7 x 68.7 (sight)
Donated by Miss E. M. Cooper, 1916

U4857 **Parliament Houses and Government Offices, Sydney (1861)**
Pencil on paper 46.4 x 70.5 (sight)
Donated by Miss E. M. Cooper, 1916

U4858 **Design for a Town Hall**
Pencil on paper 52.1 x 67.2 (sight)
Donated by Miss E. M. Cooper, 1916

M

McADOO, Violet 1896-1961 (Irish)

U821 **Haystacks (1933)**
Watercolour on paper 22.5 x 29.7
Signed, dated
Donated by J. F. Hunter, 1937

U1566 **Tiled Roofs, Spain (1933)** *(Illus.p.284)*
Pencil, charcoal, watercolour on paper 38.7 x 56.2
Signed, dated
Purchased 1944

McALDOWIE, James fl.1885-1913 (Scottish)

U1090 **'When Autumn Blasts the River Banks**

Lay Bare' *(Illus.p.284)*
Watercolour on paper 29.4 x 39.3
Purchased 1910

McALEER, Clement b.1949 (Irish)

U2700 **Day (1979)** *(Illus.p.284)*
Oil on canvas 122.5 x 114
Signed, dated
Purchased 1979

U2701 **Night (1979)** *(Illus.p.284)*
Oil on canvas 122.5 x 114
Signed, dated
Purchased 1979 .

U4759 **Studio Reflections (1989)**
Watercolour, bodycolour, chalk on paper
90.4 x 104.2
Purchased 1989

McALLISTER, John Alphonsus 1896-1925
(Irish)

U99 **W. J. Coombes 1893-1981 (1919)**
Oil on panel 58.4 x 45.1
Signed, dated
Donated by Dr. R. H. Hunter, 1935

U1091 **Off Ballycastle, Kenbane Head in the
Distance (1921)**
Pencil, watercolour on paper 28.7 x 39.5
Signed, dated
Purchased 1924

U1092 **Waterfoot Harbour, Co. Antrim (1924)**
(Illus.p.284)
Pencil, watercolour on paper 28.6 x 39.8
Signed, dated
Donated by Dr. R. H. Hunter, 1934

U1093 **Summer**
Pencil, watercolour on paper 28.6 x 39.8
Signed
Purchased 1935

U1094 **Grand Canal, Dublin**
Pencil, watercolour on paper 28 x 38.2
Signed
Purchased 1930

U1095 **The Road through the Bog (1923)**
Pencil, watercolour on paper 28.5 x 39
Signed, dated
Purchased 1924

U1096 **The Glen, Cushendun - Evening
(1920)**
Pencil, watercolour on paper 25.2 x 35.5
Signed, dated
Purchased 1924

U1097 **The Grand Canal, Dublin (1923)**
Pencil, watercolour, white on paper 28 x
38
Signed, dated
Purchased 1930

U1098 **The Brickfield** *(Illus.p.284)*
Pencil, watercolour on paper 29 x 40
Signed
Purchased 1930

U1253 **Looking from Ardsbeg, Co. Donegal
(1921)** *(Illus.p. 285)*
Pencil, watercolour on paper 37.5 x 53
(sight)

Signed, dated
Purchased 1951

U4783 **Road between Cushendun and
Murlough**
Pastel on paper 16 x 22
Bequeathed by Roberta and John Hewitt,
1987

McAULEY, Charles J. 1910-99 (Irish)

U374 **Mid-day on the Moss** *(Illus.p.285)*
Oil on board 43 x 65.9
Signed
Purchased 1948

McBRIDE, Denis b.1939 (Irish)

U367 **Variation on a Snowdrop IV (c.1967)**
(Illus.p.285)
Emulsion on canvas 121.7 x 137.6
Signed
Purchased 1967

MacBRIDE, William 1858-1913 (Scottish)

U604 **The Faggot Gatherers** *(Illus.p. 285)*
Oil on canvas 82.5 x 113
Signed
Purchased 1911

McBURNEY, John 1877-1917 (Irish)

U52 **Self-Portrait (c.1912)**
Oil on canvas 72.7 x 62.9
Donated by Mrs. Moss, 1957

U101 **Waterworks, Antrim Road (1912)**
(Illus.p.285)
Oil on canvas 45.8 x 61.2
Signed, dated
Donated by Mrs. Moss, 1957

U379 **York Dock, Belfast (1910)**
Oil on board 17.6 x 25.3
Signed, dated
Purchased 1943

U1540 **Couple on a Bench in a Garden (1916)**
(Illus.p.285)
Ink on paper 16.7 x 13.9
Signed, dated
Donated by Professor H. O. Meredith,
1933

U1975 **Sefton's House, Balmoral Avenue**
Oil on canvas 59.1 x 75.6
Donated by Mrs. Moss, 1957

MacCABE, Gladys b.1918 (Irish)

U378 **The Bus Queue (1948-49)**
Oil on panel 38.7 x 30.7
Signed
Purchased 1949

MacCABE, Max 1917-2000 (Irish)

U1086 **Aquarium**
Ink, watercolour on paper 28.6 x 35.1
Signed
Purchased 1950

MacCANN, George Galway 1909-67 (Irish)

U2251 **Death Mask of Louis MacNeice 1907-63
(1963)**

Sculpture, plaster (with surface
colouring) 27.8 x 18.2 x 12.8
Purchased 1974

McCLELLAND, George b.1931 (Irish)

U2512 **The Healing Screen (1978)**
Mixed media 230 x 220 x 23
Donated by the Friends of the National
Collections of Ireland, 1978

McCLOY, Samuel 1831-1904 (Irish)

U93 **Two Old Friends** *(Illus.p.285)*
Oil on board 47.9 x 37.5
Signed
Donated by Miss E. Maclaine, 1952

U102 **Where the White Foam Kissed my Feet
(c.1898)** *(Illus.p.285)*
Oil on board 39 x 27.3
Signed
Purchased 1906

U625 **Caught in the Act (c.1885)** *(Illus.p.285)*
Oil on board 31.5 x 24.7
Signed
Bequeathed by Sir R. Lloyd Patterson,
1919

U1440 **Espalier Apple Blossom** *(Illus.p.286)*
Watercolour on paper 12.4 x 22.6
Donated by W. Corran, 1954

U1441 **Trees and Hedge between Two Gates**
Watercolour on paper 10.5 x 24.2
Donated by W. Corran, 1954

U1442 **Trees with Stony Path**
Watercolour on paper 13.5 x 19.3
Donated by W. Corran, 1954

U1443 **Group of Trees with Wooden Fence**
Watercolour on paper 13.9 x 22.5
Signed
Donated by W. Corran, 1954

U1444 **Tree Stump and Bracken**
Watercolour on paper 13.7 x 22.4
Signed
Donated by W. Corran, 1954

U1445 **Apple Orchard with Cabbages**
Watercolour on paper 19.4 x 27.6
Signed
Donated by W. Corran, 1954

U1446 **Strickland's Glen, Bangor**
Watercolour on paper 24.5 x 34.6
Signed
Donated by W. Corran, 1954

U1447 **Lobster Pots and Fishing Boat**
Watercolour on paper 13.7 x 19.2
Signed
Donated by W. Corran, 1954

U1448 **Pieces of Armour on a Bench** *(Illus.p.286)*
Watercolour on paper 34.4 x 23.5
Signed
Donated by W. Corran, 1954

U1449 **Hutted Corn**
Watercolour on paper 13 x 18.1
Signed
Donated by W. Corran, 1954

U1450 **Felled Timber with Burdock** *(Illus.p.286)*

Watercolour on paper 12 x 17.1
Donated by W. Corran, 1954

U1451 Coltsfoot by a Stream
Watercolour on paper 12.4 x 17.4
Signed
Donated by W. Corran, 1954

U1452 River and Trees
Watercolour on paper 7.6 x 14.6
Donated by W. Corran, 1954

U1453 Stack-building *(Illus.p.286)*
Watercolour on paper 9 x 14.3
Donated by W. Corran, 1954

U1454 Rowing Boat in a Cove
Watercolour on paper 8 x 14.3
Donated by W. Corran, 1954

U1455 Donkey and Boy with Basket
Watercolour on paper 9.9 x 14
Donated by W. Corran, 1954

U1456 Spinning Wheel and Stool
Watercolour on paper 22.2 x 13.3
Donated by W. Corran, 1954

U1457 Little Girl with Open Book (1892)
(Illus.p.286)
Watercolour on paper 34.7 x 25.7
Dated
Donated by W. Corran, 1954

U1458 Dog Daisies and Clover
Watercolour on paper 22.1 x 17.2
Donated by W. Corran, 1954

U1459 Brambles and Turf
Watercolour on paper 13.6 x 19.1
Donated by W. Corran, 1954

U1460 A Bunch of Mistletoe
Pencil, watercolour on paper 20.4 x 15.1
Donated by W. Corran, 1954

**U1461 Christmas Carol - O Listen to our
Simple Song** *(Illus.p.286)*
Watercolour on paper 20.6 x 14.9
Donated by W. Corran, 1954

U1462 Little Girl at a Doorway
Watercolour on paper 19.3 x 15.8
Donated by W. Corran, 1954

U1463 Three Girls Playing Cat's Cradle
Watercolour on paper 19 x 27
Donated by W. Corran, 1954

U1464 Three Girls in a Kitchen
Watercolour on paper 26 x 19.8
Donated by W. Corran, 1954

U1465 Two Little Girls in a Kitchen
Watercolour on paper 22.1 x 27.6
Donated by W. Corran, 1954

**U1466 Interior of Cottage: Woman and a Man
Carrying a Child**
Watercolour on paper 20.7 x 26.6
Signed
Donated by W. Corran, 1954

U1467 Tired (1893)(Girl with a Child on her
Lap)
Watercolour on paper 26.4 x 34.6
Dated
Donated by W. Corran, 1954

U1468 Hawthorn Blossom and Path
Watercolour on paper 18 x 24.8
Donated by W. Corran, 1954

U1469 Shallow Woodland Pool
Watercolour on paper 22.4 x 28.5
Donated by W. Corran, 1954

U1470 Little Milkmaid: Odd One (1892)
Watercolour on paper 34.3 x 25.7
Dated
Donated by W. Corran, 1954

**U1471 Woodland Pool with Three Girls
Paddling**
Pencil, watercolour on paper 26.6 x 36.5
Donated by W. Corran, 1954

U1472 Washing Day
Watercolour on paper 34.4 x 25.3
Donated by W. Corran, 1954

U1473 Little Girl Sewing
Watercolour on paper 34.6 x 25.6
Donated by W. Corran, 1954

U2557 Lock Near Lisburn
Pencil on paper 13.3 x 21.2
Donated by S. McCloy, 1980

U4678 Corn Sheaves
Watercolour on paper 13 x 21
Signed
Donated by W. Corran, 1954

U4679 Rocky Pool
Watercolour on paper 9.8 x 17.6
Donated by W. Corran, 1954

U4680 The Dead Tree
Watercolour on paper 14.9 x 7.3
Donated by W. Corran, 1954

U4681 River and Trees, Sunset
Watercolour on paper 7.5 x 15
Donated by W. Corran, 1954

McCLUGHIN, W. J. 1900-71 (Irish)

U1575 Donegore Church (1936)
Pencil on paper 18.8 x 30 (sight)
Signed, dated
Provenance unknown

**U1581 Belfast Harbour Estate, Looking towards
Holywood (1931)**
Pencil on paper 25.2 x 35.1
Signed, dated
Provenance unknown

U4784 Cavehill (1966) *(Illus.p.286)*
Ink, watercolour on paper 9.3 x 29.5
Signed, dated
Bequeathed by Roberta and John Hewitt,
1987

U4785 Cave Hill Bridge (1933)
Ink, wash on paper 22 x 31.8
Signed, dated
Bequeathed by Roberta and John Hewitt,
1987

U4786 Portrait of a Man (Self-Portrait)
Pastel on paper 38 x 27
Bequeathed by Roberta and John Hewitt,
1987

U4787 Portrait of John Hewitt 1907-87 (1936)

Oil on board 59.7 x 49.5
Bequeathed by Roberta and John Hewitt,
1987

U4789 Sawmills (1931)
Watercolour on paper 24.5 x 30.6
Signed, dated
Bequeathed by Roberta and John Hewitt,
1987

MacCOLL, Dugald Sutherland 1859-1948
(Scottish)

U818 Pont de la Tournelle, Paris *(Illus.p.286)*
Pencil, watercolour on paper 21.5 x 28.7
Signed
Donated by the Contemporary Art
Society, 1948

McCOMB, Leonard b.1930 (Scottish)

U4812 Portrait of Jenny Scott (1987)
(Illus.p.286)
Oil on canvas 238.7 x 193
Signed, dated
Purchased 1990

MacDONAGH, Maurice b.1962 (Irish)

U4971 Axis (1993) *(Illus.p.287)*
Sculpture, welded steel, two elements,
each 118.2 x 245 x 10.4
Purchased 1993

MacDONALD, Lawrence 1799-1878 (Scottish)

U1799 Unknown Lady (1851) *(Illus.p.287)*
Sculpture, marble bust, ht.64.8
Signed, dated
Provenance unknown

McDONNELL, Hector b.1947 (Irish)

U2662 Bewley's Restaurant II (1980)
(Illus.p.287)
Oil on canvas 183 x 243.8
Purchased 1983

MacDOWELL, Patrick 1799-1870 (Irish)

U1800 Early Sorrow (1846)
Sculpture, plaster, ht. 144.8
Signed, dated
Donated by Mrs. E. B. Chisholm, 1925

U1801 A Young Man (1857)
Sculpture, plaster herm, ht. 57.2
Signed, dated
Purchased 1970

U1802 Sir James Emerson Tennent 1804-69
Sculpture, plaster bust, ht. 78
Donated by Mrs. Iris L. Marshall, 1899

U1803 Lady Tennent d.1883
Sculpture, plaster bust, ht. 64
Donated by Mrs. Iris L. Marshall, 1899

**U2569 Frederick Richard Chichester, Earl of
Belfast 1827-53 (1855)** *(Illus.p.287)*
Sculpture, marble bust, ht. 81.2
Signed
Purchased 1980

**U4839 Monument to Frederick Richard
Chichester, Earl of Belfast 1827-53**
Sculpture, marble 145x194x102

Donated by the Shaftesbury Estate of Lough Neagh Ltd., 1979

McEVOY, Ambrose 1878-1927 (English)

U370 **Miss Mary Clare (c.1915-20)** *(Illus.p.287)*
Oil on canvas 76.4 x 63.5
Purchased (Lloyd Patterson Collection) 1929

U550 **View from Aldbourne (1909-12)**
Oil on canvas 80.5 x 109.5
Purchased 1968

U822 **Portrait of a Lady** *(Illus.p.287)*
Pencil, watercolour on paper 46.5 x 34.3
Purchased 1946

U823 **Standing Nude (c.1920-25)** *(Illus.p.287)*
Pencil, watercolour on paper 35.8 x 25.5
Signed
Purchased 1968

McGLASHAN, Archibald A. b.1888 (Scottish)

U373 **Still Life (1925)** *(Illus.p.287)*
Oil on canvas 61.4 x 46.5
Signed
Purchased 1932

U377 **Head of a Child (c.1930)** *(Illus.p.287)*
Oil on canvas 38.3 x 39.8
Signed
Purchased 1932

MacGONIGAL, Maurice 1900-79 (Irish)

U369 **'The Olympia', Dublin (c.1935-36)**
(Illus.p.288)
Oil on canvas 63.6 x 76.5
Signed
Donated by the Thomas Haverty Trust, 1941

U372 **Nightfall, Connemara (1962)**
Oil on board 50.7 x 75.9
Signed, dated
Donated by the Thomas Haverty Trust, 1966

U376 **The Red Cart (1945-47)**
Oil on panel 31.3 x 39.8
Signed
Purchased 1947

McGUINNESS, Bingham 1849-1928 (Irish)

U2682 **Lisieux, Normandy** *(Illus.p.288)*
Watercolour, pencil on paper 49.5 x 42.6
Signed
Bequeathed by Miss E. Taylor, 1983

McGUINNESS, Norah 1901-80 (Irish)

U371 **Village by the Sea (1953)** *(Illus.p.288)*
Oil on canvas 68.9 x 91.6
Signed, dated
Donated by the Thomas Haverty Trust, 1957

U1254 **The Four Courts, Dublin (1940)**
(Illus.p.288)
Gouache on paper 44 x 59.5
Signed, dated
Donated by the Thomas Haverty Trust, 1945

U2365 **Pattern on the Feather Bed Mountain (1975)** *(Illus.p.288)*
Oil on canvas 91.4 x 122
Signed
Purchased 1975

McGUIRE, Edward 1932-86 (Irish)

U2107 **Portrait of Seamus Heaney b.1939 (1974)** *(Illus.p.288)*
Oil on canvas 142 x 112.1
Signed, dated
Commissioned 1974

U2278 **Francis Stuart 1902-2000 (1974)**
(Illus.p.288)
Ink on paper 30 x 21.2
Signed, dated
Purchased 1974

U2671 **John Montague b.1929 (1983)**
Oil on panel 81 x 60.8
Signed, dated
Purchased 1983

MacINTYRE, James b.1926 (Irish)

U375 **Tinker Girls (c.1956)**
Oil on board 46 x 35.1
Signed
Purchased 1957

McKELVEY, Frank 1895-1974 (Irish)

U328 **Evening, Ballycastle (c.1924)** *(Illus.p.288)*
Oil on canvas 76.5 x 102
Signed
Purchased 1924

U1099 **Study of the Head of an Old Woman (1916)** *(Illus.p.288)*
Ink, wash on paper 41.3 x 30.9
Signed, dated
Donated by the artist, 1925

U1488 **Andrew Bonar Law 1858-1923**
Catalogued erroneously ; is in the collection of the department of History, P476. 1929

U1979 **James McQuitty (1922)**
Catalogued erroneously; is in the collection of the department of History, P695.1924

U1980 **Sir Denis Stanislaus Henry, PC, DL 1864-1925**
Catalogued erroneously; is in the collection of the department of History, P315.1928

McKENNA, Stephen b.1939 (English)

U4753 **Maritime Still Life (1988)** *(Illus.p.289)*
Oil on canvas 120 x 160
Signed, dated
Purchased 1989

MACKENZIE, William Gibbes 1857-1924 (Irish)

U89 **My New Shoes! (c.1893)** *(Illus.p.289)*
Oil on canvas 120 x 79
Donated by J. C. W. Reid, 1926

U200 **The River Lagan, near Belfast (1924)**
Oil on canvas 79.6 x 91.7
Signed

Provenance unknown

U540 **River Lagan, near Belfast** *(Illus.p.289)*
Oil on panel 18.2 x 25.3
Signed
Bequeathed by Miss H. M. McCleery, 1968

U541 **Backwater, River Lagan near Edenderry, Belfast (1914)**
Oil on canvas 25.7 x 40.7
Signed, dated
Donated by the Belfast Art Society, 1927

U561 **Sunshine, Lagan Woods (1913)**
(Illus.p.289)
Oil on canvas 91.4 x 71.4
Signed, dated
Donated by the Belfast Art Society, 1927

U1982 **William Gray, MRIA 1830-1917 (1912)**
Oil on canvas 76 x 63.2
Signed, dated
Purchased 1912

U4502 **John Robb 1828-1906 (1889)**
Oil on canvas 91.5 x 71.5
Signed, dated
Donated by Lieut. B. d'A. Leitch, 1945

MacKINNON, Sine b.1901 (Irish)

U4664 **Spanish Town (1933)** *(Illus.p.289)*
Watercolour on paper 30.5 x 33.7 (sight)
Signed, dated
Purchased 1954

McKINSTRY, Cherith b.1928 (Irish)

U368 **Mary at Bethlehem (1962)**
Oil on canvas 77.5 x 99.3
Purchased 1962

McLACHLAN, W. J. 20th century (Irish)

U2449 **Sir William Turner 1872-1937 (1920)**
Oil on canvas 127.4 x 102
Signed, dated
Provenance unknown
Formerly by Unknown

U4508 **Councillor James A. Doran, JP 1848-1934**
Oil on canvas 127 x 101.6
Donated by subscribers, 1921

MACLISE, Daniel 1806-70 (Irish)

U819 **Study for Malvolio (?)**
Pencil on paper 27.8 x 13.9
Signed
Purchased 1961

U1409 **William Bullen of Kinsale (?) (1829)**
(Illus. p.289)
Pencil, wash on paper 25.2 x 19.5
Signed, dated
Donated by Rev. C. Sefton Smith, 1952

U2265 **Illustration to a Poem** *(Illus.p.289)*
Pencil, ink, sepia wash on paper 19 x 23.8
Purchased 1974

MACNEE, Sir Daniel 1806-82 (Scottish)

U201 **Rev. Henry Cooke, DD 1788-1868 (c.1856)**

Oil on canvas 127.3 x 88.9
Donated by the Misses Carruthers, 1906

MacQUOID, Percy 1852-1925 (British)

U1574 **A Man Striking Another with a Stick, above a Sluice** (Book Illustration)
Ink on card 10.8 x 16
Purchased 1928

U2048 **Penny's Ride, p.155** (Book Illustration)
Ink, white on card 10.1 x 14.5
Signed
Purchased 1928

U2049 **You Must Know, We Are a Deputation** (Book Illustration)
Ink, white on card 10.8 x 16
Purchased 1928

U2059 **Winifred Was at the Writing Table, p.186** (Book Illustration)
Ink, white on card 10.1 x 14.5
Signed
Purchased 1928

MACWHIRTER, John 1839-1911 (Scottish)

U1087 **In the Rhone Valley, near Visp**
Pencil, watercolour, white on paper 15.3 x 20.6
Signed
Donated by Meta and Robert Dunlop, 1950

McWILLIAM, F. E. 1909-92 (British)

U967 **Man and Wife (1948)** (Illus.p.39)
Sculpture, stone aggregate 91.5 x 34.3 x 33
Donated by the Contemporary Art Society, 1952

U968 **Head of William Scott 1913-89 (1956)** (Illus.p.289)
Sculpture, bronze, ht. 66.5
Signed, dated
Purchased 1956

U2076 **Women of Belfast 7 (1972)**
Sculpture, bronze 35 x 28 x 24
Signed
Donated by the Friends of the Ulster Museum, 1974

U2438 **Woman in Bomb Blast 1974/1 (1974)** (Illus.p.289)
Sculpture, bronze 56.5 x 139.2 x 57
Signed
Donated by the artist, 1977

U2461 **Study for 'Woman in Bomb Blast' (1974)** (Illus.p.290)
Watercolour, felt pen on paper 24.5 x 40.9
Signed, dated
Donated by the artist, 1978

U2462 **Study for 'Woman in Bomb Blast' (1974)**
Watercolour, felt pen on paper 18.3 x 28.3
Signed, dated
Donated by the artist, 1978

U2463 **Study for 'Woman in Bomb Blast' (1974)**
Watercolour, felt pen on paper 29.6 x 41.6

Signed, dated
Donated by the artist, 1978

U2464 **Study for 'Woman in Bomb Blast' (1974)**
Watercolour, felt pen on paper 22.9 x 38.1
Signed, dated
Donated by the artist, 1978

U2696 **Crossed Legs (c.1978)**
Sculpture, bronze 38 x 40 x 28
Signed
Purchased 1980

U4689 **Collage (1946)** (Illus.p.290)
Mixed media on paper 38.7 x 24.8
Signed, dated
Purchased 1985

U5024 **Study for 'The Unknown Political Prisoner' (c.1950-51)** (Illus.p.290)
Crayon on paper 16.8 x 13.5
Purchased 1996

McWILLIAMS, Joseph b.1938 (Irish)

U4805 **The Governors of Anguilla, Gibraltar, the Caymen Islands and the Last Governor of Northern Ireland (1989)** (Illus.p.290)
Oil on canvas 152.3 x 213.4
Signed, dated
Purchased 1989

McWILLIAMS, Simon b.1970 (Irish)

U2034 **Church** (Illus.p.290)
Oil on canvas 175.5 x 186
Donated by the Thomas Haverty Trust, 1999

MACK, F. 19th century (British?)

U4827 **Portrait of a Man (1898)**
Oil on canvas 101.2 x 76
Signed, dated
Provenance unknown

MACK, Heinz b.1931 (German)

U525 **Pyramid of Light (1964)** (Illus.p.290)
Aluminium on board 81.2 x 98.4
Signed, dated
Purchased 1965

MACKLIN, Thomas Eyre 1867-1943 (British)

U574 **City Hall, Belfast, by Floodlight (1935)** (Illus.p.290)
Oil on canvas 53.5 x 76.5
Signed, dated
Donated by the proprietors of the *Belfast Telegraph*, 1936

U654 **The City Hall and Titanic Memorial (1930)**
Oil on canvas 44.2 x 71.1
Signed, dated
Provenance unknown

U1985 **William S. Baird, JP 1824-86**
Oil on canvas 76.8 x 63.9
Signed
Donated by Sir Robert Baird, 1930

U4499 **Sir Robert Baird, KBE, DL 1855-1934 (1928)**
Oil on canvas 76.9 x 63.9

Signed, dated
Donated by Major W. Baird, 1929

MADDEN, Anne b.1932 (Irish)

U356 **Slievecarran (1963)** (Illus.p.290)
Oil, grit, flint chippings on canvas 116.1 x 89.2
Signed, dated
Purchased 1964

U4808 **Le Jardin (1988)**
Oil on canvas 127 x 178 (Diptych)
Dated
Purchased 1990

MADDOX, Conroy b.1912 (English)

U1431 **Tableau Vivant (1959)** (Illus.p.290)
Gouache, collage on board 43.2 x 29.8
Purchased 1971

MADRASSI, Luca 1861-1914 (Italian) (after)

U4852 **The Spinner**
Sculpture, bronze, ht. 96.5
Signed
Donated by John Jaffé, 1891

MAES, Nicolaes 1634-93 (Dutch)

U208 **Portrait of a Woman (1670s)** (Illus.p.291)
Oil on panel 32 x 26
Purchased 1959

MAEYER, Marcel b.1920 (Belgian)

U2451 **Fair Tent II (1976)** (Illus.p.291)
Acrylic on canvas 200 x 190
Signed, dated
Purchased 1977

MAGILL, Elizabeth b. 1959 (Canadian, works in London)

U4803 **Fly Painting (1989)** (Illus.p.291)
Oil on canvas 213.4 x 182.9
Signed, dated
Purchased 1989

MAGUIRE, Cecil b.1930 (Irish)

U2091 **The Big Hewer (1974)**
Oil on board 30.5 x 25.5
Signed, dated
Purchased 1974

MAHONEY, James 1847-79 (Irish)

U2564 **Illustration for Charles Dickens' *Our Mutual Friend*** (Illus.p.291)
Ink, white on card 10.8 x 14
Signed
Purchased 1980

MAHOOD, Kenneth b.1930 (Irish)

U361 **Crane Yellow and White (1957)**
Oil on board 76.8 x 31
Signed, dated
Purchased 1957

MAISTRE, Roy de 1894-1968 (Australian, worked in England)

U444 **Anne, Lady Butler (1954)** (Illus.p.291)

Oil on board 91.6 x 61.1
Signed
Purchased 1967

MALDONADO, José b.1962 (Spanish)

U4948 **Eclipse (1991)** *(Illus.p.291)*
Mixed media on canvas 200 x 200
Purchased 1992

MANARA, Orazio de b.1804 (Italian)

U2366 **Frederick Richard Chichester, Earl of
Belfast 1827-53 (1853)** *(Illus.p.291)*
Oil on board 25.4 x 20.2
Signed, dated
Donated by the Dowager Marchioness of
Dufferin and Ava, 1908

MANN, Harrington 1864-1937 (Scottish)

U366 **The Bird Cage (1907)** *(Illus.p.291)*
Oil on panel 46.1 x 37.8
Signed, dated
Purchased 1911

MANSFIELD, Edward b.1907 (English)

U362 **Moulding Shop - a Large 31 Ton
Casting near Completion (1942)**
Oil on canvas 51 x 61
Signed, dated
Donated by the War Artists' Advisory
Committee (per the Imperial War
Museum), 1946

MANSON, James Bolivar 1879-1945 (English)

U472 **A Freshening Breeze, St. Briac (c.1907)**
(Illus.p.291)
Oil on panel 35.3 x 45.7
Purchased (Lloyd Patterson Collection)
1933

MARCH, Elise fl.1912-39 (English)

U1988 **Rt. Hon. John Campbell White, MA, PC
1854-1923 (1923)**
Oil on canvas 76.2 x 63.5
Signed, dated
Bequeathed by Mrs. E. E. White, 1937

MARIESCHI, Michele 1710-43 (Italian) (circle
of)

U705 **Capriccio with Classical Ruins and a
Harbour** *(Illus.p.292)*
Oil on canvas 152 x 229.5
Donated by C. C. Conor, 1915

MARNY, Paul 1829-1914 (French, worked in
Ireland and England)

U1088 **Gateway** *(Illus.p.292)*
Ink, watercolour, bodycolour on paper
10.8 x 7
Signed
Bequeathed by H. Musgrave, 1922

U1089 **Windmill**
Watercolour, bodycolour on paper 20.7 x
15.4 (sight)
Signed
Bequeathed by H. Musgrave, 1922

MARTIN, John 1789-1854 (English)

U820 **Landscape with Dancing Figures (1820)**
(formerly 'Romantic Landscape')
(Illus.p.292)
Pencil, sepia on paper 21.3 x 17
Signed, dated
Purchased 1955

MARTIN, Kenneth 1905-84 (English)

U2281 **Chance and Order 12: Black (1973)**
(Illus.p.292)
Oil on canvas 121.9 x 121.9
Purchased 1974

MARTIN, Mary 1907-69 (English)

U1753 **Dispersal: On Black (1967)** *(Illus.p.292)*
Stainless steel, wood, formica 69.8 x 69.8
x 11.4
Signed, dated
Donated by the Contemporary Art
Society, 1972

MARTYN, Ferenc 1899-1986 (Hungarian)

U1762 **Abstract Composition** *(Illus.p.292)*
Watercolour, bodycolour on paper 29.8 x
40.4 (sight)
Signed
Donated by the Friends of the National
Collections of Ireland, 1972

U1763 **Abstract Composition**
Watercolour, pencil, bodycolour on paper
28.8 x 40 (sight)
Signed
Donated by the Friends of the National
Collections of Ireland, 1972

MASTER of the Female Half-Lengths fl.1520-40
(Flemish)

U1757 **Head of a Saint: possibly a Fragment of a
Nativity** *(Illus.p.292)*
Oil on panel 60.1 x 31.8
Purchased 1962

MASTER of the Legend of St. Catherine fl.1475-
1500 (Flemish)

U972 **Christ Disputing with the Doctors**
(Illus.p.292)
Oil on panel 67 x 34.1
Purchased 1970

MATEU, Assumpcio b.1952 (Spanish)

U4947 **Tres Fenestres (1992)** *(Illus.p.292)*
Mixed media on canvas 150 x 150
Signed, dated
Purchased 1992

MATSCHINSKY-DENNINGHOFF, Brigitte
b.1923 (German)

U959 **Horus II (1960)** *(Illus.p.293)*
Sculpture, welded steel 89.3 x 40.1 x
42.7
Purchased with the aid of a grant from
the Calouste Gulbenkian Foundation,
1963

MAY, J. Kelly 19th century (?) (British)

U1804 **Alexander Henderson**
Sculpture, marble bust, ht. 36.9

Signed
Donated by Messrs. Henderson and Co.,
1908

MAZE, Paul Lucien 1887-1979 (French, worked
in England)

U470 **Boulogne (1925-26)** *(Illus.p.293)*
Oil on canvas 50.4 x 65.3
Signed
Purchased (Lloyd Patterson Collection)
1933

MERCIÉ, Antonin 1845-1916 (French) (after)

U4851 **David with the Head of Goliath**
Sculpture, bronze, ht. 104.2
Signed
Purchased 1891

MESTROVIC, Ivan 1883-1962 (Yugoslavian)

U1760 **Sir John Lavery, RA, RHA, RSA 1856-
1941 (c.1925-26)** *(Illus.p.293)*
Sculpture, bronze bust, ht. 56.5
Donated by the sitter, 1931

METHUEN, Paul Ayshford, 4th Baron Methuen
1886-1974 (English)

U824 **Hampton Court (1942)** *(Illus.p.293)*
Ink, chalk on paper 45.2 x 70
Signed, dated
Donated by the Contemporary Art
Society, 1945

MICHELANGELO Buonarroti 1475-1564
(Italian) (after)

U1805 **Madonna and Child** (Cast of Bruges
Madonna)
Sculpture, plaster, ht. 127
Purchased 1890

MIDDLETON, Charles Collins 1878-1935
(English)

U591 **Off Dover**
Oil on canvas 41 x 61.5
Donated by Colin Middleton, 1949

MIDDLETON, Colin 1910-83 (Irish)

U357 **Tower with Bunting, Brugge (1965)**
Oil on board 91.3 x 91.7
Signed
Purchased 1966

U358 **Give Me to Drink (1949)** *(Illus.p.293)*
Oil on canvas 66 x 76.2
Signed
Donated by the Contemporary Art
Society, 1957

U359 **Camden Street I (1967)**
Oil on board 91 x 91.5
Signed
Purchased 1968

U360 **September Evening, Ballymote (1951)**
(Illus.p.293)
Oil on canvas 50.8 x 76.4
Signed, dated
Purchased 1954

U365 **Christ Androgyne (1943)** *(Illus.p.293)*

Oil on canvas 38.1 x 27.8
Signed, dated
Donated by M. Prescott, 1963

U582 **Coal Quay, Early Morning (1940)**
Oil on canvas 50.8 x 60.7
Signed, dated
Donated by the artist, 1943

U598 **Lagan: Annadale, October (1941)**
(Illus.p.293)
Oil on canvas 51 x 61.1
Signed, dated
Purchased 1943

U667 **Unknown (1936)**
Oil on canvas 50.3 x 40.5
Signed, dated
Provenance unknown

U1882 **Swan River, Sunset II (1972)** *(Illus.p.293)*
Gouache on paper 19.7 x 19.7 (sight)
Signed
Purchased 1973

U2452 **Dream of the Moth (1976-77)**
(Illus.p.294)
Oil on board 61 x 60.7
Signed, dated
Purchased 1977

U4690 **Barcelona Sonnet (1975)**
Ink on paper, a series of twelve drawings,
the largest 20 x 22.6, the smallest 16.5 x
17.6
Signed, dated
Donated by Mrs. Kate Middleton, 1985

U4728 **A Street Band (1926)**
Pencil on paper 18 x 20.5
Signed
Donated by Leslie Baxter, 1985

U4729 **A Punt on the Isis (1926)**
Pencil on paper 14.5 x 22
Signed, dated
Donated by Leslie Baxter, 1985

U4790 **Head (1938)** (formerly 'Untitled')*(Illus.p.294)*
Oil on board 31.7 x 15
Signed, dated
Bequeathed by Roberta and John Hewitt,
1987

U4791 **The Skylark**
Oil on canvas 27.7 x 38
Bequeathed by Roberta and John Hewitt,
1987

U4792 **If I Were a Blackbird (1941)**
Oil on canvas 50.7 x 61
Bequeathed by Roberta and John Hewitt,
1987

MIKULA, Stanislaus 20th century (Polish)

U1602 **Defence of Warsaw, September 1939
(1942)** *(Illus.p.294)*
Pastel on paper 67.9 x 101
Signed, dated
Donated by the artist, 1942

MILLAIS, Sir John Everett 1829-96 (English)

U825 **Studies**
Pencil on paper 26.9 x 23.2

Donated by J. H. Stirling, 1919

U2112 **Three Sketches of a Little Girl**
Pencil on paper 10.1 x 15.2
Signed
Donated by J. H. Stirling, 1919

MILLER, Captain Charles Keith fl. 1872-1901
(Scottish?)

U107 **The 'Walter H. Wilson' (1882)**
Oil on canvas 91.5 x 122
Signed
Provenance unknown

MILLER, William d.1779 (Irish)

U1267 **Rev. George Whitefield 1714-70,
Preaching in the Timber Yard at Lurgan,
12 July 1751** *(Illus.p.294)*
Gouache on paper 33 x 43.5
Purchased 1969

MISTRY, Dhruva b.1957 (Indian)

U4692 **Creature (1983)** *(Illus.p.294)*
Sculpture, painted plaster 156 x 151 x 40
Donated by the Contemporary Art
Society, 1986

MITCHELL, Joan 1926-92 (American)

U529 **Painting (1958)** *(Illus.p.294)*
Oil on canvas 101 x 90.8
Signed
Purchased 1964

MITCHELL, Thomas 1735-90 (English)

U4813 **A View of the River Boyne with
Gentlemen and Horses by a Statue to
William III in the Foreground, the Boyne
Obelisk beyond (1757)** *(Illus.p.294)*
Oil on canvas 106.8 x 175.5
Signed, dated
Purchased 1990

MOJOVIC, Dragen b.1942 (Yugoslavian)

U2521 **Solstitio I (1977)**
Pencil on paper 50 x 70
Signed, dated
Purchased 1977

MOLLOY, Joseph 1798-1877 (Irish)

U94 **Portrait of a Young Man (c.1820)**
(Illus.p.294)
Oil on canvas 73 x 59.7
Purchased 1895

U103 **Folkestone, Kent**
Oil on canvas on board 30.5 x 40.6
Purchased 1957

U104 **Tilbury Fort, River Thames** *(Illus.p.294)*
Oil on canvas on board 30.5 x 40.6
Purchased 1957

MONREAL, Alfonso b.1952 (Mexican, works in
Ireland)

U4821 **Tiananmen Woman** *(Illus.p.295)*
Oil on canvas 141 x 191
Purchased 1990

MONRO, Dr. Thomas 1759-1833 (British)

U826 **Sketch of Rural Scene**
Charcoal, watercolour on paper 19.4 x
27.3
Donated by Miss F. M. McTear, 1926

U1645 **Cottage and Figure**
Chalk on paper 16.4 x 21.9
Purchased 1939

U1646 **Landscape and Trees** *(Illus.p.295)*
Chalk, wash on paper 15.8 x 20.7
Purchased 1939

MONSELET, E. 19th-20th century (Belgian?)

U95 **Landscape with Sheep** *(Illus.p.295)*
Oil on canvas 46.7 x 38.7
Signed
Bequeathed by Mrs. E. Monteagle Brown,
1928

MONTÉZIN, Pierre Eugène 1874-1946 (French)

U57 **Hans Iten 1874-1930** *(Illus.p.295)*
Oil on canvas 119.4 x 76.8
Donated by Mrs. Hans Iten in memory of
her husband, 1933

U1685 **Sketch for Portrait of Hans Iten (U57)**
Oil, pencil on paper 34 x 24
Donated by Mrs. Hans Iten in memory of
her husband, 1933

MOON, Jeremy 1934-73 (English)

U693 **Crusader (1968)** *(Illus.p.295)*
Acrylic on canvas 248.6 x 247.8
Signed, dated
Purchased 1970

U5045 **Study for 'Crusader' (1968)**
Gouache, collage on paper 40.5 x 39.5
(sight)
Signed, dated
Donated by Ms. Ruth Bowman (per the
Charities Aid Foundation of America),
1997

MOONEY, Martin b.1960 (Irish)

U4841 **Arch** *(Illus.p.295)*
Oil on canvas 114.3 x 110.5
Purchased 1991

MOORE, Christopher 1790-1863 (Irish)

U1806 **James MacDonnell, MD 1764-1845
(1844)**
Sculpture, marble bust, ht.73.7
Signed, dated
Provenance unknown

U4966 **Sir Richard Griffith 1784-1878 (1859)**
(Illus.p.295)
Sculpture, marble bust, ht. 66
Signed, dated
Purchased 1993

MOORE, Henry 1898-1986 (English)

U962 **Working Model for 'Oval with Points'
(1968-69)** *(Illus.p.295)*
Sculpture, bronze 107.5 x 89 x 42; base
7.5 x 53.5 x 92
Signed

Purchased 1976

U2404 **Working Model for 'Three Piece Reclining Figure: Draped' (1975)**
(Illus.p.295)
Sculpture, bronze 63 x 102 x 63.5; base
6.2 x 111.8 x 70.2
Signed
Purchased 1976

MOORE, James, MD 1819-83 (Irish)
Most of the following works are as titled by the artist

U2305 **On the Way to the Ice House, Lady Annesley's Park, Newcastle, Co. Down (1872)**
Watercolour on paper 57.2 x 77.1
Signed, dated
Purchased 1975

U2536 **The Room in which Lord Edward Fitzgerald was Confined**
Pencil on paper 13.9 x 22.5
Provenance unknown

U2537 **Cave Hill, Co. Antrim (1880)**
Pencil on paper 17.8 x 26
Signed, dated
Provenance unknown

U2538 **Island Magee (1867)**
Ink, watercolour on paper 13.9 x 23.5
Dated
Provenance unknown

U2539 **Ballywilliam Gate, Donaghadee, Co. Down (1865)**
Ink, wash on paper 13.6 x 21.9
Signed, dated
Provenance unknown

U2540 **Lagan Lock (1868)**
Watercolour on paper 24.3 x 34.9
Dated
Provenance unknown

U2541 **The First Lock of the Lagan, Belfast (1860)**
Watercolour on paper 19 x 36.5
Dated
Provenance unknown

U2542 **The Lagan;** verso, **Annadale House from the Weir (1848)**
Watercolour on paper 24.2 x 36.8
Dated
Provenance unknown

U2543 **Ann Street, Belfast;** verso, **Fetherston's Corner (1881)**
Watercolour on paper 28.5 x 39
Dated
Provenance unknown

U2544 **Old Road, Belfast**
Watercolour on paper 30.5 x 35.2
Provenance unknown

U2546 **A House** (Annadale?)
Watercolour on paper 22.8 x 39.3
Provenance unknown

U2547 **Custom House Square**
Watercolour on paper 14.6 x 24.8
Provenance unknown

U2548 **Waring Street, Belfast (1880)**
Ink, watercolour on paper 25.4 x 35.6
Signed
Provenance unknown

U2549 **Corn Market, Ann Street, Belfast (1882)**
Ink, watercolour on paper 14.8 x 28.6
Dated
Provenance unknown

U2550 **Corn Market, Ann Street, Belfast (1882)**
Watercolour on paper 28.6 x 39.1
Dated
Provenance unknown

U2551 **Corporation Square**
Pencil, watercolour on paper 25.3 x 35.6
Provenance unknown

U2552 **Carrickfergus Shipyard (1877)**
Watercolour on paper 56.5 x 50.8
Signed, dated
Provenance unknown

U2667 **Paper Mill, Belfast (1850)**
Watercolour on paper 18.7 x 27.9
Dated
Provenance unknown

U2875 **Portpatrick (c.1836-37)**
Watercolour on paper 15 x 23.5
Dated
Provenance unknown

U2876 **Curran, Larne, Co. Antrim (1840)**
(Olderfleet Castle)
Watercolour on paper 11.8 x 18.8
Dated
Provenance unknown

U2877 **Fireplace, Curran, Larne (1840)**
Watercolour on paper 20.3 x 18.1
Dated
Provenance unknown

U2878 **From Fair Head (1840)** (Sunset or Sunrise Study)
Watercolour on paper 7 x 16.7
Dated
Provenance unknown

U2879 **Still Life with Vegetables, 8 Roxburgh Terrace, Edinburgh (1840)**
Watercolour on paper 18.5 x 27.2
Signed, dated
Provenance unknown

U2880 **Near Preston Pans (1841)**
Watercolour on paper 8.4 x 18.8
Dated
Provenance unknown

U2881 **St. Andrew's from the Edge of the Witch Lake (1841)**
Watercolour on paper 18.5 x 27
Dated
Provenance unknown

U2882 **Pulpit of John Knox in which he Preached before the Lords of the Congregation (1841)**
Watercolour on paper 27.5 x 19
Dated
Provenance unknown

U2883 **A Windmill (1841)**

Pencil, white on paper 13.3 x 16.9
Signed, dated
Provenance unknown

U2884 **Holywood Beach (1842)**
Ink, watercolour on paper 15.5 x 26.8
Dated
Provenance unknown

U2885 **Craigmillar Castle (1842)**
Watercolour on paper 18.6 x 27
Dated
Provenance unknown

U2886 **Embarkation of [Queen] Victoria 1st Viewed from the Beach near Granton [Edinburgh] (1842)**
Watercolour on paper 18.6 x 27.2
Dated
Provenance unknown

U2887 **Edinburgh from Queen's Park (1842)**
Watercolour on paper 18.4 x 26.5
Dated
Provenance unknown

U2888 **Farm Yard - Annadale, Co. Down (c.1842)**
Ink, watercolour on paper 16.2 x 26.5
Dated
Provenance unknown

U2889 **Drimleagh Castle, Co. Dublin (1843)**
Watercolour on paper 18.5 x 26.7
Dated
Provenance unknown

U2890 **Ballynahinch Spa (1844)**
Watercolour on paper 18.2 x 27
Dated
Provenance unknown

U2891 **Hill of Howth, Clontarf in the Distance (1844)**
Watercolour on paper 18.2 x 23.4
Dated
Provenance unknown

U2892 **Maynooth Castle (1844)**
Ink, watercolour on paper 18.5 x 26.8
Dated
Provenance unknown

U2893 **Old Bridge and Entrance Gate to Glenarm Castle (1844)** *(Illus.p.296)*
Watercolour on paper 18.1 x 27.1
Dated
Provenance unknown

U2894 **Glenarm (1844)**
Ink, watercolour on paper 18.4 x 27.5
Dated
Provenance unknown

U2895 **Glenarm from the Larne Old Road (1844)**
Watercolour on paper 18.2 x 26.9
Dated
Provenance unknown

U2896 **Giant's Causeway;** verso, **Port Moon (1844)**
Watercolour on paper 18.1 x 27.3
Dated
Provenance unknown

U2897 **Near Dunmurry (1844)**

Watercolour on paper 16 x 18.5
Dated
Provenance unknown

U2898 **Fishing Boats, Brighton (1845)**
Ink, watercolour on paper 27.5 x 18.8
Dated
Provenance unknown

U2899 **Rue de la Fontaine, Havre (1845)**
(Illus.p.296)
Ink, watercolour on paper 27.5 x 18.8
Dated
Provenance unknown

U2900 **Notre Dame, Paris (1845)**
Ink, watercolour on paper 18.9 x 27.6
Dated
Provenance unknown

U2901 **Baths on the Seine, Port Royal, Triumphal Arch of Napoleon, Chateau of the Tuileries, Paris, Evening (1845)**
Ink, watercolour on paper 18.6 x 27.3
Dated
Provenance unknown

U2902 **The Seine at St. Cloud Looking towards Sevres (1845)**
Ink, watercolour on paper 18.5 x 27.3
Dated
Provenance unknown

U2903 **The Garden at Versailles (1845)**
Ink, watercolour on paper 15.5 x 23.7
Dated
Provenance unknown

U2904 **Rotterdam (1845)**
Watercolour on paper 18.4 x 26.9
Dated
Provenance unknown

U2905 **Near Rotterdam (1845)**
Watercolour on paper 20.1 x 28.4
Dated
Provenance unknown

U2906 **The Church of St. Bavon, Ghent (1845)**
Ink, watercolour on paper 18.6 x 27.1
Dated
Provenance unknown

U2907 **Dover (1845)**
Watercolour on paper 14.4 x 24.9
Dated
Provenance unknown

U2908 **Macedon Point from Greencastle (1845)**
Watercolour on paper 15.6 x 23.7
Dated
Provenance unknown

U2909 **Cottage, Cavehill (1845)** *(Illus.p.296)*
Watercolour on paper 18.3 x 26.6
Dated
Provenance unknown

U2910 **Near Dunmurry (1845)** *(Illus.p.296)*
Ink, watercolour on paper 18.2 x 26.8
Dated
Provenance unknown

U2911 **Overflow on the Lagan above the Second Lock (1845)** *(Illus.p.296)*
Ink, watercolour on paper 23.2 x 33.3
Dated

Bequeathed by Mrs. Hannah Flanery, 1915

U2912 **Near Cockensie (1841)**
Watercolour on paper 8.7 x 18.9
Dated
Provenance unknown

U2913 **Richmond Hill (1846)**
Watercolour on paper 18.2 x 26.8
Dated
Provenance unknown

U2914 **Chateau, Dieppe (1846)**
Watercolour on paper 18.5 x 27.3
Dated
Provenance unknown

U2915 **Rouen from the Hill of St. Catherine (1846)**
Watercolour on paper 18.5 x 26.8
Dated
Provenance unknown

U2916 **Rouen (1846)**
Watercolour on paper 18.1 x 26.5
Dated
Provenance unknown

U2917 **In Rouen (1846)**
Watercolour on paper 18.8 x 27.2
Dated
Provenance unknown

U2918 **Fleetwood (1846)**
Watercolour on paper 17.5 x 27
Dated
Provenance unknown

U2919 **Coleraine Regatta (1847)**
Watercolour on paper 13.5 x 22.5
Dated
Provenance unknown

U2920 **Dumbarton (1848)**
Watercolour on paper 17.5 x 26
Dated
Provenance unknown

U2921 **Lough Erne from Craig Reagh (1848)**
Watercolour on paper 10.7 x 28.5
Dated
Provenance unknown

U2922 **Near Ballyleidy (1848?)** (Cottage near Clandeboye)
Watercolour on paper 11 x 19.9
Dated
Provenance unknown

U2923 **Strandtown Beach (1848)**
Watercolour on paper 10.6 x 22.4
Dated
Provenance unknown

U2924 **The Lagan (1848)** (Annadale)
Ink, watercolour on paper 18.6 x 27.2
Dated
Provenance unknown

U2925 **Folkestone, Kent;** verso, **Belfast Lough (1849)**
Watercolour on paper 17.7 x 24.3
Dated
Provenance unknown

U2926 **The Rhine at St. Goar (1849)**
Watercolour on paper 7.4 x 18.5

Dated
Provenance unknown

U2927 **Fairhead from Murlough Bay (1849)** (Fair Head)
Watercolour on paper 15.3 x 18.3
Dated
Provenance unknown

U2928 **Giant's Ring, Ballylesson, Co. Down (1849)**
Watercolour on paper 10.4 x 18
Dated
Provenance unknown

U2929 **Kempe Stones, Dundonald, Co. Down (1849)** (Kempe Stone)
Watercolour on paper 12.4 x 18.8
Dated
Provenance unknown

U2930 **Road at Barnhill, Comber (1850)**
Ink, watercolour on paper 26.9 x 18.9
Dated
Provenance unknown

U2931 **Buxton (1850)**
Watercolour on paper 10.9 x 18.8
Dated
Provenance unknown

U2932 **The Bathing Place, Dunleady (1850)**
Ink, watercolour on paper 26.9 x 21.3
Dated
Provenance unknown

U2933 **Last Overflow of the Lagan (1850)**
Watercolour on paper 9.2 x 27.2
Dated
Provenance unknown

U2934 **Cloughmore, Co. Down (1852)**
Watercolour on paper 18.1 x 26.9
Dated
Provenance unknown

U2935 **Round Tower, Armoy, near Ballycastle, Co. Antrim (1852)**
Watercolour on paper 17.8 x 17.6
Dated
Provenance unknown

U2936 **The Granny Rock, Ballycastle (1852)**
Watercolour on paper 17.7 x 26.9
Dated
Provenance unknown

U2937 **Maze (1852)**
Ink, watercolour on paper 12.5 x 18.2
Dated
Provenance unknown

U2938 **The Long Hole, Ireland's Eye/where Mrs Kirwin (sic) was Found Murdered (1853)**
Watercolour on paper 12.4 x 17.3
Dated
Provenance unknown

U2939 **Foot of High Street, Belfast, Site of the New Custom House (1854)**
Ink, watercolour on paper 18.3 x 27
Dated
Provenance unknown

U2940 **Granny Cairn or Graves - Townland of Craigarogan, Templepatrick, Co. Antrim**

(1854)
Watercolour on paper 12.1 x 17.8
Dated
Provenance unknown

U2941 **Entrance to Harbour of Havre (1855)**
Watercolour on paper 18.2 x 27.4
Dated
Provenance unknown

U2942 **Glenarm (1856)**
Ink, watercolour on paper 11.9 x 18.5
Dated
Provenance unknown

U2943 **Greenwich (1859)**
Watercolour on paper 12.8 x 17.7
Dated
Provenance unknown

U2944 **Newcastle, Evening (1859)**
Watercolour on paper 10.2 x 27.3
Signed, dated
Provenance unknown

U2945 **Greencastle, Carlingford Lough (1861)**
Watercolour on paper 14.5 x 27.2
Dated
Provenance unknown

U2946 **Greencastle, Carlingford Bay (1861)**
Watercolour on paper 12 x 17.2
Dated
Provenance unknown

U2947 **From the Broken Mountain, Mourne Range Looking towards Carlingford (1861)**
Watercolour on paper 20.8 x 27
Dated
Provenance unknown

U2948 **Newcastle Pier (1862)**
Ink, watercolour on paper 19.3 x 28.1
Signed, dated
Provenance unknown

U2949 **Prince Charlie's Point, Glencolumkille, Co. Donegal (1862)**
Watercolour on paper 11.7 x 23.9
Dated
Provenance unknown

U2950 **Miner's Cottage near Buxton (1863)**
Ink, watercolour on paper 12.4 x 17.2
Dated
Provenance unknown

U2951 **New Embankment, Hungerford, Thames, London (Morning) (1865)**
Watercolour on paper 13.7 x 22
Dated
Provenance unknown

U2952 **Castlerock, Co. Derry (1866)**
Watercolour on paper 17.5 x 25.3
Dated
Provenance unknown

U2953 **Dog Leap, Newtownlimavady, Co. Derry (1866)**
Watercolour on paper 18.9 x 27.4
Dated
Provenance unknown

U2954 **Antrim (1867)**
Watercolour on paper 13.7 x 22.6

Dated
Provenance unknown

U2955 **Reginald's Tower, Waterford (1868)**
Ink, watercolour on paper 13.3 x 22.5
Dated
Provenance unknown

U2956 **Saint Audoen's Gate, Dublin (1868)**
Watercolour on paper 17.7 x 25.3
Dated
Provenance unknown

U2957 **Bangor Regatta (1868)**
Watercolour on paper 13.4 x 22.6
Dated
Provenance unknown

U2958 **Maze Race Course (1868)**
Ink, watercolour on paper 10.3 x 22.6
Dated
Provenance unknown

U2959 **Derby (1869)** (Epsom)
Watercolour on paper 10 x 22.8
Dated
Provenance unknown

U2960 **Newcastle (1871)**
Watercolour on paper 13.2 x 22.5
Dated
Provenance unknown

U2961 **The Old Buildings, South Kensington Museum (1877)**
Ink, watercolour on paper 18.8 x 28.3
Signed, dated
Provenance unknown

U2962 **Kemp Stones, Dundonald, Co. Down (1877)** (Kempe Stone)
Watercolour on paper 17.5 x 24.7
Signed, dated
Provenance unknown

U2963 **Hampstead Heath (1879)** (Sunset Study)
Watercolour on paper 11.1 x 17.5
Dated
Provenance unknown

U2964 **From Fleetwood Steamer, Morning (1880)**
Crayon on paper 17.6 x 24.6
Dated
Provenance unknown

U2965 **Grey Abbey, Co. Down (1880)** (Greyabbey)
Watercolour on paper 25 x 17.6
Dated
Provenance unknown

U2966 **Annadale (1880)**
Bodycolour on paper 78.3 x 56.7
Donated by F. D. McIlwaine, 1949

U2967 **Oxygen Gas Works, Adelphi Arches, London (1881)**
Watercolour on paper 17.5 x 25.5
Signed, dated
Provenance unknown

U2968 **Cleopatra's Needle, Adelphi Arches, London (1881)**
Watercolour on paper 17.6 x 25.4
Signed, dated
Provenance unknown

U2969 **Eel Weir, Toome Bridge (1881)**
Watercolour on paper 17.5 x 25.3
Signed, dated
Provenance unknown

U2970 **London. Below the Adelphi Arches (1882)**
Ink, watercolour on paper 17.5 x 25.1
Signed, dated
Provenance unknown

U2971 **Slieve Bernagh from the Trassey Bog, Mourne Mountains** (Bearnagh) *(Illus.p.296)*
Watercolour, bodycolour on paper 57.2 x 77.4
Donated by subscribers (per Sir Charles Brett), 1907

U2972 **Carlin's Steps, near Glenarm**
Watercolour on paper 18.4 x 25.8
Provenance unknown

U2973 **Antonia at Annadale**
Watercolour on paper 28 x 21
Provenance unknown

U2974 **Ballywalter, Co. Down**
Watercolour on paper 13.6 x 22.2
Provenance unknown

U2975 **Bangor**
Watercolour on paper 14.3 x 18.5
Provenance unknown

U2976 **Belfast from Newtownbreda**
Watercolour on paper 18.5 x 25.8
Provenance unknown

U2977 **The Sham Fight at Scarva** *(Illus.p.296)*
Watercolour, bodycolour on paper 18 x 26
Provenance unknown

U2978 **Paris Ratcatcher**
Ink, watercolour on paper 13.9 x 11.2
Provenance unknown

U2979 **Duddingston Loch (1837)**
Watercolour on paper 18 x 27.2
Dated
Provenance unknown

U2980 **Holyrood Dairy, Edinburgh (1838)**
Pencil on paper 13 x 22
Dated
Provenance unknown

U2981 **John Knox's House, Edinburgh (1838)**
Pencil on paper 19.6 x 13.9
Dated
Provenance unknown

U2982 **Waterfall at Glendalough (1839)**
Pencil, ink, wash, white on paper 23.5 x 18.2
Dated
Provenance unknown

U2983 **White Horse Close, Edinburgh (1839)**
Pencil on paper 15.8 x 24.5
Dated
Provenance unknown

U2984 **Ruins of an Amphitheatre (?) (1839)**
Pencil on paper 16.5 x 25.8
Dated
Provenance unknown

U2985 **On the Water of Leith, Craiglockart (1840)**
Watercolour on paper 20 x 17.7
Dated
Provenance unknown

U2986 **The Antrim Headlands from near Larne (1840)**
Watercolour on paper 18.5 x 27
Dated
Provenance unknown

U2987 **Dunluce Castle (1840)**
Watercolour on paper 18.8 x 27.5
Dated
Provenance unknown

U2988 **Roslyn Castle (1840)**
Watercolour on paper 18.3 x 27.2
Dated
Provenance unknown

U2989 **Sunset, Craiglockhart, Edinburgh (1840)**
Watercolour on paper 18.4 x 27
Dated
Provenance unknown

U2990 **Edinburgh (1840)** (from the Braid Hills)
Watercolour on paper 17.2 x 26.5
Dated
Provenance unknown

U2991 **Wallace Cave, Hawthornden (1840)**
Watercolour on paper 12 x 18.6
Dated
Provenance unknown

U2992 **Samson's Ribs, Arthur's Seat, Edinburgh (1841)**
Watercolour on paper 18.6 x 26.9
Dated
Provenance unknown

U2993 **Near Innerleithen (1841)**
Watercolour on paper 7.7 x 18.5
Dated
Provenance unknown

U2994 **Tolbooth, Musselburgh (1841)**
Pencil on paper 18.9 x 27.5
Dated
Provenance unknown

U2995 **Gosford House, Firth of Forth (1841)**
Watercolour on paper 5.8 x 18.8
Dated
Provenance unknown

U2996 **Near Preston Pans (1841)**
Watercolour on paper 8 x 19
Dated
Provenance unknown

U2997 **Edinburgh (1841)** (Arthur's Seat and Craigmillar Castle)
Watercolour on paper 18.2 x 27.2
Dated
Provenance unknown

U2998 **Effie Dean's House, King's Park, Edinburgh (1841)**
Watercolour on paper 16 x 21.5
Dated
Provenance unknown

U2999 **Cairnworth's Walls, Raloo, Co. Antrim - Cave in Tom Sullivan's Land (1841)**
Watercolour on paper 13.9 x 20.6
Dated
Provenance unknown

U3000 **Fin MacCool's Grave (1841)** (The Giant, Finn McCool)
Watercolour on paper 18.5 x 27.5
Dated
Provenance unknown

U3001 **Rocking Stone, Brown's Bay, Islandmagee (1841)** (Island Magee)
Watercolour on paper 13.6 x 20
Dated
Provenance unknown

U3002 **Fin MacCool's Grave, between Larne and Glenarm (1841)**
Watercolour on paper 18.2 x 26.8
Dated
Provenance unknown

U3003 **Standing Stone near the Headless Cross, Parish of Cairncastle, Co. Antrim (1841)**
Watercolour on paper 13.3 x 18.7
Dated
Provenance unknown

U3004 **Curran, Larne (1841)**
Watercolour on paper 18.4 x 26.4
Dated
Provenance unknown

U3005 **Mountain Scene (1841)**
Watercolour on paper 10.5 x 16.6
Signed, dated
Provenance unknown

U3006 **Near Larkhill (1841)** (Study of a Tree)
Watercolour on paper 27 x 18.5
Dated
Provenance unknown

U3007 **Castle of St. Andrew's (1841)**
Watercolour on paper 18.8 x 27.3
Dated
Provenance unknown

U3008 **Cathedral of St. Andrew's (1841)**
Watercolour on paper 27.5 x 19
Dated
Provenance unknown

U3009 **View of St. Andrew's from Old City Wall (1841)**
Watercolour on paper 18.3 x 26
Dated
Provenance unknown

U3010 **Craigmillar, Edinburgh (1841)**
Watercolour on paper 18.4 x 26.8
Dated
Provenance unknown

U3011 **Two Studies of Sunsets (1841-42)**
Watercolour on paper 27.2 x 20.7
Dated
Provenance unknown

U3012 **Hawthornden (1842)**
Watercolour on paper 12.2 x 18
Dated
Provenance unknown

U3013 **Roslyn Glen (1842)**
Watercolour on paper 27.3 x 18.8
Dated

Provenance unknown

U3014 **Craigmillar Castle (1842)**
Watercolour on paper 18.8 x 26.8
Dated
Provenance unknown

U3015 **Craigmillar Castle (1842)**
Watercolour on paper 18.5 x 27.1
Dated
Provenance unknown

U3016 **Below Bridge of Allan (1842)**
Watercolour on paper 17.5 x 25.1
Dated
Provenance unknown

U3017 **Devil's Mill (1842)**
Watercolour on paper 18.8 x 27.3
Dated
Provenance unknown

U3018 **Stirling Castle from Bruce's Stone, Bannockburn (1842)**
Watercolour on paper 17.5 x 25
Dated
Provenance unknown

U3019 **Loch Leven Castle (1842)**
Watercolour on paper 15.2 x 24.8
Signed, dated
Provenance unknown

U3020 **New Charleston, Firth of Forth (1842)**
Watercolour on paper 16.4 x 26.3
Dated
Provenance unknown

U3021 **Leith (1842)**
Watercolour on paper 15.3 x 25.1
Dated
Provenance unknown

U3022 **Duddingston Loch (1842)**
Watercolour on paper 17.5 x 25
Dated
Provenance unknown

U3023 **Craigie Hall Near Edinburgh (1842)**
Watercolour on paper 18.5 x 27
Dated
Provenance unknown

U3024 **Richmond Hill (1842)**
Watercolour on paper 17.8 x 28.7
Dated
Provenance unknown

U3025 **Blackhead, Glenarm (1842)**
Watercolour on paper 18.8 x 27.2
Dated
Provenance unknown

U3026 **Castle Ruins Perched on a Rock (1842)**
Pencil, white on paper 13.7 x 18.5
Signed, dated
Provenance unknown

U3027 **Edinburgh from Braid Hills (1842)**
Watercolour on paper 17 x 26.5
Dated
Provenance unknown

U3028 **Duddingston Loch. Scene from Arthur's Seat, Samson's Ribs (1843)**
Watercolour on paper 18.4 x 26.8
Dated
Provenance unknown

U3029 **Firth of Forth from Corstorphine Hill (1843)**
Watercolour on paper 17.7 x 26.6
Dated
Provenance unknown

U3030 **Craiglockhart and the Pentland Hills (1843)**
Watercolour on paper 15.9 x 29.7
Dated
Provenance unknown

U3031 **Craiglockhart, on the Water of Leith near Slateford (1843)**
Watercolour on paper 24 x 18.4
Dated
Provenance unknown

U3032 **Glynn Abbey (1843)** (Larne)
Ink, watercolour on paper 35.3 x 26.8
Dated
Provenance unknown

U3033 **Artane Chapel (1843)**
Ink, watercolour on paper 27.2 x 18.4
Dated
Provenance unknown

U3034 **The Abbey, Malahide (1843)**
Watercolour on paper 27.2 x 36.7
Signed, dated
Provenance unknown

U3035 **Laggan (1843)** (River Lagan) (Study of Weeds)
Watercolour on paper 17.5 x 25.6
Signed, dated
Provenance unknown

U3036 **Bangor (1843)** (Lobster Pots)
Watercolour on paper 9.8 x 18.5
Dated
Provenance unknown

U3037 **Bangor (Old Pump) (1843)**
Watercolour on paper 17 x 13
Dated
Provenance unknown

U3038 **Salt Pans, Bangor (1843)**
Watercolour on paper 18.1 x 25.9
Dated
Provenance unknown

U3039 **Ballyclochan, near Bangor (1843)**
Watercolour on paper 17.1 x 24.9
Dated
Provenance unknown

U3040 **Bangor (1843)**
Watercolour on paper 9.3 x 18.4
Dated
Provenance unknown

U3041 **Bangor Bay (1843)**
Watercolour on paper 18.3 x 26.4
Dated
Provenance unknown

U3042 **The Salt Pans, Bangor (1844)**
Watercolour on paper 18.3 x 27
Dated
Provenance unknown

U3043 **Luke's Point, Bangor (1844)**
Watercolour on paper 16.2 x 24.7
Dated

Provenance unknown

U3044 **Howth Head (1844)**
Watercolour on paper 18.3 x 26.7
Dated
Provenance unknown

U3045 **Dalkey Island from Killiney (1844)**
Watercolour on paper 18.5 x 27
Dated
Provenance unknown

U3046 **Shane's Castle (1844)**
Watercolour on paper 18 x 26.7
Dated
Provenance unknown

U3047 **Fair Head and Drumakell (1844)**
Watercolour on paper 18.3 x 27.2
Dated
Provenance unknown

U3048 **Doon Point, Rathlin (1844)**
Watercolour on paper 18.1 x 27.4
Dated
Provenance unknown

U3049 **Bruce's Castle, Rathlin (1844)**
Watercolour on paper 18.5 x 26.1
Dated
Provenance unknown

U3050 **Kenban Castle, Co. Antrim (1844)** (Kenbane)
Ink, watercolour on paper 18 x 26.9
Signed, dated
Provenance unknown

U3051 **Carrick-a-Rede, Co. Antrim (1844)**
Watercolour on paper 17.8 x 26.2
Dated
Provenance unknown

U3052 **The Stack, Benandonar, Port Moon, Co. Antrim (1844)**
Watercolour on paper 18.1 x 26.2
Dated
Provenance unknown

U3053 **Giant's Causeway (1844)**
Watercolour on paper 19.6 x 27.9
Dated
Provenance unknown

U3054 **Beann Marga Church, Ballycastle (1844)** (Bonamargy Friary)
Ink, watercolour on paper 13.2 x 18.7
Dated
Provenance unknown

U3055 **Trinity College Church, Edinburgh (1845)**
Watercolour on paper 26.8 x 18.3
Dated
Provenance unknown

U3056 **Descent to the Crypt, Roslyn Chapel (1845)**
Pencil, watercolour on paper 53.4 x 39.9
Signed, dated
Provenance unknown

U3057 **On the Beach at Brighton (1845)**
Ink, watercolour on paper 18 x 27.7
Dated
Provenance unknown

U3058 **Brighton (1845)**

Ink, watercolour on paper 16 x 11.2
Dated
Provenance unknown

U3059 **Doorway in Shoreham (1845)**
Ink, watercolour on paper 13.2 x 10
Dated
Provenance unknown

U3060 **Kingston Harbour, Shoreham, Havre Packet Station (1845)**
Ink, watercolour on paper 16.2 x 25
Dated
Provenance unknown

U3061 **Gate of the Chateau of Hougoumont (1845)**
Pencil on paper 15.1 x 25.5
Signed, dated
Provenance unknown

U3062 **The Field of Waterloo (1845)**
Pencil on paper 15.7 x 24.4
Signed, dated
Provenance unknown

U3063 **Near Rotterdam (1845)**
Ink, watercolour on paper 16.4 x 25
Dated
Provenance unknown

U3064 **The Hague from the Amsterdam Railway Station (1845)**
Ink on paper 15.7 x 23.8
Dated
Provenance unknown

U3065 **Amsterdam near The Hague Railway Station (1845)**
Pencil on paper 15.8 x 24.5
Dated
Provenance unknown

U3066 **Near Rotterdam (1845)**
Watercolour on paper 9.8 x 25
Dated
Provenance unknown

U3067 **Near Whiteabbey (1845)**
Ink, watercolour on paper 16.5 x 25
Dated
Provenance unknown

U3068 **Groomsport (1845)**
Ink, watercolour on paper 18.5 x 27
Dated
Provenance unknown

U3069 **Near Salt Pans, Bangor (1845)**
Ink, watercolour on paper 27 x 18.4
Dated
Provenance unknown

U3070 **Fleetwood (1845)**
Ink, watercolour on paper 18.4 x 26.7
Dated
Provenance unknown

U3071 **Windermere Lake (1845)**
Watercolour on paper 18.3 x 27
Dated
Provenance unknown

U3072 **Grasmere Water, Cumberland (1845)**
Watercolour on paper 18.3 x 27.2
Dated
Provenance unknown

U3073 **Rydal Water, Cumberland (1845)**
Watercolour on paper 18.3 x 26.4
Dated
Provenance unknown

U3074 **Blackpool, Lancashire (1845)**
Ink, watercolour on paper 18.2 x 27
Dated
Provenance unknown

U3075 **Ballyholme Bay (1845)**
Ink, watercolour on paper 18.5 x 26.8
Dated
Provenance unknown

U3076 **Near Holywood (1845)**
Watercolour on paper 13.5 x 18.8
Dated
Provenance unknown

U3077 **Lagan Lock at Russell's (1845)**
Watercolour on paper 16.5 x 25.2
Dated
Provenance unknown

U3078 **Ward's Cottage, Lagan (1845)**
Watercolour on paper 18.3 x 26.7
Dated
Provenance unknown

U3079 **Woman with Baby and Donkey with Panniers Carrying Two Children (1845)**
Watercolour on paper 10.4 x 16.5
Dated
Provenance unknown

U3080 **Man with Donkey Carrying Two Children in Panniers (1845)**
Watercolour on paper 11.3 x 17
Dated
Provenance unknown

U3081 **Ballyholme Strand (1846)**
Watercolour on paper 13.5 x 20.3
Dated
Provenance unknown

U3082 **Greenwich (1846)**
Ink, watercolour on paper 18.5 x 26.6
Dated
Provenance unknown

U3083 **Richmond Hill (1846)**
Ink, watercolour on paper 18 x 26.3
Dated
Provenance unknown

U3084 **Richmond (1846)**
Ink, watercolour on paper 15.5 x 26.4
Dated
Provenance unknown

U3085 **Chateau d'Arques, Normandy (1846)**
Watercolour on paper 18.1 x 26.5
Dated
Provenance unknown

U3086 **Rouen (1846)**
Watercolour on paper 17.9 x 27.3
Dated
Provenance unknown

U3087 **Daventry (1846)**
Ink, watercolour on paper 17.3 x 27.1
Dated
Provenance unknown

U3088 **Madman's Hole, Collin Glen (1846)**
(Colin Glen, Belfast)
Watercolour on paper 18.5 x 27
Dated
Provenance unknown

U3089 **Fair Head from Ballycastle (1846)**
Watercolour on paper 18.4 x 27.5
Dated
Provenance unknown

U3090 **Armour's Hole, Newcastle, Co. Down; verso, Barges, Fleetwood (1846)**
Watercolour on paper 27.7 x 19.2
Dated
Provenance unknown

U3091 **First Weir, Lagan, Annadale (1846)**
Watercolour on paper 17 x 27.8
Dated
Provenance unknown

U3092 **Edinburgh Castle from Greyfriars (1847)**
Watercolour on paper 13.7 x 23
Dated
Provenance unknown

U3093 **Two Views of Kenilworth Castle; verso, Sketch View (1847)**
Pencil on paper 27.6 x 18.9
Dated
Provenance unknown

U3094 **The Lothians (1847)** (View from Arthur's Seat)
Watercolour on paper 10.8 x 17.5
Dated
Provenance unknown

U3095 **Below Greenwich (1847)**
Watercolour on paper 18.1 x 27.3
Dated
Provenance unknown

U3096 **Tollymore Park, Bryansford (the Pool in which Dr. Hunter's Daughter was Drowned) (1847)**
Watercolour on paper 18.6 x 27.2
Dated
Provenance unknown

U3097 **Holywood, Sunset (1848)**
Watercolour on paper 14.9 x 30
Dated
Provenance unknown

U3098 **Holywood Pier (?) Sunset (1848)**
Watercolour on paper 13.4 x 20.7
Dated
Provenance unknown

U3099 **Blackpool, Lancashire (1848)** (Donkeys)
Pencil, ink on paper 9.4 x 18.9
Dated
Provenance unknown

U3100 **Devenish, Lough Erne (1848)**
Ink, watercolour on paper 17.3 x 26.5
Dated
Provenance unknown

U3101 **Devenish (1848)**
Ink, watercolour on paper 19.2 x 16.7
Dated
Provenance unknown

U3102 **The Grand Trianon, Versailles (1849)**
Watercolour on paper 8.4 x 17
Dated
Provenance unknown

U3103 **Folkestone, Kent (1849)**
Watercolour on paper 17.4 x 24.8
Dated
Provenance unknown

U3104 **Folkestone (1849)** (Fishing Boat)
Ink, watercolour on paper 14.2 x 18.4
Dated
Provenance unknown

U3105 **Triumphal Arch, Paris (1849)** (Champs-Elysées)
Ink, watercolour on paper 26.2 x 18.4
Dated
Provenance unknown

U3106 **Versailles Garden (1849)**
Watercolour on paper 18.5 x 14.5
Dated
Provenance unknown

U3107 **The Cathedral, Amiens (1849)**
Ink, watercolour on paper 26.5 x 21.7
Dated
Provenance unknown

U3108 **The King's Palace from the Park, Brussels (1849)**
Watercolour on paper 18 x 18.7
Dated
Provenance unknown

U3109 **Mayence (1849)**
Ink, watercolour on paper 18.7 x 17.6
Dated
Provenance unknown

U3110 **The Rhine at St. Goar with the Castle of Rheinfels (1849)**
Watercolour on paper 18.3 x 26.1
Dated
Provenance unknown

U3111 **The Lurlei, above St. Goar, on the Rhine (1849)**
Watercolour on paper 17.4 x 26.7
Dated
Provenance unknown

U3112 **Strangford Lough from Slievnagridle (1849)**
Watercolour on paper 15 x 27
Dated
Provenance unknown

U3113 **Bangor (1849)**
Watercolour on paper 6.6 x 16.2
Dated
Provenance unknown

U3114 **Bangor (1849)**
Watercolour on paper 10.4 x 16.3
Dated
Provenance unknown

U3115 **Bangor (1849)**
Watercolour on paper 10 x 16.3
Dated
Provenance unknown

U3116 **Bangor (1849)**
Watercolour on paper 18.1 x 26.4

Dated
Provenance unknown

U3117 **Ben Vien, Murloch Bay, Fair Head, Co. Antrim (1849) (Murlough)**
Watercolour on paper 11.4 x 18.5
Dated
Provenance unknown

U3118 **Chimney Tops, from Giant's Causeway (1849)**
Watercolour on paper 17.8 x 25.8
Dated
Provenance unknown

U3119 **Holywood (1849) (Pier)**
Watercolour on paper 18.2 x 27.4
Dated
Provenance unknown

U3120 **Kempe Stones, Dundonald (1849)** (Kempe Stone)
Watercolour on paper 14.8 x 19.1
Dated
Provenance unknown

U3121 **Kempe Stones, Dundonald, Co. Down (1849)**
Sepia wash on paper 11.8 x 18.7
Dated
Provenance unknown

U3122 **Cultra, Co. Down (1849)**
Ink, watercolour on paper 18 x 26.8
Dated
Provenance unknown

U3123 **Lagan (1849)**
Watercolour on paper 8.9 x 19.5
Dated
Provenance unknown

U3124 **Rostrevor (1849)**
Watercolour on paper 17.1 x 26.4
Dated
Provenance unknown

U3125 **Craig A Vad (1850)** (Craigavad, Co. Down)
Watercolour on paper 13.1 x 18.2
Dated
Provenance unknown

U3126 **St. Peter's, Derby (Clergyman a Goth) (1850)**
Watercolour on paper 17.4 x 25.8
Dated
Provenance unknown

U3127 **Haddon Hall (1850)**
Watercolour on paper 16.2 x 12.8
Dated
Provenance unknown

U3128 **Matlock, Derbyshire (1850)**
Watercolour on paper 18.6 x 26.6
Dated
Provenance unknown

U3129 **Holywood (1850)**
Watercolour on paper 18.4 x 27.6
Dated
Provenance unknown

U3130 **Kempe Stones, Dundonald, Co. Down (1850)**
Watercolour on paper 9.1 x 15.2

Dated
Provenance unknown

U3131 **Groomsport (1852)**
Watercolour on paper 16.6 x 25.8
Dated
Provenance unknown

U3132 **Carlingford Mountains from the Woodhouse (1852)**
Watercolour on paper 15.6 x 26.9
Dated
Provenance unknown

U3133 **The Woodhouse near Rostrevor (1852)**
Watercolour on paper 15.4 x 16.7
Dated
Provenance unknown

U3134 **Caves and Castle, Red Bay, Cushendall, Co. Antrim (1852)**
Watercolour on paper 16.7 x 26.7
Dated
Provenance unknown

U3135 **The Granny Rock, Ballycastle (1852)**
Watercolour on paper 14.3 x 19.2
Dated
Provenance unknown

U3136 **Fair Head, from the Salt Pans (1852)**
Watercolour on paper 17.2 x 36.8
Dated
Provenance unknown

U3137 **Dunseverick Castle, Co. Antrim (1852)**
Watercolour on paper 18.8 x 26.8
Dated
Provenance unknown

U3138 **Fair Head (1852)**
Watercolour on paper 15.4 x 27.7
Dated
Provenance unknown

U3139 **Carrick More, Fair Head (1852)**
Watercolour on paper 17.7 x 27.2
Dated
Provenance unknown

U3140 **Sunset Study, Fair Head, Ballycastle (1852)**
Watercolour on paper 8.8 x 19.3
Dated
Provenance unknown

U3141 **Glenariff (1852)**
Ink, watercolour on paper 17.1 x 26.8
Dated
Provenance unknown

U3142 **Site of New Customs House - Foot of Waring Street, Belfast (1854)**
Ink, watercolour on paper 17.4 x 27.2
Dated
Provenance unknown

U3143 **Site of the New Custom House, Lower Part of Waring St. Store Lane (c.1854)** (Belfast)
Ink, watercolour on paper 17.8 x 26.3
Provenance unknown

U3144 **The Woodhouse, Rostrevor (1854)**
Watercolour on paper 12.5 x 17.8
Dated
Provenance unknown

U3145 **Donegall Quay (c.1854)**
Ink, watercolour on paper 17.8 x 27
Provenance unknown

U3146 **Fruit Stall Woman, Paris (1855)**
Ink, watercolour on paper 13.8 x 18.6
Dated
Provenance unknown

U3147 **Asniéres (1855)**
Watercolour on paper 18.3 x 27.2
Dated
Provenance unknown

U3148 **Sydenham (1855)** (Cedar of Lebanon)
Ink, watercolour on paper 13 x 18.5
Dated
Provenance unknown

U3149 **Glenarm, after a Storm; Seaweed being Driven in (1856)**
Ink, watercolour on paper 12.8 x 17.8
Dated
Provenance unknown

U3150 **Glenarm Castle (1856)** (with Nurse)
Ink, watercolour on paper 25.6 x 36.5
Dated
Provenance unknown

U3151 **The White Rocks, Portrush (1856)**
Watercolour on paper 15.4 x 18.7
Dated
Provenance unknown

U3152 **Ballyreagh Castle, Portrush (1856)**
Watercolour on paper 19.2 x 26.8
Dated
Provenance unknown

U3153 **Whin Dyke, Port Moon, Causeway (1857)**
Watercolour on paper 17.7 x 12.8
Dated
Provenance unknown

U3154 **Port Moon - Giant's Causeway (1857)** (Sunset)
Watercolour on paper 12.5 x 17.5
Dated
Provenance unknown

U3155 **Nurse and Child, Pleaskin, Giant's Causeway (1857)**
Watercolour on paper 18.3 x 26.9
Dated
Provenance unknown

U3156 **Ardrossan (1858)**
Ink, watercolour on paper 17.7 x 12.8
Signed, dated
Provenance unknown

U3157 **The Ivy Bridge, Bryansford (1858)**
Watercolour on paper 18.2 x 26.6
Dated
Provenance unknown

U3158 **At Cushendall (1858)**
Watercolour on paper 12.7 x 17.6
Dated
Provenance unknown

U3159 **The Traitor's Gate from the Bloody Tower, London (1859)**
Ink, watercolour on paper 26.7 x 20.3
Dated

Provenance unknown

U3160 Jersey – 'Havre des Pas' (1859)
Watercolour on paper 16.6 x 27.1
Dated
Provenance unknown

U3161 Eagle Mountain, Mourne Mountains
(1859)
Watercolour on paper 12.7 x 17.7
Dated
Provenance unknown

U3162 White Rocks, Co. Antrim, Dunluce
Castle (1861)
Watercolour on paper 13.6 x 22.2
Dated
Provenance unknown

U3163 Cross in Kilbroney Churchyard,
Rostrevor
Watercolour on paper 14 x 9.3
Dated
Provenance unknown

U3164 Top of the Broken Mountain, Mourne
(1862)
Watercolour on paper 13.5 x 22.1
Signed, dated
Provenance unknown

U3165 In Carrickfergus Jail (1862)
Ink, watercolour on paper 25 x 17.3
Signed, dated
Provenance unknown

U3166 Hampton Court (1862)
Watercolour on paper 13.4 x 22
Dated
Provenance unknown

U3167 Greenwich (1863)
Ink, watercolour on paper 13.6 x 22.3
Dated
Provenance unknown

U3168 Haddon Hall (1863)
Watercolour on paper 17.3 x 12.5
Dated
Provenance unknown

U3169 Newcastle (1864)
Watercolour on paper 13.6 x 22
Dated
Provenance unknown

U3170 Stratford on Avon (1864) (Church)
Watercolour on paper 18.8 x 15.2
Dated
Provenance unknown

U3171 The Guild Chapel and Falcon Tavern,
Stratford-upon-Avon (1864)
Ink, watercolour on paper 18.6 x 25
Signed, dated
Provenance unknown

U3172 Anne Hathaway's Cottage (1864)
Watercolour on paper 15 x 25.2
Dated
Provenance unknown

U3173 Castle Kennedy, Stranraer (1864)
Watercolour on paper 12.4 x 19.5
Signed, dated
Provenance unknown

U3174 Mourne Mountains from Terilla - where

the 'Great Britain' Stranded (1864)
(Tyrella, Co. Down)
Watercolour on paper 14.8 x 26.7
Signed, dated
Provenance unknown

U3175 Mourne Mountains (1864)
Watercolour on paper 13.6 x 21.8
Dated
Provenance unknown

U3176 Ruins of St. John the Baptist's Church,
Chester (1864); verso, Mourne
Mountains near Hilltown, Co. Down
(1865)
Pencil on paper 13.7 x 21.2
Dated
Provenance unknown

U3177 Foot of Northumberland Street, Strand,
London, now being Filled up by the New
Embankment (1865)
Ink, watercolour on paper 13.6 x 22
Signed, dated
Provenance unknown

U3178 St. Giles', Cripplegate, London (c.1865)
Pencil on paper 26.1 x 17.6
Provenance unknown

U3179 Cripplegate Church - Part of the
Remains of London Wall (1865)
Ink, watercolour on paper 25 x 22
Dated
Provenance unknown

U3180 The Gobbins, Islandmagee (1865)
(Island Magee)
Watercolour on paper 13.7 x 21.9
Dated
Provenance unknown

U3181 Castle Rock, Co. Derry (1866)
(Castlerock)
Watercolour on paper 17.6 x 25.4
Dated
Provenance unknown

U3182 At Castlerock (1866)
Watercolour on paper 16.7 x 24.4
Dated
Provenance unknown

U3183 Castlerock (1866)
Watercolour on paper 17.4 x 25.1
Dated
Provenance unknown

U3184 Gap of Memore, Co. Donegal (1866)
Watercolour on paper 18.6 x 27.5
Dated
Provenance unknown

U3185 The 'Curl', Donegal; verso, Cart at
Buxton (1866)
Watercolour on paper 12.3 x 17
Dated
Provenance unknown

U3186 Dieppe (1867)
Ink, watercolour on paper 25.3 x 17.7
Dated
Provenance unknown

U3187 Rouen (1867)
Watercolour on paper 25.3 x 17.7
Dated

Provenance unknown

U3188 Two Sketches on the Loire - Arcachon,
Tours - Boat, Baskets, Women's Head-
dresses (1867)
Ink, watercolour on paper 9.8 x 13.9 and
12.9 x 13.8
Dated
Provenance unknown

U3189 The Draining of the Pine Juice - at
Arcachon, France - so as to Get Resin
(1867)
Ink, watercolour on paper 22.4 x 13.2
Dated
Provenance unknown

U3190 The Draining of the Pine Juice,
Arcachon, France
Ink, watercolour on paper 22.4 x 11.8
Provenance unknown

U3191 Versailles (1867)
Watercolour on paper 17.1 x 25.1
Dated
Provenance unknown

U3192 Water Tank, Arcachon (1867)
Ink, watercolour on paper 22.6 x 14
Dated
Provenance unknown

U3193 Paris, Hotel de Cluny (1867)
Watercolour on paper 25.1 x 17.3
Signed, dated
Provenance unknown

U3194 St. Cloud (1867)
Watercolour on paper 13.6 x 22.6
Dated
Provenance unknown

U3195 Port Moon, Giant's Causeway (1867)
Watercolour on paper 13.8 x 22.8
Dated
Provenance unknown

U3196 Windsor (1868)
Watercolour on paper 13.6 x 22.6
Dated
Provenance unknown

U3197 Sutton Tower, Howth, Co. Dublin (1868)
Watercolour on paper 13.7 x 22.6
Dated
Provenance unknown

U3198 Bective Abbey, Co. Meath (1868)
Watercolour on paper 13.7 x 22.5
Dated
Provenance unknown

U3199 Dungiven Church, Co. Derry (1868)
Watercolour on paper 25 x 17.4
Signed, dated
Provenance unknown

U3200 Poet's Corner, Westminster Abbey
(1870) (Doorway)
Watercolour on paper 24 x 17.7
Signed, dated
Provenance unknown

U3201 Lough Shannah, Mourne Mountains
(1870)
Watercolour on paper 13.6 x 22.3
Dated
Provenance unknown

U3202 **Trassey Bog, Mourne Mountains (1870)**
Watercolour on paper 13.6 x 22.3
Dated
Provenance unknown

U3203 **The Pot, Mourne Mountains (1870)**
Watercolour on paper 13.5 x 22.3
Dated
Provenance unknown

U3204 **Mourne Mountains (1870)** (Sketch of a
Battered Fence)
Pencil on paper 11.4 x 17.8
Dated
Provenance unknown

U3205 **Shame on Co. Down, Newcastle Pier, Co.
Down (1870)**
Watercolour on paper 14.5 x 28.5
Signed, dated
Provenance unknown

U3206 **The Gobbins, Co. Antrim (1870)**
Watercolour on paper 13.4 x 22.2
Dated
Provenance unknown

U3207 **Uxbridge (1872)**
Ink, watercolour on paper 13.6 x 22
Dated
Provenance unknown

U3208 **Newcastle (1872)** (Turneresque Sky
Study)
Watercolour on paper 13.4 x 22.5
Dated
Provenance unknown

U3209 **Swakely Hall, Uxbridge, Middlesex
(1873)**
Watercolour on paper 14.4 x 35.5
Signed, dated
Provenance unknown

U3210 **The Gobbins, Co. Antrim, from Pigeon
Cove (1874)**
Watercolour on paper 12.4 x 19.6
Dated
Provenance unknown

U3211 **Richmond Hill (1874)**
Watercolour on paper 15.6 x 25.2
Signed, dated
Provenance unknown

U3212 **Newcastle (1874)** (Sunset Study)
Watercolour on paper 13.8 x 20
Dated
Provenance unknown

U3213 **Lasswade, on the North Esk, Edinburgh**
Watercolour on paper 17.3 x 25
Signed, dated
Provenance unknown

U3214 **Maidenhead - Thames (1875)**
Pencil, crayon on paper 17.5 x 25.3
Dated
Provenance unknown

U3215 **Maidenhead, on the Thames (1875)**
Watercolour on paper 17.5 x 24.9
Dated
Provenance unknown

U3216 **Crainlarick Station, Perthshire (1875)**
Watercolour on paper 17.5 x 25.2

Dated
Provenance unknown

U3217 **Borestone, Bannockburn, Stirling (1875)**
Watercolour on paper 17.6 x 25
Dated
Provenance unknown

U3218 **Carrickfergus Ship Yard (1876)**
Ink, watercolour on card 29 x 23.8
Signed, dated
Provenance unknown

U3219 **Old Houses, Kensington Museum
(1877)**
Watercolour on paper 19.6 x 27.5
Signed, dated
Provenance unknown

U3220 **Craig A Vad (1877)** (Craigavad, Co.
Down)
Watercolour on paper 17.1 x 25
Signed, dated
Provenance unknown

U3221 **Looking towards Corn Market, now
Lombard Street, Belfast (1877)**
Ink, watercolour on paper 17.4 x 27.6
Provenance unknown

U3222 **Clones Tower (1878)**
Watercolour on paper 22.2 x 13.7
Dated
Provenance unknown

U3223 **Clones (1877)** (Round Tower)
Ink, watercolour on paper 35 x 25
Provenance unknown

U3224 **Sam Bough, RSA 1822-78 at Jordanbank,
Edinburgh (1878)**
Pencil, ink on paper 22.3 x 13.6
Signed, dated
Provenance unknown

U3225 **Upper End of Lock Katrine (1878)**
Watercolour on paper 11.9 x 18.4
Dated
Provenance unknown

U3226 **Ben Venu, Trossachs (1878)**
Watercolour on paper 18 x 25.9
Dated
Provenance unknown

U3227 **Ben Venu, Trossachs (1878)**
Watercolour on paper 18 x 26.2
Dated
Provenance unknown

U3228 **Ben Venu, Trossachs Hotel (1878)**
Watercolour on paper 13.4 x 21.9
Dated
Provenance unknown

U3229 **Off Greenock (1878)**
Watercolour on paper 9.4 x 12.7
Dated
Provenance unknown

U3230 **Newcastle (1878)** (Inn Yard)
Watercolour on paper 27.4 x 25.4
Dated
Provenance unknown

U3231 **Tyrella, Co. Down (1878)**
Watercolour on paper 17.4 x 25.3
Dated

Provenance unknown

U3232 **Richmond, Surrey (1879)**
Watercolour on paper 17.4 x 24.9
Dated
Provenance unknown

U3233 **Teddington (1879)**
Watercolour on paper 17.3 x 24.9
Dated
Provenance unknown

U3234 **North Gate, Carrickfergus (1879)**
Watercolour on paper 17.4 x 25.1
Dated
Provenance unknown

U3235 **Niddry Castle, near Linlithgow (1879)**
Watercolour on paper 17.1 x 24.8
Dated
Provenance unknown

U3236 **Ruins of the Theatre Royal, Dublin
(1880)**
Ink, watercolour on paper 17.3 x 24.9
Dated
Provenance unknown

U3237 **Kew (1880)**
Watercolour, crayon on paper 25.3 x 17.5
Dated
Provenance unknown

U3238 **Putney Bridge (1880)**
Ink, watercolour on paper 17.5 x 25.5
Signed, dated
Provenance unknown

U3239 **Goragh Wood, Railway Station (1880)**
Ink, watercolour on paper 17.6 x 25.3
Signed, dated
Provenance unknown

U3240 **Fire, McKenny's, Dublin Bridge, Five
O'Clock Morning, Belfast (1880)**
Ink, crayon on paper 17.5 x 25.4
Dated
Provenance unknown

U3241 **From the Back of Dr. Wilson's House,
Bangor (1880)**
Watercolour on paper 17.5 x 25.4
Signed, dated
Provenance unknown

U3242 **Head of the Holy Loch, Clyde (1880)**
Watercolour on paper 18.1 x 26.1
Signed, dated
Provenance unknown

U3243 **Near Adelphi Arches, Strand, London
(1881)**
Watercolour on paper 17.7 x 25.3
Dated
Provenance unknown

U3244 **Oxygen Gas Works, Adelphi Arches,
London (1881)**
Watercolour on paper 17.5 x 25.5
Dated
Provenance unknown

U3245 **Drury Lane, London (1881)**
Ink, watercolour on paper 17.5 x 25.4
Dated
Provenance unknown

U3246 **Wych Street, London (1881)**

Ink, watercolour on paper 17.5 x 25.4
Dated
Provenance unknown

U3247 **Salisbury Wall, Side of the Fox under the Hill, London (1881)**
Watercolour on paper 17.6 x 25.3
Dated
Provenance unknown

U3248 **Below the Adelphi Hotel, Strand, London (1881)**
Ink, watercolour on paper 30.3 x 28.9
Signed, dated
Provenance unknown

U3249 **Ballyboley, Co. Antrim (1881)**
Watercolour on paper 17 x 26.2
Dated
Provenance unknown

U3250 **Peter and Sha (1881)** (a Parakeet and a White Persian Cat)
Ink, watercolour on paper 21 x 14.2 (irregular)
Dated
Provenance unknown

U3251 **Conlon Street, off Old Lodge Road, Belfast - Scene of Accident (1882)**
Ink, watercolour on paper 14 x 22
Dated
Provenance unknown

U3252 **Near Malahide (1882)**
Watercolour on paper 7 x 18.8
Signed, dated
Provenance unknown

U3253 **London, below the Adelphi Arches (1882)**
Ink, watercolour on paper 22.4 x 28.7
Signed, dated
Provenance unknown

U3254 **An Overgrown Grave**
Pencil on paper 19.2 x 28.2
Signed
Provenance unknown

U3255 **Font, Roslyn Chapel**
Pencil on paper 22.6 x 13.9
Provenance unknown

U3256 **Chapel (of) St. Gudule, Bruxelles (Brussels)**
Ink, watercolour on paper 60.5 x 33.6
Provenance unknown

U3257 **A Village Street**
Pencil on paper 15.6 x 24.6
Provenance unknown

U3258 **Short Castle, Mourne Mountains**
Pencil, chalk on paper 18.4 x 26.7
Provenance unknown

U3259 **A Gateway with Thatched Houses**
Pencil on paper 16.3 x 22.2
Signed
Provenance unknown

U3260 **Round Tower, Devenish Island**
Pencil, wash on paper 12.5 x 18.4
Provenance unknown

U3261 **Sketch: Sun Setting over a Mountain, Seen across a Stretch of Water with Boats**

Ink on paper 11 x 18.5
Provenance unknown

U3262 **Drinking Well - Struel, Downpatrick**
Pencil on card 20.1 x 14.9
Provenance unknown

U3263 **Eye Well - Struel, Downpatrick**
Pencil on card 16.5 x 10.5
Provenance unknown

U3264 **Landscape Seen through the Arch of a Bridge**
Ink, watercolour on paper 17.8 x 37.7
Provenance unknown

U3265 **Two Sketches of the Firth of Forth; Sketch of a Stone Urn on a Pedestal**
Pencil on paper 26.9 x 16.8
Provenance unknown

U3266 **Mourne Mountains**
Watercolour on paper 13.6 x 22.7
Provenance unknown

U3267 **Chimney Tops, Giant's Causeway (Chimney Pots)**
Watercolour on paper 18.8 x 27
Provenance unknown

U3268 **Ballyholme Bay**
Watercolour on paper 17.4 x 27
Provenance unknown

U3269 **Holywood Beach**
Watercolour on paper 14.4 x 18.9
Provenance unknown

U3270 **Ballymacarret Beach (Ballymacarrett)**
Watercolour on paper 10.6 x 17.7
Provenance unknown

U3271 **Stoke Poges Church**
Ink, watercolour on paper 18.4 x 26.3
Provenance unknown

U3272 **Well, Harrogate**
Ink, watercolour on paper 23.4 x 18.5
Provenance unknown

U3273 **Drumbo**
Watercolour on paper 17.3 x 20.3
Provenance unknown

U3274 **Sunset from Roxburgh Terrace, Edinburgh**
Watercolour on paper 12.4 x 27
Provenance unknown

U3275 **Roman Bridge, Newbattle Abbey, Dalkeith**
Watercolour on paper 18.8 x 26
Provenance unknown

U3276 **Portrush**
Watercolour on paper 12.2 x 17.8
Provenance unknown

U3277 **Graveyard, Belvoir Park**
Watercolour on paper 16.3 x 18.5
Provenance unknown

U3278 **Shakespeare's Cliff, Dover**
Watercolour on paper 10.5 x 24.7
Provenance unknown

U3279 **Chimney Tops, Giant's Causeway (Chimney Pots)**
Watercolour on paper 17.8 x 13

Provenance unknown

U3280 **Chimney Tops, Giant's Causeway**
Watercolour on paper 17.8 x 12.8
Provenance unknown

U3281 **Newcastle (Sky Study)**
Watercolour on paper 17.2 x 24.6
Provenance unknown

U3282 **Study - Armstrong's Bath Chair at Hotel, Holywood**
Ink, watercolour on paper 7 x 10.4
Provenance unknown

U3283 **Lady Annesley's Park, Study in River**
Watercolour on paper 18.4 x 26.3
Provenance unknown

U3284 **Shane's Castle**
Watercolour on paper 13 x 22.1
Provenance unknown

U4757 **The First Lock on the Lagan** *(Illus.p.296)*
Watercolour on paper 34.3 x 52.7
Signed
Purchased 1989

MOORE, James, MD 1819-83 (Irish) (attributed to)

U1420 **Dunluce Castle (1857)**
Pencil, watercolour on paper 12.7 x 17.7
Dated
Provenance unknown

MORGAN, Jane 1831-99 (Irish)

U2560 **Is That All? (1898)**
Oil on canvas 129 x 194.5
Signed, dated
Purchased 1980

MORPHEY, Garrett fl.1680-1716 (Irish) (attributed to)

U1654 **Portrait of an Unknown Man, possibly Arthur Chichester, 3rd Earl of Donegall 1666-1706** *(Illus.p.296)*
Oil on canvas 47.6 x 38.1
Purchased 1957

MORRIS, Sir Cedric 1889-1982 (Welsh)

U2289 **Birds (1928)** *(Illus.p.297)*
Oil on canvas 100.1 x 72.9
Signed, dated
Purchased (Lloyd Patterson Collection) 1929

MORRIS, William 1834-96 (English) (studio of)

U1186 **Drawing for East Window of St. Mary's Church, Tadcaster, Yorkshire**
Pencil, ink on paper 35.5 x 26.2
Purchased 1952

MORRISON, Robert Boyd 1896-1969 (Irish)

U363 **Florence M. Wilson d.1946 (1940)**
Oil on canvas 66.3 x 51.1
Signed, dated
Purchased 1957

MORROW, Edwin A. 1877-1952 (Irish)

U2272 The Spanish Walk
Oil on panel 16 x 21.6
Signed
Purchased 1974

U2273 Youngsters, Aran Island
Oil on board 35.5 x 25.5
Signed
Purchased 1974

U5048 A Cold Day, Lincoln (*Illus.p.297*)
Oil on panel 22.2 x 28 (sight)
Signed
Provenance unknown

U5049 Sea and Headland
Oil on panel 15 x 20 (sight)
Signed
Provenance unknown

MORROW, George 1870-1955 (Irish)

U1582 An African Fable: The Hare and the Lion
(*Illus.p.297*)
Ink, white on paper 31.1 x 25.7
Signed
Donated by W. R. Gordon, 1944

U1583 Cruel Sports in Olden Times: 'Stoning the Henge' on Salisbury Plain
Ink on paper 47.3 x 35.9 (sight)
Signed
Donated by the artist, 1945

U1584 The Fall of Eutychus (1904) (*Illus.p.297*)
Ink, wash, white on paper 28.1 x 36.8
Dated
Donated by J. Stoupe, 1939

Sixty-four Book Illustrations (c.1900)
Purchased 1980

U1666 Dahlias (Headpiece)
Ink on paper 25 x 30.9
Signed

U1746 Window Shopping
Ink on paper 25 x 19
Signed

U1955 The Widow's Dog
Ink on paper 25 x 30.9
Signed

U1956 Lad's Hands Seem rather Large
Ink on paper 25 x 30.9
Signed

U1957 Street Fair with Punch and Judy
Ink on paper 25 x 30.9
Signed

U1959 Honor O'Callaghan
Ink on paper 25 x 30.9
Signed

U1964 Hare Coursing
Ink on paper 25 x 30.9
Signed

U1967 Crowded Street
Ink on paper 25 x 30.9
Signed

U1973 The London Visitor
Ink on paper 25 x 30.9
Signed

U1976 Butler's Pantry
Ink on paper 25 x 30.9
Signed

U1977 Tailor at his Counter
Ink on paper 25 x 30.9
Signed

U1978 Gamekeeper Grabbing Poacher
Ink on paper 25 x 30.9
Signed

U1979 The Widow's Dog (Pheasants)
Ink on paper 25 x 30.9
Signed

U1980 The Ground Ash (Headpiece)
Ink on paper 25 x 30.9

U1983 The London Visitor
Ink on paper 25 x 30.9

U1984 The London Visitor
Ink on paper 25 x 30.9

U1986 Beauty of the Village (Headpiece)
Ink on paper 25 x 30.9

U1987 Falling into a Pond
Ink on paper 25 x 30.9

U1990 Lucy
Ink on paper 25 x 30.9

U1991 The London Visitor
Ink on paper 25 x 30.9

U1994 The Lost Dahlia
Ink on paper 25 x 30.9

U2003 Expression of Disgust
Ink on paper 25 x 30.9
Signed

U2004 Philly Firkin (Headpiece)
Ink on paper 25 x 30.9
Signed

U2005 The London Visitor
Ink on paper 25 x 30.9

U2006 Honor O'Callaghan (Headpiece)
Ink on paper 25 x 30.9
Signed

U2011 A Church Pew
Ink on paper 25 x 30.9
Signed

U2015 Country Orchard
Ink on paper 25 x 30.9
Signed

U2018 The Boy's Face Is not Nice
Ink on paper 25 x 30.9
Signed

U2020 Quarrel over a Coach
Ink on paper 25 x 30.9

U2029 A Couple Meeting
Ink on paper 25 x 30.9
Signed

U2047 Embracing Couple
Ink on paper 25 x 30.9
Signed

U2106 Widow's Dog
Ink on paper 25 x 30.9
Signed

U2283 Picking Windfalls
Ink on paper 25 x 30.9
Signed

U2340 The Lost Dahlia (Horse Leaping a Fence)
Ink on paper 25 x 30.9
Signed

U2374 Lady Walking in a Ruin
Ink on paper 25 x 30.9
Signed

U2444 House with Sheep
Ink on paper 25 x 30.9
Signed

U2454 The Widow's Dog
Ink on paper 25 x 30.9
Signed

U2607 The Widow's Dog
Ink on paper 25 x 30.9
Signed

U2608 Aunt Deborah
Ink on paper 25 x 30.9

U2658 Aunt Deborah (Charity School Boys with their Master)
Ink on paper 25 x 30.9

U2701 The Lost Dahlia
Ink on paper 25 x 30.9

U2702 The London Visitor (Headpiece)
Ink on paper 25 x 30.9
Signed

U2703 Aunt Deborah (Man and Dog)
Ink on paper 25 x 30.9

U4676 Outline of Nose Should Be quite Clean
Ink on paper 25 x 30.9
Signed

U4824 Farm (Headpiece)
Ink on paper 25 x 30.9
Signed

U4891 Man Sleeping in Chair
Ink on paper 25 x 30.9
Signed

U4937 Aunt Deborah (Boy Feeding Geese)
Ink on paper 25 x 30.9

U5072 Sorting Mail
Ink on paper 25 x 30.9
Signed

U5073 Skittle Alley ('Beauty of the Village')
Ink on paper 25 x 30.9
Signed

U5074 Philly Firkin
Ink on paper 25 x 30.9

U5075 Ragged Youth and Girl
Ink on paper 25 x 30.9
Signed

U5076 Old Red Cow (Inn)
Ink on paper 25 x 30.9
Signed

U5077 Girl and Farmer (Headpiece)
Ink on paper 25 x 30.9

U5078 Group of Ladies
Ink on paper 25 x 30.9
Signed

U5079 **Drinking at a Table**
Ink on paper 25 x 30.9
Signed

U5080 **Girl in front of House** (Headpiece)
Ink on paper 25 x 30.9
Signed

U5081 **River** (Headpiece)
Ink on paper 25 x 30.9
Signed

U5082 **Country Lodgings**
Ink on paper 25 x 30.9
Signed

U5083 **An Old Lady Rebuking a Man**
Ink on paper 25 x 30.9
Signed

U5084 **A Doctor's Visit**
Ink on paper 25 x 30.9
Signed

U5085 **Two Girls outside a Cottage**
Ink on paper 25 x 30.9
Signed

U5086 **Face not quite Impudent enough** (Tailor)
Ink on paper 25 x 30.9
Signed

U5087 **An Overturned Carriage**
Ink on paper 25 x 30.9

U5088 **Aunt Deborah** (Dog and Cat)
Ink on paper 25 x 30.9

MORROW, Norman 1879-1917 (Irish)

U1202 **Man and Woman** *(Illus.p.297)*
Pencil, gouache on paper 29.9 x 25
Signed
Purchased 1969

U1203 **Volendamers (1903)**
Pencil, watercolour on paper 41.2 x 24.2
Signed, dated
Purchased 1969

U1204 **A Suspicious-looking Couple**
Charcoal, bodycolour on board 34.7 x 26.8
Signed
Purchased 1969

MOSER, Mary (Mrs. Hugh Lloyd) 1744-1819 (English)

U98 **Flowerpiece (1769)** *(Illus.p.297)*
Pencil, watercolour, bodycolour on paper 28.5 x 66.5
Signed, dated
Donated by Dr. H. Crawford, 1955

MOYNIHAN, Rodrigo 1910-90 (British)

U471 **Apples and Plums (1943?)** *(Illus.p.297)*
Oil on canvas 50.7 x 61
Signed, dated indistinctly
Donated by the Contemporary Art Society, 1943

MUHRMAN, Henry 1854-1916 (American)

U1874 **Snow-covered Roofs** *(Illus.p.297)*
Pastel on paper 43.1 x 36.9
Purchased 1911

MULCAHY, Michael b.1952 (Irish)

U2695 **Slave**
Oil on canvas 163 x 179
Donated by the Contemporary Irish Art Society, 1983

MULHOLLAND, Carolyn b.1944 (Irish)

U4930 **Humming Head** *(Illus.p.297)*
Sculpture, bronze 40 x 34 x 16.5 (including base)
Signed
Purchased 1992

MÜLLER, Rosa fl.1845-60 (English)

U2279 **Rome from the Pincian Hill** *(Illus.p.298)*
Watercolour on paper 24.2 x 33.7
Signed
Provenance unknown

MÜLLER, William James 1812-45 (English)

U827 **Xanthus from the Theatre** *(Illus.p.298)*
Pencil, watercolour on paper 37.3 x 56.7
Purchased 1951

U828 **A Lake Scene**
Pencil, watercolour on paper 13.9 x 23.7
Bequeathed by Sir David Reid (per Lady Reid), 1951

MULREADY, William 1786-1863 (Irish)

U829 **Giving a Bite** *(Illus.p.298)*
Ink, watercolour, bodycolour on paper 41.5 x 33
Signed
Purchased 1943

MULREADY, William 1786-1863 (Irish)
(attributed to)

U92 **Young Girl with a Basket of Eggs** *(Illus.p.298)*
Oil on canvas 76.2 x 63.2
Signed
Purchased 1962

MUNCE, Iza fl.1915-25 (Irish)

U1920 **The Old Lacemaker (1914)** *(Illus.p.298)*
Oil on canvas 61 x 50
Signed
Donated by Miss Mary Munce, 1939

MUNN, Paul Sandby 1773-1845 (English)

U830 **Hugh Lloyd's Bridge, near Ffestiniog (1834)** *(Illus.p.298)*
Pencil, watercolour on paper 23.5 x 18.1
Signed, dated
Purchased 1953

MUNSTER, Ethel fl.1900-33 (Irish?)

U1101 **Harvest Evening (c.1913)**
Pencil, watercolour on paper 31.7 x 50.8
Signed
Purchased 1913

MUNTZ, Julie (Jessie) fl.1903-24 (Irish)

U100 **Miss Iza Munce** fl.1915-25
Oil on canvas 60.7 x 51

Donated by Miss J. Munce, 1946

MURPHY, Denis Brownell fl.1763-d.1842 (Irish)

U1892 **John Bridge 1755-1834, of Piddletrenthyde, Dorset (1813?)** *(Illus.p.298)*
Miniature in enamel 8.2 x 6.7
Dated indistinctly
Purchased 1963

MURPHY, Noel b.1970 (Irish)

U5016 **Searching shortsightedly for W. B. Y. (1995)** *(Illus.p.298)*
Oil on board 61 x 31
Donated by the Thomas Haverty Trust, 1995

MURRAY, Sir David 1849-1933 (Scottish)

U106 **Peace at Eve (1894)** *(Illus.p.298)*
Oil on canvas 121.9 x 182.3
Signed, dated
Bequeathed by the artist, 1939

MURRAY, Mrs. Eileen 1885-1962 (Irish)

U648 **This or Emigration (c.1926)** *(Illus.p.299)*
Oil on canvas 91.5 x 61
Signed
Purchased 1926

N

NALIN, Daniele b.1947 (Italian)

U4949 **Il Custode dei Cinque Punti Sapienti (1992)** *(Illus.p.299)*
Oil on canvas 180 x 150
Signed, dated
Purchased 1992

NASH, John Northcote 1893-1977 (English)

U474 **The Garden under Snow (c.1924-30)** *(Illus.p.299)*
Oil on canvas 76.4 x 61.2
Signed
Purchased (Lloyd Patterson Collection) 1933

U831 **View of the Plain** *(Illus.p.299)*
Ink, pencil, watercolour on paper 28.2 x 39.6
Signed
Purchased 1951

U832 **Farm at Kimble** *(Illus. p.299)*
Pencil, watercolour on paper 30.3 x 38 (sight)
Signed
Donated by the Contemporary Art Society, 1948

NASH, Paul 1889-1946 (English)

U477 **St. Pancras Lilies (1927)** *(Illus.p. 299)*
Oil on canvas 63.7 x 45.8
Purchased (Lloyd Patterson Collection) 1929

NEILL, H. Echlin 1888-1981 (Irish)

U1102 **Glenariff** *(Illus.p.299)*
Pencil, watercolour on paper 28.8 x 39.5
Signed
Purchased 1935

NELSON, Harold E. H. 1871-post 1927?
(English)

U479 **Landscape**
Oil on canvas 55.2 x 45.7
Donated by the Contemporary Art
Society, 1939

NEVINSON, Christopher Richard Wynne 1889-1946 (English)

U473 **A Mountain Landscape in Wales**
(Illus.p.299)
Oil on canvas 71.3 x 91.7
Signed
Purchased 1930

NEWTON, Herbert H. 1881-1959 (British)

U1992 **Corsican Village Square, Winter (1929)**
Oil on canvas 42.9 x 61
Signed, dated
Donated by R. C. Hanrott (for Lloyd
Patterson Collection), 1938

NICHOLL, Andrew 1804-86 (Irish)
Most of the following works are as titled by the
artist

U91 **The Old Tree in the Glen - June
(c.1843-44)** *(Illus.p.299)*
Oil on canvas 77 x 63.5
Purchased 1917

U233 **Cavehill from the Old Bridge at Ormeau
(c.1828)**
Watercolour on paper 24.5 x 34.2
Signed
Purchased 1957

U248 **Cavehill from the End of the Holywood
Road, between the New Bridge and
Strandtown (c.1828)**
Watercolour on paper 25 x 35.6
Signed
Purchased 1957

U250 **McArt's Fort from the Mountain to
between the Fort and the Caves (c.1828)**
(Illus. p.300)
Watercolour on paper 24 x 35.5
Signed
Purchased 1957

U251 **McArt's Fort (c.1828)**
Watercolour on paper 23.6 x 34.4
Signed
Purchased 1957

U266 **Temple Coran Church, Ballycarry
(c.1828) (Templecorran)**
Watercolour on paper 25.9 x 34.9
Signed
Purchased 1957

U273 **Larne Lough from the Road near
Magheramourne Lime Works (c.1828)**
(Magheramorne)
Watercolour on paper 24.7 x 35.1

Signed
Purchased 1957

U281 **From the Barnhill, Larne (c.1828)**
Watercolour on paper 24.3 x 35.5
Signed
Purchased 1957

U286 **Ballygally Head, near Larne (c.1828)**
(Ballygalley)
Watercolour on paper 23 x 35
Signed
Purchased 1957

U291 **Glenarm Castle, from the East Bank of
the River (c.1828)**
Watercolour on paper 24.2 x 34.3
Signed
Purchased 1957

U364 **Drumnasole, near Point of Garron
(c.1828)**
Watercolour on paper 24.1 x 34.7
Signed
Purchased 1957

U382 **Turnly's Road, Point of Garron (c.1828)**
Watercolour on paper 24.6 x 34.3
Signed
Purchased 1957

U398 **Clough-i-Stookan (c.1828)**
(Cloghastucan)
Watercolour on paper 21.8 x 34
Signed
Purchased 1957

U417 **Clough-i-Stookan (c.1828)**
Watercolour on paper 23.4 x 34.6
Signed
Purchased 1957

U649 **Strippen Burn, Glenariff (c.1828)**
Watercolour on paper 22.6 x 33.9
Signed
Purchased 1957

U663 **In Glenariff - First Fall - on the East
Branch of the River (c.1828)**
Watercolour on paper 23.2 x 34.8
Signed
Purchased 1957

U668 **Old Bush Mill, Co. Antrim**
Oil on panel 24 x 33
Signed
Purchased 1904

U678 **Drumnakeel and Fairhead from Murloch
Farm (c.1828) (Fair Head)**
Watercolour on paper 24.8 x 34.5
Signed
Purchased 1957

U679 **Fairhead Point from the Foot of the
Greyman's Path (c.1828)**
Watercolour on paper 24.3 x 34.5
Signed
Purchased 1957

U706 **Greyman's Path from the Base of the
Cliffs (c.1828)**
Watercolour on paper 24.8 x 33.9
Signed
Purchased 1957

U708 **Greyman's Path, Fairhead (c.1828)**

Watercolour on paper 24.3 x 34.1
Signed
Purchased 1957

U710 **Greyman's Path from the Summit of
Fairhead (c.1828)**
Watercolour on paper 24.2 x 35.2
Signed
Purchased 1957

U724 **Landscape**
Oil on panel 20.1 x 25.4
Bequeathed by Mrs. Hannah Flanery,
1915

U725 **The Giant's Causeway**
Oil on panel 20.1 x 25.2
Bequeathed by Mrs. Hannah Flanery,
1915

U727 **Fairhead from Ballycastle (1828)**
Watercolour on paper 22.9 x 35.1
Signed, dated
Purchased 1957

U740 **Bona Margey Abbey, near Ballycastle
(c.1828) (Bonamargy)**
Watercolour on paper 23.3 x 34.9
Signed
Purchased 1957

U894 **Lady Dufferin's Garden**
Pencil, white on paper 16.5 x 24.7
Donated by W. H. Kirkpatrick, 1927

U895 **Ferry Castle and Bridge, near Wexford**
Pencil, white on paper 17 x 25.9
Signed
Donated by W. H. Kirkpatrick, 1927

U896 **Devil's Glen, Co. Wicklow (1840)**
Pencil, white on paper 16.8 x 25.2
Signed, dated
Donated by W. H. Kirkpatrick, 1927

U897 **St. Kevin's Kitchen and Round Tower,
Glendalough**
Pencil, white on paper 15.5 x 25.4
Signed
Donated by W. H. Kirkpatrick, 1927

U898 **Kingstown Pier (1840)**
Pencil, white on paper 17.5 x 25.7
Signed, dated
Donated by W. H. Kirkpatrick, 1927

U899 **Moras Castle, Co. Donegal**
Pencil on paper 16.1 x 24.2
Signed
Donated by W. H. Kirkpatrick, 1927

U900 **St. Patrick's Well**
Pencil, white on paper 15.7 x 24.5
Signed
Donated by W. H. Kirkpatrick, 1927

U901 **Meeting of the Waters, Vale of Avoca
(1840)**
Pencil, white, wash on paper 17.4 x 26.1
Signed, dated
Donated by W. H. Kirkpatrick, 1927

U902 **Pass of Conlough (1838)**
Pencil, white on paper 16.8 x 24.7
Signed, dated
Donated by W. H. Kirkpatrick, 1927

U903 **Pass of Cobleagh (1838)**

Pencil, white on paper 16.4 x 24.8
Signed, dated
Donated by W. H. Kirkpatrick, 1927

U904 **Howth and Harbour;** verso, **Howth Abbey (1849)**
Pencil, white on paper 17.4 x 25.5
Signed, dated
Donated by W. H. Kirkpatrick, 1927

U905 **Fishing Boats**
Pencil, white on paper 16.9 x 24.3
Signed
Donated by W. H. Kirkpatrick, 1927

U906 **Glen with River**
Pencil, white on paper 17.1 x 24.4
Signed
Donated by W. H. Kirkpatrick, 1927

U907 **Pass of Glenoe**
Pencil, white on paper 14.3 x 23.8
Signed
Donated by W. H. Kirkpatrick, 1927

U908 **St. Finton's Church, Howth (1838)** (St. Fintan)
Pencil, white on paper 24.4 x 17.6
Signed, dated
Donated by W. H. Kirkpatrick, 1927

U909 **Lough Conn**
Pencil, white on paper 18.3 x 27.4
Signed
Donated by W. H. Kirkpatrick, 1927

U910 **Mount Sinai from the Red Sea**
Pencil, ink, watercolour on paper 38 x 54
Signed
Purchased 1956

U912 **The Long Bridge, Belfast (1835)**
Pencil, white on paper 27.4 x 38.5
Signed, dated
Donated by A. L. McCurry, 1954

U913 **Belvoir Castle from the Lagan**
Pencil, watercolour on paper 17.8 x 28.3
Donated by Mrs. H. Thompson, 1954

U914 **Agnew's Castle, Ballygally** (Ballygalley)
Watercolour on paper 26.3 x 36.3
Donated by A. L. McCurry, 1954

U915 **A Floral Design (1846)**
Pencil, white on paper 35.6 x 24.7
Signed, dated
Purchased 1959

U916 **A Bank of Flowers, with a View of Bray and the Valley of the Dargle, Co. Wicklow** *(Illus.p.300)*
Watercolour on paper 35.1 x 52.1
Signed
Purchased 1957

U917 **Belfast from Knock Old Churchyard** (formerly 'Belfast from Newtownbreda')
Watercolour on paper 47.7 x 35
Signed
Purchased 1955

U918 **Belfast from Newtownbreda Churchyard**
Watercolour on paper 35 x 52.3
Signed
Donated by Mrs. H. Chisholm, 1942

U919 **Galle Harbour, Ceylon** *(Illus.p.300)*

Watercolour on paper 51.2 x 74.4
Signed
Purchased 1957

U920 **Sketch: Dublin and Kingstown Railway**
Pencil on card 16.9 x 26
Provenance unknown

U953 **Knock Layde, near Ballycastle (c.1828)** (Knocklayde)
Watercolour on paper 23.3 x 34.6
Signed
Purchased 1957

U963 **Doonpoint, Island of Rathlin (c.1828)** *(Illus.p.300)*
Watercolour on paper 23.5 x 34.4
Signed
Purchased 1957

U983 **Kenbane Castle, near Ballycastle (c.1828)**
Watercolour on paper 24.1 x 34.2
Signed
Purchased 1957

U1100 **Bengore Head from the Interior of Port Bradden Cave (c.1828)** (Portbradden)
Watercolour on paper 23.9 x 34
Purchased 1957

U1103 **Cape St. Vincent (1846)**
Watercolour on paper 17.7 x 26
Dated
Purchased 1951

U1104 **Newtownbreda Church**
Pencil, ink, watercolour, white on paper 26.2 x 35.4
Signed
Bequeathed by Sir R. Lloyd Patterson, 1919

U1105 **Sea Cave**
Watercolour on paper 23.3 x 16.8
Donated by Miss E. M. Cooper, 1916

U1106 **Landscape with Trees, London (1840)**
Watercolour on paper 25 x 36.5
Signed, dated
Bequeathed by Mrs. Hannah Flanery, 1915

U1107 **The Old Mill, Holywood (1834)**
Pencil, watercolour on paper 35.1 x 51.8
Signed, dated
Purchased 1954

U1108 **The Long Bridge, Belfast**
Pencil, watercolour on paper 34.3 x 52.1
Signed
Donated by A. L. McCurry, 1954

U1215 **Cultra House, Co. Down**
Pencil, watercolour on paper 34.9 x 52
Signed
Purchased 1954

U1216 **Mountain Lake, Ceylon**
Pencil, watercolour on paper 52 x 71.8
Purchased 1950

U1222 **Coastal Scene in Stormy Weather**
Pencil, watercolour on paper 50.5 x 68
Signed
Purchased 1954

U1255 **Dunluce Castle** *(Illus.p.300)*

Pencil, watercolour, white on paper 50.4 x 74.4
Signed
Purchased 1954

U1256 **The Giant's Causeway from the West** *(Illus.p.300)*
Pencil, watercolour on paper 45.8 x 69.8
Signed
Purchased 1954

U1265 **Benandonar and the Stack, Portmoon (c.1828)**
Watercolour on paper 23.1 x 33.6
Signed
Purchased 1957

U1417 **Nurse and Child, Pleaskin (c.1828)**
Watercolour on paper 25 x 34.8
Signed
Purchased 1957

U1418 **Lion's Head, Pleaskin (c.1828)**
Watercolour on paper 24.2 x 34.3
Signed
Purchased 1957

U1419 **West View of Pleaskin, from above (c.1828)**
Watercolour on paper 24.7 x 34.8
Signed
Purchased 1957

U1421 **West View of the Giant's Causeway from the Stookans (c.1828)**
Watercolour on paper 25 x 34.8
Signed
Purchased 1957

U1422 **East View of the Giant's Loom (c.1828)**
Watercolour on paper 25.6 x 34.5
Signed
Purchased 1957

U1423 **East View of the Giant's Causeway (c.1828)**
Watercolour on paper 23 x 34.6
Signed
Purchased 1957

U1424 **Dunluce Castle from the Road (c.1828)**
Watercolour on paper 24.6 x 36.3
Signed
Purchased 1957

U1425 **Narrow Water Castle, near Newry (c.1828)**
Watercolour on paper 24.6 x 34.8
Purchased 1957

U1426 **Rostrevor, Co. Down (c.1828)**
Watercolour on paper 25.3 x 35
Purchased 1957

U1427 **Rostrevor (c.1828)** *(Illus.p.300)*
Watercolour on paper 23.4 x 44.1
Purchased 1957

U1428 **Mourne Mountains from the Road near Castlewellan (c.1828)**
Watercolour on paper 24.8 x 34.7
Purchased 1957

U1429 **Race Won 19 June 1829, at the Belfast Regatta, by the 'Ariel', John McCracken, Esq. against the 'Crusader', Sir Stephen May, and the 'Zoe', Marquis of Donegall**
Watercolour on paper 34.6 x 52.6

Signed
Provenance unknown

U1563 **The Old Mill, Holywood (1834)**
(Illus.p.300)
Pencil, watercolour on paper 35.1 x 51.8
Signed, dated
Purchased 1954

U1564 **The Long Bridge, Belfast (c.1835)**
Watercolour on paper 33.7 x 49
Donated by T. Morgan, 1937

U1656 **Source of the River Bann, Deer's Meadow (1843)**
Watercolour on paper 17.2 x 25.2
Signed, dated
Purchased 1966

U1667 **Clam Shell Cave, Staffa**
Pencil, white on paper 18 x 27
Signed
Donated by the Department of Education (NI), 1972

U1668 **Rocky Coast with a Natural Arch**
Pencil, white on paper 19 x 27.8
Signed
Donated by the Department of Education (NI), 1972

U1669 **A Lake with Bridges and a Ruined Church**
Pencil, white on paper 18.3 x 27
Signed
Donated by the Department of Education (NI), 1972

U1670 **A Lake with Mountains and a Wooded Island**
Pencil, white on paper 15.4 x 24.8
Signed
Donated by the Department of Education (NI), 1972

U1671 **Gougane Barra, Co. Cork**
Pencil, white on paper 18.2 x 26.6
Donated by the Department of Education (NI), 1972

U1672 **A Rocky Coast** (Staffa?)
Pencil, white on paper 18.3 x 26.6
Signed
Donated by the Department of Education (NI), 1972

U1673 **Tree Study**
Pencil, white on paper 24.1 x 15.7
Signed
Donated by the Department of Education (NI), 1972

U1674 **Tree Study**
Pencil, ink, wash, white on paper 24.6 x 15.5
Signed
Donated by the Department of Education (NI), 1972

U1675 **A Castle on a Lake**
Watercolour, pencil, gum on paper 10.3 x 15.1
Signed
Donated by the Department of Education (NI), 1972

U1676 **Stormy Sea with Ruins on a Cliff Top**

Watercolour, gum on paper 15.3 x 24.3
Signed
Donated by the Department of Education (NI), 1972

U1677 **Carrickfergus**
Watercolour, gum on paper 17.7 x 25.6
Donated by the Department of Education (NI), 1972

U1678 **Killarney (?)**
Watercolour, pencil, gum on paper 22 x 32.1
Signed
Donated by the Department of Education (NI), 1972

U1679 **Sunset** (Style of Turner)
Watercolour, gum on paper 22.7 x 34.3
Donated by the Department of Education (NI), 1972

U1680 **Choppy Sea with Sailing Ships off a Harbour**
Watercolour, pencil, gum on paper 22.9 x 32.1
Signed
Donated by the Department of Education (NI), 1972

U1690 **Fishing Boat Pulled ashore, with Three Men**
Pencil, wash, white on paper 15.6 x 16.8
Provenance unknown

U1691 **Fishing Boat Pulled ashore with Yacht and Steamer in the Distance**
Pencil, wash, white on paper 18.3 x 26.6
Purchased 1956

U1692 **Belfast from Newtownbreda Churchyard**
(Illus.p.300)
Watercolour on paper 35.4 x 52.8
Signed
Provenance unknown

U1693 **Belfast from Newtownbreda**
Watercolour on paper 14.8 x 40.1
Purchased 1893

U1694 **Tropical Lagoon**
Watercolour on paper 51.2 x 74.4
Signed
Provenance unknown

U1695 **The Pigeon Cave, Lough Swilly**
Watercolour on paper 15.5 x 23.8 (sight)
Purchased 1965

U1696 **The Long Bridge, Belfast** *(Illus.p.301)*
Watercolour on paper 44.2 x 61
Signed
Provenance unknown

U1697 **Antrim and Lough Neagh**
Watercolour on paper 43.5 x 67.8
Signed
Donated by Miss E. S. Montgomery, 1928

U1698 **The Cascade, Bryansford**
Watercolour on paper 44.7 x 33.5 (sight)
Signed
Purchased 1966

U1699 **Pigeon Cave and Dunree Fort, Lough Swilly** *(Illus.p.301)*
Watercolour on paper 35 x 49 (sight)
Signed

Purchased 1966

U1700 **Cavehill from Orangefield (c.1828)**
Watercolour on paper 24.3 x 35.6
Signed
Purchased 1957

U1701 **Cavehill from Conn's Water (c.1828)**
(River Connswater)
Watercolour on paper 24 x 37.9
Signed
Purchased 1957

U1702 **Cavehill from Solitude**
Watercolour on paper 24 x 35.4
Signed
Provenance unknown

U1703 **Irish Quarter, Carrickfergus (c.1828)**
Watercolour on paper 23.5 x 35.3
Signed
Purchased 1957

U1704 **Carrickfergus Castle (c.1828)**
Watercolour on paper 24.9 x 35.1
Signed
Purchased 1957

U1705 **Carrickfergus Castle (c.1828)**
Watercolour on paper 24.8 x 33.2
Signed
Purchased 1957

U1706 **Village of Glenoe, near Larne (c.1828)**
Watercolour on paper 24.8 x 34.1
Signed
Purchased 1957

U1707 **The Curran and Town of Larne (c.1828)**
Watercolour on paper 71.3 x 25
Signed
Purchased 1957

U1708 **North View of the Curran of Larne, from the Waterside near the Ferry (c.1828)**
Watercolour on paper 24.8 x 34.4
Signed
Purchased 1957

U1709 **Cromlech on Island Magee, commonly Called 'The Standing Stone' (c.1828)**
Watercolour on paper 26 x 35.5
Signed
Purchased 1957

U1710 **Giant's Cradle or Rocking Stone, Brown's Bay (c.1828)**
Watercolour on paper 25.7 x 34.7
Signed
Purchased 1957

U1711 **Black Cave, near Larne (c.1828)**
Watercolour on paper 34.7 x 24.6
Signed
Purchased 1957

U1751 **Carn Castle, Ballygally Head (c.1828)**
(Ballygalley)
Watercolour on paper 25.2 x 35
Signed
Purchased 1957

U1766 **Ballygally Head, near Larne (c.1828)**
Watercolour on paper 23.7 x 34.2
Signed
Purchased 1957

U1787 **Castle and Village of Glenarm (c.1828)**

Watercolour on paper 24.1 x 34.8
Signed
Purchased 1957

U1793 **Glenarm Point and Point of Garron from Glenarm** (c.1828)
Watercolour on paper 22.7 x 34.6
Signed
Purchased 1957

U1837 **Knappan, near Garron Point** (c.1828)
Watercolour on paper 23 x 35.1
Signed
Purchased 1957

U1933 **Point of Garron Looking East** (c.1828)
Watercolour on paper 23.2 x 34.3
Signed
Purchased 1957

U1974 **Turnly's Road, Point of Garron** (c.1828)
Watercolour on paper 24.6 x 34.4
Purchased 1957

U1993 **The Long Bridge, Belfast**
Oil on canvas 15.9 x 29.8 (sight)
Donated by the Misses McBride, 1917

U2057 **Point of Garron from the Sea** (c.1828)
Watercolour on paper 25.4 x 34.7
Signed
Purchased 1957

U2068 **Foran Path, Point of Garron** (c.1828)
(Foaran)
Watercolour on paper 24.5 x 34.8
Purchased 1957

U2090 **Foran Path, Garron Point** (c.1828)
Watercolour on paper 23.8 x 34.8
Signed
Purchased 1957

U2158 **Near Clough-i-Stookan** (Cloghastucan)
Watercolour on paper 24.3 x 35.1
Signed
Provenance unknown

U2159 **Red Bay Castle, near Cushendall** (c.1828)
Watercolour on paper 23 x 33.7
Signed
Purchased 1957

U2160 **Carrigmurphy from Waterfoot** (c.1828)
Watercolour on paper 24.7 x 34.7
Signed
Purchased 1957

U2161 **Glenariff from the Mountain Top above Ballinlig** (c.1828)
Watercolour on paper 23.9 x 34.4
Signed
Purchased 1957

U2162 **Essnalara, Glenariff - West Branch of the River** (c.1828) (Ess-na-laragh)
Watercolour on paper 33.3 x 24.9
Purchased 1957

U2163 **In Glenariff** (c.1828)
Watercolour on paper 24.8 x 34.6
Purchased 1957

U2164 **Turf Falls - Fidtger-a-leak, Glenariff above Ballinlig** (c.1828)
Watercolour on paper 23.6 x 34.6
Signed
Purchased 1957

U2165 **Waterfoot, near Cushendall** (c.1828)
Watercolour on paper 23.8 x 34.8
Signed
Purchased 1957

U2166 **Redbay Castle, near Cushendall** (c.1828)
(Red Bay)
Watercolour on paper 25.9 x 34.8
Signed
Purchased 1957

U2167 **Layde Church, near Cushendall** (c.1828)
Watercolour on paper 24.5 x 34.7
Signed
Purchased 1957

U2168 **Cushendun** (c.1828)
Watercolour on paper 25.4 x 35
Signed
Purchased 1957

U2169 **Fairhead from Carrick-a-feule, Murloch** (c.1828) (Fair Head from Carrick-a-feul, Murlough)
Watercolour on paper 23.4 x 34.6
Signed
Purchased 1957

U2170 **Drummakeel, Murloch, Looking towards Cushleak** (c.1828)
Watercolour on paper 23.5 x 34.3
Signed
Purchased 1957

U2171 **Entrance to the Greyman's Path, Fairhead** (c.1828) (Fair Head)
Watercolour on paper 23.7 x 33.8
Signed
Purchased 1957

U2172 **Entrance to the Greyman's Path, Looking Westward** (c.1828)
Watercolour on paper 24.6 x 34.4
Signed
Purchased 1957

U2173 **Cliffs of Fairhead** (c.1828)
Watercolour on paper 24.4 x 34.4
Signed
Purchased 1957

U2174 **Fairhead Point** (c.1828)
Watercolour on paper 23.3 x 34.7
Signed
Purchased 1957

U2175 **Fairhead Point from beyond the Collieries** (c.1828)
Watercolour on paper 23.4 x 35
Signed
Purchased 1957

U2176 **Fairhead** (c.1828)
Watercolour on paper 23.7 x 35.2
Signed
Purchased 1957

U2177 **Saltpans, Fairhead** (c.1828)
Watercolour on paper 24.7 x 35.4
Signed
Purchased 1957

U2178 **Coveton's Cave, near Ballycastle** (c.1828)
Watercolour on paper 34.5 x 24.5
Signed
Purchased 1957

U2179 **White Rocks, Ballycastle, underneath the Giant's Parlour** (c.1828)
Watercolour on paper 24.4 x 34.6
Signed
Purchased 1957

U2180 **Kenbane Castle, near Ballycastle** (c.1828)
Watercolour on paper 22.3 x 29.9
Signed
Purchased 1957

U2181 **Carrick-a-Rede** (c.1828)
Watercolour on paper 24.5 x 37.3
Signed
Purchased 1957

U2182 **East View of Bengore Head** (c.1828)
Watercolour on paper 24.3 x 34.4
Signed
Purchased 1957

U2183 **Dunseverick Castle** (c.1828)
Watercolour on paper 25.4 x 34.5
Signed
Purchased 1957

U2184 **East View of the Four Brothers** (c.1828)
Watercolour on paper 23.9 x 33.9
Signed
Purchased 1957

U2185 **Bengore Head** (c.1828)
Watercolour on paper 24.5 x 34.5
Signed
Purchased 1957

U2186 **The Four Brothers, from below** (1828)
Watercolour on paper 21.5 x 33.1
Signed, dated
Purchased 1957

U2187 **Pleaskin Head** (c.1828)
Watercolour on paper 25.6 x 35.1
Signed
Purchased 1957

U2188 **East View of Pleaskin, from the Rock Heads** (c.1828)
Watercolour on paper 24.2 x 33.9
Purchased 1957

U2189 **Chimney Tops, Giant's Causeway** (c.1828) (Chimney Pots)
Watercolour on paper 24.2 x 35
Signed
Purchased 1957

U2190 **Chimney Tops, Giant's Causeway** (c.1828)
Watercolour on paper 24.4 x 34.5
Signed
Purchased 1957

U2191 **Roveran Valley from the Rock Head Looking Westward** (c.1828)
Watercolour on paper 23.6 x 37.6
Signed
Purchased 1957

U2192 **Seagull Isle, Portcoon** (c.1828)
Watercolour on paper 24.6 x 35.4
Signed
Purchased 1957

U2193 **Dunluce Castle** (c.1828)
Watercolour on paper 24 x 34.8

Signed
Purchased 1957

U2194 **S.E. View of Dunluce Castle from the Rock Heads (c.1828)**
Watercolour on paper 24.7 x 34.9
Signed
Purchased 1957

U2195 **White Rocks from Dunluce Castle (c.1828)**
Watercolour on paper 24.6 x 34.9
Signed
Purchased 1957

U2196 **Gull's Point, near Dunluce (c.1828)**
Watercolour on paper 22.6 x 33.8
Signed
Purchased 1957

U2197 **Port Na-ale, near Dunluce (c.1828)**
Watercolour on paper 24.8 x 35.7
Signed
Purchased 1957

U2198 **Craig-a-neskie, near Dunluce (c.1828)**
Watercolour on paper 24 x 34.6
Signed
Purchased 1957

U2199 **Craig-a-neskie, near Dunluce (c.1828)**
Watercolour on paper 23.7 x 33.2
Purchased 1957

U2200 **Lime Quarry, beyond Dunluce (c.1828)**
Watercolour on paper 24.6 x 34.6
Signed
Purchased 1957

U2201 **Limestone Cavern, Called 'Long Gilbert', beyond Dunluce Castle (c.1828)**
Watercolour on paper 25.2 x 35
Signed
Purchased 1957

U2202 **West View of the White Rocks beyond Dunluce (c.1828)**
Watercolour on paper 24.3 x 35
Signed
Purchased 1957

U2203 **On the Coast near Portrush (c.1828)**
Watercolour on paper 24.6 x 34
Signed
Purchased 1957

U2204 **On the Lagan at Lambeg from the Bridge, Looking up the River (c.1828)**
Watercolour on paper 24 x 35.4
Signed
Purchased 1957

U2205 **On the Lagan (c.1828)**
Watercolour on paper 22.5 x 41.7
Purchased 1957

U2206 **Rostrevor, near Newry (c.1828)**
Watercolour on paper 24.7 x 35.6
Purchased 1957

U2207 **Parkmount, Shore Road, Belfast (c.1828)**
Watercolour on paper 23.8 x 33.6
Signed
Purchased 1957

U2208 **The Long Bridge, Belfast (1835)**
Pencil, white on paper 17.2 x 37
Signed, dated

Purchased 1893

U2209 **Coast Scene with Steamboat on Horizon (1835)**
Pencil on paper; measurements unknown
Dated
Donated by J. E. Robson, 1960

U2210 **Steaming Cauldron on Fire, with Kegs at Right and Two Open Tubs at Left (1835)**
Pencil, wash on paper; measurements unknown
Dated
Donated by J. E. Robson, 1960

U2211 **Waterloo Bridge, Clifton, Connemara (1836)**
Pencil on paper; measurements unknown
Dated
Donated by J. E. Robson, 1960

U2212 **Bay with Breakwater**
Watercolour on paper 25 x 34.4
Signed
Provenance unknown

U2213 **Belfast from Newtownbreda**
Watercolour on paper 27.8 x 46.7 (sight)
Purchased 1909

U2214 **The Hermitage, Tollymore Park**
Watercolour on paper 22 x 40.2 (sight)
Signed
Purchased 1962

U2215 **Deramore**
Watercolour on paper 23 x 32
Purchased 1965

U2235 **Dunree Fort, Lough Swilly**
Pencil, white on paper 16.8 x 24.8
Signed
Donated by W. H. Patterson, pre-1918

U2236 **Killadreenan Church near Newtownmountkennedy (1838)** (Newtown Mountkennedy)
Pencil, watercolour on paper 17.1 x 26
Signed, dated
Donated by W. H. Patterson, pre-1918

U2237 **St. Kevin's Well, Glendalough (1840)**
Pencil, watercolour, white on paper 16.9 x 25.4
Signed, dated
Donated by W. H. Patterson, pre-1918

U2238 **Cloughnastucan, Co. Antrim** (Cloghastucan)
Pencil, white on paper 17.4 x 25.4
Signed
Donated by W. H. Patterson, pre-1918

U2239 **Deeps Castle / Ferry Castle (1840)**
Pencil, white on paper 17.1 x 26
Signed, dated
Donated by W. H. Patterson, pre-1918

U2240 **Deeps Castle / Ruined Mansion (1860)**
Pencil, white on paper 23.5 x 16.5
Signed, dated
Donated by W. H. Patterson, pre-1918

U2241 **Dunree Fort, Lough Swilly**
Pencil, white on paper 16.4 x 24.8
Signed

Donated by W. H. Patterson, pre-1918

U2242 **Capstans, Masts and Rigging**
Pencil, white on paper 16.8 x 26
Signed
Donated by W. H. Patterson, pre-1918

U2243 **Fishing Boat**
Pencil, white on paper 22.8 x 15.9
Signed
Donated by W. H. Patterson, pre-1918

U2244 **Kendlestown Castle near Delgany (1838)** (Kindelestown)
Pencil, white on paper 13.6 x 22.2
Dated
Donated by W. H. Patterson, pre-1918

U2245 **Fishing Boats**
Pencil on paper 16.5 x 25.6
Signed
Donated by W. H. Patterson, pre-1918

U2246 **Fishing Boats ashore**
Pencil, white on paper 16.1 x 25.4
Signed
Donated by W. H. Patterson, pre-1918

U2247 **Two Fishing Boats**
Pencil, white on paper 16.1 x 24.1
Signed
Donated by W. H. Patterson, pre-1918

U2248 **Pontoon Bridge, Lough Conn, Co. Sligo**
Pencil, white, watercolour on paper 15.9 x 24.4
Signed
Donated by W. H. Patterson, pre-1918

U2249 **Statue of the Late Earl of Belfast**
Pencil on paper 18.4 x 25.1
Signed
Donated by W. H. Patterson, pre-1918

U2250 **Opening of the Cork-Bandon Railway**
Pencil on paper 14 x 16.1
Donated by W. H. Patterson, pre-1918

U2383 **Fingal's Cave, Staffa** *(Illus.p.301)*
Watercolour, gum on paper 70.8 x 51.4
Signed
Purchased 1976

U2591 **Salmon Leap (1835)** (Coleraine)
Pencil, white on paper 17.1 x 25.4
Signed, dated
Donated by J. Higginson, 1962

U2592 **New Portrush (1838)**
Pencil, wash, white on paper 15.9 x 24.5
Signed, dated
Donated by J. Higginson, 1962

U2593 **Port Moon and Stack, Giant's Causeway**
Pencil, wash, white on paper 15.9 x 25.4
Signed
Donated by J. Higginson, 1962

U2594 **Upper Lake, Killarney**
Pencil, white on paper 16.5 x 27.3
Signed
Donated by J. Higginson, 1962

U3285 **Album of Sixty-seven Drawings of Irish**
-3351 **Antiquities (c.1834-37)**
Album size 38 x 27.5
Donated by Dr. Nesca Robb, 1957

U3285 **Blarney Castle, near Cork**
Ink, wash on paper

U3286 **The Tunnel, Upper Lake, Killarney**
Ink, wash on paper

U3287 **Ballylough Castle, Co. Antrim - the Ancient Seat of the McQuillans**
Ink, wash on paper

U3288 **Round Tower, Antrim**
Ink on paper

U3289 **Round Tower, Clondalkin, Co. Dublin**
Ink on paper

U3290 **Muckross Abbey, Killarney**
Ink on paper

U3291 **The Belfry Tower, Chancel Arch, Muckross Abbey**
Ink, wash on paper

U3292 **Muckross Abbey, Killarney**
Ink on paper

U3293 **O'Sullivan's Cascade, Killarney**
Ink, watercolour, wash on paper

U3294 **Waterfall in the Devil's Glen, Co. Wicklow**
Ink, wash on paper

U3295 **Mellifont Abbey - Ruins**
Ink on paper

U3296 **Mellifont Abbey**
Ink, wash on paper

U3297 **Mellifont Castle**
Ink, wash on paper

U3298 **Boyle Abbey**
Pencil, ink on paper

U3299 **Temple Coran Church** (Templecorran)
Pencil, ink on paper

U3300 **Round Tower and Church, Donaghmore**
Ink, wash on paper

U3301 **Athlumney Church**
Pencil, ink on paper

U3302 **Round Tower and Church of Lusk, Co. Dublin**
Ink on paper

U3303 **The Hermitage, Slane, Co. Meath**
Ink, wash on paper

U3304 **Slane Abbey**
Ink on paper

U3305 **Ancient Abbey and College of Slane**
Pencil, ink on paper

U3306 **New Grange** (Newgrange) (Inner Chamber)
Ink, wash on paper

U3307 **New Grange** (Inner Chamber)
Ink, wash on paper

U3308 **New Grange** (Inner Chamber)
Ink, wash on paper

U3309 **Kilclief Castle, Strangford Lough**
Ink, wash on paper

U3310 **Church of St. Peter and St. Paul, Trim**

Ink on paper

U3311 **Quoile Castle, Strangford Lough**
Ink on paper

U3312 **Murrisk Abbey, under Croagh Patrick, Co. Mayo**
Ink on paper

U3313 **Grace O'Malley's Castle, Westport Bay**
Ink on paper

U3314 **Baldongan Castle and Church**
Ink on paper

U3315 **Athlumney Castle**
Ink on paper

U3316 **Eastern Gable, Greyabbey, Co. Down**
Ink on paper

U3317 **Ballyalton Cromlech, near Downpatrick**
Ink on paper

U3318 **Cromlech at Glasakeeran, Co. Derry**
Ink, wash on paper

U3319 **Drumachose Old Church, Co. Derry**
Ink on paper

U3320 **Dungiven Old Church, Co. Derry**
Ink, wash on paper

U3321 **Dungiven Castle, Co. Derry**
Ink, wash on paper

U3322 **The Old Tree over the Grave of the Persecutor at Ballintubber, Co. Mayo** (Ballintober)
Ink on paper

U3323 **Tomb of the Burkes, Ballintubber, Co. Mayo**
Ink on paper

U3324 **Cromlech, near Dunloy, commonly Called the 'Giant's Grave', Co. Antrim**
Ink, wash on paper

U3325 **Standing Stone near Dundrum, Co. Down**
Ink on paper

U3326 **Cromlech, Island Magee, commonly Called the 'Standing Stone'**
Ink on paper

U3327 **Grey Horse near Yellow Water Bridge, Mourne Mountains**
Ink, wash on paper

U3328 **Standing Stone, Carrownacaw, near Downpatrick**
Pencil, ink on paper

U3329 **Round Tower, Drumbo, Co. Down**
Pencil, ink on paper

U3330 **King John's Castle, Ardglass**
Ink on paper

U3331 **North Gate, Carrickfergus**
Ink on paper

U3332 **Old Church of Layde, near Cushendall, Co. Antrim**
Pencil, ink on paper

U3333 **Dalkey Castle, Co. Dublin**
Ink on paper

U3334 **Quintin Bay Castle, Strangford Lough**
Ink on paper

U3335 **Round and Square Towers, Co. Dublin** (Swords)
Ink, wash on paper
Signed

U3336 **Old Castle, Swords, Co. Dublin**
Pencil, ink on paper

U3337 **Carlingford Castle**
Ink, wash on paper

U3338 **Carlingford Abbey**
Ink on paper

U3339 **Ancient Church and Monastery, Banagher, Co. Derry**
Ink on paper

U3340 **Old Church and Round Tower, Devenish Island, Lough Erne, Co. Fermanagh**
Ink on paper

U3341 **Clonmacnoise** (Clonmacnois)
Pencil, wash on paper

U3342 **Monasterboice, Co. Louth**
Ink on paper

U3343 **Jordan's Castle, Ardglass**
Ink on paper

U3344 **The King's Castle, Ardglass**
Ink, wash on paper

U3345 **Ross Cottage, Lower Lake, Killarney**
Ink, wash on paper

U3346 **Waterfall at Hermitage, Co. Wicklow**
Ink, wash on paper

U3347 **Salmon Leap on the Liffey**
Pencil, ink on paper

U3348 **The Larch House, Lower Lake, Killarney**
Pencil, ink, wash on paper

U3349 **Devil's Glen, Co. Wicklow**
Pencil, ink, wash on paper

U3350 **King John's Castle, Ardglass**
Ink, wash on paper

U3351 **Entrance to Glenarm Park, Co. Antrim**
Ink on paper

U3352 **Album of Fifty-four Drawings of**
-3405 **Irish Antiquities (late 1830s)**
Album size 38 x 27.5
Purchased 1942

U3352 **Grey Abbey** (Greyabbey, Co. Down)
Ink on paper

U3353 **Chancel Arch, Grey Abbey**
Ink, wash on paper

U3354 **East Gable, Grey Abbey**
Ink, wash on paper

U3355 **St. Lawrence's Gate, Drogheda**
Ink, wash on paper

U3356 **St. Mary de Urso, Drogheda** (St. Mary d'Urso)
Ink, wash on paper

U3357 **Dungiven Church**
Ink on paper

U3358 **Chancel Arch, Dungiven**
Ink, wash on paper

U3359 **Tomb of Cumaighe-na-Gal, Dungiven ('Cooey-na-Gal')**
Ink, watercolour on paper

U3360 **Old Castle, Swords, Co. Dublin**
Ink, wash on paper

U3361 **The Round and Square Towers, Swords, Co. Dublin**
Ink, wash on paper

U3362 **Abbey of St. Peter and St. Paul near Trim**
Ink, wash on paper

U3363 **Dalkey Castle, Co. Dublin**
Ink, wash on paper

U3364 **Carlingford Abbey**
Ink, wash, watercolour on paper

U3365 **Carlingford Abbey**
Ink, wash, watercolour on paper

U3366 **Cromlech at Dundrum, Co. Down**
Ink, wash on paper

U3367 **Glasakeeran, Co. Derry**
Ink, wash on paper

U3368 **The Temple of the Sun**
Watercolour on paper

U3369 **Cloughmore Stone, Rostrevor (Cloghmore)**
Ink, wash on paper

U3370 **Cromlech, Island Magee**
Ink on paper

U3371 **The Rocking Stone, Island Magee, near Larne**
Ink, wash on paper

U3372 **Jordan's Castle, Ardglass**
Ink, wash on paper

U3373 **The King's Castle, Ardglass**
Ink, wash on paper

U3374 **Standing Stone, near Dundrum**
Ink, wash on paper

U3375 **Ballyalton Cromlech, near Downpatrick**
Ink, wash on paper

U3376 **Cromlech. The Grey Horse**
Ink, wash on paper

U3377 **Pict's Pipes. 'Flint Arrow Head, Co. Wicklow'. 'Spear Head'. 'Stone Hatchet Found at Ferns'. 'Stone Bead Found near the Round Tower, Co. Antrim'. 'Hatchet or Socketed Celt'**
Ink, watercolour on paper

U3378 **Old Church, Newtownards, Co. Down**
Ink, wash on paper

U3379 **North Gate, Carrickfergus**
Ink, wash on paper

U3380 **Holywood Church**
Ink, watercolour on paper

U3381 **Knockbreda Old Church, near Belfast**
Ink, watercolour on paper

U3382 **Cromlech, Giant's Ring, near Belfast**

Ink, wash on paper

U3383 **The Kemp Stones, Dundonald (Kempe Stone)**
Ink, wash on paper

U3384 **Cromlech at Kilkeel**
Ink, watercolour on paper

U3385 **Entrance to Donard's Cave, near Newcastle, Co. Down**
Ink on paper

U3386 **The Keep of the Old Castle, Dundrum, Co. Down**
Ink, watercolour on paper

U3387 **St. Donard's Church**
Ink, watercolour on paper

U3388 **The Seven Castles of Clonmines**
Ink, wash on paper

U3389 **Ruins on Devenish Island, Lough Erne, Co. Fermanagh**
Ink on paper

U3390 **Old Church and Round Tower, Devenish Island**
Ink, wash on paper

U3391 **Cromlech near Roughfort, Co. Antrim**
Ink, wash on paper

U3392 **Round Tower, Armoy**
Ink, wash on paper

U3393 **Armoy Round Tower, Co. Antrim**
Ink, wash on paper

U3394 **Round Tower Called 'The Steeple', Antrim**
Ink, wash on paper

U3395 **Ballylough Castle, Co. Antrim**
Ink, wash on paper

U3396 **Grace Staples Cave, Co. Antrim**
Ink, wash on paper

U3397 **Clough-i-Stookan, or White Woman (Cloghastucan or White Lady)**
Ink, wash on paper

U3398 **The Nurse and Child, Pleaskin, Co. Antrim**
Ink, wash, watercolour on paper

U3399 **The King and his Nobles, Pleaskin, Co. Antrim**
Ink, wash on paper

U3400 **Dunluce Castle**
Ink, wash on paper

U3401 **Layde Old Church, near Cushendall**
Ink, wash on paper

U3402 **Interior of the Abbey of Inch**
Ink, wash on paper

U3403 **Temple Coran Church (Templecorran)**
Ink on paper

U3404 **Untitled**
Ink, wash on paper

U3405 **The Grey Man's Path, Co. Antrim**
Ink, wash on paper

U3406 **Album of Sixty-six Drawings of Irish**

-3471 **Antiquities (late 1830s)**
Album size 38 x 27.5
Purchased 1942

U3406 **Torc Waterfall, Killarney**
Ink, wash, watercolour on paper

U3407 **Selskar Old Church**
Ink on paper

U3408 **Old Castle at Ferns, Co. Wexford**
Ink on paper

U3409 **Stone Cross. Untitled**
Ink, wash on paper

U3410 **St. Mogue's Monument, Ferns Cathedral**
Ink, wash on paper

U3411 **A Tomb in Bannow Old Church, Co. Wexford. A Stone Coffin in Bannow Old Church, Co. Wexford**
Ink, watercolour on paper

U3412 **Round Tower and Church of Lusk, Co. Dublin**
Ink, wash on paper

U3413 **Baldongan Castle, Church and Abbey**
Ink, wash on paper

U3414 **Bona Margey Abbey (Bonamargy)**
Ink, watercolour on paper

U3415 **Monasterboice, Co. Louth**
Ink on paper

U3416 **Monasterboice, Co. Louth**
Ink, wash on paper

U3417 **Donaghmore Church and Round Tower**
Ink, wash on paper

U3418 **Lot's Wife, Stalagmite Caves, Co. Kilkenny (1837)**
Pencil, wash, white on paper
Dated

U3419 **St. Michael's Cave, Gibraltar**
Ink, wash on paper

U3420 **Athlumney Castle**
Ink, wash on paper

U3421 **Athlumney Church**
Ink, wash on paper

U3422 **Kilclief Castle**
Ink, wash on paper

U3423 **Castle, Lough Corrib, Co. Galway**
Ink, wash on paper

U3424 **Banagher Old Church**
Ink, wash on paper

U3425 **Drum-a-Chose Church, Co. Derry (Drumachose)**
Ink on paper

U3426 **Blarney Castle, Co. Cork**
Ink, wash on paper

U3427 **Grace O'Malley's Castle, Westport Bay**
Ink, wash on paper

U3428 **Muckross Abbey, Killarney**
Ink on paper

U3429 **West Door of Muckross Abbey**
Ink, wash on paper

U3430 **Chancel Arch, Muckross Abbey**
Ink, wash on paper

U3431 **Muckross Abbey, Killarney**
Ink, wash on paper

U3432 **Ballinrobe Abbey, Co. Mayo**
Ink, wash on paper

U3433 **St. Patrick's Well**
Ink, wash on paper

U3434 **Murrisk Abbey, Croagh Patrick**
Ink, wash on paper

U3435 **Aghaboe Church**
Ink, wash on paper

U3436 **Aghaboe Church and Tower**
Ink on paper

U3437 **Innisfallen**
Ink, wash on paper

U3438 **Gougane Barra, Hermitage of St. Finbarr, Co. Cork. Source of the River Lee**
Ink, wash on paper

U3439 **St. Erek's Chapel, Co. Mayo**
Ink, wash on paper

U3440 **Slane Abbey, Co. Meath**
Ink, wash on paper

U3441 **Ancient Abbey and College of Slane**
Ink, wash on paper

U3442 **Tomb of the Burkes, Ballintubber, Co. Mayo** (Ballintober)
Ink, wash on paper

U3443 **The Grave of the Persecutor**
Ink, wash on paper

U3444 **Sligo Abbey**
Ink, wash, watercolour on paper

U3445 **Roscommon Abbey**
Ink, wash on paper

U3446 **Boyle Abbey**
Ink, wash on paper

U3447 **The Gates of the City of Glendalough**
Ink, wash on paper

U3448 **Kirk Castle, Lough Corrib**
Ink, watercolour on paper

U3449 **Ross Castle, Lough Corrib**
Ink, wash on paper

U3450 **Grand Triumphal Arch, Church of the Holy Trinity, Glendalough**
Ink, watercolour on paper

U3451 **The Monastery, Glendalough (1840)**
Ink, watercolour on paper

U3452 **Glendalough**
Pencil on paper

U3453 **Baptismal Font, Cathedral, Glendalough**
Pencil, white on paper

U3454 **St. Kevin's Loaf, Glendalough, Co. Wicklow**
Ink, watercolour on paper

U3455 **St. Kevin's Hill, Glendalough**

Ink, wash on paper

U3456 **The Mares' Cross, Glendalough, Co. Wicklow**
Ink, watercolour on paper

U3457 **Tomb of King Mactrole**
Ink, watercolour on paper

U3458 **Mellifont Abbey**
Ink, wash on paper

U3459 **Mellifont Abbey**
Ink, wash on paper

U3460 **Mellifont**
Ink, wash on paper

U3461 **Ballisodare River, Co. Sligo** (Ballysadare)
Pencil, white on paper

U3462 **Clondalkin Round Tower**
Ink, wash on paper

U3463 **St. Finnan's Church, Clonmacnoise** (Clonmacnois)
Ink, wash on paper

U3464 **Plan of Clonmacnoise**
Ink on paper

U3465 **All Saints' Cross, Clonmacnoise**
Ink, wash on paper

U3466 **New Grange, near Drogheda** (Newgrange)
Ink, wash on paper

U3467 **New Grange**
Ink, wash on paper

U3468 **New Grange, near Drogheda**
Ink, wash on paper

U3469 **King John's Castle, Ardglass**
Ink, wash on paper

U3470 **O'Donaghue's Castle, Lower Lake, Killarney**
Ink, wash on paper

U3471 **Doorway, Cong Abbey**
Ink, wash on paper

U4794 **Shane's Castle, Lough Neagh**
Pencil, white on paper 17.8 x 25.8
Bequeathed by Roberta and John Hewitt, 1987

NICHOLL, William 1794-1840 (Irish)

U627 **Landscape with Trees** *(Illus.p.301)*
Oil on paper 35 x 25
Bequeathed by Mrs. Hannah Flanery, 1915

U921 **Sunset over Farm and Lake**
Watercolour on paper 18.4 x 26
Bequeathed by Mrs. Hannah Flanery, 1915

U922 **Knock, near Belfast** *(Illus.p.301)*
Watercolour, pencil on paper 23.8 x 34.2
Signed
Provenance unknown

U1109 **View from Strandtown with Ballymacarrett Church and Cavehill in the Distance** *(Illus.p.301)*

Wash on paper 20.8 x 28.4
Purchased 1927

U1110 **A Rocky Stream** (formerly 'A Waterfall')
Pencil, watercolour on paper 24.7 x 35.8
Bequeathed by Mrs. Hannah Flanery, 1915

U1364 **Tree Study**
Pencil, wash on paper 19.7 x 11.1 (sight)
Donated by Miss Nicholl, 1953

U1365 **Tree Study**
Pencil, wash on paper 20.6 x 13.8
Donated by Miss Nicholl, 1953

U1366 **Tree Study**
Pencil, wash on paper 20.5 x 16.5
Donated by Miss Nicholl, 1953

U1367 **The Halfpenny Bridge, Belfast, with the Ballymacarrett Glass Works beyond** (formerly 'Bridge over a River by a Factory'); verso, **Tree Study**
Watercolour, sepia on paper 21.3 x 30.5
Signed
Provenance unknown

U1368 **The Throne, Cavehill**
Pencil, watercolour on paper 23.1 x 35
Signed
Purchased 1957

NICHOLLS, Bertram 1883-1952 (English)

U476 **Ebb Tide, Padstow (1947)** *(Illus.p.301)*
Oil on canvas 50.7 x 76.2
Signed, dated
Purchased 1947

NICHOLSON, Ben 1894-1982 (English)

U519 **Painting (1935)** *(Illus.p.301)*
Oil on canvas 71.1 x 92.1
Signed
Purchased 1967

NICHOLSON, Sir Charles fl.1894-1923 (English)

U1845 **Capital of the Arts: Architecture (1926-28)**
Ink on paper 38.6 x 41.7
Donated by B. Law, 1971
One of eighteen designs for capitals, etc. of columns in St. Anne's Cathedral, Belfast (executed by Morris Harding)

U1846 **Capital of the Arts: Sculpture (1926-28)**
Ink on paper 63 x 39.4
Donated by B. Law, 1971
One of eighteen designs for capitals, etc. of columns in St. Anne's Cathedral, Belfast (executed by Morris Harding)

U1847 **Capital of the Arts: Painting (1928)**
Ink on paper 39.1 x 44
Signed, dated
Donated by B. Law, 1971
One of eighteen designs for capitals, etc. of columns in St. Anne's Cathedral, Belfast (executed by Morris Harding)

U1848 **Capital of the Arts: Drama (1928)**
Ink on paper 39.5 x 42
Signed, dated

Donated by B. Law, 1971
One of eighteen designs for capitals, etc.
of columns in St. Anne's Cathedral,
Belfast (executed by Morris Harding)

U1849 **Capital of Healing: Three Elevations (1927)**
Ink, pencil on paper 52.5 x 51.3
Signed, dated
Donated by B. Law, 1971
One of eighteen designs for capitals, etc.
of columns in St. Anne's Cathedral,
Belfast (executed by Morris Harding)

U1850 **Capital of Healing: Healing a Lame Man (1927)**
Ink, pencil on paper 57 x 45.4
Signed, dated
Donated by B. Law, 1971
One of eighteen designs for capitals, etc.
of columns in St. Anne's Cathedral,
Belfast (executed by Morris Harding)

U1852 **Capital of Science (1927)**
Ink, pencil on paper 75 x 47.5
Signed, dated
Donated by B. Law, 1971
One of eighteen designs for capitals, etc.
of columns in St. Anne's Cathedral,
Belfast (executed by Morris Harding)

U1853 **Spur of Arts Column (1928)**
Ink on paper 33 x 40
Signed, dated
Donated by B. Law, 1971
One of eighteen designs for capitals, etc.
of columns in St. Anne's Cathedral,
Belfast (executed by Morris Harding)

U1854 **Spur: Grotesque Snake (1926-28)**
Ink, pencil on paper 44.5 x 39.6
Signed
Donated by B. Law, 1971
One of eighteen designs for capitals, etc.
of columns in St. Anne's Cathedral,
Belfast (executed by Morris Harding)

U1855 **Spur: Grotesque Animal (1926-28)**
Ink, pencil on paper 56 x 37
Signed
Donated by B. Law, 1971
One of eighteen designs for capitals, etc.
of columns in St. Anne's Cathedral,
Belfast (executed by Morris Harding)

U1856 **Spur: Stylised Leaf (1926-28)**
Ink, pencil on paper 47.5 x 34
Signed
Donated by B. Law, 1971
One of eighteen designs for capitals, etc.
of columns in St. Anne's Cathedral,
Belfast (executed by Morris Harding)

U1858 **Spur: Volute (1927)**
Ink, pencil on paper 38.4 x 28.5
Signed, dated
Donated by B. Law, 1971
One of eighteen designs for capitals, etc.
of columns in St. Anne's Cathedral,
Belfast (executed by Morris Harding)

U1859 **Spur: Heraldic Bird and Shield (1928)**
Pencil, wash on paper 41 x 75
Signed, dated
Donated by B. Law, 1971
One of eighteen designs for capitals, etc.

of columns in St. Anne's Cathedral,
Belfast (executed by Morris Harding)

U1860 **Capitals to North and South Windows (1926)**
Ink, pencil on paper 47.5 x 32.3
Signed, dated
Donated by B. Law, 1971
One of eighteen designs for capitals etc.
of columns in St. Anne's Cathedral,
Belfast (executed by Morris Harding)

U1861 **Capitals to Central Window (1926)**
Ink on paper 56.5 x 37.7
Signed, dated
Donated by B. Law, 1971
One of eighteen designs for capitals, etc.
of columns in St. Anne's Cathedral,
Belfast (executed by Morris Harding)

U1862 **Middle Capital, North Side of Central Window (1926)**
Ink, pencil on paper 35.3 x 50.7
Signed, dated
Donated by B. Law, 1971
One of eighteen designs for capitals, etc.
of columns in St. Anne's Cathedral,
Belfast (executed by Morris Harding)

U1863 **Three Capitals of North Porch (1927)**
Ink, pencil on paper 23 x 75.8
Signed, dated
Donated by B. Law, 1971
One of eighteen designs for capitals, etc.
of columns in St. Anne's Cathedral,
Belfast (executed by Morris Harding)

U2041 **Capital of Linen (1926)**
Ink, pencil on paper 56 x 55.2
Signed, dated
Donated by B. Law, 1971
One of eighteen designs for capitals, etc.
of columns in St. Anne's Cathedral,
Belfast (executed by Morris Harding)

NICHOLSON, Francis 1753-1844 (English)
(attributed to)

U1158 **Edinburgh**
Now by Unknown, 19th century
(English)

NICHOLSON, Margaret Dorothy fl.1920-40
(English)

U559 **The Model (1928)** *(Illus.p.301)*
Oil on canvas 51 x 76.5
Signed, dated
Donated by the Contemporary Art
Society, 1935

NICHOLSON, Sir William 1872-1949 (English)

U475 **Cinerarias (c.1928)** *(Illus.p.302)*
Oil on panel 59.5 x 54.2
Signed
Purchased (Lloyd Patterson Collection)
1929

NICOL, Erskine 1825-1904 (Scottish)

U603 **Rejected (1865)** *(Illus.p.302)*
Oil on canvas 59 x 40
Signed, dated
Purchased 1911

U1111 **Paddy at Versailles (1856)** *(Illus.p.302)*
Pencil, watercolour, bodycolour on paper
36.2 x 26.4
Signed, dated
Purchased 1930

U2453 **'The Merican Difficulty' (1862)**
(Illus.p.302)
Watercolour, bodycolour on paper 30.7 x
23.2
Signed, dated
Purchased 1977

NIEBLA, Josep Alvarez b.1945 (Spanish)

U4946 **Temps de Separacio (1991)** *(Illus.p.302)*
Oil on canvas 162 x 130
Signed, dated
Purchased 1992

NIETSCHE, Paul 1885-1950 (Russian, worked in
Ireland)

U110 **Portrait of Mr. F. W. H. (1935)** (Frederick
W. Hull 1867-1953)
Oil on board 51.8 x 45
Signed, dated
Purchased 1957

U126 **Woman on a Sofa (1934)** (Dorothy V.
Williamson)
Oil on canvas 116.9 x 157.5
Signed, dated
Donated by Sir W. Edmenson, 1966

U380 **James Humbert Craig 1878-1944 (1940)**
(Illus.p.302)
Oil on board 187.8 x 86.4
Signed, dated
Purchased 1952

U381 **Green Apples (1949)** *(Illus.p.302)*
Oil on board 61 x 50.8
Signed, dated
Purchased 1949

U566 **Self-Portrait (1929)**
Gouache on board 50.8 x 38.8
Signed, dated
Purchased 1930

U2673 **Portrait of F. L. Green 1902-53 (1946)**
(Illus.p.302)
Chalk on paper 61 x 50.8
Signed
Purchased 1983

U4980 **Portrait of Zoltan Lewinter-Frankl 1894-
1961 (1943)** *(Illus.p.302)*
Oil on canvas 112.5 x 86.5
Signed, dated
Donated by Mrs. A. Lewinter-Frankl in
memory of her husband, Zoltan
Lewinter-Frankl, 1994

NISBET, Noel Laura 1887-1956 (English)

U1875 **The Dance, or The Followers of Pan (1)**
(Illus.p.303)
Watercolour, bodycolour on paper 68.3 x
100.5
Signed
Purchased 1934

U1876 **The Dance, or The Followers of Pan (2)**
Watercolour, bodycolour on paper

James Arthur O'Connor 1792-1841 **Scene in Co. Wicklow (1820)** U680

Sir Joshua Reynolds 1723-92 **Miss Theodosia Magill 1744-1817, afterwards Countess of Clanwilliam (1765)** U692

Giovanni Francesco Romanelli c. 1610 62 **St. Cecilia** U142

William Scott 1913-89 **Egypt Series No.3 (1972)** U2288

Sir Stanley Spencer 1891-1959 **The Betrayal (1922-23)** U487

Graham Sutherland 1903-80 **Gorse on a Sea Wall (1939)** U503

Joseph Mallord William Turner 1775-1851 **The Dawn of Christianity (The Flight into Egypt) (1841)** U224

Jack Butler Yeats 1871-1957 **Riverside Long Ago (1923)** U428

67.7 x 101
Signed
Purchased 1934

NIXON, John c.1750-1818 (English)

U2262 **Belturbet, Co. Cavan (1798)**
Ink, wash, watercolour on paper 19.6 x
28.4
Dated
Purchased 1974

U2263 **Belturbet, Co. Cavan**
Watercolour, wash on paper 17.2 x 24.1
Purchased 1974

U2562 **Magilligan Mountain (1791)** *(Illus.p.303)*
Watercolour, wash on paper 19.7 x 28.6
Signed, dated
Purchased 1980

U2563 **Rostrevor (1791)** *(Illus.p.303)*
Watercolour, wash on paper 18.2 x 26
Signed, dated
Purchased 1980

U2580 **The Old Walls of Londonderry, with the
Market House and Church Taken from
Ship Quay Street (1793)**
Ink, watercolour on paper 22.2 x 14
Signed, dated
Purchased 1980

U2581 **The Glin near Newtown-Limavady
(1791)**
Watercolour on paper 19.8 x 27.6
Signed, dated
Purchased 1980

U2582 **Giant's Chair at the Causeway, Co.
Antrim (1790)** *(Illus.p.303)*
Watercolour, wash on paper 19.8 x 28
Signed, dated
Purchased 1980

NIXON, William Charles 1813-78 (Irish)

U109 **James Hope 1764-1847 (c.1830-35)**
Oil on canvas 77.5 x 64.5
Purchased 1927

NOGUCHI, Isamu 1904-88 (American)

U980 **Black Sun (1967)** *(Illus.p.40)*
Sculpture, lacquered bronze 76.2 x 24.8
(circular)
Purchased with the aid of a grant from
the Calouste Gulbenkian Foundation,
1971

NOLAND, Kenneth b.1924 (American)

U522 **Newlight (1963)** *(Illus.p.303)*
Acrylic on canvas 176.8 x 177.2
Signed, dated
Purchased 1965

U715 **Crystal (1959)** *(Illus.p.303)*
Acrylic on canvas 238.7 x 238.7
Dated
Donated by the artist (per the American
Federation of Arts), 1970

NORTCLIFFE, Frank fl.1930s (English)

U478 **Ferragudo, Algarve** *(Illus.p.303)*

Oil on canvas 40.6 x 50.8
Signed
Donated by the Contemporary Art
Society, 1939

NORTH, John William 1842-1924 (English)

U1112 **Near Lough Awe** *(Illus.p.303)*
Pencil, watercolour on paper 30.3 x 47.2
Signed
Purchased 1911

O

OAKLEY, Charles b.1925 (English)

U2290 **Ship's Interior (1)**
Watercolour on board 68.6 x 91.5
Signed
Purchased 1975

U2291 **Tanker Interior (2)** *(Illus.p.303)*
Watercolour on board 68.6 x 91.5
Signed
Purchased 1975

OBEN, James George fl.1779-1819 (Irish)

U833 **Rock of Fennor on the River Boyne**
(Illus.p.304)
Watercolour, gum on card 49.8 x 64.5
Signed
Purchased 1970

O'BRIEN, Dermod 1865-1945 (Irish)

U383 **Lennox Robinson 1886-1958 (1918)**
Oil on canvas 100.7 x 75.6
Signed, dated
Donated by the sitter, 1952

U629 **The Estuary of the Shannon (1935)**
(Illus.p.304)
Oil on canvas 50.7 x 60.9
Signed, dated
Bequeathed by Dr. R. I. Best (per the
Friends of the National Collections of
Ireland), 1959

U2643 **The Fine Art Academy, Antwerp (1890)**
(Illus.p.304)
Oil on canvas 79.5 x 59.7
Purchased 1982

O'CONNELL, Eilis b.1953 (Irish)

U4845 **Inuit Bay (1985)**
Sculpture, painted steel 136 x 136 x 6
Donated by Mervyn Solomon, 1991

O'CONNOR, James Arthur 1792-1841 (Irish)

U626 **Wooded Glen with Angler (1831)**
Oil on board 22.8 x 19
Signed, dated
Purchased 1964

U655 **Castle Arras, near Alf, on the Moselle
(c.1833)** *(Illus.p.304)*
Oil on board 22.9 x 28
Signed
Purchased 1956

U680 **Scene in Co. Wicklow (1820)** *(Illus.p.89)*
Oil on canvas 70.8 x 91.3

Signed, dated
Purchased 1970

O'CONNOR, John 1830-89 (Irish)

U112 **The Market Place, Vicenza (1881)**
(Illus.p.304)
Oil on canvas 169.5 x 132
Signed, dated
Purchased 1956

O'CONNOR, Joseph b.1936 (Irish)

U689 **Small Dutch Head (1968)**
Oil on board 47.4 x 36.7
Signed, dated
Purchased 1970

O'CONOR, Roderic 1860-1940 (Irish)

U389 **Field of Corn, Pont Aven (1892)**
(Illus.p.304)
Oil on canvas 38 x 38
Signed, dated
Purchased 1963

U1752 **Portrait of Alden Brooks 1883-1964
(1916)** (formerly 'Portrait of a Man')
Oil on canvas 92 x 73.5
Purchased 1972

U2323 **Un Bouquet** *(Illus.p.304)*
Oil on canvas 55.1 x 46.3
Purchased 1975

U2565 **Reclining Nude (c.1906)** *(Illus.p.304)*
Oil on canvas 54.2 x 65
Purchased 1980

U2566 **La Colline Noir** *(Illus.p.304)*
Oil on canvas 42.6 x 56
Purchased 1980

U2675 **View of Pont Aven (1899)** *(Illus.p.305)*
Oil on canvas 54.5 x 65
Signed, dated
Purchased 1983

U4696 **Woman in White (c.1910)**
Oil on canvas 81.3 x 64.8
Donated by Dr. Terence Fulton in
memory of Zoltan Lewinter-Frankl, 1986

U5037 **Self-Portrait (c.1923-26)** *(Illus.p.305)*
Oil on panel 36.2 x 37
Donated by Ms. Corinne B. Cornish,
1996

O'HARA, Helen 1846-1920 (Irish)

U1320 **Evening** *(Illus.p.305)*
Watercolour, white on paper 36.7 x 54
Signed
Bequeathed by Miss A. Finley, 1950

O'KELLY, Aloysius 1850-1929 (Irish)

U5035 **Huckleberry Finn (1885)** *(Illus.p.305)*
Oil on canvas 91.3 x 59.3 (sight)
Signed
Donated by Mervyn Solomon, 1996

O'MALLEY, Power 1870-1946 (Irish)

U4820 **Aran Woman** *(Illus.p.305)*
Oil on canvas 71.1 x 55.8
Signed

Purchased 1990

O'MALLEY, Tony b.1913 (Irish)

U2335 **Autumn (1974)**
Gouache on paper 51.2 x 39.2
Signed, dated
Purchased 1975

U2429 **Farm in Winter (1966)**
Gouache, acrylic on paper 45.7 x 72.5
Dated
Purchased 1977

U2430 **Bird in Window (1974)** *(Illus.p.305)*
Gouache on paper 29.6 x 20.8
Purchased 1977

U2431 **Still Life (1975)** *(Illus.p.305)*
Gouache on paper 20.9 x 29.7
Purchased 1977

U2469 **Still Life with Onions on a Table (1962)**
(Illus.p.305)
Charcoal, chalk on paper 37.8 x 50.8
Signed, dated
Purchased 1977

U2470 **The Warehouse Yard, New Ross (1962)**
Gouache, acrylic on paper 42.2 x 59.7
Signed, dated
Purchased 1977

U2680 **Ghost of a Place (1981)**
Oil on board 91 x 122.2
Signed
Purchased 1983

O'MEARA, Frank 1853-88 (Irish)

U2556 **Autumnal Sorrows (1878)** *(Illus.p.305)*
Oil on canvas 48.5 x 99.8
Signed, dated
Purchased 1980

U4804 **Old Woman Gathering Faggots**
Oil on canvas 40 x 75
Donated by Mervyn Solomon, 1989

O'MURNAGHAN, Art 1872-1954 (Irish)

U1113 **Nature Rhythm - Dawn (Sunrise Meditation) (1930)** *(Illus.p.306)*
Ink, gouache on card 26.5 x 19
Signed, dated
Donated by the artist, 1937

U1114 **Nature Rhythm - Flames in a Bush (1933)** *(Illus.p.306)*
Watercolour, ink, bodycolour on paper
20.2 x 25.4
Signed, dated
Donated by the artist, 1937

O'NEILL, Daniel 1920-74 (Irish)

U384 **The Blue Skirt (1949)** *(Illus.p.306)*
Oil on canvas 60 x 73
Signed
Donated by the Thomas Haverty Trust, 1951

U386 **Knockalla Hills, Donegal (1951)**
(Illus.p.306)
Oil on board 50.8 x 60.9
Signed
Purchased 1952

U387 **The First Born (1949)**
Oil on canvas 60.7 x 50.7
Signed
Purchased 1960

U713 **Flowers and Fruit (1969-70)**
Oil on board 35.4 x 53.3
Signed
Donated by the McClelland Galleries, 1970

U714 **Three Friends (1969-70)** *(Illus.p.306)*
Oil on board 68.6 x 50.8
Purchased 1970

U716 **Girl with Fan (1969-70)** *(Illus.p.306)*
Oil on board 68.4 x 50.8
Signed
Purchased 1970

U2069 **Place du Tertre (1949)** *(Illus.p.306)*
Oil on canvas 64 x 76.7
Signed
Bequeathed by Mrs. S. A. Forbes, 1974

U4795 **Flowers on a Shore (1951)**
Oil on board 40.5 x 51.2
Bequeathed by Roberta and John Hewitt, 1987

O'NEILL, Henry 1798-1880 (Irish)

U1257 **Cashel (1875)** *(Illus.p.306)*
Pencil, white, watercolour on paper 35.5 x 45.8
Signed, dated
Donated by Mrs. C. Stallard, 1942

OOST, Jacob van 1601-71 (Flemish)

U1867 **The Holy Family with St. John and St. Elizabeth (1643)** *(Illus.p.306)*
Oil on panel 119.4 x 194
Signed, dated
Purchased 1973

OPIE, John 1761-1807 (English)

U115 **Sir John Borlase Warren 1753-1822 (1794)** *(Illus.p.307)*
Oil on canvas 76.2 x 62.8
Signed, dated
Donated by the Hon. William Warren-Vernon, 1915

OPIE, John 1761-1807 (English) (attributed to)

U113 **Portrait of a Young Girl**
Oil on canvas 154.4 x 123
Donated by Lady Edith Dixon, 1959

ORCHARDSON, Sir William Quiller 1832-1910 (Scottish)

U1634 **Portrait of Emma Joseph (1904)**
(Illus.p.307)
Oil on canvas 120 x 99.5
Signed, dated
Bequeathed by C. M. S. Nissin, 1971

ORPEN, Sir William 1878-1931 (Irish)

U114 **Resting (1905)** *(Illus.p.307)*
Oil on canvas 76.2 x 55.6
Signed, dated
Donated by Miss Penelope Andrews and

Miss Helen M. Brett (on behalf of subscribers), 1906

U480 **Summer Time** *(Illus.p.307)*
Oil on panel 61 x 49.9
Signed
Purchased 1951

U481 **Self-Portrait (c.1905-10)** *(Illus.p.307)*
Oil on canvas 50.8 x 40.7
Signed
Purchased (Lloyd Patterson Collection) 1933

U834 **Nude Woman**
Pencil on paper 32.1 x 18.4
Donated by Mrs. Aileen Bodkin (per the Friends of the National Collections of Ireland) in memory of her husband, Professor Thomas Bodkin, 1963

U1217 **Male Nude Studies** *(Illus.p.307)*
Chalk on paper 62.7 x 48.2
Signed
Donated by the Friends of the National Collections of Ireland, 1928

ORR, Barry 20th century (Irish)

U1851 **Flight of Fancy (1971)**
Sculpture, kinetic work in aluminium 38.1 x 49.5 x 21
Purchased 1971

ORROCK, James 1829-1913 (Scottish)

U1115 **Near Border Tower**
Pencil, watercolour on paper 34.8 x 52.7
Signed
Purchased 1929

OSBORNE, Walter Frederick 1859-1903 (Irish)

U116 **Cherry Ripe (1889)** *(Illus.p.307)*
Oil on canvas 68.5 x 50.5
Signed, dated
Purchased 1951

U2382 **Estuary at Walberswick (c.1884-85)**
(Illus.p.307)
Oil on canvas 45.5 x 61
Purchased 1976

O'SULLIVAN, Séan 1906-64 (Irish)

U388 **Neach (1928)** *(Illus.p.307)*
Oil on canvas on board 60.5 x 50.6
Signed, dated
Donated by the Thomas Haverty Trust, 1936

U1869 **George Russell ('AE') 1867-1935 on his Death-bed (1935)** *(Illus.p.308)*
Charcoal on paper 38.1 x 50.8
Signed, dated
Donated by Mrs. E. Solterer (per the Friends of the National Collections of Ireland) in memory of her father, C. P. Curran, 1973

U1877 **Henry Harrison 1867-1954 (1941)**
Charcoal on paper 46.3 x 33.5 (sight)
Signed, dated
Donated by Miss Mary McNeill, 1954

P

PAGET, Henry Marriot 1856-1936 (English)

U613 **W. B. Yeats 1865-1939 (1889)**
(*Illus.p.308*)
Oil on canvas 52.1 x 42.1
Signed, dated
Donated by the Friends of the National
Collections of Ireland, 1932

PALMER, James Lynwood 1867-1941 (English)

U610 **Trigo (1929)** (*Illus.p.308*)
Oil on canvas 96.5 x 127
Signed, dated
Bequeathed by W. Barnett, 1946

PALMER, Samuel 1805-81 (English)

U835 **The Piping Shepherd** (*Illus.p.308*)
Watercolour, bodycolour on paper 18.5 x
39.9
Signed
Purchased 1949

PANINI, Giovanni Paolo 1691-1765 (Italian)
(and studio)

U117 **Roman Ruins and Figures** (*Illus.p.308*)
Oil on canvas 121.5 x 142.5
Donated by Miss A. P. Norris, 1941

PAOLOZZI, Sir Eduardo b.1924 (British)

U951 **Crash (1964)** (*Illus.p.308*)
Sculpture, welded aluminium 150 x 244
x 97
Purchased 1967

PARK, John A. 1880-1962 (English)

U118 **The Haven under the Hill**
Oil on canvas 101.6 x 127
Signed
Donated by J. W. Corry, 1943

PARKER, Brynhild fl.1930-38 (British)

U484 **Quayside, Appledore (c.1930-33)**
(*Illus.p.308*)
Oil on canvas 42.2 x 76.2
Signed
Donated by the Contemporary Art
Society, 1933

PARKER, Richard Dunscombe 1805-81 (Irish)

**'Illustrations of the Irish Birds', a Collection of
One Hundred and Seventy Works**
Watercolour, pencil, gum on paper, each 62.2 x
77.5
Bequeathed by Miss E. S. M. Parker, 1932
All of the following works are as titled by the
artist

U2216 **The Golden Eagle** (Aquila chrysaetos)

U2222 **The White-tailed Eagle, or Sea Eagle**
(Haliaetus albicilla)

U2253 **The Spotted Eagle, with a Rabbit** (Aquila
clanga)

U2310 **The Osprey Eagle, with a Salmon**
(Osprey) (Pandion haliaetus)

U2313 **The Peregrine Falcon, Male and Female,
one Devouring a Snipe** (Falco peregrinus)

U2314 **The Marsh Harrier, Devouring a Water-
rail** (Circus aeruginosus)

U2315 **The Hen Harrier, Male and Female**
(Circus cyaneus)

U2316 **Sparrow Hawks, Male and Female**
(Accipiter nisus)

U2317 **Kestrels, Male and Female** (Falco
tinnunculus)

U2318 **Merlins, Male and Female** (Falco
columbarius)

U2319 **The Hobby** (Falco subbuteo)

U2320 **The White Barn Owl** (Tyto alba)

U2321 **The Long-eared Owl** (Asio otus)

U2347 **The Short-eared Owl** (Asio flammeus)

U2348 **The Ring-necked Pheasant** (Phasianius
colchicus)

U2387 **Common Pheasants, Male and Female**
(Pheasant) (Phasianius colchicus)

U2388 **Grouse, Male and Female** (Red Grouse)
(Lagopus lagopus) (*Illus.p.308*)

U2389 **Partridge, Male and Female** (Perdix
perdix)

U2390 **Quails, Male and Female** (Coturnix
coturnix)

U2391 **The Virginian Colin** (Bobwhite) (Colinus
virginianus)

U2392 **The Swan** (Bewick's Swan) (Cygnus
columbianus)

U2393 **The Bean Goose** (Anser fabalis)

U2394 **The Bernicle Goose** (Barnacle Goose)
(Branta leucopsis)

U2395 **The Brent Goose** (Branta bernicla hrota)

U2396 **The Shell Drake** (Shelduck) (Tadorna
tadorna)

U2397 **Mallard and Duck** (Anas platyrhynchos)

U2398 **Scaup Ducks, Male and Female** (Aythya
marila)

U2399 **The Tufted Duck** (Aythya fuligula)

U2400 **The Blue-winged Shoveller** (Shoveler)
(Anas clypeata)

U2401 **The Golden Eye, Male and Female**
(Bucephala clangula)

U2402 **Pintail Ducks, Male and Female** (Anas
acuta)

U2403 **Widgeon, Male and Female** (Widgeon)
(Anas penelope)

U2405 **Pochards, Male and Female** (Aythya
ferina)

U2406 **Teal, Male and Female** (Anas crecca)

U2407 **The Summer Duck, Male and Female**
(Wood Duck or Carolina Duck) (Aix
sponsa)

U2408 **The Long-tailed Duck, Male and Female**
(Clangula hyemalis)

U2409 **The Common Scoter, Male and Female**
(Melanitta nigra)

U2420 **The Red-breasted Mergansers, Male and
Female** (Mergus serrator)

U2422 **The Goosanders, Male and Female**
(Mergus merganser)

U2423 **Coots, Male and Female** (Fulica atra)

U2535 **The Grey Phalarope, in Summer and
Winter Plumage** (Phalaropus fulicarius)

U2545 **Moor-hens, Male and Female** (Gallinula
chloropus)

U2609 **Water-rails, Male and Female** (Rallus
aquaticus)

U2692 **The Land-rail or Corn Crake** (Crex crex)

U3472 **The Spotted Crake** (Porzana porzana)

U3473 **The Crane** (Grus grus)

U3474 **Herons, Male and Female** (Grey heron)
(Ardea cinerea)

U3475 **The Night Heron, Immature and Adult**
(Nycticorax nycticorax)

U3476 **The White Stork, with an Eel** (Ciconia
ciconia)

U3477 **The Squacco Heron** (Ardeola ralloides)

U3478 **The Bittern** (Botaurus stellaris)

U3479 **The Little Bittern** (Ixobrychus minutus)

U3480 **The Curlew** (Numenius arquata)

U3481 **The Whimbrel** (Numenius phaeopus)

U3482 **The Red-shank** (Tringa totanus)

U3483 **The Green Sandpipers, Male and Female**
(Tringa ochropus)

U3484 **The Common Sandpiper** (Tringa
hypoleucos)

U3485 **The Green-shank** (Tringa nebularia)

U3486 **The Avocet** (Recurvirostra avosetta)

U3487 **The Bar-tailed Godwit, in Summer and
Winter Plumage** (Limosa lapponica)

U3488 **The Black-tailed Godwit, in Summer and
Winter Plumage** (Limosa limosa)

U3489 **The Woodcock** (Scolopax rusticola)

U3490 **Snipe, Male and Female** (Gallinago
gallinago)(*Illus.p.308*)

U3491 **Jack-snipe, Male and Female**
(Lymnocryptes minimus)

U3492 **Sabine's Snipe**

U3493 **The Pigmy or Curlew Sandpiper**
(Calidris ferruginea)

U3494 **The Sanderlings, in Three Stages of
Plumage** (Calidris alba)

U3495 **The Little Stint, in Summer and Winter Plumage** (Calidris minuta)

U3496 **The Dunlin or Purre** (Calidris alpina)

U3497 **The Grey Plover, in Winter Plumage** (Pluvialis squatarola)

U3498 **The Golden Plover, in Summer and Winter Plumage** (Pluvialis apricaria)

U3499 **The Green Plover, Male and Female** (Lapwing) (Vanellus vanellus)

U3500 **The Knot, in Summer and Winter Plumage** (Calidris canutus)

U3501 **Ringed Plovers, Male and Female** (Charadrius hiaticula)

U3502 **The Rock Doves** (Columba livia)

U3503 **The Oyster Catcher, in Summer Plumage** (Haematopus ostralegus)

U3504 **The Magpie** (Pica pica)

U3505 **The Raven** (Corvus corax)

U3506 **The Hooded Crow** (Corvus corone cornix)

U3507 **The Rook** (Corvus frugilegus)

U3508 **Jackdaws, Male and Female** (Corvus monedula)

U3509 **The Chough, or Red-legged Crow** (Pyrrhocorax pyrrhocorax)

U3510 **Starlings, Male and Female** (Sturnus vulgaris)

U3511 **The Rose-coloured Pastor** (Rose-coloured Starling) (Sturnus roseus)

U3512 **The Jay** (Garrulus glandarius)

U3513 **The Night Jar** (Caprimulgus europaeus)

U3514 **The Cuckoo** (Cuculus canorus)

U3515 **The American Cuckoo** (Yellow-billed Cuckoo) (Coccyzus americanius)

U3516 **Wood Pigeons, Male and Female** (Columba palumbus)

U3517 **The Turtle Dove** (Streptopelia turtur)

U3518 **The King-fisher** (Alcedo atthis)

U3519 **Gannets, in Two Stages of Plumage, Adult and Immature, 1st Year** (Sula bassana) *(Illus.p.309)*

U3520 **The Great Diver, in Winter and Summer Plumage** (Great Northern Diver) (Gravia immer)

U3521 **The Red Throated Diver, in Summer and Winter Plumage** (Gravia stellata)

U3522 **The Great Crested Grebe, in Winter Plumage** (Podiceps cristatus)

U3523 **The Eared Grebe, in Summer and Winter Plumage** (Black-necked Grebe) (Podiceps nigricollis)

U3524 **The Little Grebes or Dabchicks, in Summer and Winter Plumage (?)** (Tachytaptus ruficollis)

U3525 **The Green Cormorant** (Shag) (Phalacrocorax aristotelis)

U3526 **The Common Cormorants, Adult and Immature** (Phalacrocorax carbo)

U3527 **The Guillemot, in Summer and Winter Plumage** (Uria aalge)

U3528 **The Black Guillemot, in Three Stages of Plumage** (Cepphus grylle)

U3529 **The Puffins or Sea Parrots, Male and Female** (Fratercula arctica)

U3530 **The Little Auks, Male and Female** (Alle alle)

U3531 **Razorbills, in Summer and Winter Plumage** (Alca torda)

U3532 **The Great Black-backed Gull, in Three Stages of Plumage** (Larus marinus)

U3533 **The Lesser Black-backed Gull** (Larus fuscus)

U3534 **The Herring Gull, in Three Stages of Plumage** (Larus argentatus)

U3535 **The Black-headed Gull, in Three Stages of Plumage** (Larus ridibundus)

U3536 **The Iceland Gull, Adult and Immature** (Larus glaucoides)

U3537 **The Ivory Gull** (Pagophila eburnea)

U3538 **The Common Gull, Immature** (Larus canus)

U3539 **The Kittiwake Gull, Immature and Adult** (Rissa tridactyla)

U3540 **The Arctic Gull** (Arctic Skua) (Stercorarius parasiticus)

U3541 **The Greater Shearwater** (Great Shearwater, Puffinus gravis. This, however, is the Sooty Shearwater, Puffinus griseus)

U3542 **The Manx Shearwater** (Puffinus puffinus)

U3543 **The Common Tern** (Sterna hirundo)

U3544 **The Black Tern, in Winter and Summer Plumage** (Childonias niger)

U3545 **The Sandwich Tern, in Summer Plumage** (Sterna sandvicensis)

U3546 **The Stormy Petrel** (Hydrobates pelagicus)

U3547 **The Water Ouzel** (Dipper) (Cinclus cinclus)

U3548 **The Great Grey Shrike, with a Fieldmouse** (Lanius excubitor)

U3549 **The Field Fare** (Turdus pilaris)

U3550 **The Ring Ouzel, Male and Female** (Turdus torquatus)

U3551 **The Missel Thrush** (Mistle Thrush) (Turdus viscovorus)

U3552 **The Song Thrush** (Turdus philomelos)

U3553 **The Red Wing** (Turdus iliacus)

U3554 **The Black Birds, Male and Female** (Turdus merula)

U3555 **The Golden Oriole, Male and Female** (Oriolus oriolus)

U3556 **The Hedge Accentor** (Hedge Sparrow or Dunnock) (Prunella modularis)

U3557 **The Robin** (Erithacus rubicula)

U3558 **The Blue Redstart** (Black Redstart) (Phoenicurus ochruros)

U3559 **The Stone Chats, Male and Female** (Saxicola torquata)

U3560 **The Wheatear, in Summer and Winter Plumage** (Oenanthe oenanthe)

U3561 **The Willow Warbler** (Phylloscopus trochilus. However, this is more like the Reedwarbler, Acrocephalus scirpaceus)

U3562 **The Black Cap Warbler** (Blackcap) (Sylvia atricapilla)

U3563 **The Spotted Flycatcher** (Muscicapa striata)

U3564 **The Gold Crested Regulus, Male and Female** (Goldcrest) (Regulus regulus)

U3565 **The Great Titmouse, Male and Female** (Great Tit) (Parus major)

U3566 **The Cole Titmouse, Male and Female** (Coal Tit) (Parus ater)

U3567 **The Long-tailed Titmouse** (Long-tailed Tit) (Aegithalos caudatus)

U3568 **The Bohemian Waxwing** (Waxwing) (Bombycilla garrulus)

U3569 **The Common Wren, Male and Female** (Troglodytes troglodytes)

U3570 **The Common Creeper** (Tree Creeper) (Certhia familiaris)

U3571 **The Hoopoe** (Upupa epops)

U3572 **Grey Wagtails, Male and Female** (Motacilla cinerea)

U3573 **The Pied Wagtails, Male and Female** (Motacilla alba yarrellii)

U3574 **The Sky Lark** (Alaunda arvensis)

U3575 **The Meadow Pipit** (Anthus pratensis)

U3576 **The Rock Pipit** (Anthus spinoletta)

U3577 **The Snow Bunting, in Winter Plumage** (Plectrophenax invalis)

U3578 **The Common Bunting** (Corn Bunting) (Emberiza calandra)

U3579 **The Black-headed Buntings, Male and Female** (Reed Bunting) (Emberiza schoenicus)

U3580 **The Yellow Ammers, Male and Female** (Yellow Hammer) (Emberiza citrinella)

U3581 **Chaffinches, Male and Female** (Fringilla coelebs)

U3582 **The Mountain Finches, Male and Female**

(Brambling in Winter Plumage) (Fringilla montifringilla)

U3583 **Green Finches, Male and Female**
(Carduelis chloris)

U3584 **Hawfinches, Male and Female**
(Coccothraustes coccothraustes)

U3585 **The House Sparrows, Male and Female**
(Passer domesticus)

U3586 **Bull Finches, Male and Female** (Pyrrhula pyrrhula)

U3587 **Common Crossbills, Male, Female and Immature** (Crossbill) (Loxia curvirostra)

U3588 **Gold Finches, Male and Female**
(Carduelis carduelis)

U3589 **Siskins, Male and Female** (Carduelis spinus)

U3590 **Common Linnets, Male and Female, in Summer Plumage** (Carduelis cannabina)

U3591 **Lesser Redpoles, Male and Female**
(Lesser Redpoll) (Carduelis flammea cabarct)

U3592 **The Mountain Linnets or Twites**
(Carduelis flavirostris)

U3593 **The Common Swift** (Apus apus)

U3594 **Swallow, Male and Female** (Hirundo rustica)

U3595 **Martins, Male and Female** (House Martin) (Delichon urbica)

U3596 **The Sand Martin** (Riparia riparia)

U4683 **The Blue Titmouse, Male and Female**
(Blue Tit) (Parus caerulus)

PARTRIDGE, Sir Bernard 1861-1945 (English)

U1399 **An Interval for Reflection (1924)**
(Illus.p.309)
Pencil, ink on paper 36.9 x 26.9
Signed
Donated by the National Art Collections
Fund, 1949

U1412 **A Son of Liberty (1922)**
Pencil, ink on paper 27.8 x 36.5
Signed
Donated by the National Art Collections
Fund, 1949

PASMORE, Victor 1908-98 (English)

U523 **Abstract in Black, White and Indigo
(Floating World) (1960-61)** *(Illus.p.309)*
Cellulose on formica 151 x 151
Signed, dated
Purchased 1964

U681 **Abstract Collage (1949)**
Paper on board 60.3 x 45.1
Signed
Purchased 1970

U697 **Still Life with Flowers (c.1939)**
(Illus.p.309)
Oil on canvas 45.8 x 35.6
Signed

Purchased 1970

PASTERNAK, Leonid 1862-1945 (Russian)

U4796 **Portrait of Lydia and Josephine
Pasternak (1920)**
Crayon on paper 36 x 24
Signed, dated
Bequeathed by Roberta and John Hewitt,
1987

PATERSON, Emily Murray 1855-1934 (Scottish)

U486 **The Gulls, Polperro** *(Illus.p.309)*
Oil on canvas 37.5 x 45.1
Signed
Donated by the artist's family (per Mrs.
H. Stevens), 1935

U836 **Wet Evening on the Riva, Venice**
(Illus.p.309)
Watercolour, bodycolour on paper 19.2 x
26.7
Signed
Donated by the artist's family (per Mrs.
H. Stevens), 1935

U837 **Street, Dordrecht**
Watercolour, bodycolour on paper 37.7. x
27.5
Signed
Donated by the artist's family (per Mrs.
H. Stevens), 1935

PATERSON, W. H. fl.c.1880-1910 (Irish)

U1321 **The 'W. J. Pirie' in Abercorn Basin,
Belfast (1883)**
Pencil, watercolour on paper 36.8 x 27
Signed, dated
Donated by the artist, 1907

PAUL, Joseph (of Norwich and London) d.1887
(English)

U619 **Mill Scene** *(Illus.p.309)*
Oil on canvas 122 x 91
Donated by Lady Edith Dixon, 1959

PAYNE, William fl.1776-1830 (English)

U1116 **View of the Wye, Monmouth, Moonlight**
Pencil, watercolour on paper 12 x 17.3
Purchased 1938

U1117 **View of the Tamar, Cornwall, Moonlight**
(Illus.p.309)
Ink, watercolour on paper 12 x 16.8
Signed
Purchased 1938

U1981 **Derwent Lake** *(Illus.p.309)*
Watercolour on paper 30.5 x 42.5
Provenance unknown

PEACOCK, Joseph 1783-1837 (Irish)

U120 **The Patron, or the Festival of St. Kevin at
the Seven Churches, Glendalough
(1813)** *(Illus.p.310)*
Oil on panel 86.4 x 137.8
Signed, dated
Purchased 1964

PEARSON, William fl.1772-1849 (English)

U838 **Landscape Composition** *(Illus.p.310)*
Pencil, watercolour on paper 20.6 x 32.2
Purchased 1954

PENLEY, Aaron Edwin 1807-70 (English)

U1118 **Loch Long, Argyle (1868)** *(Illus.p.310)*
Pencil, watercolour, white on paper 24.2
x 34.2
Signed, dated
Purchased 1938

PENPRAZE, Newton 1888-1978 (English,
worked in Ireland)

U2672 **The Mystic (c.1930s-'40s)** *(Illus.p.310)*
Sculpture, plaster on paper 65 x 39 x 46
Donated by R. N. Penpraze, 1983

U2677 **The Dawn of a New Day – Progress**
Oil on canvas 142.5 x 192.8
Donated by D. Penpraze, 1983

U2686 **Laughter**
Pencil on paper 54.5 x 35.6
Donated by R. N. Penpraze, 1983

U2687 **Rage**
Pencil on paper 54.5 x 35.6
Donated by R. N. Penpraze, 1983

U2688 **Remorse**
Pencil on paper 54.5 x 35.6
Donated by R. N. Penpraze, 1983

U2689 **Contemplation**
Pencil on paper 54.5 x 35.6
Donated by R. N. Penpraze, 1983

U2690 **Fear**
Pencil on paper 54.5 x 35.6
Donated by R. N. Penpraze, 1983

U2691 **Pain**
Pencil on paper 54.5 x 35.6
Donated by R. N. Penpraze, 1983

U2706 **Human Skeleton**
Charcoal, white on paper 74.5 x 40.8
Donated by J Warwick, 1984

U2707 **Ecorché Figure**
Chalk on paper 74.5 x 46.2
Donated by J. Warwick, 1984

PEPLOE, Samuel John 1871-1935 (Scottish)

U483 **Roses** *(Illus.p.310)*
Oil on canvas 50.9 x 40.5
Signed
Purchased 1932

PETERS, Rev. Matthew William 1741-1814
(Irish)

U717 **Portrait of a Lady with a Large Pointed
Hat (c.1786-93)** *(Illus.p. 310)*
Oil on panel 21.5 x 16.5
Signed
Purchased 1970

PETLEY, Roy b.1951 (English)

U4822 **Passing Storm, Norfolk**
Oil on canvas 60.9 x 91.5
Signed
Donated by Philip Solomon, 1990

PETRIE, George 1790-1866 (Irish)

U839 **Belfast from Turf Lodge**
Pencil, watercolour on paper 23.8 x 37.3
Purchased 1949

U840 **The Black Castle, Wicklow, from the
South (1819)** (formerly 'Rocky Coast
with Castle')
Pencil, wash on paper 20.3 x 29.7
Signed, dated
Purchased 1956

U1119 **Eagle's Nest, Killarney** *(Illus.p.310)*
Pencil, watercolour on paper 26.2 x 36.4
Purchased 1910

PHILLIPS, James J. 1843-1936 (Irish)

U2625 **Library of Rouen Cathedral**
Watercolour on card 31.1 x 22.2
Signed
Provenance unknown

U2626 **'La Turboise' (1905)**
Watercolour on card 24.1 x 15.9
Signed, dated
Provenance unknown

U2627 **Capital with Two Winged Creatures**
Watercolour on card 22.1 x 23.2
Provenance unknown

U2628 **L'Hotel de Colombey, Caen (1891)**
(Illus.p.310)
Watercolour on card 33 x 24.4
Signed, dated
Provenance unknown

U2629 **Capital with Winged Creature and Head**
Watercolour on card 22.1 x 21
Signed
Provenance unknown

U2630 **Capital with Human Heads**
Watercolour on card 18.4 x 22.2
Signed
Provenance unknown

U2631 **Capital with Leaves**
Watercolour on card 24.1 x 22.2
Provenance unknown

U2632 **Capital with Leaves and Berries**
Watercolour on card 24.3 x 20.9
Provenance unknown

U2633 **Capital with Human Head and Two
Birds**
Watercolour on card 19.7 x 21.9
Provenance unknown

U2634 **Steps and Iron Railing**
Watercolour on card 33.7 x 23.5
Provenance unknown

U2635 **Caernarvon Castle**
Watercolour on card 25.3 x 35.5
Signed
Provenance unknown

U2636 **Theatre of Dionysius, Athens**
Watercolour on card 11.1 x 36.5
Signed
Provenance unknown

U2637 **Mutilated Effigy**
Watercolour on card 15.9 x 34

Provenance unknown

U2638 **Capital with Human Head and Leaves**
Watercolour on card 23.8 x 27.9
Provenance unknown

U2639 **Down Cathedral**
Watercolour on card 36.2 x 25.1
Signed
Provenance unknown

U2640 **Sketch for a Head**
Watercolour, pencil on card 9.5 x 9.5
Provenance unknown

U2641 **Three Niches of Down Cathedral**
Watercolour on card 16.8 x 9.5
Provenance unknown

U2642 **Sketch of a Horse**
Pencil on card 9.5 x 9.8
Provenance unknown

PHILLIPS, Peter b.1939 (English)

U2414 **Mosaikbild 6 x 11 (1975)**
Acrylic on canvas 170.8 x 300.2
Signed, dated
Purchased 1976

PHILLIPS, Tom b.1937 (English)

U4826 **Portrait of Barry Douglas b.1960 (1990)**
(Illus.p.310)
Oil on three canvases, 60.7 x 127 overall
Commissioned 1989

PHILP, James George 1816-85 (English)

U1120 **View Looking towards Falmouth (1855)**
(Illus.p.311)
Pencil, watercolour on paper 38.2 x 63.5
Signed, dated
Purchased 1936

PHILPOT, Glyn Warren 1884-1937 (English)

U390 **Portrait of a Young Man (c.1920)**
(Illus.p.311)
Oil on canvas on board 44.2 x 41.2
Signed
Purchased (Lloyd Patterson Collection)
1929

PIENE, Otto b.1928 (German)

U530 **Purgatory Flower (1963-64)** *(Illus.p.311)*
Oil, smoke, fire on canvas 100.3 x 81.2
Signed, dated
Purchased 1965

PILKINGTON, Sir William, Bt. c.1775-1850
(English)

U2109 **View on the Palatine Hill, Rome**
(Illus.p.311)
Pencil, watercolour on paper 22.2 x 28.6
Purchased 1956

PINWELL, George John 1842-75 (English)

U1121 **The Last Load (1869)** *(Illus.p.311)*
Watercolour on paper 41.7 x 61.1
Signed, dated
Purchased 1952

PIPER, John 1903-92 (English)

U4686 **Bladon (1945)** *(Illus.p.311)*
Watercolour on paper 55.9 x 74.2 (sight)
Signed, dated
Bequeathed by Norah McGuinness (per
the Friends of the National Collections of
Ireland), 1982

PIPER, Raymond b.1923 (English, works in
Ireland)

U1218 **William Conor 1881-1968 (1962)**
(Illus.p.311)
Pencil on paper 38.3 x 28.1
Signed, dated
Donated by the artist, 1967

U1538 **Carlingford Lough (1956)**
Pencil on paper 28 x 38.5
Signed, dated
Purchased 1963

U5040 **Councillor Mrs. Florence E. Breakie,
OBE, JP (1959)**
Oil on canvas 75.8 x 63
Signed, dated
Donated by J. Harcourt, 1996

PISSARRO, Lucien 1863-1944 (French,
naturalised British)

U124 **The Allotments (1917)** *(Illus.p.311)*
Oil on canvas 53.5 x 65.1
Purchased 1923

U485 **Trippleton Farm (1932)** *(Illus.p.311)*
Oil on canvas 53.9 x 43.2
Signed, dated
Purchased (Lloyd Patterson Collection)
1932

PITCHFORTH, Roland Vivian 1895-1982
(English)

U1122 **Londonderry Base (1944)** *(Illus.p.312)*
Pencil, watercolour on paper 46.8 x 77
Signed, dated
Donated by the War Artists' Advisory
Committee (per the Imperial War
Museum), 1946

U1219 **Frigate at Pollock Dock, Belfast (1944)**
(Illus.p.312)
Pencil, watercolour on paper 55.8 x 76.1
Signed, dated
Donated by the War Artists' Advisory
Committee (per the Imperial War
Museum), 1946

U4703 **Frigates at Pollock Dock, Belfast (1944)**
Watercolour on paper 45.8 x 79
Signed, dated
Donated by the War Artists' Advisory
Committee (per the Imperial War
Museum), 1946

U4704 **Submarines at Londonderry for Training
Escorts (1944)**
Watercolour, pencil on paper 56 x 76
Signed, dated
Donated by the War Artists' Advisory
Committee (per the Imperial War
Museum), 1946

U4705 **Ferry to Naval Barracks, Londonderry
(1944)**
Watercolour, pencil on paper 51.5 x 76

Signed, dated
Donated by the War Artists' Advisory
Committee (per the Imperial War
Museum), 1946

**U4706 Castle Class Escort at Londonderry Base
(1944)**
Watercolour, pencil on paper 56 x 76
Signed, dated
Donated by the War Artists' Advisory
Committee (per the Imperial War
Museum), 1946

PLACE, George c.1750-1805 (Irish)

U1902 William Ware (c.1790) *(Illus.p.312)*
Miniature, watercolour on ivory 6 x 5.1
Purchased 1973

POCOCK, Nicholas 1740-1821 (British)

**U122 Attack of the French Squadron under
Mons. Bompart Chef d'Escadre upon the
Coast of Ireland by a Detachment of His
Majesty's Ships under Command of Sir J.
B. Warren, Oct. 12, 1798 (1799)**
(Illus.p.312)
Oil on canvas 69.4 x 99.5
Signed, dated
Donated by the Hon. William Warren-
Vernon, 1915

**U123 Pursuit of the French Squadron after the
Surrender of 'Le Hoche 84' and
'Coquille 44', with the Action of the
'Ethalion' and 'Bellone' and the 'Anson',
Bearing Down the Van Ships of the
Enemy, Oct. 12, 1798**
Oil on canvas 70 x 100
Signed
Donated by the Hon. William Warren-
Vernon, 1915

U2302 Stormy Scene on Rocky Coast (1792)
(Illus.p.312)
Watercolour on paper 35 x 48.5
Signed, dated
Purchased 1956

POLIDORO da Caravaggio 1492-1543 (Italian)
(after)

U2114 Two Putti *(Illus.p.312)*
Ink, gouache on paper 21.2 x 20.7
Donated by J. H. Stirling, 1919

POLIS, Miervaldis b.1948 (Russian)

U2520 Self-Portrait (1975) *(Illus.p.312)*
Pencil on paper 24.1 x 16.8
Signed, dated
Purchased 1977

POMEROY, Frederick William 1856-1924
(English)

**U1807 Frederick Temple, 1st Marquess of
Dufferin and Ava 1826-1902 (1905)**
Sculpture, bronze statuette, ht. 21.3; base
17
Signed, dated
Donated by R. Turtle, 1941

POPE-STEVENS, Thomas fl.1765-80 (Irish)

U5010 John Reilly of Scarva, Co. Down, MP

1745-1804 (1775) *(Illus.p.312)*
Oil on canvas 123 x 99
Dated
Purchased 1994

PORTA, Fra Guglielmo della d.1577 (Italian)
(after)

U1786 Dante Alighieri 1265-1321
Sculpture, bronze, ht. 31.8
Purchased 1891

PORTER, Frederick James 1883-1944 (British)

U482 A View from the Artist's Studio (1931)
(Illus.p.312)
Oil on canvas 59.9 x 73.5
Signed, dated
Purchased (Lloyd Patterson Collection)
1932

PRAEGER, Sophia Rosamond 1867-1954 (Irish)

U1176 The Philosopher (1908)
Sculpture, bronze 43.2 x 16.3 x 22.5
Signed
Donated by the artist, 1947

U1177 The Philosopher (c.1920) *(Illus.p.313)*
Sculpture, marble 43.2 x 16.3 x 22.5
Signed
Donated by the artist, 1929

U1767 The Fairy Fountain (c.1900-1)
(Illus.p.313)
Sculpture, marble 64.8 x 76.5 x 16.5
Signed
Purchased 1926

U2028 Robert Lloyd Praeger 1865-1953
Sculpture, plaster bust, ht. 30
Donated by Mr. and Mrs. Richard
McLachlan, 1999

U2217 Tug-of-War in Hopton Wood (c.1934)
Sculpture, relief in Irish limestone 18.5 x
72.5 x 6
Purchased 1947

U2218 Spring (c.1934)
Sculpture, relief in Irish limestone 18.5 x
72.5 x 6
Purchased 1947

U2221 Old Hannah (c.1900-20)
Sculpture, plaster bust, ht. 32.4
Donated by J. A. Cleland, DL, 1941

U2224 Child Feeding Birds (c.1900-30)
Sculpture, plaster frieze, 33.4 x 18
Signed
Bequeathed by Miss H. M. McCleery,
1968

**U2226 Fionnuala, the Daughter of Lir (c.1910-
11)**
Sculpture, plaster frieze, 32.4 x 20.5
Bequeathed by Miss H. M. McCleery,
1968

**U2227 Fionnuala, the Daughter of Lir (c.1910-
11)**
Sculpture, plaster frieze, 49.5 x 30
Bequeathed by Miss H. M. McCleery,
1968

U2228 By Donegal Bay (c.1910)

Sculpture, plaster frieze, 33.2 x 17.4
Signed
Donated by Judge Arnold Praeger, 1969

U2229 Three Figures with Baskets (c.1900-30)
Sculpture, plaster 30.5 x 20.3
Signed
Donated by Judge Arnold Praeger, 1969

U2230 The Shawls (c.1930)
Sculpture, plaster frieze, 30.2 x 63.5
Signed
Donated by Dr. A. Boyd, 1969

U2478 Two Seated Children (1928-29)
Sculpture, lead, concrete 136.5 x 61.6
Signed
Donated by C. Lindsay, 1978

U4712 Two Children
Sculpture, plaster 25 x 13 x 18
Bequeathed by Miss H. M. McCleery,
1968

U4713 Girl with a Baby
Sculpture, plaster 17 x 9 x 15.4
Bequeathed by Miss H. M. McCleery,
1968

U4714 Pulman Statuette
Sculpture, plaster 11 x 12.5 x 5.5
Bequeathed by Miss H. M. McCleery,
1968

U4715 Safety First (1931)
Sculpture, plaster 17.8 x 6.5 x 9.5
Signed, dated
Bequeathed by Miss H. M. McCleery,
1968

U4716 St. Fiachra (c.1938)
Sculpture, plaster 21.8 x 7.5 x 14.2
Signed
Bequeathed by Miss H. M. McCleery,
1968

U4717 Sleeping Boy
Sculpture, plaster 21.3 x 9.6 x 5
Signed
Bequeathed by Miss H. M. McCleery,
1968

U4718 The First Aeroplane (c.1927)
Sculpture, plaster 17 x 17 x 11.7
Signed
Bequeathed by Miss H. M. McCleery,
1968

U4719 The Philosopher
Sculpture, plaster, ht. 19
Signed
Bequeathed by Miss H. M. McCleery,
1968

U4720 St. Brigid of Kildare
Sculpture, plaster, ht. 15
Bequeathed by Miss H. M. McCleery,
1968

PRATT, William b.1855 fl.1880-1936 (Scottish)

U564 Burning the Shaws *(Illus.p.313)*
Oil on canvas 50.9 x 41
Signed
Donated by Mrs. A. Thompson and Miss
L. Stevenson, 1935

PRIESTMAN, Bertram 1868-1951 (English)

U127 **Wooded Hillside (1910)**
Oil on canvas 87 x 122
Signed, dated
Purchased 1911

PRITCHETT, Edward 1828-64 (English)

U125 **Piazza San Marco, Venice** *(Illus.p.339)*
Now by Unknown, 19th century (Italian)

PROUT, John Skinner 1806-76 (English)

U1123 **Kenilworth Castle** *(Illus.p.313)*
Pencil, watercolour on paper 23.8 x 36
Purchased 1914

PROUT, Samuel 1783-1852 (English)

U841 **Chapel in the Château d'Amboise**
(Illus.p.313)
Ink, watercolour, white on paper 46 x
33.1
Signed
Purchased 1948

PUECH, Denys Pierre 1854-1942 (French)
(after)

U1809 **La Syrène**
Sculpture, bronze, ht. 81.2
Purchased 1892

PURSER, Sarah Henrietta 1848-1943 (Irish)

U121 **An Irish Idyll** *(Illus.p.313)*
Oil on canvas 76.5 x 64.7
Bequeathed by Dr. R. I. Best (per the
Friends of the National Collections of
Ireland), 1959

U1258 **John Kells Ingram 1823-1907 (1890)**
(Illus.p.313)
Pastel on paper 60.9 x 45.5
Signed, dated
Donated by W. A. Ingram, 1931

U4963 **John Butler Yeats 1839-1922 (c.1901)**
(Illus.p.313)
Pencil on paper 12 x 21 (sight)
Purchased 1993

PYE, Patrick b.1929 (Irish)

U1759 **Still Life Study with Flowers** *(Illus.p.313)*
Pastel on paper 17.6 x 11.5
Purchased 1966

PYNAS, Jan Symonsz 1583/84-1631 (Dutch)

U721 **Adoration of the Golden Calf**
(Illus.p.314)
Oil on canvas 120.5 x 179.6
Purchased 1967

Q

QUINTON, Eugène d.1892 (French) (after)

U4854 **Chasseur à la Source (1888)**
Sculpture, bronze, ht. 96.5
Signed, dated
Purchased 1893

R

R., H. H. [H. H. R.] 20th century (British?)

U4505 **Portrait of a Man (1937)**
Oil on canvas 91.5 x 71
Signed, dated
Provenance unknown

RABINOWITCH, Royden b.1943 (Canadian)

U2694 **Barrel Construction (1964)** *(Illus.p.314)*
Sculpture, wood 88.5 x 88.5 x 9.5
Dated
Donated by the artist, 1983

RAE, Henrietta 1859-1928 (English)

U662 **John Horner 1858-1919 (1913)**
Oil on canvas 89 x 73.8 (oval)
Signed, dated
Donated by Mrs. S. G. Callender-Bullock,
1928

RAINEY, Clifford b.1948 (Irish)

U2336 **Waiting for the Morrow in the
Knowledge that Yesterday's Gone (1974)**
Sculpture, glass, mirror, chromed steel
132.3 x 139.3 x 108.4
Purchased 1975

U2410 **Portrait of William Scott 1913-89 (1976)**
(Illus.p.314)
Pencil on paper 57 x 76
Signed, dated
Purchased 1976

U2411 **Portrait of F. E. McWilliam 1909-92
(1976)** *(Illus.p.314)*
Pencil on paper 57 x 76
Signed, dated
Purchased 1976

U2697 **Bristol Maquette (1978)**
Sculpture, mixed media, stone, glass
304.8 x 91.5 x 91.5
Signed
Purchased 1981

RAKOCZI, Basil 1908-79 (English)

U4892 **Chez les Sinclair (c.1956)** *(Illus.p.314)*
Oil on canvas 130 x 162
Signed
Purchased 1992

U4893 **Nature Morte au Téléphone (1958)**
(Illus.p.314)
Oil on canvas 73 x 92
Donated by Mme. Jacqueline Robinson,
1992

RAMSAY, Sinclair 19th-20th century (British)

U1995 **Artillery Barracks**
Oil on canvas 46.3 x 30.5
Purchased 1917

U1996 **Front of Cooney's Court**
Oil on canvas 36.5 x 26.6
Purchased 1917

U1997 **Old Houses, High Street (1888)**
Oil on canvas 40.6 x 30.5

Purchased 1917

U1998 **Site of Belfast Castle**
Oil on canvas 35.5 x 25.3
Purchased 1917

RANDALL-PAGE, Peter b.1954 (English)

U4938 **Dark Fruit (1989)** *(Illus.p.314)*
Sculpture, Kilkenny limestone (two
components) 106.7 x 50.8 x 50.8
Donated by the Contemporary Art
Society, 1992

RANKIN, William Bruce Ellis 1881-1941
(British)

U1600 **Sketch for 'The Winning Eight' (1921)**
(Illus.p.314)
Pastel on paper 80.8 x 65.7
Signed, dated
Donated by Mrs. E. Thesiger, 1946

U1655 **Stormy Day (1926)**
Oil on board 66 x 50.7
Signed, dated
Donated by Mrs. E. Thesiger, 1946

RAYNER, Margaret fl.1866-95 (English)

U2683 **Haddon Hall Chapel** *(Illus.p.314)*
Watercolour, bodycolour on paper 47 x
59.7
Bequeathed by Miss E. Taylor, 1983

RAYNER, Samuel fl.1821-72 d.1874 (English)

U1124 **West Porch, Lichfield Cathedral**
(Illus.p.315)
Watercolour, bodycolour on paper 34.6 x
24.4
Purchased 1937

READ, Samuel 1815-83 (English)

U2481 **Glenarm, July 26 (1874)**
Pencil on paper 8.5 x 12.3
Dated
Purchased 1978

U2482 **Glenarm, Ireland, July 26 (1874)**
Pencil on paper 8.5 x 12.3
Dated
Purchased 1978

U2483 **Giant's Causeway, July 30 (1874)**
Pencil on paper 8.5 x 12.3
Dated
Purchased 1978

U2484 **Gateway, Glenarm Castle, July 27 (1874)**
Pencil on paper 12.3 x 8.5
Dated
Purchased 1978

U2485 **Amphitheatre, Causeway, July 29 (1874)**
Pencil, white on paper 8.5 x 12.3
Dated
Purchased 1978

U2486 **Fairhead from Ballycastle, July 27 (1874)**
(Fair Head)
Pencil on paper 8.5 x 12.3
Dated
Purchased 1978

U2487 **On the Walls, Londonderry, August 2**

(1874)
Pencil on paper 12.3 x 8.5
Dated
Purchased 1978

U2488 **Carrick-a-Rede, July 29 (1874)**
Pencil, white on paper 8.5 x 12.3
Dated
Purchased 1978

U2489 **Carrickfergus Castle, July 25 (1874)**
Pencil on paper 8.5 x 12.3
Dated
Purchased 1978

U2490 **The Grey Man, July 28 (1874)**
(Illus.p.315)
Pencil, white on paper 12.3 x 8.5
Dated
Purchased 1978

U2491 **The Grey Man's Path, Co. Antrim, July 28 (1874)**
Pencil on paper 12.3 x 8.5
Dated
Purchased 1978

U2492 **The Grey Man's Path, July 28 (1874)**
Pencil, white on paper 12.3 x 8.5
Dated
Purchased 1978

U2493 **The White Rocks, Portrush, August 1 (1874)**
Pencil, white on paper 8.5 x 12.3
Dated
Purchased 1978

U2494 **Portrush, August 1 (1874)**
Pencil, white on paper 8.5 x 12.3
Dated
Purchased 1978

U2495 **White Rocks, Portrush, July 31 (1874)**
Pencil, white on paper 8.5 x 12.3
Dated
Purchased 1978

U2496 **Portrush, August 1 (1874)**
Pencil, white on paper 12.3 x 8.5
Dated
Purchased 1978

U2497 **Portrush, August 1 (1874)**
Pencil, white on paper 8.5 x 12.3
Dated
Purchased 1978

U2498 **Dunluce, Ireland, August 1 (1874)**
Pencil, white on paper 8.5 x 12.3
Dated
Purchased 1978

U2499 **Dunluce Castle, July 31 (1874)**
Pencil, white on paper 8.5 x 12.3
Dated
Purchased 1978

U2500 **Garron Point, July 27 (1874)**
Pencil on paper 8.5 x 12.3
Dated
Purchased 1978

U2501 **Fair Head, July 28 (1874)**
Pencil, white on paper 8.5 x 12.3
Dated
Purchased 1978

U2502 **Fair Head, Co. Antrim, July 28 (1874)**
Pencil, white on paper 8.5 x 12.3
Dated
Purchased 1978

U2503 **Hill of Howth, Dublin Bay, May 11 (1865)**
Pencil on paper 8.5 x 12.3
Dated
Purchased 1978

U2504 **Bray Head, Ireland, May 7 (1865)**
Pencil, white on paper 12.3 x 8.5
Dated
Purchased 1978

U2505 **Hill of Howth, Ireland's Eye, May 11 (1865)**
Pencil on paper 8.5 x 12.3
Dated
Purchased 1978

REEVE, Russell Sidney 1895-1970 (English)

U1125 **Riverside, Norwich (1923)** *(Illus.p.315)*
Watercolour on paper 22.8 x 29.1
Signed, dated
Purchased 1927

REID, Nano 1910-81 (Irish)

U397 **Old Stables (early 1960s)**
Oil on board 45.7 x 61.1
Signed
Purchased 1964

U400 **The Lilter (1933)** *(Illus.p.315)*
Oil on canvas 51.2 x 40.6
Signed
Donated by the Thomas Haverty Trust, 1941

U401 **Galway Peasant (1929)** *(Illus.p.315)*
Oil on canvas 41 x 30.7
Signed
Donated by the Thomas Haverty Trust, 1936

REYNOLDS, Sir Joshua 1723-92 (English)

U692 **Miss Theodosia Magill 1744-1817, afterwards Countess of Clanwilliam (1765)** *(Illus.p.90)*
Oil on canvas 127 x 101.6
Purchased with the aid of grants from the Pilgrim Trust, the Gallaher-Mitchell Trust, the National Art Collections Fund and public subscription, 1970

RICCI, Sebastiano 1659-1734 (Italian)

U145 **Archimedes and Hiero at the Siege of Syracuse**
Oil on canvas 105.2 x 84.8
Donated by Miss A. P. Norris (per Portstewart Urban District Council), 1941

RICE, Noreen fl.1956-90 (Irish)

U4806 **Dun Aengus**
Pastel on paper; measurements unknown
Purchased 1990

RICH, Alfred William 1856-1921 (English)

U1126 **Distant View of Lincoln** *(Illus.p.315)*
Watercolour on paper 28.4 x 40
Signed
Purchased 1955

U1322 **Landscape with Distant Windmill**
Pencil, watercolour on paper 13 x 27.5
Signed
Purchased 1954

RICHARD, W. 19th century (French)

U1487 **Italian Farm and Stream** *(Illus.p.315)*
Watercolour, wash, pencil on paper 29.4 x 35.3
Donated by J. H. Bland, 1910

RICHARDS, Ceri 1903-71 (Welsh)

U516 **La Cathédrale Engloutie (Dialogue du Vent et de la Mer) (1962)** *(Illus.p.315)*
Oil on canvas 127 x 127
Signed, dated
Purchased 1963

RICHARDSON, Jennifer b.1944 (Scottish, works in Ireland)

U2292 **In the Fields (1974)** *(Illus.p.315)*
Acrylic on board 76.5 x 60.9
Signed
Purchased 1975

RICKATSON, Octavius fl.1880-93 (British)

U719 **Landscape**
Oil on panel 24.1 x 35.5
Signed
Provenance unknown

RICKETTS, Charles de Sousy 1866-1931 (British)

U842 **Costume for 'The Mikado' (1926)** *(Illus.p.316)*
Pencil, watercolour on paper 50.6 x 49.5
Dated
Donated by the National Art Collections Fund, 1933

RILEY, Bridget b.1931 (English)

U533 **Cataract IV (1967)** *(Illus.p.316)*
Emulsion on canvas 221 x 223.5
Purchased 1968

RILEY, John 1646-91 (British) (attributed to)

U223 **Man in Armour**
Oil on canvas 75.5 x 63.3 (oval)
Purchased 1959

RITCHIE, Anna b.1937 (Australian, worked in Ireland)

U393 **Dark Composition**
Oil on canvas 91.5 x 81.3
Signed
Purchased 1962

U402 **Sudden Flight**
Oil on canvas on board 28.2 x 31.7
Signed
Provenance unknown

RIVERS, Elizabeth 1903-64 (English, worked in

Ireland)

U495 **Cat and Egg** *(Illus.p.316)*
Oil on canvas 56 x 68.5
Signed
Purchased 1953

ROBERTS, David 1796-1864 (Scottish)

U1323 **Church of San Iago, Jerez, Spain
(c.1833)** *(Illus.p.316)*
Pencil, watercolour, white on paper 41.2
x 28.8
Purchased 1937

ROBERTS, David 1796-1864 (Scottish)
(attributed to)

U140 **Roman Remains at Nijmegen** *(Illus.p.316)*
Oil on board 20.3 x 39.3
Bequeathed by H. Musgrave, 1922

ROBERTS, Hilda 1901-82 (Irish)

U392 **Portrait of George Russell ('AE') 1867-
1935 (1929)** *(Illus.p.316)*
Oil on canvas 76.2 x 63.8
Signed, dated
Purchased 1936

U1866 **John Lyle Donaghy 1902-47 (1928)**
(Illus.p.316)
Oil on panel 75.9 x 54.3
Signed
Purchased 1973

ROBERTS, William Patrick 1895-1980 (English)

U492 **Les Routiers (c.1931)** *(Illus.p. 316)*
Oil on canvas 101.7 x 76.3
Signed
Purchased (Lloyd Patterson Collection)
1933

U496 **Sawing Wood (c.1930)** *(Illus p.316)*
Oil on canvas 46 x 61.1
Signed
Purchased (Lloyd Patterson Collection)
1930

U1324 **Watching a Raid** *(Illus.p.317)*
Pencil, watercolour on paper 35.4 x 25.3
Signed
Donated by the Contemporary Art
Society, 1964

ROBINSON, Anne Marjorie 1858-1924 (Irish)

U97 **Self-Portrait**
Oil on canvas 66.2 x 50.8
Donated by John B. Robinson, 1929

U1127 **Cavehill from Belfast Harbour**
(Illus.p.317)
Watercolour on card 21.3 x 46.6
Signed
Donated by the Belfast Art Society in
memory of the artist, 1927

U2256 **Fate, Love and Life (c.1913)**
Sculpture, bronze 18.4 x 13.3 x 12.1
Signed
Donated by John B. Robinson, 1925

U2276 **A Study from Life (c.1911)**
Sculpture, plaster 29.2 x 17.1 x 18.4
Purchased 1911

U4515 **Twenty-two Miniatures Donated by the
-4536** **Artist's Brother, John B. Robinson as a
Memorial, 1925**

U4515 **Unknown Lady in Widow's Weeds**
Watercolour on ivory 4.5 x 3.5 (sight)
(oval)

U4516 **Man in an Elizabethan Ruff**
Watercolour on ivory 10 x 7.5 (sight)
Signed

U4517 **Reverie (1914)** *(Illus.p.317)*
Watercolour on ivory 9 x 7.5 (sight)
Signed, dated

U4518 **Girl with Long Dark Hair**
Watercolour on ivory 9 x 6.8 (sight)
Signed

U4519 **Lady in Fur Coat and Broad-brimmed
Hat**
Watercolour on ivory 7.8 x 6.7 (sight)

U4520 **A Study** (Bearded Man in White Tie)
Watercolour on ivory 9 x 7.2 (sight)

U4521 **The Gipsy**
Watercolour on ivory 9 x 7 (sight)

U4522 **Lady with Red Hair**
Watercolour on ivory 7 x 5.6 (sight)
Signed

U4523 **Lady with Dark Hair**
Watercolour on ivory 8.5 x 7 (sight)

U4524 **Woman in Picturesque Costume Peeling
a Vegetable**
Watercolour on ivory 11.5 x 7.7 (sight)

U4525 **Seated Man in Red Coat**
Watercolour on ivory 10.5 x 7.5 (sight)

U4526 **Reverie**
Watercolour on ivory 8 x 10.5 (sight)
(oval)
Signed

U4527 **The Fortune Teller**
Watercolour on ivory 9.2 x 7 (sight)

U4528 **Head of a Girl in an Orange Blouse**
Watercolour on ivory, diameter 3 (sight)
(circular)

U4529 **Young Girl with Red Plaited Hair**
Watercolour on ivory 6 x 4.7 (sight)
(oval)

U4530 **An Early Victorian** *(Illus.p.317)*
Watercolour on ivory 9 x 7 (sight)
Signed

U4531 **A Study** (Girl with Brown Plaited Hair)
Watercolour on ivory 7 x 5.5 (sight)

U4532 **The Velvet Cap**
Watercolour on ivory 8.3 x 6.5 (sight)
Signed

U4533 **A Study** (White-haired Lady)
Watercolour on ivory 6 x 4.8 (sight)
(oval)

U4534 **Man with White Pointed Beard**
Watercolour on ivory 8.7 x 7.5 (sight)
(oval)

U4535 **Girl in Empire Dress with Black Bonnet**

Watercolour on ivory 9 x 7.5 (sight)
(oval)

U4536 **Dark-haired Girl in Black Evening Dress**
Watercolour on ivory 10 x 7.8 (sight)

U4828 **Brigid, the Mary of the Gaels**
Pencil on paper 134.6 x 58.4
Donated by John B. Robinson as a
memorial to the artist, 1925

U4829 **St. Cecilia (?)**
Pencil on paper 134.6 x 58.4
Donated by John B. Robinson as a
memorial to the artist, 1925

U4830 **Brigit**
Pencil on paper 99 x 54.6
Donated by John B. Robinson as a
memorial to the artist, 1925

U5004 **Brigit Feeding the Poor; The Baptism of
St. Brigit by Angels; It was Brigit Wove
the First Cloth in Ireland (1918)**
(Two Illus.p.317)
Oil on canvas, three panels, each 134 x
58.5
Signed, dated
Donated by John B. Robinson as a
memorial to the artist, 1925

ROBINSON, Markey 1918-99 (Irish)

U395 **Bomb Crater in Eglinton Street (1941)**
Gouache on cardboard 49.5 x 58.5
Signed
Donated by Councillor P. Brown, 1943

U2433 **Unknown (1945)**
Oil on canvas 53.2 x 69
Signed, dated
Provenance unknown

U4798 **Woman in White** *(Illus.p.317)*
Oil on board 74 x 46
Bequeathed by Roberta and John Hewitt,
1987

U5051 **Flower Market near the Madeleine**
(Illus.p.317)
Oil on panel 50.8 x 69.2 (sight)
Signed
Provenance unknown

ROBINSON, Thomas d.1810 (English, worked in
Ireland)

U136 **Portrait of a Young Man, possibly a
United Irishman (1798)** *(Illus.p.317)*
Oil on canvas 76.8 x 63.1
Signed, dated
Purchased 1967

U137 **William Ritchie 1756-1834 (c.1800-8)**
Oil on canvas 75.5 x 63.2
Donated by J. J. Ritchie, 1943

U141 **Colonel William Sharman 1731-1803
(1798)** *(Illus.p.317)*
Oil on canvas 127 x 101
Signed, dated
Purchased 1947

U144 **William Ritchie 1756-1834 (c.1802)**
(Illus.p.318)
Oil on canvas 93.7 x 74.6
Donated by A. MacLaine, JP, 1892

ROBINSON, William Heath 1872-1944
(English)

U1400 A Missionary Being Boiled by Cannibals
(Illus.p.318)
Ink, wash on card 31.1 x 29.6
Signed
Provenance unknown

ROBSON, George Fennel 1788-1833 (English)

U1128 Farmstead with Figures and Trees
(Illus.p.318)
Pencil, watercolour, white on paper 24.3
x 33.2
Purchased 1935

ROCH[E], Sampson Towgood 1757/59-1847
(Irish)

U2516 Rustics Dancing outside an Inn
(Illus.p.318)
Watercolour on paper 19.3 x 26.2
Signed
Purchased 1979

ROCHE, Vivienne b.1953 (Irish)

U5007 Quinata
Sculpture, metal 75 x 90
Donated by the Contemporary Irish Art
Society (per Gordon Lambert), 1994

RODGERS, Patsy Dan 20th century (Irish)

U2445 Tory in a Storm (c.1977) *(Illus.p.318)*
Acrylic on board 79.2 x 67.7
Signed
Purchased 1977

ROGERS, Claude 1907-79 (British)

U722 Bonding Warehouses, Bristol
Oil on canvas 13.3 x 17.8
Signed
Purchased 1970

ROLDAN, Alfredo 20th century (Spanish)

U650 Antes de la Ducha (1997) *(Illus.p.318)*
Oil on canvas 162 x 97
Signed, dated
Donated by Philip Solomon, 1998

ROMANELLI, Giovanni Francesco c.1610-62
(Italian)

U142 St. Cecilia *(Illus.p.91)*
Oil on canvas 100 x 137
Purchased 1965

ROMBOUTS, Adriaen fl.1660-67 (Flemish)

U138 Pancake Night (1667) *(Illus.p.318)*
Oil on panel 44.5 x 34.9
Signed, dated
Donated by W. T. Braithwaite (per J.
Horner), 1906

ROOKER, Michael 'Angelo' 1743-1801 (English)

U1647 View in Hyde Park *(Illus.p.318)*
Ink, watercolour on paper 21.9 x 30.8
Signed
Purchased 1937

ROSANDIC, Toma 1878-1958 (Yugoslavian)

U1811 Ecce Homo (1915) *(Illus.p.318)*
Sculpture, bronze 104.1 x 20.3 x 18.4
Purchased 1931

**U2074 The Laying of Christ in the Tomb:
Altarpiece from the Petrinovic
Mausoleum in Brac, Dalmatia (1925)**
Sculpture, wood 92.4 x 236.2 x 7.6
Signed
Purchased 1931

**U4835 Study for 'The Laying of Christ in the
Tomb' (U2074)**
Pencil on paper 63.5 x 203.2
Signed
Provenance unknown

ROSLYN, Louis Frederick 1878-1949 (English)

**U2257 Sir Robert Baird, KBE, DL 1855-1934
(1925)**
Sculpture, bronze bust, ht. 64.1
Signed, dated
Donated by subscribers, 1929-30

ROSSETTI, Dante Gabriel 1828-82 (English)

**U843 Study of Elizabeth Siddal 1834-62, for
'The Return of Tibullus to Delia'**
(Illus.p.319)
Pencil on paper 32.9 x 19.4
Donated by the National Art Collections
Fund, 1947

**U3598 Study of Elizabeth Siddal 1834-62, for
'The Return of Tibullus to Delia' (1851)**
(Illus.p.319)
Pencil on paper 28.7 x 18.7
Dated
Donated by the National Art Collections
Fund, 1947

ROTHENSTEIN, Sir William 1872-1945
(English)

U494 Oakridge Farm, Late Summer (c.1925)
(Illus.p.319)
Oil on canvas 61.5 x 101.7
Purchased (Lloyd Patterson Collection)
1929

**U1750 John Rothenstein as a Child, Feeding
Hens (1904)** *(Illus.p.319)*
Pastel on paper 31.6 x 24.4
Signed, dated
Purchased 1956

ROTHWELL, Marguerita Rosalie fl.1881-89
(Irish)

**U157 Robert Patterson, FRS, MRIA 1802-72
(1889)** *(Illus.p.319)*
Oil on canvas 45.7 x 40.5
Signed, dated
Donated by the Misses R. and F. F. and
Mr. R. R. Patterson, 1943 (the Rothwell
Bequest)

U4493 Isabella M. S. Tod 1836-96 (1897)
Oil on canvas 114.8 x 86
Donated by the Presentation Committee,
1897

ROTHWELL, Richard 1800-68 (Irish)

U148 Rev. John Scott Porter 1801-80 (c.1845)
Oil on canvas 85.2 x 67
Donated by Miss M. E. Porter, 1927

U149 Miss Knowles (1840-50)
Oil on canvas 91.5 x 71
Donated by Miss Nixon, 1902

U150 Self-Portrait (c.1820-25)
Oil on canvas 92.8 x 72
Provenance unknown

U151 John Lawless 1773-1837
Oil on canvas 76.5 x 63.3
Purchased 1927

U152 Stella in Rome (c.1831-34) *(Illus.p.319)*
Oil on canvas 65.3 x 65.3
Signed
Donated by the Misses R. and F. F. and
Mr. R. R. Patterson, 1943 (the Rothwell
Bequest)

U153 Marcus Ward 1806-47 *(Illus.p.319)*
Oil on canvas 61 x 51
Purchased 1938

U154 Self-Portrait
Oil on canvas 61 x 51
Donated by L. M. Ewart, JP, 1895

U155 Francis McCracken 1762-1842 (c.1835)
Oil on canvas 75 x 63
Donated by Mrs. H. Chisholm, 1943

U156 Portrait of a Young Man
Oil on cardboard 58.6 x 48.4
Donated by Surgeon-General Sinclair,
KHP (per Mrs. Ring), 1920

**U204 Frederick Richard Chichester, Earl of
Belfast 1827-53**
Oil on canvas 91.8 x 71.4
Donated by C. V. Smylie, 1934

U660 Copy of a Rembrandt Self-Portrait
Oil on panel 37.5 x 27.7
Donated by the Misses R. and F. F. and
Mr. R. R. Patterson, 1943 (the
Rothwell Bequest)

**U685 Frederic William Macaulay 1801-39
(c.1826)** *(Illus.p.319)*
Oil on canvas 76 x 63
Donated by F. R. V. Macaulay, 1970

**U686 Anna Macaulay, née Hyndman 1801-91
(c.1826)** *(Illus.p.319)*
Oil on canvas 76 x 63.7
Donated by F. R. V. Macaulay, 1970

**U688 James Warwick Macaulay 1824-53
(c.1826)**
Oil on canvas 76.2 x 63.5
Donated by F. R. V. Macaulay, 1970

U2000 The Blinding of Cupid (after Titian)
Oil on canvas 65.4 x 99.1
Donated by the Misses R. and F. F. and
Mr. R. R. Patterson, 1943 (the Rothwell
Bequest); sold 1970

U2001 Henrietta Maria (after Rubens)
Oil on panel 43.2 x 27.9
Donated by the Misses R. and F. F. and
Mr. R. R. Patterson, 1943 (the Rothwell
Bequest); sold 1970

U2277 **Portrait of a Boy** *(Illus.p.320)*
Watercolour, bodycolour, gum on paper
26.3 x 19.7 (oval)
Purchased 1974

U4482 **The Night Watch** (after Rembrandt)
Oil on canvas 76.2 x 96.5
Donated by the Misses R. and F. F. and
Mr. R. R. Patterson, 1943 (the Rothwell
Bequest); sold 1970

ROWAN, Nathaniel fl.1913-25 (Irish)

U1411 **The Lost Tip (1913)**
Pencil, ink, watercolour on paper 36 x
28.2
Signed, dated
Purchased 1949

ROWBOTHAM, Thomas Leeson, Jnr. 1823-75
(Irish)

U1129 **Bay of Naples (1873)**
Pencil, watercolour, white on paper 19.7
x 47.1
Signed, dated
Bequeathed by Miss D. Fitzgerald, 1955

U2561 **Mountainous Landscape with Bridge
(1868)** *(Illus.p.320)*
Watercolour, white on paper 20.7 x 31.1
(sight)
Signed, dated
Bequeathed anonymously (per Canon S.
Smart), 1980

ROWLANDSON, Thomas 1756-1827 (English)

U844 **A Tour in Flanders (1792)** *(Illus.p.320)*
Ink, watercolour on paper 20.5 x 30.4
Signed, dated
Purchased 1935

U1201 **Study of a Man in Riding Dress**
(Illus.p.320)
Pencil on paper 24.4 x 17.9
Donated by J. H. Stirling, 1919

RUSKIN, John 1819-1900 (English)

U845 **Leaf from a Sketch Book**
Pencil, watercolour, white on paper 17.5
x 25.3
Donated by the National Art Collections
Fund, 1947

RUSSELL, George William ('AE') 1867-1935
(Irish)

U394 **The Watcher** *(Illus.p.320)*
Oil on canvas 53.6 x 81.6
Signed
Donated by the Misses Macnaughten (per
Miss E. Macnaughten), 1950

U396 **The Skipping Rope** *(Illus.p.320)*
Oil on canvas 53.6 x 81.4
Signed
Donated by the Misses Macnaughten (per
Miss E. Macnaughten), 1950

U399 **River in the Sand (1924)** *(Illus.p.320)*
Oil on canvas 53.8 x 81.5
Signed
Donated by the artist, 1924

RUSSIAN Icon, Crimean School, late 16th-early
17th century

U2231 **St. Demetrius Plunging King John into
an Abyss** *(Illus.p.320)*
Oil, tempera on panel 43.6 x 34.2
Donated by Major E. S. Mercer, 1910

RUSSIAN Icon, Russian School, 17th-18th
century

U2232 **St. Nicholas** *(Illus.p.320)*
Mixed media on panel 42.2 x 33.8
Donated by Major E. S. Mercer, 1910

RUSSIAN Icon, Moscow School, late 17th
century

U2233 **The Old Testament Trinity: Abraham
Entertaining the Angels**
Mixed media on canvas on panel 54 x
43.8
Donated by Major E. S. Mercer, 1910

RUSSIAN Icon, Russian School, 18th century

U2234 **Dormition of the Virgin** *(Illus.p.321)*
Mixed media on canvas on panel 31 x
27.3
Donated by Mrs. E. M. Peacock, 1932

RUSSSIAN Icon, Provincial School, 18th century

U2367 **Joy of All who Grieve**
Mixed media on panel 29.8 x 25.5
Provenance unknown

RUTHERSTON, Albert 1881-1953 (English)

U1754 **The Maypole in Dorset (1920)**
(Illus.p.321)
Watercolour on silk 23 x 31 (sight) (oval)
Signed, dated
Purchased 1972

RYAN, Adrian 1920-98 (English)

U493 **Mousehole (1946)** *(Illus.p.321)*
Oil on canvas 91 x 71.5
Signed, dated
Donated by the Contemporary Art
Society, 1950

S

SADLER, William II 1782-1839 (Irish)

U166 **The Relief of Derry**
Oil on panel 48.5 x 82.4
Donated by J. F. Johnson, 1896

U227 **The Eagle's Nest, Killarney** *(Illus.p.321)*
Oil on panel 48.5 x 80
Purchased 1969

SAITO, Kikuo b.1939 (Japanese, works in USA)

U2577 **Windy Paw (1979)** *(Illus.p.321)*
Acrylic on canvas 271 x 162.5
Signed
Purchased 1980

SANDBY, Paul 1731-1809 (English)

U170 **Carrick Ferry, near Wexford, Ireland**

Oil on canvas 25.4 x 31
Bequeathed by W. A. Sandby, 1904

U846 **Caernarvon Castle (1794)** *(Illus.p.321)*
Watercolour, bodycolour on paper 37.6 x
54
Signed, dated
Purchased 1967

U847 **St. George's Chapel, Windsor, from
inside Henry VIII Gate** *(Illus.p.321)*
Watercolour, bodycolour on paper on
board 31.5 x 46.9
Bequeathed by W. A. Sandby, 1904

U848 **Lake and Town of Nemi** (after Richard
Wilson 1714-82)
Watercolour, bodycolour, white on paper
23.9 x 30
Signed
Bequeathed by W. A Sandby, 1904

U849 **Rochester Castle**
Pencil, watercolour on paper 20.8 x 27.5
Bequeathed by W. A. Sandby, 1904

U850 **Edwinsford, Carmarthenshire**
(Illus.p.321)
Watercolour, white on paper 31.4 x 50.2
Bequeathed by W. A Sandby, 1904

U851 **View near the Woodyard, Windsor Great
Park** *(Illus.p.321)*
Watercolour, white on paper 65.7 x 37.7
Bequeathed by W. A. Sandby, 1904

U2568 **South East Prospect of the Cathedral
Church of London-Derry, Ireland**
Ink, watercolour, pencil on paper 18.7 x
24.4
Purchased 1980

SANDBY, Thomas 1721-98 (after)

U800 **The South Terrace, Windsor Castle**
(Illus.p.322)
Ink, watercolour on paper 34.6 x 29.2
Purchased 1935

SANDFORD, Matt 20th century (Irish)

U4862 **Sir Hugh O'Neill, MP**
Ink, crayon on paper 18.4 x 13.3
Signed
Donated by Kemsley Newspapers Ltd.,
1944

U4863 **Lord Carson 1854-1935**
Ink, crayon on paper 24.7 x 17.8
Signed
Donated by Kemsley Newspapers Ltd.,
1944

U4864 **Major Sir Ronald Ross, MP b.1888**
Ink, crayon on paper 18.4 x 13.3
Signed
Donated by Kemsley Newspapers Ltd.,
1944

U4865 **Marquess of Londonderry 1878-1949**
Ink, crayon on paper 21.6 x 14
Signed
Donated by Kemsley Newspapers Ltd.,
1944

U4866 **Viscount Castlereagh, MP 1902-55**
Ink on paper 22.8 x 14

Signed
Donated by Kemsley Newspapers Ltd.,
1944

U4867 **Serjeant A. M. Sullivan, KC**
Ink on paper 20.3 x 11.4
Signed
Donated by Kemsley Newspapers Ltd.,
1944

U4868 **Lennox Robinson 1886-1958**
Ink, crayon on paper 22.8 x 14.6
Signed
Donated by Kemsley Newspapers Ltd.,
1944

U4869 **Sean O'Casey 1880-1964**
Ink on board 21 x 13.3
Signed
Donated by Kemsley Newspapers Ltd.,
1944

U4870 **Liam O'Flaherty 1896 1984**
Ink on board 20.3 x 13.6
Donated by Kemsley Newspapers Ltd.,
1944

U4871 **Count John McCormack 1884-1945**
Ink on board 23.5 x 17.2
Signed
Donated by Kemsley Newspapers Ltd.,
1944

U4872 **Fourteen Caricatures of Ulster
Celebrities**
Ink, crayon on paper 52.1 x 46.8
Signed
Donated by the *Belfast Telegraph* (per R.
M. Sayers), 1944

U4873 **Sir Robert McConnell, Bt., b.1902**
Ink on card 21 x 16.9
Donated by the *Belfast Telegraph* (per R.
M. Sayers), 1944

SANDYS, Edwin d.1708 (Irish)

U5012 **A True Prospect of the Giant's Causeway
(1696)**
Ink, watercolour on paper 66 x 96.5
Purchased 1994

SANDYS, Frederick 1829-1904 (English)

U168 **Cassandra** *(Illus.p.322)*
Oil on board 30.2 x 25.4
Purchased 1929

U852 **Study of a Head (1890)** *(Illus.p.322)*
Pencil, chalk on paper 35.8 x 26.4
Signed, dated
Purchased 1931

SCANLAN, Robert b.1908 (Irish)

U1259 **Northern Ireland Coast (1941)**
(Illus.p.322)
Gouache on paper 35.6 x 48.9
Signed, dated
Donated by the War Artists' Advisory
Committee (per the Imperial War
Museum), 1946

SCARFE, Gerald b.1936 (English) (after)

U1660 **'The Beggar's Opera' Backcloths**

Oil on canvas, series of fifteen, each 427 x
610
Donated by Opera Northern Ireland,
1999; painted in the Lyric Theatre,
Belfast

SCHMID (?), Carl 19th century (German)

U618 **General Francis Rawdon Chesney 1789-
1872 (1853)** *(Illus.p.322)*
Oil on canvas 92 x 71.3
Signed, dated
Donated by Miss K. Chesney, 1962

SCHONZEIT, Ben b.1942 (American)

U2578 **Hot House, Black and White (1979)**
(Illus.p.322)
Oil on canvas 122 x 243
Signed
Purchased 1980

SCHOTZ, Benno 1891-1984 (Scottish)

U1812 **Anna May Wong 1907 61 (1933)**
(Illus.p.322)
Sculpture, bronze head, ht. 34.3
Signed, dated
Purchased 1937

SCOTT, David Winfield b.1916 (American)

U923 **Mist and Hills, Pomona Valley (1936)**
Watercolour on paper 36.6 x 22
Signed, dated
Donated by Dr. B. D. Scott, 1936

U924 **Valley Farm, Pomona Valley (1936)**
Watercolour on paper 18 x 32.5
Signed, dated
Donated by Dr. B. D. Scott, 1936

SCOTT, Edith b.1885 (American)

U1130 **California Beach, Venice, California**
Pencil, watercolour on paper 24 x 37.8
Signed
Donated by the artist (per Dr. B. D.
Scott), 1936

U1132 **Neighbours, Apple Valley, California
(Mohave Desert)**
Pencil, watercolour on paper 24 x 37.8
Signed
Donated by the artist (per Dr. B. D.
Scott), 1936

SCOTT, Patrick b.1921 (Irish)

U410 **Bog Reflection (1960-61)** *(Illus.p.322)*
Tempera on canvas on board 61 x 50.8
Signed
Purchased 1961

U703 **Yellow Device (1962)**
Tempera on canvas 96.7 x 81.5
Signed, dated
Purchased 1962

SCOTT, William 1913-89 (British)

U403 **Untitled (1959)**
Oil on canvas 86.6 x 111.7
Signed
Purchased with the aid of a grant from
the Friends of the National Collections of

Ireland, 1962

U404 **Brown Still Life (1958)** *(Illus.p.322)*
Oil on canvas 89.5 x 99
Purchased 1958

U2288 **Egypt Series No. 3 (1972)** *(Illus.p.92)*
Oil on canvas 203.2 x 254
Signed, dated
Donated by the artist, 1974

U2475 **Still Life (1949)** *(Illus.p.323)*
Oil on canvas 57.5 x 66
Signed
Purchased 1978

U2663 **Whites (1964)** *(Illus.p.323)*
Oil on canvas 185 x 122
Signed, dated
Purchased 1983

U2664 **White with Red Lines (1962)**
(Illus.p.323)
Oil on canvas 86 x 111.5
Signed
Purchased 1983

U2665 **Shapes and Shadows (1962)** *(Illus.p.323)*
Oil on canvas 86 x 111.5
Signed
Purchased 1983

U2669 **1st Aegean Suite No. 1 Jan 1969 (1968)**
(Illus.p.323)
Pencil, watercolour, bodycolour on paper
26 x 33.5
Signed, dated
Purchased 1983

U2670 **Grey Circle (1961)** *(Illus.p.323)*
Bodycolour on paper 40.5 x 43.5
Signed
Purchased 1983

SCOTT, William fl.1880-1907 (British)

U2610 **Old Town, Bordighera** *(Illus.p. 323)*
Ink on card 21.9 x 31.4
Signed
Donated by Mrs. E. M. Peacock, 1933

U2611 **S. Agnese**
Ink on card 31.4 x 21.9
Signed
Donated by Mrs. E. M. Peacock, 1933

U2612 **Vallecrosia, Corner of Piazza Nuova
(1897)**
Ink on card 32.3 x 25.1
Signed, dated
Donated by Mrs. E. M. Peacock, 1933

U2613 **Sanzeno from the Sborigo Road**
Ink on board 8.9 x 19.2
Signed
Donated by Mrs. E. M. Peacock, 1933

U2614 **Street in San Biaggio (1897)**
Ink on card 24.3 x 31.8
Signed, dated
Donated by Mrs. E. M. Peacock, 1933

U2615 **Sorpello**
Ink on card 23.5 x 31.7
Signed
Donated by Mrs. E. M. Peacock, 1933

U2616 Street in Vallecrosia (1897)
Ink on card 24.7 x 10.8
Signed, dated
Donated by Mrs. E. M. Peacock, 1933

U2617 St. Michele, La Roya Valley
Ink on card 16.6 x 25.1
Donated by Mrs. E. M. Peacock, 1933

U2618 Castle of the Doria at Dolceacqua
Ink on card 25.1 x 16.9
Signed
Donated by Mrs. E. M. Peacock, 1933

U2619 Street in Vallecrosia (1897)
Ink on card 32.4 x 24.8
Signed, dated
Donated by Mrs. E. M. Peacock, 1933

U2620 Fountain at Contes
Ink on card 33.6 x 24.4
Signed
Donated by Mrs. E. M. Peacock, 1933

U2621 Coast at Bordighera
Ink on card 16.5 x 24.2
Signed
Donated by Mrs. E. M. Peacock, 1933

U2622 Old Houses at St. Martin, Vésubre (1907)
Ink on card 20.6 x 12.7
Signed, dated
Donated by Mrs. E. M. Peacock, 1933

U2623 Escarène
Ink on card 14.6 x 23.8
Signed
Donated by Mrs. E. M. Peacock, 1933

U2624 View of Village
Ink on card 15.2 x 21.2
Signed
Donated by Mrs. E. M. Peacock, 1933

SCOTT-SMITH, Jessie fl.1883-1903 (English)

U718 Mr. and Mrs. Webster (after Thomas Webster 1800-86)
Oil on panel 26.7 x 21.4
Donated by Miss F. M. McTear, 1926

U4487 Portrait of a Man
Oil on canvas 147.8 x 112.4
Signed
Provenance unknown

U4537 Francis George King as a Baby
Miniature, watercolour on ivory, diameter 2.3 (circular)
Donated by Miss F. M. McTear, 1926

SCULLY, Sean b.1945 (Irish)

U2079 Fourth Layer (1973) *(Illus.p.323)*
Acrylic on canvas 244 x 244
Signed, dated
Purchased 1974

SEABROOKE, Elliott 1886-1950 (English)

U502 Fruit (1928) *(Illus.p.323)*
Oil on canvas 50.6 x 61
Signed, dated
Purchased (Lloyd Patterson Collection) 1929

SEABY, Wilfred Arthur 1910-91 (English)

U1880 Slieve Bignion from the Beatings (1972)
Watercolour, gouache, felt pen on paper 49.9 x 64.9
Signed, dated
Donated by the artist, 1973

U1881 Tom King's Cottage, Tolloeragh (1970) *(Illus.p.324)*
Watercolour, ballpoint, ink on paper 42 x 59.3
Signed, dated
Donated by the artist, 1973

SEARLE, Ronald b.1920 (English)

U1410 The Shoe Cleaner, Belgrade (1948) *(Illus.p.324)*
Ink on paper 25.2 x 17.8
Signed
Purchased 1955

SEDGLEY, Peter b.1930 (English)

U1632 Colour Cycle II (1970)
Acrylic on canvas 121.5 x 121.5, with four coloured lamps and programmed control gear
Purchased 1971

SELONS, Dorothea Medley 20th century (British?)

U2002 Mauve Chrysanthemums
Oil on panel 45.7 x 40.6
Signed
Purchased 1936

SEVERDONCK, Franz van 1809-89 (Belgian)

U180 Goats (1859) *(Illus.p.324)*
Oil on panel 17.4 x 22.6
Signed, dated
Donated by W. T. Braithwaite (per J. Horner), 1906

SHACKLETON, William 1872-1933 (English)

U1601 Study (1903) *(Illus.p.324)*
Pencil on paper 33.5 x 30.2
Signed, dated
Acquired by exchange (Lloyd Patterson Collection), 1930

SHAW, Kathleen T. 1870-1958 (English)

U1813 Primate William Alexander 1824-1911, Archbishop of Armagh (1914)
Sculpture, plaster bust, ht. 91.4
Signed, dated
Purchased 1920

SHAWCROSS, Neil b.1940 (English, works in Ireland)

U2094 Nude II (1974) *(Illus.p.324)*
Gouache on paper 14.6 x 18.4
Signed, dated
Purchased 1974

U2448 Flowers (1976) *(Illus.p.324)*
Watercolour, pencil on paper 36.8 x 31.1
Signed, dated
Purchased 1977

U2474 Portrait of Francis Stuart 1902-2000 (1978) *(Illus.p.324)*
Oil on canvas 122 x 92
Commissioned 1978

U2511 Portrait of Paul Muldoon b.1951 (1978) *(Illus.p.324)*
Watercolour, pencil on paper 78.7 x 54.6 (sight)
Signed, dated
Commissioned 1978

SHERIDAN, Clare Consuelo 1885-1970 (English)

U1814 Sir Winston Churchill, OM, CH, MP 1874-1965 (1942)
Sculpture, bronze head, ht. 44.4
Signed, dated
Purchased 1951

SHERRIN, John 1819-96 (English)

U1133 Bird's Nest and Hawthorn (1869) *(Illus.p.324)*
Watercolour, bodycolour on paper 20 x 25.6
Signed, dated
Purchased 1938

SHIELDS, Mark b.1963 (Irish)

U5015 Self-Portrait: The Troubled Look (1995) *(Illus.p.325)*
Acrylic on linen 37 x 18
Signed, dated
Donated by the Thomas Haverty Trust, 1995

U5019 Skull - Bianco e Vermiglio (1994) *(Illus.p.325)*
Acrylic on linen 33 x 31.4 (sight)
Signed, dated
Donated by the Thomas Haverty Trust, 1995

SHOESMITH, Kenneth Denton 1890-1939 (English)
A Collection of Three Hundred and Fourteen Works
Bequeathed by Mrs. S. Shoesmith, 1975

U2284 Istanbul, S. Sophia
Watercolour, pencil on board 26.6 x 36.8
Signed

U2285 Cranes, Baker Street *(Illus.p.325)*
Watercolour, bodycolour, pencil on board 75.9 x 50.8
Signed

U2356 Shanghai River *(Illus.p.325)*
Oil on canvas 91.5 x 139.7
Signed

U2357 Royal Yacht at Cowes
Oil on canvas 91.5 x 139.7
Signed

U2358 Tangier - the Flower Seller *(Illus.p.325)*
Oil on canvas 91.5 x 139.7
Signed

U3599 Junks in a Harbour by Night (1919)
Watercolour, bodycolour on board 34.6 x 46.7

Signed, dated

U3600 **Two Destroyers (?) by Moonlight (1919)**
Watercolour, bodycolour on board 46.3 x 58.4
Signed, dated

U3601 **RMSP 'Cardiganshire' Leaving Port Said, Homeward (1915)**
Watercolour, bodycolour on board 38.1 x 53.1
Signed, dated

U3602 **P & O 'Egypt' Hospital Ship (1917)**
Watercolour, bodycolour on paper 25.1 x 56.5
Signed, dated

U3603 **Sunset Memory (1906)**
Pencil, wash on card 16.2 x 23.8 (sight)
Signed, dated

U3604 **The P & O Mailboat in the Suez Canal (1918)**
Watercolour, bodycolour on card 51.1 x 38.3
Signed, dated

U3605 **Hong Kong from Kow Loon, RMS 'Empress of Asia' (1916)**
Watercolour on paper 35 x 56.2
Signed, dated

U3606 **HMS 'Suffolk' and 'Cumberland' (1916)**
Watercolour on card 24.1 x 30.5
Signed, dated

U3607 **'Montezuma' as 'Iron Duke', 'Ruthenea' as 'King George V'**
Pencil on paper 30.5 x 48.9 (sight)
Signed

U3608 **RMSP 'Magdelene', Carlisle Bay, Barbados (1915)**
Bodycolour on card 27.6 x 38.8
Signed, dated

U3609 **RMSP 'Cardiganshire' Homeward Bound from New Orleans (1918)**
Bodycolour on card 33 x 20.9
Signed, dated

U3610 **Liner in Open Sea**
Watercolour on paper 12 x 26.3

U3611 **HMS 'Glorious'. Launch 20 April 1916**
Pencil on paper 30.5 x 49.2
Signed

U3612 **'Montezuma' as 'Iron Duke'**
Pencil on paper 30.5 x 48.9 (sight)
Signed

U3613 **Rowing Boat Approaching Battle Cruiser, Twilight**
Watercolour, bodycolour on board 29.2 x 23.1

U3614 **'HMS Avenger' (1916)**
Watercolour on board 15.2 x 29.5
Signed, dated

U3615 **Battle Cruiser in Open Sea**
Watercolour, bodycolour on board 43.2 x 51.7

U3616 **Picket Boats from the Grand Fleet (1917)**

Watercolour, bodycolour on paper 35.9 x 53.1
Signed, dated

U3617 **'Merion' as 'Tiger'**
Pencil on paper 30.2 x 48.9
Signed

U3618 **Sailing Ship in Open Sea (1911)**
Watercolour on paper 30.5 x 50.8
Signed, dated

U3619 **TBD 'Brisk' (1916)**
Watercolour, bodycolour on paper 13.3 x 21
Signed, dated

U3620 **HMS 'Tiger' (1919)**
Pencil on paper 26.3 x 61.6 (sight)
Signed, dated

U3621 **'Oruba' as 'Orion'**
Pencil on paper 30.2 x 49.2 (sight)
Signed

U3622 **New Orleans, Camouflaged Merchant Ship (1918)** *(Illus.p.325)*
Watercolour, bodycolour on card 22.8 x 29.2
Signed, dated

U3623 **Sailing Ships in the Estuary (1916)**
Watercolour, pencil on card 26 x 38.1
Signed, dated

U3624 **Cruiser Entering Dock, Liverpool**
Watercolour, bodycolour on paper 50.8 x 31.8

U3625 **Trawlers on the North Sea (1912)**
Watercolour on paper 21.5 x 48.2 (sight)
Signed, dated

U3626 **Design for Decoration on the 'Queen Mary' (squared)**
Bodycolour on board 40.6 x 37.1 (sight)

U3627 **'Lusitania' Dropping her Pilot, New York (1912)**
Watercolour, bodycolour on board 27.9 x 43.2 (sight)
Signed, dated

U3628 **A Harbour by Sunset (1913)**
Watercolour, bodycolour on board 28.1 x 46.8
Signed, dated

U3629 **Small Passenger Steamer in Open Sea**
Watercolour, bodycolour on board 31.1 x 49.5

U3630 **'Lindisfarne' Unloading into Barges**
Watercolour, bodycolour on board 26.6 x 27.3

U3631 **Evening on the Nile**
Watercolour, pencil on board 27 x 37.8
Signed

U3632 **A Destroyer**
Watercolour, bodycolour on board 22.9 x 30.5
Signed

U3633 **An Eastern Street Scene**
Watercolour, bodycolour on board 21.2 x 30.2 (sight)
Signed

U3634 **Gibraltar, 1 June 1933**
Pencil, watercolour, bodycolour on board 25.4 x 35.5 (sight)
Signed

U3635 **Palermo, June 1933**
Watercolour, bodycolour on board 24.8 x 35.5 (sight)
Signed

U3636 **Sailing Ships in Open Sea**
Watercolour, bodycolour on board 36.8 x 53.3 (sight)

U3637 **The Green Parrot**
Watercolour, bodycolour on board 26.2 x 36.5 (sight)
Signed

U3638 **Cunard RMS 'Mauretania' Leaving New York, off Fire Island**
Watercolour on paper 20.3 x 37.1

U3639 **RMSP 'Cardiganshire' on the Mississippi (1918)**
Bodycolour on paper 20.3 x 50.2
Signed, dated

U3640 **RMS 'Thames' Leaving St. Michael's, Azores**
Watercolour, bodycolour on paper 21 x 35.5

U3641 **RMSP 'Amazon' off Cape Frio (1911)**
Watercolour, bodycolour on paper 20 x 29.5
Signed, dated

U3642 **Making Queenstown (1919)**
Watercolour on paper 16.9 x 34.2
Signed, dated

U3643 **Thunderstorm in Suez Canal (1910)**
Watercolour on paper 20.3 x 34.6
Signed, dated

U3644 **'Danube' in Pernambuco Roads (1911)**
Watercolour on paper 20.6 x 36.1
Signed, dated

U3645 **Entering St. Vincent**
Watercolour on paper 21.2 x 34.2

U3646 **Off the North Coast of Sumatra (1910)**
Watercolour on paper 22.1 x 36.5
Signed, dated

U3647 **Rowing Boats Approaching a Battle Cruiser**
Watercolour on paper 16.8 x 50.8

U3648 **Steamboat off a Mountainous Coast (1912)**
Watercolour, bodycolour on paper 24.1 x 50.2
Signed, dated

U3649 **Convoy of Merchant Ships with a Warship**
Watercolour, bodycolour on paper 25.3 x 56.2

U3650 **RMSP 'Danube' Picking up the Lisbon Pilot (1910)**
Watercolour, bodycolour on paper 18.4 x 27.9
Signed, dated

U3651   **Orient Line RMS 'Otway' in Colombo Harbour (1909)**
Watercolour, bodycolour on paper 21.2 x 35.2
Signed, dated

U3652   **Fine Weather on the China Sea (1910)**
Watercolour on paper 17.4 x 25.3
Signed, dated

U3653   **Warship in Open Sea (1912)**
Watercolour on paper 23.2 x 49.5
Signed, dated

U3654   **P & O Company's RMS 'Mantua' (1911)**
Watercolour, bodycolour on paper 20.6 x 35.8
Signed, dated

U3655   **'Inflexible' and 'Invincible'**
Watercolour, bodycolour on paper 21.9 x 44.1

U3656   **RMSP 'Danube' (1911)**
Watercolour on paper 20.9 x 35.5
Signed, dated

U3657   **Mersey Estuary - Low Tide**
Watercolour on paper on card 13.3 x 21.6

U3658   **Hamburg American SS 'Victoria Luise', Norway (1912)**
Ink on paper 25.3 x 42.9
Signed, dated

U3659   **Steamboat in Open Sea**
Watercolour on paper 22.8 x 33

U3660   **Rolling Ship in Heavy Sea (1911)**
Watercolour on paper 21.2 x 36.8
Signed, dated

U3661   **Colombo Harbour (1910)**
Watercolour, bodycolour on paper 17.8 x 35.2
Signed, dated

U3662   **German Armoured Cruiser SMS 'Scharnhorst' off Kobe, Japan**
Watercolour, bodycolour on paper 18.4 x 26

U3663   **Harbour of Penang, Straits Settlements (1910)**
Watercolour, bodycolour on paper 19.7 x 34.9
Signed, dated

U3664   **Royal Mail Steamers 'Danube' and 'Avon' in Bahia, Brazil (1911)**
Watercolour, bodycolour on paper 22.8 x 34.6
Signed, dated

U3665   **The Fleet at Spithead Three Days before the Review. The Ship Nearest is the Latest Cruiser, HMS 'Indefatigable' (1911)**
Watercolour on paper 17.8 x 37.1
Signed, dated

U3666   **RMS 'Avon' (1910)**
Watercolour on paper 19.7 x 34.6
Signed, dated

U3667   **Warship Viewed from astern**
Watercolour on paper on card 28 x 28

U3668   **Isle of Man Steamer Leaving Barrow**
Watercolour on paper 16.5 x 24.8
Signed

U3669   **Turbine Boat 'Viking', Isle of Man (1905)**
Watercolour on paper 15.5 x 24.3
Signed, dated

U3670   **The River Mersey, Memory age 13 (1903)**
Pencil, watercolour on paper 32.1 x 50.2
Signed, dated

U3671   **Cruisers Accompanying His Majesty's Yacht at Liverpool, July 19, 1904. Memory (1904)**
Ink, watercolour on paper 33 x 48.2
Signed, dated

U3672   **The Launch of HMS 'Sentinel', Scout, at the Vickers' Sons and Maxim Works, Barrow-in-Furness. Snap Shot, aged 13 (1904)**
Pencil, watercolour on paper 34 x 51.1
Signed, dated

U3673   **The Arrival of the RMSP 'Danube' in the Harbour of Rio de Janeiro (1914)**
Watercolour, bodycolour on board 32.4 x 54.3
Signed, dated

U3674   **HMS 'Cornwall', Grassy Bay, Bermuda (1912)**
Watercolour on paper 33 x 53.6
Signed, dated

U3675   **Sailing Boat in Estuary**
Watercolour, bodycolour on card 35.8 x 50.8

U3676   **A Steamship (1916)** (RMSP 'Danube'?); verso, **Two Pen Sketches of Same Ship**
Ink on board 26.6 x 38.1
Signed, dated

U3677   **Design for Leaflet, 'Europe by Famous Cabin Liners - Royal Mail The Comfort Route' (1926)** (Shows One of the Company's Early Paddle Steamers of 1839 and RMS 'Ohio' of 1926)
Bodycolour on paper 36.8 x 31.1
Signed

U3678   **'Patrician' and 'Invincible'**
Pencil on paper 31.8 x 51.1

U3679   **Two Ships offshore by Night**
Watercolour, bodycolour on card 26.7 x 36.8

U3680   **Patrol in the North Sea 'Town' Class Light Cruiser (1914)**
Pencil, white on card 30.5 x 24.2
Signed, dated

U3681   **Steamboat offshore by Night**
Watercolour, bodycolour on paper 25.3 x 45.7

U3682   **Coast with Snow-covered Peaks**
Bodycolour on card 23.7 x 33.6
Signed

U3683   **A Launch Excursion on Lyngen Fjord, Norway (1912)**

Watercolour, bodycolour on paper 24.8 x 46.3
Signed, dated

U3684   **From Norheimsund**
Watercolour, bodycolour on card 17.8 x 34.3
Signed

U3685   **A Sailing Ship**
Watercolour on paper 28.5 x 33.6

U3686   **Royal Mail Steamboat in a Fjord**
Bodycolour on paper 39 x 28.5
Signed

U3687   **P & O 'Mantua'**
Watercolour on paper 25.1 x 40.3

U3688   **HMT 'Brisk' (1916)**
Wash, white on paper 12 x 19.7 (sight)
Signed, dated

U3689   **Prize Day on HMS 'Conway', Summer 1908 (1909)**
Ink on paper 22.9 x 29.2
Signed, dated

U3690   **HMS 'Cumberland' and HMS 'Magdelena' (1916)**
Watercolour, bodycolour on board 26.6 x 38.1
Signed, dated

U3691   **Ships in a Mediterranean Harbour, probably Algiers (1918)**
Watercolour, bodycolour on board 67.2 x 100.4 (sight)
Signed, dated

U3692   **Eastern Street Scene**
Watercolour, bodycolour on board 24.7 x 35.5
Signed

U3693   **A Byzantine Church, Daphni, Greece** (formerly 'San Vitale, Ravenna (?)')
Watercolour, bodycolour on board 35.2 x 25 (sight)
Signed

U3694   **Convoy of Warships (1919)**
Watercolour, bodycolour on board 28.5 x 48 (sight)
Signed, dated

U3695   **The Landing** (formerly 'Rowing Boats and Yachts on a River by Night')
Watercolour, bodycolour on board 34 x 46.3 (sight)
Signed

U3696   **American Cargo Ship at Sea (1918)**
Watercolour, bodycolour on board 35.5 x 53.1
Signed, dated

U3697   **Rolling Home**
Watercolour, bodycolour on board 66.7 x 100.4
Signed

U3698   **Santa Maria della Salute, Venice**
Watercolour, bodycolour on board 66.7 x 99.7

U3699   **Four Master in Open Sea**
Watercolour, bodycolour on board 68.2 x

100.6
Signed

U3700 **Junks in a Chinese Harbour**
Watercolour, bodycolour on board 68.2 x 101
Signed

U3701 **The Piazzetta, Venice. Design for Poster**
Bodycolour on board 78.4 x 63.1
Signed

U3702 **Gibraltar, Starlight (1913)**
Watercolour, bodycolour on board 60.7 x 83.5 (sight)
Signed, dated

U3703 **The Golden Horn**
Watercolour on board 22.5 x 35
Signed

U3704 **A Following Gale**
Watercolour, bodycolour on board 34.6 x 50.5 (sight)
Signed

U3705 **Hagia Sophia, Istanbul**
Watercolour, pencil on paper 22.9 x 34.3 (sight)
Signed

U3706 **Two Warships at Sea**
Watercolour on paper 22.8 x 40.6 (sight)

U3707 **The Harbour of Piraeus, Athens**
(Illus.p.325)
Watercolour, bodycolour on board 26 x 45.1
Signed

U3708 **Boats on a Seashore**
Bodycolour on board 36.9 x 52.4 (sight)

U3709 **A Four-funnel Battleship, HMS 'Drake' (1917)**
Watercolour, bodycolour on paper 29.8 x 48.2 (sight)
Signed, dated

U3710 **Venice, Santa Maria della Salute** (Night)
Bodycolour on board 50.2 x 75.6
Signed

U3711 **Portuguese Fishing Village**
Watercolour, bodycolour on board 37.8 x 63.2
Signed

U3712 **Drawing for Painted Doors to Chapel in 'Queen Mary'** (to scale and squared 1/8 in = 1 in)
Pencil on paper 56.5 x 53.6

U3713 **RMSP 'Danube', Bahia, Brazil (1911)**
Watercolour on paper 33 x 52.1
Signed, dated

U3714 **Cunard Line Hospital Ship, 'Mauretania' (1918)**
Bodycolour on board 38.8 x 50.8
Signed, dated

U3715 **Eastern Street Scene**
Watercolour on board 38.1 x 53.4

U3716 **Eastern Street Scene**
Watercolour on board 38.1 x 53.1

U3717 **Scale Study for 'Richard Hakluyt Recording the Voyages of the Elizabethan Sailors' (1936)** (for the 'Queen Mary') (squared)
Pencil, watercolour, bodycolour on card 40 x 57.9

U3718 **Scale Study for 'Samuel Pepys, Diarist and Secty. to the Admty. at the Royal Dockyard, Deptford' (1936)** (for the 'Queen Mary') (squared)
Pencil, watercolour, bodycolour on card 40 x 57.9

U3719 **Steam Yacht (1917)**
Bodycolour on paper 21 x 50.8
Signed, dated

U3720 **Tritons and Sea-nymphs Riding White Sea-horses** (Decorative Design)
Bodycolour on card 40 x 55

U3721 **Hospital Ship 'Guildford Castle', Alexandria (1917)**
Watercolour, bodycolour on paper 27.9 x 48.2
Signed, dated

U3722 **French Armoured Cruiser 'Marseillaise' off Oran, Algeria (1916)**
Watercolour, bodycolour on paper 33 x 49.2
Signed, dated

U3723 **'Montcalm', French Cruiser (1917)**
Watercolour on paper 29.8 x 48
Signed, dated

U3724 **P & O Express Mail Steamer 'Strathmore'**
Bodycolour on board 53.1 x 75.9

U3725 **Camouflaged Ship in Eastern Harbour**
Watercolour, bodycolour on board 50.8 x 75.6
Signed

U3726 **TBDs in the Channel (1917)**
Watercolour, bodycolour on paper 25.3 x 56.5
Signed, dated

U3727 **Patrol Cruiser Picking up Survivors of a Torpedoed Vessel (1917)**
Watercolour on paper 34.2 x 51.8
Signed, dated

U3728 **Towing to Safety a Torpedoed Merchantman (1918)**
Watercolour, bodycolour on board 34.3 x 77.1
Signed, dated

U3729 **Passing Harland & Wolff's, Approaching Donegall Quay** (Royal Yacht 'Victoria & Albert' Taking George V and Queen Mary to the Opening of the Stormont Parliament)
Watercolour, bodycolour on board 45.1 x 75.9
Signed

U3730 **Pencil Studies of Arms** (Front and Back of Sheet)
Pencil on paper 35.5 x 54

U3731 **Study for First Class 'Queen Mary' Madonna** (Altarpiece 'The Madonna of the Atlantic' for First Class Catholic Chapel on the 'Queen Mary'). Also Layouts of Lettering for Samuel Pepys Panel (U3718); verso, **Sketch for Madonna's Left Hand**
Pencil on board 53.6 x 33

U3732 **Study for First Class 'Queen Mary' Madonna**
Pencil on paper 53.6 x 36.2

U3733 **Study for First Class 'Queen Mary' Madonna**
Pencil, chalk on paper 53.6 x 36.2

U3734 **Study for First Class 'Queen Mary' Madonna**
Pencil on paper 53.6 x 36.2

U3735 **Study for First Class 'Queen Mary' Madonna** (squared)
Pencil on paper 54 x 36.2

U3736 **Studies for Left Arm and Right Hand of First Class 'Queen Mary' Madonna**
Pencil on paper 28.5 x 38.8

U3737 **Studies of Hands of First Class 'Queen Mary' Madonna** (squared)
Pencil on paper 36.8 x 27

U3738 **Studies of Arms** (for 'Queen Mary' Madonna?); verso, **Sketch of a Woman** (squared)
Pencil on paper 37.2 x 26.6

U3739 **Studies of Left Hand of First Class 'Queen Mary' Madonna** (Both Sides of Paper)
Pencil on paper 36.5 x 26.8

U3740 **Tracing for Left Arm of First Class 'Queen Mary' Madonna**
Pencil on paper 22.5 x 28.6

U3741 **Two Tracings for Left Hand of First Class 'Queen Mary' Madonna**
Pencil on paper 22.5 x 28.5

U3742 **Two Tracings for Left Hand of First Class 'Queen Mary' Madonna**
Pencil on paper 22.5 x 28.5

U3743 **Two Studies for Right Hand of First Class 'Queen Mary' Madonna; a Sketch Plan of the Chapel and a Sketch of a Cat** (squared)
Pencil, white on paper 22.5 x 28.5

U3744 **Study of a Seated Girl wearing a Short Dress and Pointed Hat**
Pencil, white on paper 36.9 x 25.1

U3745 **Sketch of a Nude Girl Seated, Elbows on Knees; Small Sketch of Sandalled Feet**
Pencil, white on paper 24.1 x 36.2

U3746 **Study of a Nude Girl Seated**
Pencil, white, chalk on paper 34.9 x 25.5

U3747 **Composition Study for 'Loot', 'Queen Mary'** (First Class Lounge?)
Pencil on paper 22.5 x 28.6

U3748 **The 'Conway', Liverpool** *(Illus.p.325)*
Watercolour, bodycolour on board 76.9 x 119.4
Signed

U3749　**Cunard RMS 'Mauretania' (1910)**
Watercolour, bodycolour on paper 18.1 x
22.8
Signed, dated

U3750　**View of a Deck and Wheelhouse, Sunrise
or Sunset**
Ink, bodycolour on paper 18.1 x 22.8

U3751　**'Mauretania' Coaling**
Pencil, watercolour, bodycolour on paper
15.9 x 20

U3752　**'Monmouthshire'**
Watercolour, bodycolour, pencil on paper
16.5 x 20

U3753　**View of Ship's Deck with Lifeboats**
Watercolour, bodycolour on paper 15.9 x
20.3

U3754　**HMS 'Conway', Rock Ferry, Cheshire;
verso, Pencil Sketch of a Trawler and a
Straight Bow**
Watercolour, bodycolour on paper 19.2 x
27

U3755　**Sandy Hook Pilot Boat (1912)**
Watercolour on paper 17.8 x 25.4
Signed, dated

U3756　**Junks at Sea off Pedro Blanco (1910)**
Watercolour on paper 17.8 x 22.9
Signed, dated

U3757　**Hospital Ship 'Essequibo', Alexandria
(1916)**
Watercolour, bodycolour on paper 21.2 x
36.2
Signed, dated

U3758　**Three West Indians in a Boat**
Pencil, watercolour on paper 12.7 x 22.8

U3759　**Four Sketches of Sea and Ships**
Watercolour on paper 20 x 15.9

U3760　**Sketch of a Junk; Sketch of Figures and
Boats**
Watercolour, pencil on paper 20 x 15.5

U3761　**Two-funnelled Ships** (Orient Line?)
Ink, wash on board 20.7 x 33

U3762　**'Montezuma' as 'Iron Duke'**
Pencil on paper 30.4 x 49.2 (sight)
Signed

U3763　**'Perthshire' as 'Vanguard'**
Pencil on paper 30.5 x 49.9 (sight)
Signed

U3764　**Two-funnelled Battleship with Signal
Flags**
Watercolour, bodycolour on board 35.5 x
50.8
Signed

U3765　**Dummy Battleships, l. to r.- 'Montezuma'
as 'Iron Duke', 'Oruba' as 'Orion',
'Tyrolia' as 'King George V' (1918)**
Watercolour, bodycolour on board 36.9 x
51.5
Signed, dated

U3766　**Sailing Ships in Heavy Wind**
Watercolour, bodycolour on board 35.5 x
50.5

U3767　**'Buenos Ayres'**
Bodycolour on board 26.6 x 37.5
Signed

U3768　**Sea and Distant Coast by Moonlight**
Watercolour on paper 12 x 17.1

U3769　**Royal Mail Steamer (?)** (Poster Design)
Watercolour, bodycolour on board 20.9 x
22.2

U3770　**Spanish Galleons with Rowing Boats
Landing** (Sketch for Larger Composition)
Pencil, watercolour on board 27 x 38.1

U3771　**Armoured Cruisers 'Black Prince' and
'Duke of Edinburgh' (1916)**
Watercolour, bodycolour on board 27.9 x
27.9
Signed, dated

U3772　**RMSP 'Cardiganshire', Yokohama, Japan
(1917)**
Bodycolour on card 32.7 x 20.6
Signed, dated

U3773　**SS 'Conway', Camouflaged (1918)**
Watercolour, bodycolour on board 26.6 x
36.9
Signed, dated

U3774　**Royal Mail Fleet, Port of Spain, Trinidad
(1912)**
Watercolour, bodycolour on board 29.5 x
23.7 (sight)
Signed, dated

U3775　**An Ocean Convoy (1918)**
Watercolour, bodycolour on board 38.1 x
54
Signed, dated

U3776　**Convoy of Battleships (1914)**
Watercolour, bodycolour on board 37.1 x
54
Signed, dated

U3777　**Passenger Steamer (from Memory)
(1902)**
Pencil on paper 30.1 x 36.2
Signed, dated

U3778　**Junks (1919)**
Watercolour, bodycolour on board 11 x
20.6
Signed, dated

U3779　**Three Sketches of Ships (1902)**
Pencil on paper 16 x 36, 24.5 x 30, 23.5
x 30.5
Dated

U3780　**Four Paintings of Ships at Sea (c.1905)**
Watercolour on paper 16.8 x 12.2, 9.5 x
16.3, 8 x 15.5, 14.8 x 22.2
Dated

U3781　**Tracing for Left Hand of First Class
'Queen Mary' Madonna** (squared)
Pencil on paper 17.1 x 29.2

U3782　**Study for First Class 'Queen Mary'
Madonna**
Pencil on paper 53.3 x 36.5

U3783　**Study for Head of First Class 'Queen
Mary' Madonna** (squared); verso, **Two
Studies for Full Figure of Madonna**

Pencil on paper 53.6 x 36.8

U3784　**Studies for Second Class 'Queen Mary'
Madonna** (squared)
Pencil on paper 54 x 37.2

U3785　**Study for Second Class 'Queen Mary'
Madonna**
Pencil on paper 53.6 x 37.2

U3786　**Study for Altar, Tourist Class, 'Queen
Mary'**
Pencil on paper 40 x 58.6

U3787　**Study for Folding Screen in Tourist Class
Library, 'Queen Mary' ('Continental
Flower Market')**
Bodycolour on paper 16.3 x 14

U3788　**Arab on a Camel, Poster Design**
Bodycolour, ink on paper 52.4 x 32.3

U3789　**Sketch for Poster Design with Ships:
Seville and Southern Spain**
Bodycolour, ink, pencil on card 51.4 x
31.8

U3790　**Sketch for Poster with Ships at Night:
Cunard, Europe-America**
Bodycolour, ink, pencil on card 37.5 x
27.3

U3791　**Sketch for Poster with Ship: Scotland and
Ireland, Royal Mail Route; verso, Another
Sketch**
Bodycolour, ink, pencil on card 33.6 x
21.2

U3792　**Sketches for Poster, Ship at Night: New
York, Royal Mail**
Bodycolour, ink on board 33.6 x 21.2
Signed

U3793　**Sketch for Poster with Ships: New York,
RMSP**
Bodycolour, ink on card 51.1 x 31.4

U3794　**Sketch for Poster: New York by RMSP
(c.1923-27)**
Bodycolour, ink on card 51.1 x 32

U3795　**Sketch for Poster with Ships: New York
by RMSP**
Bodycolour, ink on card 51.7 x 32.1

U3796　**Poster Design with RMSP Ship in
Norwegian Fjord**
Bodycolour, ink on paper 35.5 x 30.5

U3797　**Sketch for Poster: Norway, Summer
Cruises by the Orient Line (c.1930)**
Bodycolour, ink on card 50.8 x 31.8

U3798　**Painting (1916)**
Bodycolour on card 10.8 x 14.2
Signed, dated

U3799　**Painting of Ships**
Bodycolour on card 12.4 x 19
Signed

U3800　**Small Painting**
Bodycolour on card 24.5 x 18.4
Signed

U3801　**Poster (?) Design 'The Tall Ship'**
Bodycolour, ink on paper 33.6 x 26

U3802　**RMSP 'Tagus' (1915)**

Bodycolour on card 41.2 x 26.7
Signed, dated

U3803 **Sketch for Advertisement: Player's Navy Cut Virginia Cigarettes and Tobacco (c.1930)**
Bodycolour, ink on board 31.4 x 41.9

U3804 **Rigged Arab Dhow**
Pencil, ink on card 37.5 x 26.7

U3805 **Sketch for Calendar: Union Castle Line to South and East Africa**
Bodycolour on paper 15.9 x 11.4

U3806 **Sketch for Advertisement: Brighton and Hove; verso, Another Sketch**
Bodycolour, ink on paper 9.8 x 13.6

U3807 **Sketch for Advertisement: Asiatic Petroleum Co. Ltd.**
Bodycolour, ink on paper 13.6 x 17.1

U3808 **Sketch for Menu Cover: Royal Mail Cruising**
Pencil, bodycolour on paper 21.6 x 12.7

U3809 **Sketch for Advertisement: Royal Mail Atlantic East Indies Cruise**
Bodycolour, ink on paper 22.9 x 15.2

U3810 **Sketch for Advertisement: Royal Mail Atlantic Eastern Cruise**
Bodycolour on paper 17.7 x 11.7

U3811 **Sketch for Advertisement: Rio de Janeiro by Royal Mail**
Bodycolour, ink on paper 18.1 x 11.4

U3812 **Sketch for Advertisement: Rio by Royal Mail; verso, Another Sketch**
Bodycolour, ink on paper 5.7 x 4.1

U3813 **Sketch for Poster: Norway, Araguaya; verso, Another Sketch**
Pencil, bodycolour on paper 14 x 8.9

U3814 **Sketch for Advertisement: Arcadian**
Pencil, chalk on paper 9.5 x 6.3

U3815 **Sketch for Advertisement: Norway by RMSP The Land of the Midnight Sun**
Bodycolour, ink on paper 9.5 x 5.3

U3816 **Sketch for Advertisement: Norwegian Fjord, Royal Mail**
Bodycolour, ink, pencil on paper 12.7 x 10.1

U3817 **Sketch for Advertisement: Norwegian Fjord, Atlantic Norway Cruises**
Bodycolour, pencil, ink on paper 12.7 x 8.9

U3818 **Sketch for Advertisement: Royal Mail Atlantic Cruises**
Pencil on paper 12.7 x 8.9

U3819 **Sketch for Advertisement: Royal Mail Atlantic Cruises**
Bodycolour on paper 12.7 x 8.9

U3820 **Sketch for Advertisement: Royal Mail Atlantic Cruises**
Bodycolour, ink on paper 7 x 4.4

U3821 **Sketch for Advertisement: Royal Mail Atlantic Cruises**
Bodycolour on paper 7.5 x 5.1

U3822 **Sketch for Advertisement: Royal Mail Atlantic Mediterranean Cruises; verso, Fragment of Life Drawing**
Bodycolour on paper 7.6 x 5.1

U3823 **Sketch for Poster: Orient Line to Australia**
Bodycolour on paper 12.6 x 10.1

U3824 **Sketch for Poster: Orient Line Mediterranean Cruises**
Bodycolour on paper 10.1 x 6.3

U3825 **Sketch for Poster: Orient Line Norway Cruises**
Bodycolour on paper 15.1 x 9.5

U3826 **Sketch for Poster: Orient Line Norway Cruises**
Bodycolour on board 20.2 x 12.6

U3827 **Sketch for Poster: Orient Line Norway Cruises**
Bodycolour on paper 9.9 x 6.3

U3828 **Sketch for Poster: Orient Line Norway Cruises; verso, Fragment of Life Drawing**
Bodycolour on paper 12 x 7.9

U3829 **Sketch for Poster: Orient Line Norway Cruises**
Bodycolour on paper 7.9 x 5.7

U3830 **Sketch for Poster: Orient Line Norway Cruises**
Bodycolour on paper 10.1 x 6.3

U3831 **Sketch for Poster: Orient Line Norway Cruises; verso, Fragment of Life Drawing**
Bodycolour on paper 9.9 x 6.4

U3832 **Sketch for Poster: Orient Line Norway Cruises; verso, Fragment of Life Drawing**
Bodycolour on paper 10.1 x 6

U3833 **Sketch for Poster: Orient Line Norway Cruises; verso, Fragment of Life Drawing**
Bodycolour on paper 10.4 x 6.3

U3834 **Sketch for Poster: Norway Orient Line Cruises; verso, Fragment of Life Drawing**
Bodycolour on paper 9.9 x 6.3

U3835 **Sketch for Poster: Norway Cruises by Orient Line; verso, Another Sketch**
Bodycolour on paper 10.4 x 6.4

U3836 **Sketch for Poster: Norway**
Bodycolour on paper 9.9 x 6.7

U3837 **Sketch for Poster: Norway Cruises**
Bodycolour on paper 9.5 x 6.3

U3838 **Sketch for Poster: Norwegian Flag**
Bodycolour on paper 9.5 x 6.6

U3839 **Sketch for Poster: Norway**
Bodycolour on paper 8.2 x 5.7

U3840 **Sketch for Poster, probably Norway; verso, Fragment of Life Drawing**
Bodycolour on paper 20 x 15.2

U3841 **Sketch for Poster: Canada, Canadian Pacific**
Bodycolour on paper 20.3 x 12.6

U3842 **Sketch for Poster: Canada**
Bodycolour on paper 14 x 8.2

U3843 **Sketch for Poster: West Indies Cruise, Canadian Pacific**
Pencil, watercolour on paper 14 x 8.2

U3844 **Layout for Folding Card: Canadian Pacific**
Watercolour on paper 12.6 x 17.8

U3845 **Sketch for Poster: Blue Star, Mediterranean Cruises**
Bodycolour on paper 9.2 x 5.7

U3846 **Sketch for Poster: 'Arandora Star', Blue Star Cruises, Mediterranean Cruises**
Bodycolour on paper 7.9 x 5.3

U3847 **Sketch for Poster: Blue Star Line, Mediterranean Cruises**
Bodycolour on paper 9.5 x 6.3

U3848 **Sketch for Poster: Norway Cruises, Blue Star Line**
Bodycolour on paper 7 x 5.6

U3849 **Sketch for Poster: Norway Cruises, Blue Star Line**
Bodycolour on paper 8.5 x 6

U3850 **Sketch for Poster: Cunard White Star**
Bodycolour on paper 7.6 x 5

U3851 **Two Sketches for Posters: White Star RMS 'Majestic' (two sides)**
Bodycolour on paper 10.7 x 6.3

U3852 **Six Designs for Backs of Playing Cards, Cunard White Star, RMS 'Maurctania'**
Ink, bodycolour on paper 8.9 x 5.6

U3853 **Design for Back of Playing Cards**
Ink, bodycolour on paper 8.9 x 5.6

U3854 **Nine Designs for Backs of Playing Cards**
Bodycolour on paper 8.9 x 5.6

U3855 **Design with a Celestial Globe**
Bodycolour, ink on paper 9.8 x 7.6

U3856 **Design with a Celestial Globe**
Bodycolour on paper 17.1 x 7.6

U3857 **Sketch for Poster: Royal Mail**
Bodycolour on paper 10.1 x 6.3

U3858 **Sketch for Poster: Buenos Aires, by Royal Mail**
Bodycolour on paper 5.6 x 4.1

U3859 **Sketch for Poster: Royal Mail, Fourth Cruising Gala**
Bodycolour, ink on paper 13 x 8.2

U3860 **Sketch for Poster: West Indies**
Bodycolour on paper 8.5 x 6.3

U3861 **Sketch for Poster: Alcantara**
Bodycolour on paper 9.5 x 15.9

U3862 **Sketch for Book Jacket: *The Citadel* by A. J. Cronin**
Pencil, watercolour on paper 12.7 x 10.1

U3863 **Sketch for Poster: Come back to Erin**
Bodycolour on paper 12.6 x 9.5

U3864 **Sketch for Christmas Greeting Card**
Ink, watercolour on paper 16.1 x 12.6

U3865 **Sketch for Poster: 'Galatea'. 'Screen'**
Pencil on paper 13.6 x 10.4

U3866 **Sketch for Poster: Riverside**
Ink, watercolour on paper 5.6 x 8.5

U3867 **Sketch for Poster: Milwall**
Pencil on paper 10.4 x 6.6

U3868 **Sketch for Poster: South America; verso,
Part Drawing in Pencil of HMS 'Conway'**
Pencil on paper 11.4 x 13.5

U3869 **Sketch for Poster: Caravan**
Ink on paper 7 x 6.3

U3870 **Sketch for Poster: West Indies**
Bodycolour on paper 7.3 x 5.2

U3871 **Sketch for Poster: Harwich**
Ink, bodycolour on paper 9.2 x 6.4

U3872 **Shambles Light Ship**
Bodycolour on paper 8.5 x 10.8

U3873 **Yachts**
Bodycolour on paper 11.1 x 16.5

U3874 **Interior of a Room with Chinese Décor**
Pencil, watercolour on paper 14 x 13.6

U3875 **Sketch of a Boat: Off Malaga**
Pencil on paper 12.3 x 10.2

U3876 **Sketch of a Mountain from the Sea**
Pencil on paper 22.6 x 14.9

U3877 **Palm Trees and Ships**
Ink on paper 8.5 x 12.1

U3878 **Sketch for Poster: Oil Tanker**
Bodycolour on paper 8.9 x 10.8

U3879 **Sketch for Poster: Ship's Lights at Night**
Bodycolour on paper 12.1 x 7.9

U3880 **Composition Sketch**
Pencil on paper 5.4 x 4.4

U3881 **Composition Sketch, Venice (?)**
Pencil on paper 9.9 x 8.6

U3882 **Sketch for Poster: Bowsprit**
Bodycolour on paper 9.5 x 9.5

U3883 **Sketch for Poster: Bowsprit**
Ink on paper 13.6 x 13

U3884 **Sketch for Poster: Prow of Ship**
Ink on paper 9.2 x 8.2

U3885 **Sketch for Poster: Men in a Boat**
Ink on paper 9.5 x 8.9

U3886 **Sketch for Poster: Gondola**
Ink on paper 8.6 x 6.3

U3887 **Sketch for Poster: Sailing Ship**
Ink on paper 8.9 x 7.3

U3888 **Sketch for Poster: Sailing Ship**
Bodycolour on paper 17.5 x 11.4

U3889 **Sketch for Poster: Man on a Donkey**
Bodycolour on paper 8.5 x 11.4

U3890 **Sketch for Poster: Mosque**
Bodycolour on paper 7.3 x 6.3

U3891 **Sketch for Poster: African Woman**
Bodycolour on paper 9.2 x 7.3

U3892 **Sketch for Poster: Crow's Nest**
Bodycolour on paper 6.4 x 4.1

U3893 **Sketch for Poster: Harbour**
Pencil on paper 5.1 x 3.7

U3894 **Sketch for Poster: Dusk, Flowers**
Bodycolour on paper 4.8 x 6.3

U3895 **Sketch for Poster: Seated Arab
Stallholder**
Bodycolour on paper 9.5 x 6.1

U3896 **Sketch for Poster: Gondola**
Bodycolour on paper 7 x 3.8

U3897 **Sketch for Poster: Palm Trees**
Bodycolour on paper 9.2 x 13.6

U3898 **Sketch for Poster: Tropical Harbour**
Bodycolour on paper 6.3 x 12.1

U3899 **Sketch for Poster: Ship of the Line?**
Bodycolour on paper 10.4 x 7

U3900 **Sketch for Poster: Bridge**
Ink, white on paper 4.4 x 7

U3901 **Design for Christmas Greeting Card**
(Both Sides)
Bodycolour, pencil on paper 12.3 x 9.5

U3902 **Design for Christmas Greeting Card**
(rounded)
Bodycolour on paper, diameter 7.3

U3903 **Design for Christmas Greeting Card**
Pencil on paper 12.3 x 10.8

U3904 **Roundel** (London Bridge?)
Pencil on paper 12.3 x 10.2

U3905 **Roundel** (Sailing Ship from Rigging)
Pencil on paper 12.3 x 10.2

U4488 **Marseille (1916)**
Bodycolour on paper 10.8 x 14.3
Signed, dated

U4504 **A Norwegian Fjord**
Bodycolour on card 23.8 x 33.7
Signed

SIBBETT, Beryl 19th-20th century (Irish)

U411 **Flowers**
Oil on canvas 61 x 50.6
Provenance unknown

SICKERT, Walter Richard 1860-1942 (British)

U490 **Suspense (c.1916)** *(Illus.p.325)*
Oil on canvas 76.5 x 59
Signed
Purchased (Lloyd Patterson Collection)
1929

U500 **Easter (c.1928)** *(Illus.p.326)*
Oil on canvas 66.1 x 77.2
Signed
Purchased (Lloyd Patterson Collection)
1929

U853 **Studies for 'Suspense'**
Pencil, ink on paper 44.1 x 30.6
Signed
Purchased 1967

U854 **Study for 'Suspense'** (squared)
(Illus.p.326)
Pencil, ink on paper 43.3 x 31.5
Signed

Purchased 1962

U925 **Aerial Mast on Seashore**
Pencil, ink on paper 18.1 x 27.1
Donated by the Sickert Trust, 1947

U926 **Country Road with Trees**
Ink on paper 19 x 27.8
Donated by the Sickert Trust, 1947

U927 **Two Sketches of Women**
Pencil, ink on paper 29.4 x 18.8
Donated by the Sickert Trust, 1947

U928 **Reclining Female Nude**
Pencil, ink on paper 26 x 37.4
Donated by the Sickert Trust, 1947

U929 **Music Hall Comedian**
Pencil, ink on paper 11.9 x 11.4
Donated by the Sickert Trust, 1947

U930 **Woman Seated at a Table**
Pencil on paper 28.1 x 21.3
Donated by the Sickert Trust, 1947

U931 **Lady in a Coat and Hat**
Pencil on paper 28.1 x 22
Donated by the Sickert Trust, 1947

U932 **Music Hall Artiste**
Pencil on paper 30.5 x 23.8
Donated by the Sickert Trust, 1947

U933 **Reclining Female Nude**
Pencil on paper 22.8 x 31.7
Donated by the Sickert Trust, 1947

U934 **Woman Drinking**
Pencil on paper 32.3 x 20
Donated by the Sickert Trust, 1947

SIMMS, Charles 1873-1928 (British)

U409 **Saints and Sinners**
Oil on canvas on board 76.9 x 55.9
Bequeathed by Violet Gertrude,
Marchioness of Donegall (per the
National Art Collections Fund), 1953

U419 **Sketch for 'Someone Passes'**
Oil on paper 24 x 32
Bequeathed by Violet Gertrude,
Marchioness of Donegall (per the
National Art Collections Fund), 1953

U421 **Man's Last Pretence of Consummation in
Indifference**
Oil on paper on board 32.5 x 24.7
Bequeathed by Violet Gertrude,
Marchioness of Donegall (per the
National Art Collections Fund), 1953

SINGLETON, Henry 1766-1839 (English)

U1325 **Allegory of the Napoleonic Wars**
(Illus.p.326)
Pencil, watercolour, gum on paper 24.3 x
19
Purchased 1959

SIVELL, Robert 1888-1958 (Scottish)

U497 **Sisters (1927)** *(Illus.p.326)*
Oil on canvas 109.3 x 96.2
Purchased 1928

SKEAPING, John 1901-80 (English)

U1221 **Bullfight (1934)** *(Illus.p.326)*
Ink, chalk on paper 29 x 45.5
Signed, dated
Donated by the Contemporary Art
Society, 1938

SLADE, Adam (Frank) b.1875 (English)

U607 **Cliff End, Sussex** *(Illus.p.326)*
Oil on canvas 61.9 x 91.4
Donated by the Friends of the National
Collections of Ireland (per Sarah Purser),
1928

SLATTERY, John Joseph d.1859 (Irish)

U1609 **Nude Study: Eve and the Serpent**
Chalk on paper 38.5 x 22.6 (sight)
Donated by J. H. Bland, 1917

U1610 **Draped Classical Female Figure**
(Maenad?)
Chalk on paper 38.5 x 22.4 (sight)
Donated by J. H. Bland, 1917

U1611 **Pensive Female Figure**
Chalk on paper 23.9 x 22.6 (sight)
Signed
Donated by J. H. Bland, 1917

U1612 **Seated Male Nude with Spear**
Chalk on paper 21.5 x 22.5 (sight)
Signed
Donated by J. H. Bland, 1917

U1613 **Nude Study** (Penitent Magdelene ?)
Chalk on paper 36.7 x 26.6 (sight)
Donated by J. H. Bland, 1917

U1614 **Figure Group with Stabbed Woman**
(Death of Lucretia? Non Dolet?)
Chalk on paper 22.7 x 42.7 (sight)
Signed
Donated by J. H. Bland, 1917

U1615 **Three Classical Figures**
Chalk on paper 20.8 x 12 (sight)
Donated by J. H. Bland, 1917

U1616 **Girl with Arms Crossed on Breast**
Chalk on paper 20.8 x 12.2
Donated by J. H. Bland, 1917

U1617 **Sketch** (Risen Christ?)
Chalk on paper 20.6 x 11.6
Donated by J. H. Bland, 1917

U1618 **Kneeling Helmeted Archer**
Chalk on paper 15.1 x 11.8 (sight)
Donated by J. H. Bland, 1917

U1619 **Sketch** (Cupid and Psyche?)
Chalk on paper 17.5 x 12.2
Donated by J. H. Bland, 1917

U1620 **Kneeling Archer**
Chalk on paper 11.9 x 11.6 (sight)
Donated by J. H. Bland, 1917

U1621 **Male Nude with Cloak**
Chalk on paper 17.8 x 9.4 (sight)
Signed
Donated by J. H. Bland, 1917

U1622 **Male Nude with Cloak**
Chalk on paper 15.5 x 7.1 (sight)
Signed
Donated by J. H. Bland, 1917

U1623 **Crouching Female Nude**
Chalk on paper 12.2 x 7.4 (sight)
Signed
Donated by J. H. Bland, 1917

U1624 **Female Nude with Left Arm Upraised**
Chalk on paper 21.5 x 7.2
Donated by J. H. Bland, 1917

U1625 **Seated Female Nude**
Chalk on paper 29 x 21.5 (sight)
Signed
Donated by J. H. Bland, 1917

U1626 **Abraham and Isaac (?)** *(Illus.p.326)*
Chalk on paper 29 x 21.4 (sight)
Signed
Donated by J. H. Bland, 1917

U1627 **Cain and Abel; Cain Killing Abel**
Chalk on paper 30 x 44.3 (sight)
Signed
Donated by J. H. Bland, 1917

U1628 **Abraham Sacrificing Isaac** *(Illus.p.326)*
Chalk on paper 28.8 x 29.4 (sight)
Donated by J. H. Bland, 1917

U1629 **Ten Classical Figures**
Chalk on paper 29.3 x 42.8 (sight)
Donated by J. H. Bland, 1917

SLAUGHTER, Stephen 1697-1765 (English,
worked in Ireland) (attributed to)

U147 **Portrait of a Gentleman (c.1745)**
(Illus.p.326)
Oil on canvas 126.4 x 101.5
Purchased 1959

SLEATOR, James Sinton 1885-1950 (Irish)

U163 **Portrait of Forrest Reid 1875-1947**
(1924) *(Illus.p.327)*
Oil on canvas 76.2 x 63.5
Signed, dated
Purchased 1926

U407 **Still Life (1923)** *(Illus.p.327)*
Oil on canvas 76 x 63.5
Signed, dated
Donated by the artist, 1926

U4962 **Self-Portrait (1945-49)**
Oil on canvas 80 x 70
Purchased 1993

U5069 **White Marguerites in a Vase** *(Illus.p.327)*
Oil on canvas 66 x 56
Donated by Mrs. Pauline P. Johnstone in
memory of Mrs. Roberta Raine, 1998

SLOAN, Bob b.1940 (Irish)

U4731 **Still Life for Sarah (1983-88)**
Sculpture, aluminium, bronze, concrete,
ht. 87
Purchased 1988

SMITH, J. Carson 19th-20th century (British)

U4500 **Fisherman in a Hut**
Oil on canvas 63 x 91
Signed

Provenance unknown

SMITH, John 'Warwick' 1749-1831 (English)

U950 **Naples from the Arinelli** *(Illus.p.327)*
Watercolour, pencil on paper 34.4 x 50.9
Purchased 1938

SMITH, Sir Matthew 1879-1959 (English)

U499 **Daisies and Pears (c.1920-29)**
(Illus.p.327)
Oil on canvas 81.2 x 54.5
Purchased (Lloyd Patterson Collection)
1929

SMITH, Richard b.1931 (English)

U537 **Penny (1960)** *(Illus.p.327)*
Oil on canvas 226.1 x 210.8
Signed, dated
Donated by the Contemporary Art
Society, 1965

SMITH, Sidney 1912-82 (Irish)

U412 **Balloon in Tramway Depot, Evening**
(1941)
Oil on canvas 50.8 x 60.9
Signed, dated
Donated by the War Artists' Advisory
Committee (per the Imperial War
Museum), 1946

U413 **Just a Song at Twilight (1941)**
Oil on canvas 50.6 x 60.9
Signed, dated
Donated by the War Artists' Advisory
Committee (per the
Imperial War Museum), 1946

U414 **Gossip**
Oil on canvas 71.2 x 45.7
Signed
Purchased 1946

U415 **From the Flies (1943-44)** *(Illus.p.327)*
Oil on canvas 45.7 x 71.1
Signed
Purchased 1944

U1490 **Arnott's, April 1941**
Crayon on paper 30.7 x 24.4
Purchased 1943

U1491 **R[oyal] E[ngineer]'s on Demolition Duty**
(1941)
Crayon on paper 24.4 x 30.6
Signed, dated
Purchased 1943

U1492 **Demolition, York Street Mill**
Crayon on paper 24.5 x 30.6
Purchased 1943

U1493 **Corner of Bridge Street (1941)**
Crayon on paper 30.6 x 24.4
Signed, dated
Purchased 1943

U1494 **Demolition, Donegall Street**
Congregational Church
Crayon on paper 24.3 x 30.7
Purchased 1943

U1495 **Portrait of Michael McLaverty 1907-92**
Pencil on paper 33.9 x 23.5

Donated anonymously, 1947

U1544 **Demolition Squad, North Street**
Crayon on paper 30.7 x 24.4
Signed
Purchased 1943

U1545 **Welder Cutting Girders (1941)**
Crayon on paper 30.7 x 24.4
Signed, dated
Purchased 1943

U1546 **Demolition Squad, North Street**
(Illus.p.327)
Crayon on paper 30.5 x 24.4
Signed
Purchased 1943

U2590 **Portrait of W. R. Rodgers 1909-69 (1941)**
(Illus.p.327)
Pencil on paper 36.2 x 26
Signed, dated
Donated by John Hewitt, 1981

U2648 **Outside Fiesole, Florence (1965)**
(Illus.p.328)
Oil on board 25.3 x 35.3
Signed, dated
Donated by Mrs. P. Chabanais, 1982

U2649 **Castlewellan, Co. Down (1940s)**
(Illus.p.328)
Oil on canvas 45.5 x 61
Signed
Donated by Mrs. P. Chabanais, 1982

U2650 **Self-Portrait (1946)** *(Illus.p.328)*
Oil on canvas 71.3 x 45.8
Signed, dated
Donated by Mrs. P. Chabanais, 1982

SMYTH, Edward and **John,** 1749-1812 and
c.1773-1840 (Irish)

U1164 **Francis Johnston 1760-1829** *(Illus p 328)*
Sculpture, marble bust, ht. 70.5
Signed
Purchased 1971

U1165 **Mrs. Francis Johnston, née Anne Barnes
1769-1841** *(Illus.p.328)*
Sculpture, marble bust, ht. 64.8
Purchased 1971

SMYTH, J. B. 19th century (English?)

U1326 **Landscape with Church (1874)**
(Illus.p.328)
Watercolour, white on paper 20.9 x 29.3
Signed, dated
Provenance unknown

SOLIMENA, Francesco 1657-1747 (Italian)

U158 **Study for Circe** *(Illus.p.328)*
Oil on canvas 65.2 x 51
Purchased 1965

SOLOMONS, Estella F. 1882-1968 (Irish)

U405 **Portrait of Alice Milligan 1866-1953
(1918)** *(Illus.p.328)*
Oil on canvas 92 x 71.5
Signed, dated
Donated by the Thomas Haverty Trust,
1945

U416 **Portrait of Joseph Campbell 1879-1944
(1919)** *(Illus.p.328)*
Oil on canvas 61 x 50.9
Signed, dated
Donated by the Thomas Haverty Trust,
1945

SOMERVILLE, Edith Oenone 1858-1949 (Irish)

U1565 **Bearded Man at the Tiller of a Yacht
(1881)**
Pencil on paper 15.2 x 24.2
Signed, dated
Purchased 1971

U2088 **Stage Design for 'A Horse! A Horse!':
Castle by Moonlight (c.1930)**
(Illus.p.329)
Pastel on paper 36.8 x 43.2 (sight)
Signed
Purchased 1974

U2089 **Stage Design for 'A Horse! A Horse!':
Camp in the Mountains (c.1930)**
Pastel on paper 30.5 x 40 (sight)
Purchased 1974

SOTO, Jesús-Rafael b.1923 (Venezuelan)

U391 **Un Carré Argenté (1966)**
Wood, painted metal on board 158 x
107.1
Signed, dated
Purchased 1967

SOUTER, Camille b.1929 (English, works in
Ireland)

U406 **Forgotten Island near Venice (1964)**
Oil on paper on board 78.3 x 57.9
Signed, dated
Purchased 1965

U704 **The Last of the Radicio (1964)**
(Illus.p.329)
Oil on paper on board 58.2 x 78.5
Signed, dated
Purchased 1965

U2259 **Red Brick and It's not a Game (1973)**
Oil on board 58.3 x 44.7
Signed, dated
Purchased 1974

U2260 **Belfast (1973)**
Oil on panel 51.5 x 30.9
Signed, dated
Purchased 1974

SPENCER, Gilbert 1892-1979 (English)

U491 **Little Milton near Garsington (1926)**
(Illus.p.329)
Oil on canvas 67.5 x 89.2
Signed, dated
Purchased (Lloyd Patterson Collection)
1932

U855 **Farm Cart (1929)** *(Illus.p.329)*
Pencil, watercolour on paper 35.4 x 25.6
Signed, dated
Purchased 1951

SPENCER, Sir Stanley 1891-1959 (English)

U487 **The Betrayal (1922-23)** *(Illus.p.93)*

Oil on canvas 122.7 x 137.2
Purchased (Lloyd Patterson Collection)
1929

U488 **Scene from the Marriage at Cana in
Galilee (1935)** *(Illus.p.329)*
Oil on canvas 84.2 x 183.2
Donated by the Hon. Bryan Guinness
(per the Friends of the National
Collections of Ireland), 1939

U489 **Portrait of Daphne Spencer b.1932
(1951)** *(Illus.p.329)*
Oil on canvas 92.3 x 61.6
Purchased 1953

U5022 **Portrait of Zoltan Lewinter-Frankl 1894-
1961 (c.1954-57)**
Pencil on paper 35.5 x 25.5
Purchased 1995

SPENDER, John Humphrey b.1910 (English)

U1131 **Ruined Square (1948)** *(Illus.p.329)*
Watercolour, oil, gouache on paper 28 x
40.8
Signed, dated
Purchased 1954

STANFIELD, Clarkson 1793-1867 (English)

U167 **The Stack Rock, Co. Antrim (1861)**
(Illus.p.329)
Oil on canvas 38 x 61.2
Signed, dated
Donated by R. B. Dunwoody, CBE, 1964

U856 **Carrickfergus Castle**
Pencil, wash, white on paper 14.5 x 11.4
Purchased 1948

U857 **Shakespeare's Cliff, Dover (1849)**
(formerly 'A Coast Scene') *(Illus.p.329)*
Pencil, watercolour, white on paper 20.9
x 32.5
Signed, dated
Purchased 1912

STANLEY, Mrs. Catherine 1792-1862 (English)

U4905 **Panoramic View of the Mourne
Mountains and Mourne Park (1814)**
Ink, sepia wash on paper 23.5 x 127
Dated
Purchased 1992

STANNUS, Anthony Carey 1830-1919 (Irish)

U162 **The Last of the Spanish Armada
(c.1884)**
Oil on canvas 89.8 x 135.5 (sight)
Signed
Donated by Sir R. Lloyd Patterson, 1888

U560 **Dinant** *(Illus.p.330)*
Watercolour, white on paper 73 x 129
Signed
Bequeathed by Sir R. Lloyd Patterson,
1919

U599 **Land's End, Cornwall (1897)**
Oil on canvas 78.7 x 130.8
Signed, dated
Donated by Miss K. Emerson, 1955

U628 **Evening on the Dogger Bank**

Watercolour, bodycolour, white on paper
78 x 125
Signed
Donated by the artist (per Sir James
Henderson), 1906

U858 **An Irish Interior** *(Illus.p.330)*
Watercolour, white on paper 24.5 x 34.3
Signed
Purchased 1955

U859 **Beating into Port** *(Illus.p.330)*
Pencil, watercolour, white on paper 23.1
x 32.2
Signed
Bequeathed by Sir R. Lloyd Patterson,
1919

U1205 **Bude**
Watercolour, white on paper 17.9 x 28.2
Signed
Bequeathed by Miss H. M. McCleery,
1968

U1206 **A Highland River**
Pencil, watercolour, bodycolour, gum on
paper 23.7 x 44.7
Signed
Bequeathed by Miss H. M. McCleery,
1968

U1401 **The Haymakers, Warkworth Castle,
Northumberland** *(Illus.p.330)*
Pencil, watercolour, white on paper 27.5
x 43.1
Signed
Purchased 1955

U2007 **Canon John Grainger, DD, MRIA 1830-
91**
Oil on canvas 240.6 x 147.6
Signed
Donated by the Presentation Committee,
1892
Formerly 'Portrait of a Man' by Unknown,
Art dept. U4484

U4491 **Alderman William John Johnston, JP
1821-97**
Oil on canvas 142.9 x 112.7
Donated by the Presentation Committee,
1892

U5023 **Mexico City (c.1868)**
Watercolour on paper 19 x 53.5
Donated by R. H. S. Robertson, 1996

STANNUS, Anthony Carey 1830-1919 (Irish)
(after)

U4955 **The Launch of the 'Norah Graeme' at
the Queen's Island, Belfast, 1858**
Watercolour, white on paper 32 x 48
Donated by F. T. C. Lloyd, 1993

STAPLES, Sir Robert Ponsonby, Bt. 1853-1943
(Irish)

U159 **Liner on Stocks (1904-24)** (Central Panel
of Triptych 'Shipbuilding in Belfast')
(Illus.p.330)
Oil on canvas 124.4 x 170.7
Signed
Purchased 1913

U573 **Bangor Boat (1904-24)** (Right-hand

Panel of Triptych 'Shipbuilding in
Belfast') *(Illus.p.330)*
Oil on canvas 124.7 x 86.6
Purchased 1913

U597 **Turbine Makers (1904-24)** (Left-hand
Panel of Triptych 'Shipbuilding in
Belfast') *(Illus.p.330)*
Oil on canvas 124.7 x 86.6
Signed
Purchased 1913

U694 **Flax Pullers (c.1908)** *(Illus.p.330)*
Oil on canvas 124.7 x 168.3
Signed
Donated by the Flax Spinners'
Association, 1930

U1768 **Sketches for Triptych of 'Shipbuilding in
Belfast' (1906)**
Pencil on paper 17.5 x 9.8
Donated by the artist, 1913

U1769 **Sketches for 'Shipbuilding' (1906)**
Pencil on paper 9.6 x 17.6
Donated by the artist, 1913

U1770 **Sketches for 'Shipbuilding' (1906)**
Pencil on paper 6.5 x 17.6
Donated by the artist, 1913

U1771 **Sketches for 'Shipbuilding' (1906)**
Pencil on paper 7.6 x 12.6
Donated by the artist, 1913

U1772 **Sketches for 'Shipbuilding' (1906)**
Pencil on paper 17.5 x 9.6
Signed, dated
Donated by the artist, 1913

U1773 **Sketches for 'Shipbuilding' (1906)**
Pencil on paper 17.5 x 9.4
Donated by the artist, 1913

U1774 **Sketches for 'Shipbuilding' (1906)**
Pencil on paper 12.2 x 9.5
Donated by the artist, 1913

U1775 **Sketches for 'Shipbuilding' (1906)**
Pencil on paper 17.6 x 9.6
Donated by the artist, 1913

U1776 **Sketches for 'Shipbuilding' (1906)**
Pencil on paper 7.1 x 14.8
Donated by the artist, 1913

U1823 **Fife Arms, Braemar (1897)**
Charcoal, ink, watercolour, white on
paper 40.5 x 58
Signed, dated
Provenance unknown

U1824 **George Moore 1852-1933, at Grey
House, Kensington (1894)**
Pencil on card 21.6 x 18.3
Purchased 1958

U1825 **Percy French 1854-1920** *(Illus.p.330)*
Watercolour on paper 22.2 x 15.3
Purchased 1958

U1826 **Sir Nathaniel Alexander Staples, 10th
Baronet 1817-99 (1870-71)**
Pencil, sanguine, chalk on paper 31.2 x
23.5
Signed
Purchased 1958

U1827 **Rt. Hon. Alexander Carlisle in Harland
and Wolff's Office (1909)**
Pencil, crayon on card 16.8 x 15
Signed
Purchased 1958

U1828 **Beerbohm Tree at Her Majesty's Theatre**
(Sir Herbert Beerbohm Tree 1853-1917)
Pencil, crayon on paper 32.7 x 23.7
Provenance unknown

U1829 **Captain Craig (afterwards Lord
Craigavon) 1871-1940 at the Slieve
Donard Hotel, Newcastle, Co. Down
(1912)**
Pencil on paper 17.7 x 22.2
Signed, dated
Purchased 1958

U1830 **Captain Craig (afterwards Lord
Craigavon) 1871-1940 at
Holywood, Co. Down (1911)**
Pencil, charcoal, watercolour on paper
19.1 x 15.5
Signed, dated
Purchased 1958

U1831 **Michael, Cardinal Logue 1840-1924,
Lissan Chapel (1921)**
Pencil on card 18 x 15
Signed, dated
Purchased 1958

U1832 **Self-Portrait (1916)** *(Illus.p.331)*
Watercolour, crayon on paper 28.4 x 19.9
Signed, dated
Purchased 1958

U1833 **Bob (1910)**
Chalk, white on paper 56.8 x 39.3
Signed, dated
Provenance unknown

U1834 **'Sir Edward [Carson] Considers the Next
Move'**
Ink, watercolour, white on card 45.8 x 29
Signed
Purchased 1958

U1835 **The Most Rev. William Alexander 1824-
1911, Archbishop of Armagh and
Primate of All Ireland (1899)**
(Illus.p.331)
Charcoal, sanguine, white on paper 33 x
25.5
Dated
Purchased 1958

U1836 **Joe Devlin, MP 1871-1934 (1910)**
Chalk, white on paper 32.5 x 23.5
Signed, dated
Purchased 1958

U1838 **Falls Road, Belfast**
Pencil, crayon on paper 36.4 x 26
Signed
Provenance unknown

U1839 **Study for 'Shipbuilding' Triptych (1906)**
Pencil on paper 17.6 x 9.5
Donated by the artist, 1913

U1840 **Men Making a Turbine (1906)**
Pencil on paper 17.5 x 9.6
Signed, dated
Donated by the artist, 1913

U1841　**Group at Salvation Army Meeting (1906)**
Pencil on paper 9.6 x 13.2
Donated by the artist, 1913

STEENWYCK, Hendrik van, the Younger
c.1580-1649 (Dutch)

U161　**Church Interior** *(Illus.p.331)*
Oil on canvas 80.2 x 107.1
Purchased 1962

STEER, Philip Wilson 1860-1942 (English)

U498　**Yachts on the Solent (1920)** *(Illus.p.331)*
Oil on canvas 51.1 x 81.4
Signed, dated
Purchased (Lloyd Patterson Collection)
1929

U501　**The Teme at Ludlow (1900)** *(Illus.p.331)*
Oil on canvas 45.9 x 61.1
Signed, dated
Acquired by exchange (Lloyd Patterson
Collection), 1930

U860　**Haweswater (1904)** *(Illus.p.331)*
Watercolour, bodycolour on paper 24 x
36.3
Signed
Acquired by exchange (Lloyd Patterson
Collection), 1930

STEVENSON, Patric 1909-83 (Irish)

U861　**Cows in a Byre: 1 (1952)**
Ink, gouache on paper 30 x 48
Signed, dated
Bequeathed by Very Rev. L. C. Stevenson,
1962

U1437　**Breakers, Achill (1953)** *(Illus.p.331)*
Gouache on paper 30.1 x 44.4 (sight)
Signed, dated
Bequeathed by Very Rev. L. C. Stevenson,
1962

STEYN, Stella 1907-87 (Irish)

U5020　**Woman Seated at a Table (1951)**
(Illus.p.331)
Oil on canvas 91 x 60.5
Signed, dated
Purchased 1995

STIVEN, Fred b.1929 (Scottish)

U2468　**August Suite II (1976)**
Sculpture, wood, metal 27.4 x 42.5 x 9.8
Signed, dated
Purchased 1978

STORCK, Abraham c.1635-c.1710 (Dutch)

U160　**River Scene** *(Illus.p.331)*
Oil on canvas 99 x 86.4
Donated by W. T. Braithwaite (per J.
Horner), 1906

STOTHARD, Thomas 1755-1834 (English)

U862　**Sketch for Decorative Design**
Ink, wash on paper 20.2 x 11.1
Provenance unknown

U1435　**Mother's Present** *(Illus.p.332)*
Sepia on card 17.5 x 15.4

Donated by J. H. Stirling, 1919

U2008　**Sketch for Decorative Design**
Ink, wash on paper 16.5 x 5.4
Provenance unknown

U3906　**Sketch for Decorative Design**
Ink, wash on paper 20.2 x 12.1
Provenance unknown

STOUPE, James (Seamus) 1872-1949 (Irish)

U27　**French Barque in York Dock (1912)**
Oil on panel 15.2 x 21.6
Signed
Purchased 1950

U418　**After Milking Time** *(Illus.p.332)*
Oil on board 50.7 x 61.1
Signed
Provenance unknown

U420　**Study for 'After Milking Time'**
Oil on board 38 x 45.5
Signed
Provenance unknown

U665　**Autumn**
Oil on board 40.4 x 55.9
Signed
Provenance unknown

U1543　**Self-Portrait (1941)**
Pastel on paper 40.5 x 60.4
Signed, dated
Donated by the artist, 1943

U2009　**Belfast from the Castle Grounds**
Oil on canvas 49.4 x 57.1
Purchased 1950

U2010　**William Gray 1830-1917**
Copper medallion, diameter 20.3
Donated by the artist, 1940

U2219　**Alderman James A. Doran, JP 1848-1934
(c.1921)**
Sculpture, bronze bust, ht. 61
Signed
Donated by the sitter, 1930

U2350　**The Park Walk (1916)**
Oil on board 37.9 x 45.4
Signed
Purchased 1950

U2351　**Hillfoot Road (?)**
Oil on board 45.6 x 58.3
Signed
Provenance unknown

U2352　**Ballylesson** *(Illus.p.332)*
Oil on canvas 50.7 x 61.1
Signed
Provenance unknown

STROEBEL, Johannes Antonie Balthasar 1825-
1905 (Dutch)

U165　**Dutch Interior** *(Illus.p.332)*
Oil on panel 65.4 x 50
Bequeathed by H. Musgrave, 1922

U658　**Dutch Family Scene**
Oil on canvas 47.8 x 63.6
Signed
Bequeathed by H. Musgrave, 1922

STUART, Ian b.1926 (Irish)

U957　**Grey Box (1967)** *(Illus.p.332)*
Sculpture, welded aluminium 230 x 160
x 109.2
Purchased 1967

U1764　**Dromos (c.1962-63)**
Sculpture, welded metal 57.4 x 35.2 x 26
Purchased with the aid of a grant from
Ulster Television Ltd., 1963

STUART (or STEUART), Sir John James 1779-
1849 (Scottish) (attributed to)

U1489　**Battlescene**
Pencil, sepia wash on paper 9.9 x 17.7
Provenance unknown

STUART, William fl.1850-67 (British)

U29　**George I Arriving at the Nore in 1714**
(Illus.p.332)
Oil on canvas 113.2 x 158
Donated by Sir R. Lloyd Patterson, 1891

STUART-HILL, A. H. fl.c.1920-50 (British)

U460　**Santa Margherita, Italy (c.1927-28)**
(Illus.p.332)
Oil on board 66.2 x 76.6
Signed
Purchased 1928

STUBBS, Ralph R. 19th century (British)

U171　**The Nab, Scarborough, South Side
(1858)** *(Illus.p.332)*
Oil on board 20.8 x 31
Signed, dated
Donated by W. T. Braithwaite (per J.
Horner), 1906

SULLIVAN, Edmund Joseph 1869-1933
(English)

U1268　**The Art Class** *(Illus.p.332)*
Ink on paper 23.4 x 19.1
Donated by Mrs. Stewart, 1970

U1269　**Portrait of Kathleen Barry (later Mrs.
Graham Sutherland)**
Pencil on paper 20.5 x 15.6
Donated by Mrs. Stewart, 1970

SUNDERLAND, Thomas 1744-1823 (English)

U1134　**Ullswater** *(Illus.p.333)*
Charcoal, wash on paper 24.3 x 34.6
Purchased 1955

SUTER, Paul 20th century (Swiss)

U4950　**Tristan (1992)**
Sculpture, welded steel 200 x 140 x 100
Purchased 1992

SUTHERLAND, Graham 1903-80 (English)

U503　**Gorse on a Sea Wall (1939)** *(Illus.p.94)*
Oil on canvas 62.2 x 48.3
Signed, dated
Purchased 1967

SWANZY, Mary 1882-1978 (Irish)

U2087　**Reading the 'Employment Offers'**

Column (1972) *(Illus.p.333)*
Oil on board 34.8 x 26.8
Signed
Purchased 1974

U2324 **Flowerpiece (c.1913)** *(Illus.p.333)*
Oil on canvas 98.8 x 81.5
Signed
Purchased 1975

U2558 **Woman in a Green Dress and Cameo (1920-40)** *(Illus.p.333)*
Oil on canvas 76.2 x 64
Donated by the Friends of the National Collections of Ireland, 1980

U2559 **Abstract**
Oil on canvas 81.4 x 101.4
Donated by the Friends of the National Collections of Ireland, 1980

U4932 **Samoan Scene**
Oil on canvas 152.6 x 91.5
Bequeathed by M. Kennedy, 1992

SWEETMAN, Thomas H. fl.1812-c.35 (Irish)

U169 **John Philpot Curran 1750-1817 (c.1809)**
Oil on canvas 25.4 x 21.6
Signed, dated
Purchased 1962

SWIFT, Patrick 1927-83 (Irish)

U5003 **Positano** *(Illus.p.333)*
Oil on canvas 59.6 x 82.2
Donated by Stephen O'Meara and the Swift family, 1994

SYMONS, Mark Lancelot 1887-1935 (English)

U1402 **Family Breakfasting (1934)** *(Illus.p.333)*
Pencil, wash on paper 28.2 x 37.2
Dated
Purchased 1955

SZTABINSKI, Grzegorz 20th century (Polish)

U2517 **Permutations I** *(Illus.p.333)*
Ink on paper 66 x 48.2
Purchased 1979

T

TAANMAN, Jacob 1836-1923 (Dutch)

U190 **Woman and Child (1867)** *(Illus.p.333)*
Oil on panel 28.3 x 20.7
Signed, dated
Bequeathed by H. Musgrave, 1922

TANSEY, Francis b.1959 (Irish)

U4822 **Translucent Projection I**
Acrylic on canvas 99.1 x 99.1
Donated by the artist, 1990

TAPIES, Antoni b.1923 (Spanish)

U513 **Peinture Verte (1954)** *(Illus.p.333)*
Oil on canvas 97.1 x 146
Signed
Purchased 1964

TASSI, Agostino 1565-1644 (Italian)

U186 **Landscape with Figures** *(Illus.p.334)*
Oil on canvas 35 x 52.3
Purchased 1963

TAYLER, J. Frederick 1802-89 (English)

U1136 **The Homestead (1853)** *(Illus.p.334)*
Pencil, watercolour, white on paper 26 x 37.5
Signed, dated
Purchased 1934

TAYLOR, Ernest E. 1863-1907 (English, worked in Ireland)

U2014 **John Vinycomb, MRIA 1833-1928 (1892)** *(Illus.p.334)*
Oil on canvas 91.6 x 71.6
Signed, dated
Donated by T. V. Vinycomb, 1928

TAYLOR, Francis b.1899 (English)

U1135 **The Windows of Kensington, London (1927)** *(Illus.p.334)*
Pencil, ink, watercolour on paper 33.5 x 47
Signed, dated
Purchased 1927

TAYLOR, Wendy b.1945 (English)

U2012 **Sky Hook (1975)**
Sculpture, steel, fibreglass 175.2 x 188 x 101.6
Purchased 1979

TENIERS, David, the Younger 1610-90 (Flemish) (attributed to)

U212 **Rocky Arch with Figures**
Oil on panel 39.2 x 55.6
Signed
Purchased 1959

U2040 **Interior with Figures**
Oil on canvas on panel 41.9 x 34.3
Purchased 1959; sold 1970

THOMPSON, Miss M. O. fl.1883-88 (Irish)

U439 **Mug, Holly and Ivy**
Pencil, white on paper 35.4 x 23.6
Donated by B. Jackson and Dr. T. Jackson, 1998

U611 **A March Landscape (1888)**
Watercolour on paper 14.5 x 20.3
Signed, dated
Donated by B. Jackson and Dr. T. Jackson, 1998

THOMPSON, Sidney Mary (Mrs. Rodolphe Christen) 1847-1923 (Irish)

U2016 **Samuel Alexander Stewart, ALS, FBSE 1827-1910 (1896)**
Oil on canvas 61.8 x 48.8
Signed, dated
Donated by the Belfast Naturalists' Field Club, 1930

THOMPSON, Thomas Clement c.1780-1857 (Irish)

U188 **Searching the Scriptures (1841)**

Oil on canvas 95.2 x 73.6
Signed, dated
Purchased 1967

U226 **John McCance 1772-1835 (1825)**
Oil on canvas 130 x 101.5
Signed, dated
Donated by the Northern Bank Ltd., 1969

U729 **Francis Johnston 1760-1829 (early 1820s)** *(Illus.p.334)*
Oil on canvas 131 x 103
Purchased 1971

U730 **Mrs. Francis Johnston, neé Anne Barnes 1769-1841 (early 1820s)**
Oil on canvas 130 x 103
Purchased 1971

THOMSON, Hugh 1860-1920 (Irish)

U1138 **'Aaron Peeping' (1907)** (Illustration for George Eliot's *Silas Marner*, 1907, ch. 10)
Ink, watercolour on paper 32.1 x 25.9
Signed, dated
Purchased 1936

U1139 **'The Same Kind of Delicate Flattery' (1897)** (Illustration for Jane Austen's *Northanger Abbey*, 1897, ch. 12)
Ink, watercolour on paper 22 x 16 (sight)
Signed, dated
Purchased 1936

U1140 **'Bringing Him to the Point' (1898)** (Illustration for Stephen Gwynn's *An Irish Horse Fair*, 1901) *(Illus.p.334)*
Pencil, ink, watercolour on paper 38 x 53.6
Signed, dated
Purchased 1936

U1141 **Illustration for Robert Browning's 'The Pied Piper of Hamelin' (1894)** *(Illus.p.334)*
Ink, watercolour on paper 30.5 x 24.1
Signed, dated
Purchased 1954

U1142 **'Laying the Cloth' (1899)** (Illustration for Oliver Goldsmith's *The Vicar of Wakefield*, 1890) *(Illus.p.334)*
Ink, watercolour on paper 29.2 x 21.9 (sight)
Signed, dated
Purchased 1951

U1143 **Illustration for Mrs. M. H. Spielmann's *My Son and I* (1908)**
Ink, watercolour on paper 32 x 25.9
Signed, dated
Purchased 1951

U1144 **'The Shanachie' (1906)** (Frontispiece to Stephen Gwynn's *Fair Hills of Ireland*, 1906) *(Illus.p.334)*
Pencil, charcoal, watercolour on paper 30.2 x 22.6 (sight)
Signed, dated
Purchased 1936

U1145 **'Hester Seated Herself on the Bed' (1915)** (Illustration for Nathaniel Hawthorne's *The Scarlet Letter*, 1915)

Pencil, watercolour on paper 27 x 21.2
(sight)
Signed, dated
Donated by Mrs. J.N. Thomson, 1935

U1369   **'Delighted in his Dry Bon-mots and
Cackling Laughter' (1892)** (Illustration
for 'A Gentlewoman of the Old School'
in Austin Dobson's *Ballad of Beau
Brocade*, 1892)
Ink on paper 30.5 x 24.1
Signed, dated
Purchased 1936

U1585   **Caricature of Harry Lauder 1870-1950**
(Illus.p.335)
Charcoal on paper 40.6 x 27.9
Purchased 1954

THOMSON, Rev. John 1778-1840 (Scottish)

U187   **Dunluce Castle**
Oil on canvas 78 x 107
Donated by R. B. Dunwoody, 1963;
destroyed in Malone House fire, 1976

TIBBLE, Geoffrey 1909-52 (English)

U504   **Pietà (1950)** *(Illus.p.335)*
Oil on canvas 76.4 x 63.8
Signed
Purchased 1953

TINDLE, David b.1932 (British)

U4799   **Fishing Boats (1957)**
Oil on board 18 x 25
Bequeathed by Roberta and John Hewitt,
1987

TONKS, Henry 1862-1937 (English)

U863   **Girl in a Green Dress** *(Illus.p.335)*
Ink, pastel on paper 24.8 x 18.4
Purchased 1970

TOOGOOD, Romeo Charles 1902-66 (Irish)

U575   **Dan Nancy's, Cushendun (1933)**
(Illus.p.335)
Oil on canvas 63.6 x 76.4
Signed
Donated by the Thomas Haverty Trust,
1936

U653   **Barge at Edenderry (1936)** *(Illus.p.335)*
Oil on canvas 71.4 x 82
Signed, dated
Donated by the Thomas Haverty Trust,
1941

TOPHAM, Francis William 1808-77 (English)

U1413   **Cottage Interior, Claddagh, Galway
(1845)** *(Illus.p.335)*
Pencil, watercolour, white on paper 25.2
x 31
Dated
Purchased 1956

TOWNE, Francis 1739-1816 (English)

U864   **Trees and Rocks, Ambleside** *(Illus.p.335)*
Ink, watercolour on paper 26.9 x 37.9
Purchased 1936

TREVOR, Helen Mabel 1831-1900 (Irish)

U189   **The Young Eve (1882)** *(Illus.p.335)*
Oil on canvas 122.5 x 88.5
Signed, dated
Purchased 1959

TROBRIDGE, George 1856-1909 (English,
worked in Ireland)

U1146   **Looking East towards the Castlereagh
Hills from Malone, Arthur James Ward's
Cottage in Foreground** *(Illus.p.335)*
Pencil, watercolour on paper 35.8 x 54.2
Signed
Donated by the Misses Brett, 1935

U1147   **Riverside Meadows, Belvoir Park**
(Illus.p.336)
Pencil, watercolour on paper 36.2 x 53.8
Signed
Purchased 1908

TROSCHKE, Wolfgang b.1947 (German)

U5021   **Ohne Titel (1993)** *(Illus.p.336)*
Oil on canvas 180.5 x 250.2
Signed, dated
Purchased 1994

TUMALTI (or TUMALTY), Bernard M. fl.1821-
47 (British)

U2017   **Portrait of Thomas Henry Hull 1859-64**
Oil on canvas 57.1 x 44.4
Donated by F. W. Hull, 1943

TUOHY, Patrick J. 1894-1930 (Irish)

U5042   **The Baptism of Christ (c.1922)**
Oil on canvas 180 x 303
Signed
Donated by Dr. J. O'Brien, 1996

TURNER, Desmond b.1923 (Irish)

U5052   **Cottages in Keel (1996)**
Oil on canvas 49.6 x 60 (sight)
Signed, dated
Donated by the Thomas Haverty Trust,
1997

TURNER, John b.1916 (Irish)

U408   **The Family (1945)** *(Illus.p.336)*
Oil on canvas 76.4 x 63.5
Signed, dated
Purchased 1945

U2554   **Death of the First Born (1948)**
(Illus.p.336)
Oil on canvas 68.8 x 76.4
Signed, dated
Donated by the artist, 1980

U2595   **Ecce Homo (1948)**
Oil on canvas 76 x 45
Signed, dated
Donated by the artist, 1980

TURNER, Joseph Mallord William 1775-1851
(English)

U224   **The Dawn of Christianity (The Flight
into Egypt) (1841)** *(Illus.p.95)*
Oil on canvas 79 x 79 (circular image,

diameter 79)
Donated by Lady Margaret Currie, 1913

U865   **Beeston Castle, Cheshire** *(Illus.p.336)*
Watercolour, pencil on paper 21 x 32.8
Donated by F. J. Nettlefold, 1948

U866   **Beachy Head Looking towards
Newhaven** (formerly 'Sandy Cove with
Boats, Beachy Head') *(Illus.p.336)*
Watercolour on paper 29.4 x 43.9
Bequeathed by Sir David Reid (per Lady
Reid), 1951

U2019   **Leaf from an Early Sketch Book (?)**
Oil on paper 25.4 x 10.2 (sight)
Donated by Mrs. W. R. Mackenzie, 1925

TURNER, William (of Oxford) 1789-1862
(English)

U1148   **View of Magdalen College Tower and
Bridge, Oxford** *(Illus.p.336)*
Pencil, watercolour on paper 26.5 x 44.3
Purchased 1953

U

UDEN, Lucas van 1595-c.1672 (Flemish)

U230   **Landscape with Figures** *(Illus.p.336)*
Oil on panel 36.6 x 57
Signed
Purchased 1959

UECKER, Günther b.1930 (German)

U539   **Tisch (1963)**
Relief, painted nails on canvas on board
149.9 x 149.9
Signed, dated
Donated by the Contemporary Art
Society, 1968

UNKNOWN

These artists are arranged alphabetically by
School and thereafter, by Century within Schools

UNKNOWN, 16th century (British)

U642   **Robert Devereux, 2nd Earl of Essex
1566-1601** *(Illus.p.336)*
Oil on panel 57 x 44.5
Purchased 1955

U4755   **Walter Devereux, 1st Earl of Essex 1539-
76 (1572)** *(Illus.p.337)*
Oil on panel 87.1 x 70.1
Dated
Purchased with the aid of a grant from
the National Art Collections Fund, 1989

UNKNOWN, 17th century (British)

U195   **'Le Chandelier'** *(Illus.p.337)*
Oil on canvas 90.2 x 109.2
Purchased 1959

UNKNOWN, 18th century (British)

U196   **Portrait of a Woman**
Oil on canvas 76.2 x 63.5
Provenance unknown

U1923 **William Scott (Tantra Barbus) (c.1776)**
Oil on canvas 34.8 x 41.9
Donated by J. A. Culbert, 1936

U1989 **Mary, First Wife of Hugh, 1st Baron Massy (1776)**
Oil on canvas 76.2 x 63.5
Dated
Donated by Mrs. G. Haddon, 1933

U2417 **William III 1650-1702**
Miniature, watercolour on ivory 7.2 x 5.7
Donated by Dr. Nesca Robb, 1976

UNKNOWN, 19th century (British)

U672 **Landscape**
Oil on panel 26.3 x 33
Purchased 1959

U873 **Woody Landscape** *(Illus.p.337)*
Watercolour, gum on paper 40.7 x 33.2
Purchased 1954
Formerly attributed to Hugh William 'Grecian' Williams 1773-1829

U1363 **Borthwick Castle, Midlothian** *(Illus.p.337)*
Ink, wash, white on paper 18.1 x 26.6
Bequeathed by Mrs Hannah Flanery, 1915
Formerly attributed to William Nichol 1794-1840

U1665 **Portrait of a Lady** (Style of Sir Thomas Lawrence 1769-1830)
Oil on canvas 75.8 x 63.5
Provenance unknown

U2073 **Portrait of a Woman**
Now **Lola Montez 1818-61** by H. K. (19th century French or German)

U2708 **Mrs. Elizabeth Gaskell 1810-65 (?)**
Sculpture, wax bust, ht. 19.8
Donated by J. St. Clair Boyd, 1939

U4483 **Portrait of a Woman**
Oil on canvas 240 x 147.8
Provenance unknown

U4484 **Portrait of a Man**
Now **Canon John Grainger, DD, MRIA 1830-91**, by Anthony Carey Stannus 1830-1919, Art dept. U2007

U4498 **Portrait of a Man** *(Illus.p.337)*
Oil on canvas 76.4 x 64
Provenance unknown

U4507 **Portrait of a Man**
Oil on canvas 127 x 102
Provenance unknown

U4538 **Girl with Brown Hair**
Miniature, watercolour on ivory 5.5 x 4 (oval)
Donated by Miss F. McTear, 1926

U4726 **Portrait of a Man**
Oil on canvas 92 x 71
Provenance unknown

U4906 **Emily Sophia Arnott, née Fletcher 1814-74 (c.1840)**
Miniature, watercolour on paper 8.3 x 14 (sight) (oval)
Donated by Miss Ileene Chesney, 1980

U4908 **Captain Charles Cornwallis Chesney 1791-1830 (c.1820s)**
Watercolour, gum, white on paper 16 x 12 (sight)
Donated by Miss Ileene Chesney, 1980

U4909 **Eliza, Lady Blunt, née Simmons 1744-1836 (c.1820)**
Miniature, watercolour on ivory 7 x 5.5 (sight) (oval)
Donated by Miss Ileene Chesney, 1980

U4911 **Dorothea Fletcher, née Blunt 1781-1848 (c.1820)**
Miniature, watercolour on ivory 8.5 x 7 (sight) (oval)
Donated by Miss Ileene Chesney, 1980

U4913 **Everilda Chesney, née Fraser 1792-1840 (c.1830)**
Miniature, watercolour on ivory 7.5 x 6 (sight) (oval)
Donated by Miss Ileene Chesney, 1980

U4914 **James Fraser (c.1830)**
Miniature, watercolour on ivory 7.5 x 6 (sight) (oval)
Donated by Miss Ileene Chesney, 1980

U4915 **General Francis Rawdon Chesney 1789-1872 (c.1850)**
Miniature, watercolour on ivory 8.9 x 6.3 (sight) (oval)
Donated by Miss Ileene Chesney, 1980

U4917 **Georgette Chesney, née Foster 1788-1825 (c.1820)**
Silhouette, ink on silk 6 x 5.6 (sight) (oval)
Donated by Miss Ileene Chesney, 1980

U4918 **Louisa Chesney, née Fletcher, as a Child (c.1820)**
Silhouette, ink on paper 7.5 x 6 (sight) (oval)
Donated by Miss Ilene Chesney, 1980

U4919 **Louisa Chesney, née Fletcher (c.1848)**
Miniature, watercolour on ivory 10.5 x 8.3 (sight) (oval)
Donated by Miss Ileene Chesney, 1980

U4921 **Edward Fletcher and his Son, Edward Charles Fletcher (c.1830)**
Two silhouettes. ink on paper 11 x 15 overall
Donated by Miss Ileene Chesney, 1980

U4922 **Helena, Louisa and Dorothea Fletcher (c.1830)**
Three cut-out silhouettes on paper 10.7 x 12.7 overall
Donated by Miss Ileene Chesney, 1980

U4923 **Sophia Charlotte, Charles Philip and Charlotte Jane Fletcher (c.1830)**
Three silhouettes. ink on paper 10.7 x 22.6 overall
Donated by Miss Ileene Chesney, 1980

U4924 **James Fletcher as a Child (c.1820)**
Cut-out silhouette on paper 22 x 13 (sight)
Donated by Miss Ileene Chesney, 1980

UNKNOWN, 20th century (British)

U4490 **Portrait of an Unknown Man (1924)**
Now by Harry R. Douglas 1862-1934, Art dept. U2459

UNKNOWN, 19th century (British or Irish)

U939 **Landscape Sketch**
Watercolour on paper 8.3 x 23.8
Donated by Mrs. W. R. Mackenzie, 1925

UNKNOWN, 17th century (Dutch)

U25 **Louis Crommelin 1652-1727 (c.1690-95)**
Oil on canvas 50.8 x 45.7
Donated by Miss May de la Cherois Crommelin, 1927

U675 **Adoration of the Infant Jesus**
Oil on canvas 72.5 x 91.5
Purchased 1959

UNKNOWN, 18th century (Dutch)

U2116 **A Bull and Two Cows in a Stream**
Ink, wash on paper 14.8 x 20.2
Donated by J. H. Stirling, 1919

UNKNOWN, 18th century (English)

U937 **Grove of Trees Looking onto a River**
Pencil, watercolour on paper 20 x 27.8
Donated by R V Williams ('Richard Rowley'), 1930

U1160 **Landscape with Village**
Pencil, watercolour on paper 35 x 48.4
Purchased 1937

U1474 **Roman Theatre at Taormina, Sicily**
Watercolour, pencil, ink on paper 39 x 152
Donated by J. H. Bland, 1916

UNKNOWN, 19th century (English)

U759 **Seated Girl;** verso, **Tree Branch** *(Illus.p.337)*
Pencil, watercolour on paper 14.5 x 13.1
Purchased 1948

U768 **River Gorge** *(Illus.p.337)*
Watercolour on paper 22.5 x 30.2
Purchased 1938

U935 **Boy on a Donkey**
Ink, pencil, watercolour on paper 18.3 x 12.1
Signed
Purchased 1952
Formerly attributed to J. F. Lewis 1805-76

U936 **Rome** *(Illus.p.337)*
Ink, watercolour on paper 12.6 x 18.3
Signed
Donated by R. V. Williams ('Richard Rowley'), 1930
Formerly attributed to J. F. Lewis 1805-76

U938 **London from Greenwich**
Watercolour on paper 11.3 x 15.4
Provenance unknown

U940 **Riverside Scene in London** *(Illus.p.337)*
Pencil on card 23.8 x 29.6
Provenance unknown

U941 **Fishing Boats**
Ink, pencil on paper 26.4 x 18
Purchased 1944

U942 **Lahneck on the Rhine**
Ink, watercolour on paper 27.4 x 18.2
Purchased 1912

U943 **Landscape with Bridge**
Watercolour on paper 21 x 29.8
Signed
Donated by R. V. Williams ('Richard
Rowley'), 1930

U944 **Church Porch** (Regensburg Cathedral?)
Ink, watercolour, white on paper 32.1 x
24.3
Purchased 1912

U946 **La Ferté** (Style of Richard Parkes
Bonington 1801-28) *(Illus.p.338)*
Watercolour on paper 20.1 x 28.5
Purchased 1949

U947 **Rustic Bridge over Stream** (Style of
William James Müller 1812-45)
Pencil, watercolour on paper 20.1 x 24.8
Purchased 1928

U1137 **Caister Castle, Norfolk**
Pencil, wash on paper 31.2 x 50.4
Donated by J. F. Johnson, 1896
Formerly attributed to John Thirtle 1777-
1839

U1149 **Conway Castle** (after Thomas Girtin
1775-1802)
Pencil, wash on paper 32.3 x 53
Donated by J. F. Johnson, 1896
Formerly attributed to John Varley 1778-
1842

U1158 **Edinburgh**
Watercolour on paper 24 x 28.8
Purchased 1911
Formerly attributed to Francis Nicholson
1753-1844

U1159 **Llanrwst Bridge (?)**
Ink, watercolour on paper 14.3 x 19.5
Donated by Miss F. M. McTear, 1917

U1161 **Mule Train**
Now after Robert Hills 1769-1844

U1166 **Sand Dunes and Sea** (Leaf from a
Sketchbook)
Watercolour, white on paper 8.3 x 23.8
Donated by Mrs. W. R. MacKenzie, 1925

U1403 **Warkworth Castle**
Pencil, watercolour on paper 36 x 51.6
Purchased 1911

UNKNOWN, 16th century (Flemish)

U669 **St. Jerome in his Study** *(Illus.p.338)*
Oil on panel 73 x 106
Purchased 1959

UNKNOWN, 19th century (French)

U676 **Lady with a Fan**
Oil on panel 34 x 28

Purchased 1959

U2070 **Napoleon Bonaparte 1769-1821**
Miniature, watercolour on ivory 8.5 x 6.6
(oval)
Donated by W. Kinning Crone, 1947

U2071 **Empress Joséphine 1763-1814**
Miniature, watercolour on ivory 8.5 x 6.6
(oval)
Donated by W. Kinning Crone, 1947

UNKNOWN, 17th century (French or Flemish)

U210 **Lady with a Guitar**
Oil on canvas 132.8 x 99
Donated by Mrs. Wood, 1960

UNKNOWN, 19th century (French or English)

U945 **Arch of Septimus Severus, Rome**
(Illus.p.338)
Watercolour on paper 13.4 x 18
Donated by M. Mercer, 1954

UNKNOWN, 17th century (German?)

U674 **Head of Christ**
Oil on canvas 58.5 x 45.5
Purchased 1959

UNKNOWN, 17th century (Irish)

U217 **Portrait of a Man, probably John King,
1st Baron Kingston d.1676 (1670s)**
(formerly thought to be John King, 3rd
Baron Kingston c.1664-1728)
Oil on canvas 228 x 124.4
Purchased 1959

U2337 **Sir James Ware 1594-1666**
Oil on canvas 76.2 x 64.2
Provenance unknown

U2515 **Captain William Jackson d.1688 (late
1660s)** *(Illus.p.338)*
Oil on canvas 120.2 x 99.5
Purchased 1977
Formerly attributed to John Michael
Wright the Younger fl.1680-1710

UNKNOWN, 18th century (Irish)

U105 **George Macartney 1671-1757 (c.1750)**
(Illus.p.225)
Now attributed to Francis Bindon c.1690-
1765

U131 **George Macartney 1671-1757 (c.1750)**
Now attributed to Francis Bindon c.1690-
1765

U135 **Dr. William Gamble 1689-1778 (c.1740)**
Oil on canvas 76.4 x 63.1
Bequeathed by H. Musgrave, 1922

U206 **Stewart Banks 1725-1802 (c.1760-65)**
Now attributed to Strickland Lowry
1737-c.85

U207 **Portrait of a Man**
Oil on canvas 60 x 49.5
Donated by J. F. Johnson, 1896

U213 **John Echlin of Thomastown 1723-89
(c.1787)** *(Illus.p.338)*

Oil on canvas 175.5 x 121.8
Donated by Mrs. Doreen Echlin, 1961

U214 **Portrait of a Man, possibly James King,
4th Baron Kingston 1693-1761 (late
1720s)** (formerly thought to be Sir
Edward King 1726-97)
Oil on canvas 243.8 x 152.4
Purchased 1959

U222 **Mrs. Banks or Mrs. Catherine Macartney
(c.1760-65)**
Now attributed to Strickland Lowry
1737-c.85

U1901 **Portrait of a Man (c.1790)** (Style of
Horace Hone 1756-1825)
Miniature, watercolour on ivory 4.4 x 3.2
(oval)
Provenance unknown

U2037 **Mrs. James McTear 1703-96**
Oil on canvas 83.8 x 71.1
Donated by Mrs. F. Riddell and Miss E.
McTear, 1920

U2255 **A View of Glenarm Castle (c.1768-1812)**
(Illus.p.338)
Oil on canvas 93.3 x 126.3
Purchased 1974

U2339 **Rev. John Campbell 1663-1730 (c.1705-
10)**
Oil on canvas 78 x 61
Bequeathed by Rev. Chancellor Archer,
1937

UNKNOWN, 19th century (Irish)

U34 **Dr. James Forsythe 1756-1849 (c.1815-
20)**
Oil on canvas 141.5 x 105.5
Donated by Mrs. N. Forsythe, 1933
Formerly 'Portrait of a man' (c.1830s) by
Samuel Hawksett 1801-59

U90 **Major Lachlan MacLaine b.1780
(c.1830)**
Oil on canvas 91.7 x 71
Donated by Miss E. MacLaine,1952

U108 **Elizabeth McTear, née Crawford 1765-
1836 (c.1830)** *(Illus.p.338)*
Oil on canvas 91 x 73.4
Donated by Mrs. F. Riddell and Miss E.
McTear, 1920

U134 **Rev. Dr. James Armstrong 1780-1839
(c.1815-20)**
Oil on canvas 71 x 61.6
Donated by Miss Clara Crozier, 1949

U139 **Valentine Rennie 1795-1837 (1814)**
Oil on board 38 x 28
Donated by Miss E. Rennie, 1948

U203 **Burning the Effigy of Lundy in Derry
(c.1830)** *(Illus.p.338)*
Oil on canvas 71 x 91.8
Purchased 1946

U205 **Commander Francis Anderson Calder
1787-1855 (1843-46)**
Oil on canvas 75.8 x 63.5
Donated by Mrs. M. G. Graham, 1932

U220 **Mrs. John Neilson b.1758 (c.1815)**

Oil on canvas 101.5 x 81.5
Donated by Miss J. F. L'Estrange, 1912

U542 **Shipwreck off Co. Down Coast**
Oil on paper on board 24.5 x 43.5
Bequeathed by Miss H. M. McCleery,
1968

U614 **River Lagan and Long Bridge**
Oil on canvas 34.4 x 48.9
Purchased 1937

U684 **Frederic William Macaulay 1801-39
(1814-18)**
Oil on canvas 76.5 x 63.4
Donated by F. R. V. Macaulay, 1970

U687 **Lieutenant-Colonel Hugh Kyd b.1787
(1819)**
Oil on canvas 76.5 x 63.5
Donated by F. R. V. Macaulay,1970

U911 **Castle with Cattle**
Pencil, watercolour on paper 33.2 x 47.1
Donated by Meta and Robert Dunlop,
1950

U1439 **Mountains and Pool**
Watercolour on paper 23.4 x 31.9
Provenance unknown

U1571 **The Blind Harper, Patrick Quin c.1745-
1812 (c.1800)** *(Illus.p.338)*
Pencil, watercolour, gum on paper 19.7 x
14.2
Purchased 1927

U1587 **Dublin from Phoenix Park**
Pencil, ink on paper 35.6 x 99.7
Donated by J. H. Bland, 1916

U1657 **Philip Johnston 1804-82**
Oil on canvas 59.8 x 43
Donated by Philip Johnston and Sons
Ltd., 1964

U1659 **William Tennent 1760-1832 (c.1810)**
Oil on canvas 61 x 50
Provenance unknown

U1663 **Portrait of an Unknown Man**
Now by Sir Thomas Alfred Jones c.1823-
93

U1778 **William Herdman 1777-1855**
Sculpture, plaster, ht. 72.4
Donated by R. E. Herdman, 1928

U2105 **The Curran, Larne** *(Illus.p.339)*
Ink, wash on paper 11.1 x 16.9
Provenance unknown

U2268 **Samuel Tennent b.1779 (c.1830)**
Oil on canvas 77.5 x 63.2
Donated by Mrs. H. Chisholm, 1942

U2269 **John Tennent 1772/77-1813 (c.1810)**
Oil on canvas 76.2 x 64.8
Donated by Mrs. H. Chisholm, 1942

U2270 **William Tennent 1760-1832 (c.1810)**
(Illus.p.339)
Oil on canvas 92.7 x 74
Donated by Mrs. H. Chisholm, 1942

U2274 **Robert Tennent, MD, RN 1765-1837
(c.1815)**
Oil on canvas 91 x 70.2
Donated by Mrs. H. Chisholm, 1942

U2280 **Slieve Roe**
Oil on canvas 61.3 x 92
Purchased 1939

U2299 **Hugh O'Neill, 2nd Earl of Tyrone 1540?-
1616**
Oil on panel 20 x 17.6
Donated by Canon John Grainger, 1891

U2300 **Hugh O'Neill, 2nd Earl of Tyrone 1540?-
1616**
Oil on panel 19.4 x 15
Donated by Canon John Grainger, 1891

U2342 **Rev. Thomas Drew, DD 1800-70**
Oil on canvas 91.5 x 71.5
Bequeathed by Lady Adelaide Drew,
1913

U2344 **Dr. William McGee 1793-1874 (c.1830-
35)**
Oil on canvas 76.5 x 63.7
Donated by Miss K. Armstrong and Mrs.
M. Merryweather, 1939

U2345 **Miss Margaret Smith 1774-1884**
Oil on canvas 62.5 x 47.1
Donated by Mrs. E. M. Sinclair, 1942

U2346 **Mrs. John Sauvage**
Oil on canvas 91.3 x 71.6
Provenance unknown

U2380 **Thomas Moore 1779-1852**
Miniature, watercolour on ivory 6.8 x 5.4
Provenance unknown

U2412 **John Russell of Newforge** *(Illus.p.339)*
Miniature, watercolour on ivory 7.5 x 5.7
Donated by Miss Isobel Pordon, 1929

U2457 **Rev. Samuel Martin Stephenson 1742-
1833 (c.1800)**
Oil on canvas 91.3 x 71.5
Provenance unknown

U2472 **Samuel Neilson 1761-1803 (c.1795)**
(after Charles Byrne 1757-1810)
Oil on cardboard 17.5 x 14.8
Donated by J. W. Bigger, 1927

U2477 **Portrait of a Young Man (c.1820)**
Oil on canvas 69.8 x 57
Donated by R. F. McCance, 1978

U3907 **Dundalk Bay**
Oil on canvas 50.8 x 61
Donated by R. B. Dunwoody, CBE, 1964

U4485 **Sir Hugh McCalmont Cairns, 1st Earl
Cairns 1819-85**
Oil on canvas 53.5 x 43.2
Donated by J. A. Cleland, DL, 1935

U4495 **James Bryce, LLD, FGS 1806-77**
Oil on canvas 112 x 86
Donated by the Belfast Natural History
and Philosophical Society, 1910

U4497 **Portrait of a Man**
Oil on canvas 76 x 63.5
Provenance unknown

U4727 **The Arrival of William III at
Carrickfergus, 1690**
Oil on canvas 71 x 129
Purchased 1987

UNKNOWN, 20th century (Irish)

U2449 **Sir William Turner 1872-1937 (1920)**
Now by W. J. McLachlan, 20th century
(Irish)

UNKNOWN, 17th century (Italian)

U211 **Ecce Homo** *(Illus.p.339)*
Oil on canvas 90.5 x 79
Purchased 1965

U218 **La Pittura**
Oil on canvas 136.4 x 107
Donated by W. T. Braithwaite (per J.
Horner), 1906

U670 **St. Francis (?)**
Oil on canvas 61.8 x 51.3
Purchased 1959

U2115 **Ecce Homo** *(Illus.p.339)*
Ink, wash on paper 25.4 x 39.8
Donated by J. H. Stirling, 1919

UNKNOWN, 18th century (Italian)

U671 **Feast of Belshazzar**
Oil on canvas 146.4 x 174.5
Purchased 1959

UNKNOWN, 19th century (Italian)

U125 **Piazza San Marco, Venice** *(Illus.p.339)*
Oil on canvas 53.3 x 43.2
Bequeathed by Dr. R. I. Best (per the
Friends of the National Collections of
Ireland), 1959
Formerly attributed to Edward Pritchett
1828-64

UNKNOWN CENTURY

UNKNOWN (English)

U2021 **Boats on Lake with Storm Clouds**
Oil on canvas; measurements unknown
Donated by W. T. Braithwaite (per J.
Horner), 1906

UNKNOWN (Italian)

U1946 **Samson and Delilah**
Oil on canvas; measurements unknown
Donated by Major Blackly, 1891

U1947 **Sisera and Jael (?)**
Oil on canvas; measurements unknown
Donated by Major Blackly, 1891

U2024 **Esther before Ahasuerus**
Oil; support and measurements unknown
Donated by J. F. Johnson, 1891

U2050 **Figure Group**
Oil on canvas 132.1 x 99.1
Donated by Mrs. Wood, 1960

UNKNOWN SCHOOL

UNKNOWN, 18th century

U1898 **Rev. Samuel Barber** *(Illus.p.339)*
Miniature, watercolour on ivory 12.7 x
10.2
Donated by Miss F. M. McTear, 1914

U2603 North East View of Garron Point (1794)
(Illus.p.222)
Now attributed to John James Barralet
c.1747-1815 or Pupil

U2604 Presbyterian Meeting House, Glenarm
(Illus.p.222)
Now attributed to Barralet Pupil

U2605 Glenarm Church (1796) *(Illus.p.222)*
Now attributed to Barralet Pupil

UNKNOWN, 19th century

U198 Head of a Man
Oil on board 20.8 x 16.3
Bequeathed by H. Musgrave, 1922

U806 The Link Boy *(Illus.p.339)*
Watercolour, bodycolour on paper 57.7 x
45.4
Purchased 1952
Formerly by William Henry Hunt 1790-
1864

U1810 Scipio Africanus
Sculpture, bronze bust, ht. 59.7
Provenance unknown

U1844 Unknown Man (c.1840)
Sculpture, marble bust, ht. 74
Donated by the French Consul in Belfast,
1971

U1893 Rev. Samuel Hanna
Miniature, watercolour on ivory 7.2 x 5.7
(sight)
Provenance unknown

U1894 William Russell (c.1806)
Miniature, watercolour on ivory 7 x 5.8
(oval)
Donated by Miss Isobel Pordon, 1929

U1896 Mrs. Cherry
Miniature, watercolour on ivory 4.7 x 3.5
(sight)
Donated by Miss F. M. McTear, 1926

U1897 Hugh Ritchie *(Illus.p.339)*
Miniature, watercolour on ivory 7 x 6
Donated by Miss E. MacLaine, 1952

U1899 Unknown Man
Miniature, watercolour on ivory 6.2 x 4.7
Provenance unknown

U1900 Mrs. Samuel Smith, née Galt
Miniature, watercolour on ivory 8.2 x 7
(oval)
Donated by Miss F. M. McTear, 1923

**U2044 Dr. William Alexander McKeown 1844-
1904**
Oil on canvas 91.8 x 71
Donated by Dr. K. McKeown, 1965

U2353 Painting of the Ship 'Glenericht'
Oil on board 50.6 x 61
Donated by Mr. Croft, 1975

U2360 James Russell (c.1806)
Miniature, watercolour on ivory 7.3 x 5.7
(oval)
Donated by Miss Isobel Pordon, 1929

U4823 Portrait of a Woman
Oil on canvas 80 x 64.5

Provenance unknown

U4848 Berenice (after Greek Antique)
Sculpture, bronze bust, ht. 53.3
Purchased 1885

U4849 Dionysus (after Greek Antique)
Sculpture, bronze bust, ht. 48.2
Purchased 1885

UNKNOWN CENTURY and SCHOOL

U661 Madonna of the Rose (after Raphael)
Oil on canvas 87.7 x 72.6
Donated by Mrs. T. A. Shillington, 1933

U1782 Allegory of the Via Aemilia
Sculpture, marble relief 118.1 x 156.8 x
25.4
Donated by the executors of Letitia and
D. E. Lowry, 1936
Formerly 'Reconciliation of the Queens',
after Antonio Canova 1757-1822

U1948 Abraham Sacrificing Isaac
Details unavailable
Donated by J. F. Johnson, 1896; destroyed
1945

U2013 William III on Horseback
Oil on canvas on board 74.2 x 53.6
Purchased 1961

**U2023 England, Scotland and Ireland
Lamenting Charles I**
Oil on canvas 76.2 x 56.5
Donated by R. M. Young, 1925

U2025 Head of a Man
Oil on board 19.7 x 14.6
Bequeathed by H. Musgrave, 1922

U2030 John O'Donovan
Oil on canvas 20.7 x 18.1
Donated by F. J. Bigger, 1906

U2286 The Holy Family with Saints (c.1530)
(Illus.p.281)
Now attributed to Luca Longhi 1507-80

U3908 Stylised Figure of a Woman
Oil on canvas 60.8 x 45.6
Provenance unknown

V

VAILLANT, Wallerand 1623-77 (Dutch)

U193 Portrait of a Woman (c.1660-70)
(Illus.p.340)
Oil on canvas 97 x 78.6
Donated by Mrs. J. Brooks, 1911

VALLELY, Dara b.1946 (Irish)

U4934 Chicago Pipers' Club *(Illus.p.340)*
Oil on canvas 244 x 186.5
Purchased 1992

VALLELY, John B. b.1941 (Irish)

U1870 Trio (1973) *(Illus.p.340)*
Oil on board 122 x 135
Signed
Purchased 1973

VANSTON, Doreen 1903-88 (Irish)

U4879 A Dying Animal (c.1943) *(Illus.p.340)*
Oil on canvas 62.7 x 76.1
Signed
Donated by Louis le Brocquy, 1991

VARLEY, Cornelius 1781-1873 (English)

U1648 Lixnaw Castle, Co. Kerry (1842)
(Illus.p.340)
Watercolour on paper 38 x 55.4
Signed, dated
Purchased 1943

U1868 Sketch of a Rough Shelter
Pencil on paper 11.5 x 19.2
Purchased 1973

U4985 A Cottage
Pencil on paper 34.5 x 25
Purchased 1994

U4986 Killarney
Pencil on paper 12.5 x 39
Purchased 1994

**U4987 Irish Maidens at the Spring, Earl
Gosford's Grounds (1808)**
Pencil on paper 22.5 x 37
Signed, dated
Purchased 1994

U4988 Study of a Cart
Pencil on paper 26.5 x 41.5
Purchased 1994

U4989 Young Ash
Pencil on paper 23.5 x 38.5
Signed
Purchased 1994

U4990 Thorn/Ireland (1808)
Pencil on paper 37.5 x 28
Signed, dated
Purchased 1994

U4991 Landscape with Cottages
Pencil on paper 22.5 x 38.5
Purchased 1994

**U4992 Mangerton Mt./Ross Castle/Killarney
Lake (1808)**
Pencil on paper 20 x 50
Signed, dated
Purchased 1994

U4993 In Ireland (1808)
Pencil on paper 25 x 37
Signed, dated
Purchased 1994

U4994 Kerry House
Pencil on paper 18.5 x 37
Purchased 1994

U4995 Muckross Abbey (?)
Pencil on paper 29 x 42.5
Purchased 1994

U4996 Blenaville near Tralee, Ireland (1808)
Pencil on paper 19.5 x 49.5
Signed, dated
Purchased 1994

U4997 Mourne Mt. from Market Hill, Ireland
Pencil on paper 22 x 32.5
Signed

Purchased 1994

U4998 **Landscape**
Pencil on paper 20 x 50
Purchased 1994

VARLEY, John 1778-1842 (English)

U867 **Waborne Hall, Norfolk** *(Illus.p.340)*
Pencil, watercolour, gum on paper 16.5 x
24.1
Signed
Bequeathed by Sir David Reid (per Lady
Reid), 1951

U868 **Harlech Castle**
Pencil, watercolour on paper 18.7 x 26.7
Bequeathed by Sir David Reid (per Lady
Reid), 1951

U869 **River Scene with Church (1842)**
Watercolour, gum on paper 18.3 x 31.1
Signed, dated
Purchased 1938

U1149 **Conway Castle**
Now by Unknown, 19th century
(English)

VASARELY, Victor 1908-97 (Hungarian)

U514 **Geta (c.1960-63)** *(Illus.p.340)*
Oil on canvas 126.4 x 101
Purchased 1963

VICKERS, Alfred 1786-1868 (English)

U732 **In the Vale of Amersham** *(Illus.p.340)*
Oil on canvas 26 x 36
Signed
Bequeathed by Dr. R. M. Jones (per Mrs.
Jones), 1949

VIEGERS, B. 19th-20th century (British?)

U2053 **View at Katwyck**
Oil on canvas 81.2 x 48.2
Bequeathed by Mrs. E. Monteagle Brown,
1928

VOLLAERT, Jan Christian 1709-69 (German)

U181 **River View** *(Illus.p.340)*
Oil on panel 15.2 x 21
Donated by W. T. Braithwaite (per J.
Horner), 1906

VOS, Cornelis de 1584-1651 (Flemish)

U31 **The Raising of Lazarus** *(Illus.p.341)*
Oil on canvas 156.8 x 193
Signed
Purchased 1959

W

W., Richard [Richard W.] early 19th century
(French)

U1487 **Italian Farm with Stream**
Watercolour, pencil, gum on paper 29.4 x
35.3
Signed
Donated by J. H. Bland, 1910

WADSWORTH, Edward 1889-1949 (English)

U510 **Gastropoda (1927)** *(Illus.p.341)*
Tempera on panel 53.3 x 37.7
Signed
Purchased (Lloyd Patterson Collection)
1929

WAGEMAKER, Jaap 1906-72 (Dutch)

U531 **Image in Relief (1961)** *(Illus.p.341)*
Acrylic, wood, metal on board 121.9 x
104.1
Signed, dated
Purchased 1963

WAGHORN, Tom 1900-59 (British)

U4667 **Downpatrick (1943)** *(Illus.p.341)*
Watercolour, ink on paper 36.9 x 26
Signed, dated
Purchased 1944

WAKEMAN, William Frederick 1822-1900
(Irish)

U2375 **Cromlech in the Townland of
Tawnatruffaun, Co. Sligo (1891)**
(Illus.p.341)
Ink, sepia, watercolour on paper 17.5 x
21
Dated
Purchased 1891

U2376 **Cromlech at Levally, near Athenry, Co.
Galway (1891)**
Ink, sepia, watercolour on paper 17.5 x
23.8
Signed
Purchased 1891

U2377 **The 'Giant's Table', near Ballina, Co.
Mayo (1891)**
Ink, sepia, watercolour on paper 17.5 x
22.2
Purchased 1891

U2378 **The Giant's Grave, Kilternan, Co. Dublin
(1891)**
Ink, sepia, watercolour on paper 17.5 x
21.9
Purchased 1891

WALKER, David Bond 1891-1977 (Irish)

U422 **The Pensive Maiden (1925)**
Oil on canvas 91.7 x 76.5
Signed, dated
Purchased 1926

U4486 **F. A. C. Mills (c.1929-30)**
Oil on canvas on board 30.7 x 27
Purchased 1950

WALKER, Dame Ethel 1861-1951 (British)

U507 **Summer Afternoon** *(Illus.p.341)*
Oil on canvas 63.4 x 76.8
Signed
Purchased (Lloyd Patterson Collection)
1933

WALKER, John b.1939 (English)

U1886 **Touch (1970)** *(Illus.p.341)*
Acrylic on canvas 274 x 609.5

Purchased 1973

WALKER, John Crampton 1890-1942 (Irish)

U595 **Geums (c.1930-31)** *(Illus.p.341)*
Oil on canvas 61 x 45.7
Signed
Donated by the Thomas Haverty Trust,
1936

WALLACE, Patricia (Mrs. Patricia Griffith)
1913-73 (Irish)

U1150 **The Haggard** *(Illus.p.341)*
Gouache on paper 27.5 x 45.2 (sight)
Signed
Donated by the Thomas Haverty Trust,
1941

WALLIS, Alfred 1855-1942 (English)

U690 **'Consols Mine Raswall Hill and the Road
Zennor to Farms. The White you See is
Granite' (c.1936)** *(Illus.p.342)*
Oil, gouache on board 31.8 x 50.8
Signed
Purchased 1970

WALMSLEY, Thomas 1763-1806 (Irish)

U2303 **Mouth of the Suir, Ireland** *(Illus.p.342)*
Watercolour, bodycolour on paper 31.6 x
44
Signed
Purchased 1952

WALSH, George Stephen (20th century)

U4941 **The Vision of St. Bernadette**
Ink, watercolour on paper 46.5 x 10.8
(sight)
Donated by Harold Clokey, 1992

WALSH, Ronan b.1958 (Irish)

U5009 **Young Man Seated: Study I (1992)**
Mixed media on paper 62.7 x 43.3
(sight)
Signed, dated
Donated by the Contemporary Irish Art
Society (per Gordon Lambert), 1994

WALTON, Elijah 1833-80 (English)

U1151 **Abu Simbel, Nubia (1876)** *(Illus.p.342)*
Pencil, watercolour, white on paper 25.1
x 18
Signed, dated
Donated by J. Cunningham, 1928

WARD, Leslie Moffat b.1888 (English)

U1260 **A Medway Boat Building Yard**
(Illus.p.342)
Pencil, ink, watercolour, bodycolour on
paper 35.6 x 54.3
Signed
Donated by J. Connel, 1924

WARREN, Barbara b.1925 (Irish)

U426 **Child among Rocks (1965-66)**
(Illus.p.342)
Oil on canvas 50.7 x 66
Signed

Donated by the Thomas Haverty Trust, 1966

WARREN, Michael, b.1950 (Irish)

U4741   **Torso, Diptych I**
Sculpture, wood 78.7 x 19 x 16.5
Donated by the Contemporary Irish Art Society, 1988

U4943   **Chi (1984)**
Sculpture, carbonised wood (in two separate elements) 270 x 270 x 35
Purchased 1992

WATERS, George 1863-1947 (Irish)

U1152   **On the Dodder (c.1937)**
Pencil, watercolour on card 19.1 x 26.8
Signed
Donated by the Thomas Haverty Trust, 1941

U1327   **Spring's Advent, Belvoir Park**
Pencil, watercolour on paper 20 x 27
Signed
Purchased 1930

U4668   **April, Colin Glen, Belfast** *(Illus.p.342)*
Watercolour on paper 34.2 x 22.9
Purchased 1931

U4669   **In the Dargle (c.1937)**
Watercolour on paper 19 x 27.9 (sight)
Signed
Donated by the Thomas Haverty Trust, 1941

WATKINS, Bartholomew Colles 1833-91 (Irish)

U172   **Ecclesiastical Ruins on Inniscaltra, or Holy Island, Lough Derg, Co. Galway, after Sunset: "This Island is One of Great Historic Interest …" - Petrie (c.1863)** *(Illus.p.342)*
Oil on canvas 104.3 x 153
Signed
Purchased 1968

WAY, Emily C. fl.1887-1907 (Irish)

U4489   **Portrait of a Man (1896)**
Oil on canvas 143 x 112.5
Signed, dated
Provenance unknown

WEBB, Kenneth b.1927 (Irish)

U558   **Farm and Trees (1960)**
Oil on board 33.5 x 89
Signed, dated
Donated by the Thomas Haverty Trust, 1966

WEENIX, Jan Baptist 1621-c.1660/61 (Dutch)

U194   **Shepherds and Flocks among Classical Ruins** *(Illus.p.342)*
Oil on canvas 88.2 x 113
Donated by Miss A. P. Norris (per Portstewart Urban District Council), 1941

WELD, Isaac 1774-1856 (Irish)

U1415   **Crook Haven, Cape Clear Island**

Pencil, wash on paper 16.9 x 26.5
Purchased 1967

WELLS, John b.1907 (British)

U423   **Harbour Facade (1961)**
Oil on board 61 x 106
Purchased 1962

WELLS, William fl.1893-1923 (Scottish)

U2038   **Field Workers** *(Illus.p.342)*
Oil on canvas 30.5 x 26
Signed
Purchased 1931

WENDELS, Franziskus b.1960 (German)

U4894   **Großstadt I (1991)**
Oil on canvas 180 x 280 (Diptych)
Purchased 1992

U4951   **Shaftesbury Square, Belfast (1992)** *(Illus.p.343)*
Oil, acrylic on canvas 120.3 x 150
Donated by the artist, 1992

U4952   **Sandy Row, Belfast (1992)**
Oil, acrylic on canvas 100 x 120.3
Purchased 1992

WESTALL, Richard 1765-1836 (English)

U1178   **The Three Marys at the Sepulchre** *(Illus.p.343)*
Ink, gum, wash on paper 18.6 x 15.5
Signed
Purchased 1971

WHALL, Dick b.1939 (English)

U2576   **Some Demarcatory Features Sited within the English Cultural 'Landscapism' - Milan Model 2.1978-4.1979 (1978-79)**
Pencil, watercolour on paper 83.2 x 59.1
Signed, dated
Purchased 1979

WHEATLEY, Francis 1747-1801 (English)

U146   **John, 1st Viscount O'Neill of Shane's Castle 1740-98 (c.1780)** *(Illus.p.343)*
Oil on canvas 76.5 x 63.6
Purchased 1940

U2439   **The Belfry Tower, Furness Abbey, Lancashire (1798)** *(Illus.p.343)*
Watercolour on paper 38.3 x 48
Signed, dated
Purchased 1977

WHELAN, Leo 1892-1956 (Irish)

U508   **Interior of a Kitchen (c.1934)** *(Illus.p.343)*
Oil on canvas 68.3 x 57.5
Signed
Donated by the Thomas Haverty Trust, 1941

WHICHELO, Augustus George fl.1873-76 (English)

U4494   **Rev. Hugh Hanna 1824-90 (1876)**
Oil on canvas 111.9 x 86.4
Signed, dated

Bequeathed by Mrs. A. H. Moulds, 1938

WHITE, Ethelbert 1891-1972 (English)

U425   **Sun through the Wood (c.1932)** *(Illus.p.343)*
Oil on canvas 63.8 x 77.2
Signed
Purchased (Lloyd Patterson Collection) 1933

U431   **In the Garden**
Oil on canvas 47.5 x 57.5
Signed
Purchased 1928

U870   **Below the Mournes** *(Illus.p.343)*
Pencil, watercolour on card 46.2 x 55.9
Signed
Purchased 1936

U871   **Cold Kitchen Farm (1915)** *(Illus.p.343)*
Pencil, watercolour on paper 38.4 x 46.8
Signed, dated
Purchased 1927

U4801   **The Mourne Mountains** *(Illus.p.343)*
Pencil, watercolour on paper 34 x 42 (sight)
Signed
Bequeathed by Roberta and John Hewitt, 1987

WILES, Francis 1889-1956 (Irish)

U1816   **The Dawn of Womanhood (1914)** *(Illus.p.344)*
Sculpture, marble 99.5 x 33 x 57
Signed, dated
Purchased 1931

U2039   **The Dawn of Womanhood (1914)**
Sculpture, bronze 99.5 x 33 x 57
Signed, dated
Donated by the artist's sisters, 1980

U2698   **Reclining Woman (The Butterfly) (c.1928)**
Sculpture, marble 19.7 x 68 x 13.9
Signed
Donated by the artist's sisters, 1980

U2699   **Kneeling Woman**
Sculpture, plaster relief 29.5 x 28.9 x 3.1
Donated by the artist's sisters, 1980

WILKIE, Sir David 1785-1841 (Scottish)

U872   **Studies of Houses (1817)**
Pencil, crayon, white on paper 17.3 x 26.1
Signed, dated
Donated by J. H. Stirling, 1919

WILKIE, Sir David 1785-1841 (Scottish) (attributed to)

U182   **A Doctor Bleeding a Patient**
Oil on panel 13 x 15.8
Purchased 1959

WILKS, Maurice C. 1910-84 (Irish)

U424   **The Seafarer (1939)**
Oil on canvas 91.4 x 71
Signed

Donated by the Thomas Haverty Trust, 1941

U4814 James Quigley d.1945 (1930s)
Chalk on paper 35 x 24.5 (sight)
Signed
Provenance unknown

WILLIAMS, Hugh William 'Grecian' 1773-1829 (Scottish)

U1649 Lake of Avernus (1816) *(Illus.p.344)*
Ink, wash on paper 18.5 x 27.8
Signed, dated
Purchased 1952

WILLIAMS, Hugh William 'Grecian' 1773-1829 (Scottish) (attributed to)

U873 Woody Landscape *(Illus.p.337)*
Now by Unknown, 19th century (British)

WILLIAMS, Terrick John 1860-1936 (English)

U511 A Rain Squall, Concarneau *(Illus.p.344)*
Oil on canvas 26.9 x 40.7
Signed
Donated by Dr. R. H. Hunter, 1941

WILSON, Alistair b.1951 (English)

U4691 Still (1982)
Sculpture, mixed media 268 x 143 x 47
Donated by P. H. Nicholl, 1986

WILSON, David 1873-1934 (Irish, worked in England)

U1153 Irish Boglands, Donaghmore, Co. Tyrone
Pencil, watercolour on paper 27.2 x 37.5
Signed
Purchased 1929

U1154 Walberswick Ferry, Suffolk
Pencil, ink, watercolour on paper 26 x 37
Signed
Purchased 1929

U1155 The Godstone Road, Surrey
Pencil, watercolour on paper 28.2 x 38.5
Signed
Purchased 1929

U1261 Telscombe, Sussex *(Illus.p.344)*
Pencil, watercolour on paper 37.6 x 56.5
Signed
Purchased 1929

U1262 A Sussex Barn *(Illus.p.344)*
Watercolour on paper 37.5 x 56.4
Signed
Purchased 1929

U1591 Magpie
Ink, watercolour on card 16.3 x 22
Signed
Purchased 1925

U1592 F. Frankfort Moore on 'Toast' (1899)
Ink, crayon on paper 36.4 x 27.1
Signed
Purchased 1925

U1593 General Sir George White 1835-1912 *(Illus.p.344)*
Ink, crayon on paper 36.1 x 24.6
Signed

Purchased 1925

U1594 General Booth 1829-1912 Looks for New Worlds to Conquer (1912) *(Illus.p.344)*
Pencil, ink, watercolour, bodycolour on paper 31.8 x 25.3
Signed
Donated by A. S. Moore, 1944

U1603 The Fatal War (1): 'A Story for Grown-up Children'
Ink, crayon on board 18.2 x 32.6
Signed
Purchased 1925

U1604 The Fatal War (2): 'The Prince Approached cautiously'
Ink, crayon on board 19 x 26
Signed
Purchased 1925

U1605 The Fatal War (3): 'The Party Was on its Way Returning'
Ink, crayon on board 19 x 25.5
Signed
Purchased 1925

U1606 The Fatal War (4): 'He Was Swayed between his Philosophy and his Heart'
Ink, crayon on board 18.9 x 25.8
Purchased 1925

U1607 The Fatal War (5): 'Raw Middle-class Recruits'
Ink, crayon on board 19.2 x 25.9
Signed
Purchased 1925

U1608 The Fatal War (6): 'He Gets the Princess to Sing to him'
Ink, crayon on board 19 x 27.3
Signed
Purchased 1925

U2678 Helianthus
Pencil, watercolour on paper 48.4 x 54.7
Signed
Purchased 1930

U4836 View in Hyde Park, London *(Illus.p.344)*
Watercolour on paper 12.1 x 16.5 (sight)
Signed
Donated by R. P. Smyth, 1991

U5025 View on the Sussex Downs
Watercolour on paper 24.5 x 34
Signed
Bequeathed by Mrs. Peggy Hoppin, 1996

U5026 Birmingham from the Walsall Road
Watercolour on paper 24.5 x 34.5
Signed
Bequeathed by Mrs. Peggy Hoppin, 1996

U5027 Shoreham-by-Sea, Sussex
Watercolour on paper 32 x 42.5
Signed
Bequeathed by Mrs. Peggy Hoppin, 1996

U5028 Barn at Limpsfield, Surrey
Watercolour on paper 34.2 x 50.5
Signed
Bequeathed by Mrs. Peggy Hoppin, 1996

U5029 Border of Sussex and Surrey
Watercolour on paper 33 x 49.5
Signed

Bequeathed by Mrs. Peggy Hoppin, 1996

U5030 Chrysanthemums in a Flowered Jug
Watercolour on paper 35.5 x 51.8
Signed
Bequeathed by Mrs. Peggy Hoppin, 1996

U5031 White Roses in a Glass (1927) *(Illus.p.344)*
Watercolour on paper 47 x 36.5
Signed
Bequeathed by Mrs. Peggy Hoppin, 1996

U5032 Sweet Peas *(Illus.p.345)*
Watercolour on paper 48 x 31.5
Signed
Bequeathed by Mrs. Peggy Hoppin, 1996

WILSON, James Glen 1827-63 (Irish)

U178 Emigrant Ship Leaving Belfast (1852) *(Illus.p.345)*
Oil on canvas 71.4 x 91.3
Signed, dated
Purchased 1953

U572 Belfast Quay (1851) *(Illus.p.345)*
Oil on canvas 41 x 61
Signed, dated
Donated by W. H. McLaughlin, 1903

U2656 'Herald' and 'Torch' off a Rocky Coast (1853)
Watercolour on paper 16.8 x 27.7
Signed, dated
Donated by Mervyn Solomon, 1982

U4970 The First Lock at Stranmillis (1850) *(Illus.p.345)*
Oil on canvas 60.8 x 91.5
Signed, dated
Purchased 1993

WILSON, Joseph fl. c.1766-93, d.1793 (Irish)

U174 Rev. William Bruce, DD, 1757-1841 (c.1784)
Oil on canvas 73.6 x 60.6
Donated by Miss Bruce, 1928

U175 Mrs. William Magee 1764-1800 (c.1782)
Oil on canvas 76 x 62.8
Bequeathed by Miss E. F. Thompson, 1915

U176 William Dawson 1759-1834 (c.1780) *(Illus.p.345)*
Oil on canvas 76.5 x 63.6
Bequeathed by R. Baxter, 1922

U177 Elizabeth McTear, née Crawford 1765-1836 (1789)
Oil on canvas 76.4 x 63.2
Signed, dated
Donated by Miss F. M. McTear, 1926

U183 Miss Maxwell (c.1782) *(Illus.p.345)*
Oil on panel 22.8 x 18.5 (oval)
Bequeathed by Miss E. Munce, 1967

U185 John Magee 1752-1809 (c.1782) *(Illus.p.345)*
Oil on panel 24.2 x 19.6 (oval)
Purchased 1933

U645 William Magee 1750-1827 (c.1782)
Oil on canvas 76 x 63.2

Bequeathed by Miss E. F. Thompson, 1915

U695 **William Magee 1750-1827 (c.1782)**
(Illus.p.345)
Oil on panel 23.8 x 20.2 (oval)
Purchased 1933

U707 **Mrs. William Magee 1764-1800 (1782)**
Oil on panel 24.4 x 20 (oval)
Purchased 1933

U2060 **Mrs. James McTear 1703-96 (c.1780)**
Oil on canvas 72.5 x 59.7
Donated by Miss F. M. McTear, 1926

U2254 **Lieutenant Hugh Hyndman (c.1782)**
(Illus.p.345)
Oil on canvas 77 x 64
Purchased 1974

WILSON, Richard 1713/14-82 (English)

U6 **Landscape with Banditti (c.1755-58)**
(Illus.p.346)
Oil on canvas 117 x 167
Purchased 1959

U2301 **Farm with Pond (c.1776)**
Oil on copper 21.8 x 26.9
Donated by Miss A. P. Norris (per Portstewart Urban District Council), 1941

WILSON, Ross b.1958 (Irish)

U2572 **Portrait of John Carson b.1951 (1980)**
Charcoal on paper 55.3 x 77.5 (sight)
Signed, dated
Purchased 1980

U2661 **Portrait of Anthony C. West b.1910 (1982)** *(Illus.p.346)*
Charcoal on paper 88.2 x 61.9
Purchased 1982

U4688 **Portrait of Brian Moore 1921-99 (1985)** *(Illus.p.346)*
Charcoal on paper 81.3 x 55.9 (sight)
Signed, dated
Purchased 1985

WIMPERIS, Edmund Morison 1835-1900 (English)

U1156 **A Sunny Vale (1884)** *(Illus.p.346)*
Watercolour on paper 29.7 x 48
Signed, dated
Donated by Meta and Robert Dunlop, 1950

U1270 **Moorland with Trees**
Pencil, watercolour on paper 24.7 x 35
Purchased 1926

U1328 **Wensleydale (1895)**
Watercolour on paper 16.5 x 25.5
Signed, dated
Donated by Meta and Robert Dunlop, 1950

U1650 **The Riverside Pasture (1898)**
(Illus.p.346)
Watercolour on paper 25.5 x 35.6
Signed, dated
Purchased 1946

U2062 **Landscape (1888)** *(Illus.p.346)*
Oil on canvas 127.5 x 77
Signed, dated
Donated by Lady Cleaver in memory of her husband, Sir J. F. Cleaver, 1936

WIRGMAN, Theodore Blake 1848-1925 (British)

U2471 **Henry Jones McCance, DL 1829-1900 (1896)** *(Illus.p.346)*
Oil on canvas 76.1 x 63.5
Signed, dated
Donated by Mrs. M. Hollins, 1935

WISNIEWSKI, Janusz 20th century (Polish)

U2518 **Winter Headquarters of Condemned Angels (1977)**
Ink on paper 59.1 x 83.2
Signed, dated
Purchased 1977

WISSING, Willem 1653-87 (Dutch)

U640 **William III 1650-1702**
Oil on canvas 238.8 x 149.8
Donated by G. T. Weir, 1937

WOLFE, Edward 1897-1983 (British)

U506 **The Doorway (c.1929-30)** *(Illus.p.346)*
Oil on board 80.7 x 65.6
Signed
Purchased (Lloyd Patterson Collection) 1933

WOLMARK, Alfred Aaron 1877-1961 (British)

U427 **Concarneau (1911)**
Oil on panel 45.8 x 37.8
Signed
Donated by Mr. and Mrs. T. Pitt, 1962

U4967 **Sir John Lavery 1856-1941 (1926)**
Ink on paper 34 x 24
Signed, dated
Donated by Dr. Michael Goldberger, 1993

WOOD, Christopher 1901-30 (English)

U509 **Village in Italy (1925)** *(Illus.p.346)*
Oil on canvas 55.1 x 46.3
Signed, dated
Purchased 1952

U512 **Street Scene with Trees** *(Illus.p.347)*
Oil on canvas 55.1 x 46
Purchased 1952

WOOD, Shakspere 1827-86 (English)

U1817 **Henry MacCormac, MD 1800-86 (1869)**
Sculpture, marble bust, ht. 68.6
Signed, dated
Donated by Sir William MacCormac, 1892

U1818 **Sir William MacCormac Bt., KCB 1836-1901 (1867)**
Sculpture, marble bust, ht. 82.6
Signed, dated
Bequeathed by Lady MacCormac, 1923

U1819 **Lady MacCormac 1835-1923 (1869)**

Sculpture, marble bust, ht. 74.9
Signed, dated
Bequeathed by the sitter, 1923

U1820 **John Charters 1796-1874 (1869)**
Sculpture, marble bust, ht. 81.3
Signed, dated
Donated by Sir William MacCormac, 1892

U1821 **Alexander Mitchell 1780-1868**
(Illus.p.347)
Sculpture, marble bust, ht. 48.2
Donated by Mrs. M. Garrett, 1907

WOOD, William 1769-1810 (British)

U4910 **Dorothea Fletcher, née Blunt 1781-1848**
Miniature, watercolour on ivory 9 x 7.2 (sight) (oval)
Donated by Miss Ileene Chesney, 1980

U4912 **James Fletcher**
Miniature, watercolour on ivory 7.7 x 6.3 (sight) (oval)
Donated by Miss Ileene Chesney, 1980

WOODS, Gordon b.1938 (Irish)

U2437 **Graph (1976)**
Oil on paper 39.5 x 36.7
Signed, dated
Purchased 1977

WOOLMER, Alfred Joseph 1805-92 (English)

U606 **Scene in Chelsea Park** *(Illus.p.347)*
Oil on canvas 66.1 x 50.6
Bequeathed by H. Musgrave, 1922

WRIGHT, John Michael, the Elder 1617-94 (English)

U179 **Gentleman in Armour, possibly a Member of the King Family (1680)**
(Illus.p.347)
Oil on canvas 136.5 x 111.1
Purchased 1959

U216 **Robert King, 2nd Baron Kingston 1657-93 (c.1676)** *(Illus.p.347)*
Oil on canvas 239.4 x 146.6
Purchased 1959

WRIGHT, John Michael, the Younger fl.1680-1710 (Irish) (attributed to)

U2515 **Captain William Jackson d.1688 (late 1660s)** *(Illus.p.338)*
Now by Unknown, 17th century (Irish)

WRIGHT, Joseph, of Derby 1734-97 (English)

U2368 **Virgil's Tomb: Sun Breaking through a Cloud (1785)** *(Illus.p.347)*
Oil on canvas 47 x 65
Signed, dated
Purchased 1975

WYCK, Jan c.1640-1702 (Dutch)

U173 **A Cavalry Skirmish** *(Illus.p.347)*
Oil on canvas 96 x 131.5
Signed
Purchased 1958

WYCK, Jan c.1640-1702 (Dutch) (attributed to)

U698 **William III 1650-1702** *(Illus.p.347)*
Oil on canvas 98 x 77.3
Purchased 1969

WYNDHAM, Guy Richard Charles 1896-1948
(English)

U505 **Summer Landscape** *(Illus.p.347)*
Oil on canvas 63.7 x 76.5
Signed
Purchased (Lloyd Patterson Collection)
1932

WYNTER, Bryan 1915-75 (English)

U956 **Imoos (1967)**
Kinetic construction in wood, painted
card, mirror, electric light and motor
205.5 x 62 x 73.7
Purchased 1967

Y

YEAMES, William Frederick 1835-1918 (British)

U191 **Choir Boys (1891)** *(Illus.p.348)*
Oil on canvas 106 x 78
Signed, dated
Donated by Mrs. M. Garner, 1957

YEATS, Anne b.1919 (Irish)

U429 **Woman Watching (1948)**
Watercolour, bodycolour, wax on paper
78.5 x 56.3
Donated by the Thomas Haverty Trust,
1950

U432 **One Room (c.1954)** *(Illus.p.348)*
Oil on canvas 40.6 x 45.6
Signed
Donated by the Thomas Haverty Trust,
1957

YEATS, Jack Butler 1871-1957 (Irish)

U428 **Riverside Long Ago (1923)** *(Illus.p.96)*
Oil on canvas 61.4 x 91.7
Signed
Purchased 1967

U430 **On Through the Silent Lands (1951)**
(Illus.p.348)
Oil on canvas 50.6 x 68.3
Signed
Purchased 1962

U433 **Grafton Street/Conversation Piece
(1923)** *(Illus.p.348)*
Oil on panel 23.1 x 36.2
Signed
Donated by the Contemporary Art
Society, 1945

U874 **A Soft Day (1908)** (formerly 'A Soft Day:
Jockey and his Horse') *(Illus.p.348)*
Gouache on paper 44.4 x 32.1
Signed
Purchased 1954

U1329 **The End of the World (1909)**
(Illus.p.348)
Pencil, ink, watercolour on paper 20.5 x
30.5
Signed
Purchased 1956

U2436 **Untitled** (Two Jockeys on Horses,
Leaping a Stone Wall) *(Illus.p.348)*
Oil on panel 14.2 x 18.3
Signed
Bequeathed by J. N. Bryson, 1977

U4888 **Darrynane (in the Sun) (1927)**
(Derrynane) *(Illus.p.348)*
Oil on board 23.1 x 36
Signed
Bequeathed by Greta and Norbert
Magnus (per the National Art Collections
Fund), 1991

YEATS, John Butler 1839-1922 (Irish)

U192 **Portrait of Acheson T. Henderson, QC
1812-1909 (1891)** *(Illus.p.348)*
Oil on canvas 91.5 x 71.5
Signed, dated
Donated by A. F. G. Henderson, 1953

YOUNG, Robert 1822-1917 (Irish)

U1157 **Rocky Coastline**
Pencil, charcoal, watercolour on paper
32.2 x 48.4
Bequeathed by H. Musgrave, 1922

U1651 **Eagle Rock, with Ben Bulben in Distance
(1875)**
Pencil, watercolour on paper 34.3 x 51
Signed, dated
Bequeathed by H. Musgrave, 1922

YÜ-FENG (alias Chu Ch'üan) 18th-19th century
(?) (Chinese)

U346 **Riding Home with his Bag after a Night's
Fowling**
Ink, watercolour on paper 128 x 63.5
Signed
Donated by Frederick McKibbin in
memory of his father, Commander
McKibbin, 1964

YULE, Ainslie b.1941 (Scottish)

U2032 **Grid Drawing (1978)**
Mixed media on paper 110.5 x 96 (sight)
Signed, dated
Purchased 1978

U2455 **White Reclining Object (1975)**
Pencil, charcoal on paper 49.5 x 66.7
(sight)
Signed, dated
Purchased 1978

Z

ZOCCHI, Cesare 1851-1922 (Italian)

U4802 **Faust and Marguerite**
Sculpture, marble 133 x 73 x 53
Donated by Henry Matier, 1891

drawings paintings & sculptures

the
ulster museum
botany and
zoology
collections

A

ALEXANDER, Edwin 1870-1926 (Scottish)

N70   **Barn Owl**
       Watercolour on card 32.8 x 18.3
       Signed
       Purchased 1966

AUSTEN, Winifred 1876-1964 (English)

N36   **Helter-skelter Coots** *(Illus.p.350)*
       Watercolour on paper 35.8 x 50
       Purchased 1965

B

BARYE, Antoine-Louis 1795-1875 (French)

S16   **Lion Sitting**
       Sculpture, bronze 27 x 34.5 x 14
       Donated by Delia Whittaker, 1968

S17   **Lioness Standing**
       Sculpture, bronze 21.2 x 42 x 7.5
       Signed
       Donated by Delia Whittaker, 1968

S18   **Greyhound and Hare** *(Illus.p.350)*
       Sculpture, bronze 27 x 45 x 13
       Signed
       Donated by Delia Whittaker, 1968

S19   **Lion Standing**
       Sculpture, bronze 23 x 41 x 9
       Signed
       Donated by Delia Whittaker, 1968

S20   **Stag and Young** *(Illus.p.350)*
       Sculpture, bronze 21.7 x 22 x 8
       Signed
       Donated by Delia Whittaker, 1968

BATTERSBY, Miss 19th century (Irish)
The following works are as titled by the artist

N501   **Sketchbook, Twenty-three Illustrations of
       Birds (1804-41)**
       Watercolour, pencil on paper, each 47.5 x
       34.4
       Provenance unknown

1. **Bird of Paradise (1804)** (Lesser Bird of
    Paradise) (Paradisea minor)

2. **Whidah Bunting, Africa (1808)** (Paradise
    Whydah) (Vidua paradisaea)

3. **Pompadore Chatterer, Cayenne (1806)**
    (Illus.p.350)

4. **Cinnamon Woodpecker, North America
    (1806)** (Chestnut Woodpecker, South
    America) (Celeus elegans)

5. **Green Woodpecker, England. A Young Bird**
    (Picus viridis) *(Illus.p.350)*

6. **Golden Wing Woodpecker Picus Auratus,
    Canada (1810)** (Yellow-shafted Flicker)
    (Colaptes auratus)

7. **Great Spotted Woodpecker (1806)**
    (Dendrocopos major)

8. **Bee Eater, New South Wales (1806)** (possibly
    Ground Cuckoo Shrike) (Pteropodocys
    maxima)

9. **Migratory Thrush, North America (1809)**
    (American Robin) (Turdus migratorius)

10. **Ring Dove (1807)** (Collared Dove)
    (Streptopelia decaoto)

11. **Blue-tailed Thrush (1806)** *(Illus.p.350)*

12. **Butcher Bird, England (1806)** (Lesser Grey
    Shrike) (Lanius minor)

13. **Crested Manakin Female, South America
    (1810)** (Golden Cock-of-the-Rock)
    (Rupicola rupicola)

14. **Merops Cafer (1808)** (White-backed
    Mousebird) (Colius colius)

15. **Mergus Albellus. Shot on the Dublin Coast
    (1814)** (Smew) (Mergellus albellus)

16. **Toucan** (Black-necked Aracari) (Pteroglossus
    sp)

17. **Psittacus Hamatodie, Botany Bay** (Rainbow
    Lorikeet) (Trichoglossus haematodus)

18. **Sun Creeper; Strawberry Creeper** (Scarlet-
    chested Sunbird) (Nectarinia senegalensis);
    Sugar Creeper, Africa (1840) (Beautiful
    Sunbird) (Nectarinia pulchella)

19. **Cardinal Gross Beaks, Male and Female
    (1830)** (Red-crested Cardinal) (Paroaria
    coronata)

20. **Trogan Couroucan, Mexico (1830)** (Collared
    Trogon) (Trogon collaris)

21. **Nonpareil Paraquet, Botany Bay (1806)**
    (Rosella Parakeet) (Platycerus eximius)

22. **Motmot, Brazil (1806)** (Blue-crowned
    Motmot) (Momotus momota)

23. **Humming Birds (1841)**

N 502 **Sketchbook, Twenty-four Illustrations of
       Flowers (1832)**
       Watercolour, pencil on paper, each 35.2 x
       26.3
       Provenance unknown

1. **Pelargonium Loronesis Perfection**

2. **Polyanthus**

3. **Commelina Coelestris, Belfast** (Day Flower)
    (Commelina coelestis)

4. **Dwarf Pomegranet, Belfast** (Pomegranate)

5. **China Mallow, Belfast** *(Illus.p.350)*

6. **Salvia Involucrata, Belfast**

7. **Salvia Splendens, Belfast** (Scarlet Sage)

8. **China Primrose**

9. **Ixia Bicolor** *(Illus.p.350)*

10. **Pelargonium Coruscans**

11. **Pelargonium Youngii**

12. **Pelargonium Shakespeare**

13. **Dog's Tooth Violet**

14. **Azalea Pontica** (Rhododendron luteum)

15. **Auricula**

16. **Diosma Uniflora**

17. **Fuchsia Microphilla** (Fuchsia minimiflora)

18. **Gloccina Alba** (Gloxinia alba)

19. **Sarracenia Purpurea, Belfast** (Huntsman's
    Cap)

20. **Dahlia, from a Prize Flower at the
    Horticultural Show at Belfast (1831)**

21. **Erica Ventricosa Superba, Belfast**

22. **China Pink, Belfast**

23. **Anemone**

24. **Eschscholtzi Calafornica, Belfast** (California
    Poppy) (Eschscholzia californica)

BENINGTON, J. M. 20th century (British)

N94   **Great Spotted Woodpecker** *(Illus.p.350)*
       Ink on board 16.5 x 15.7
       Purchased 1959

N95   **Snowy Owl**
       Ink on board 18.8 x 16.2
       Signed
       Purchased 1959

N96   **Redwing on Nest in Iceland (1955)**
       (Illus.p.351)
       Ink on board 19.8 x 15.8
       Signed, dated
       Purchased 1959

N97   **Peregrine (1955)**
       Ink on board 22.8 x 18.2
       Signed, dated
       Purchased 1959

N98   **Golden Eagle (1955)** *(Illus.p.351)*
       Ink on board 25.5 x 19.8
       Signed, dated
       Purchased 1959

N152   **Eiders at Sea (1964)**
       Oil on canvas 76.8 x 51
       Signed, dated
       Purchased 1967

N153   **Heron Fishing (1966)**
       Watercolour on card 30 x 27.7
       Signed, dated
       Purchased 1967

BOOTH, L. G. Jackson 20th century (British)

N14   **The Unfortunate Oiled Guillemot**
       (Illus.p.351)
       Watercolour on paper 41.5 x 57.3
       Signed
       Purchased 1965

BOOTH, Raymond 20th century (British)

N319   **Stoat in Winter (1974)** *(Illus.p.351)*
       Oil on canvas 18.8 x 40.1
       Signed, dated
       Purchased 1975

BROWN, Alan b.1908 (British)

N41   **Locust (1945)**
       Watercolour on paper 33 x 26.6
       Signed, dated
       Purchased 1965

BURTON, Philip J. K. b.1935 (English)

N62   **Black-tailed Godwits over the Mud
       (1966)**
       Oil on board 49.6 x 90.4 (sight)
       Signed, dated
       Purchased 1966

BUSBY, John Philip b.1928 (English)

N75   **Fulmars (1966)**

Oil on board 63.5 x 60.7
Signed, dated
Purchased 1966

N230 **Studies of a Tawny Owl (1968)**
Pencil on paper 34.6 x 25.3
Signed, dated
Purchased 1968

N234 **Bass Rock Gannets (1968)**
Watercolour, charcoal, ink on paper 31 x
44 (sight)
Signed, dated
Purchased 1968

N249 **Snowy Owl (1968)**
Pencil on paper 12 x 15 (sight)
Signed, dated
Purchased 1969

N250 **Goldfinch (1968)**
Crayon on paper 15 x 18.8
Signed, dated
Purchased 1969

N284 **Great Crested Grebes (1967)**
Oil on canvas 60.6 x 60.6
Signed, dated
Purchased 1970

N393 **September Greys (Grey Plover and
Dunlin) (1972)**
Pencil, watercolour on paper 33 x 50
(sight)
Signed, dated
Purchased 1972

BYERS, Heather 20th century (Irish)

Twenty Paintings (1971-73)
Commissioned 1972

N383 **Perch (1972)** *(Illus.p.351)*
Watercolour on paper 31 x 41.5
Signed, dated

N398 **Brown Trout**
Watercolour on paper 37.5 x 52.8
Signed

N399 **Dace**
Watercolour on paper 38 x 56
Signed

N400 **Rainbow Trout (1971)** *(Illus.p.351)*
Watercolour on paper 37.3 x 55.8
Signed, dated

N401 **Charr (1972)** *(Illus.p.351)*
Watercolour on paper 36.5 x 51.3
Signed, dated

N402 **Gudgeon (1972)**
Watercolour on paper 25.5 x 38
Signed, dated

N403 **Stone Loach (1972)**
Watercolour on paper 26.7 x 36.8
Signed, dated

N404 **Common Carp**
Watercolour on paper 38 x 56.2
Signed

N405 **Brown Trout**
Watercolour on paper 38.5 x 48.5
Signed

N406 **Minnow and Stickleback**
Watercolour on paper 29 x 39
Signed

N407 **Killarney Shad (1973)**
Watercolour on paper 38 x 51.6
Signed, dated

N408 **Tench**
Watercolour on paper 35 x 55.5
Signed

N409 **Roach**
Watercolour on paper 36 x 43.2
Signed

N410 **Bream (1971)**
Watercolour on paper 38 x 50.5
Signed, dated

N411 **Rainbow Trout**
Watercolour on paper 36.2 x 52.8

N412 **Salmon (Female) (1972)**
Watercolour on paper 36 x 56
Signed, dated

N413 **Chub (1972)**
Watercolour on paper 37.2 x 51.4
Signed, dated

N414 **Rudd (1971)**
Watercolour on paper 33 x 44.4
Signed, dated

N415 **Pollan (1973)**
Watercolour on paper 38.4 x 56.2
Signed, dated

N416 **Pike**
Watercolour on paper 38.2 x 56.2
Signed

C

CAMPBELL, Con 20th century (British)

N315 **Arkle and Pat Taaffe** *(Illus.p.351)*
Acrylic on canvas 60.5 x 74.7 (sight)
Signed
Donated by the artist, 1974

CARTER, Allan 20th century (British?)

N359 **Gazelle (1972)**
Watercolour on paper 22.5 x 38.2 (sight)
Signed, dated
Purchased 1972

CAYLEY, Neville Henry Pennington 1853-1903
(Australian)

N78 **Kookaburra** *(Illus.p.351)*
Watercolour on paper 32 x 25.4
Signed
Purchased 1966

CHING, Raymond Harris b.1939 (New
Zealander)

N289 **Great Northern Diver**
Pencil on paper 56.7 x 42
Purchased 1971

CLENDINNING, Norman 20th century (Irish)

N500 **Whales (1959)**
Watercolour on paper 43 x 58
Signed, dated
Provenance unknown

COLLINS, George Edward 1880-1968 (English)

N43 **Jay** *(Illus.p.352)*
Watercolour on paper 36.2 x 26.5
Signed
Purchased 1966

N286 **Kingfishers** *(Illus.p.352)*
Ink on paper 20.2 x 27.4
Signed
Purchased 1959

COOK, Alan M. 20th century (British?)

N270 **Foxes (1970)**
Ink on board 30.4 x 49.7
Signed, dated
Purchased 1970

COOMBES, Dr. Charles John F. b.1908 (English)

N63 **Egyptian Vultures (1966)**
Oil on canvas 127 x 81
Signed, dated
Purchased 1966

N68 **Magpie (1966)** *(Illus.p.352)*
Watercolour on paper 33 x 43.2
Signed, dated
Purchased 1966

N186 **Otter (1967)**
Oil on canvas 74.6 x 61.8 (sight)
Signed, dated
Purchased 1968

COTT, Dr. Hugh B. 20th century (English)

N188 **The Mud Wallow (1967)**
Ink on paper 37 x 47.8
Signed
Purchased 1967

COX, John H. 20th century (English)

N237 **Buzzard**
Pencil on paper 23.6 x 35.8
Signed
Purchased 1968

CUSA, Noel William 1909-91 (English)

N13 **Roseate Terns (1964)** *(Illus.p.352)*
Watercolour on paper 38.8 x 57
Signed, dated
Purchased 1965

N32 **Guillemots (1965)** *(Illus.p.352)*
Watercolour on paper 39 x 56.5
Signed, dated
Purchased 1965

N69 **Goshawk (1965)**
Watercolour on paper 33.5 x 50.3 (sight)
Signed, dated
Purchased 1966

D

D'ARCY, Gordon b.1947 (Irish)

N287   **Pectoral Sandpiper (1970)**
Ink on paper 31 x 38.2
Signed, dated
Purchased 1971

DETVOLD, Edward Julius 1883-1957 (British)

N288   **Eagle (1900)** *(Illus.p.352)*
Watercolour on paper 56.3 x 40.5
Signed, dated
Purchased 1971

DOENGES, Ernst 20th century (British)

N292   **Fallow Buck**
Pencil on paper 61 x 45.7
Purchased 1971

N293   **Roe in Snow (1970)**
Oil on canvas 45 x 60 (sight)
Signed, dated
Purchased 1971

E

ECKLEBERRY, Don Richard 20th century
(British?)

N316   **Shorebirds**
Oil on board 26.8 x 105.2 (sight)
Signed
Purchased 1973

EDE, Basil b.1931 (British)

N47   **Cock Capercaillie in Display** *(Illus.p.352)*
Watercolour on paper 32.6 x 44
Signed
Purchased 1966

EDWARDS, John b.1940 (English)

N294   **Rabbit**
Pencil on paper 20.4 x 33.1
Signed
Purchased 1971

N295   **Squirrel**
Pencil on paper 20 x 23.8 (sight)
Signed
Purchased 1971

N296   **Wood Mouse**
Pencil on paper sight 17 x 26
Signed
Purchased 1971

ENNION, Eric Arnold R. 1900-81 (English)

N17   **Widgeon Resting** *(Illus.p.352)*
Watercolour on paper 25 x 33.3
Signed
Purchased 1965

N150   **Stone Curlew**
Watercolour on paper 19 x 13.5
Signed
Purchased 1967

N193   **Shags and Cormorants**
Watercolour on paper 11.9 x 19.4
Signed
Purchased 1968

N194 **Herring Gull**

Watercolour on paper 16.5 x 18.2
Signed
Purchased 1968

N239   **California Quails**
Watercolour on paper 26.8 x 36
Signed
Purchased 1968

N245   **Wood Sandpiper**
Pencil, watercolour on paper 21.5 x 15.5
Signed
Purchased 1968

N246   **Waxwings**
Pencil, watercolour on paper 21.5 x 14.2
Signed
Purchased 1968

N258   **Woodland Birds (1967-68)** (Wryneck,
Redstarts and Others)
Pencil, watercolour on paper 28.5 x 35.7
Signed
Purchased 1969

N261   **Storks and Other Waterfowl**
Pencil, watercolour on paper 34.5 x 25.2
Signed
Purchased 1969

F

FAULKNER, Trevor 20th century (British?)

S22   **Lady Amherst Pheasant (1970)**
(Illus.p.352)
Sculpture, steel 13.5 x 35 x 5.5
Signed, dated
Purchased 1970

S23   **Sparrowhawk** (Head Study)
Sculpture, steel 8 x 5 x 8
Purchased 1970

G

G., A. H. [A. H. G.] 20th century (British?)

N388   **Widgeon**
Watercolour on paper 18.5 x 30
Signed
Provenance unknown

GILLMOR, Robert A. F. b.1936 (English)

N187   **Grebe Family** *(Illus.p.353)*
Watercolour on paper 20 x 27.9 (sight)
Signed
Purchased 1968

N254   **Group of Ptarmigan**
Ink on paper 33 x 20.5
Signed
Purchased 1969

N255   **Oystercatcher** *(Illus.p.353)*
Pencil, wash on paper 20.2 x 15.5
Signed
Purchased 1969

N256   **Young Magpie**
Charcoal, chalk on paper 16.4 x 24
Signed
Purchased 1969

GRIERSON, Mary 20th century (British?)

N396   **Neottia nidus-avis (Bird's Nest Orchid)
(1970)** *(Illus.p.353)*
Watercolour, ink on paper 55.4 x 37.1
Signed, dated
Purchased 1976

H

HARDING, Morris 1874-1964 (English, worked
in Ireland)

Twelve Sculptures (1914-40)
Donated by Miss Rita Harding, 1966

S1   **Leopard and the Pangolin**
Plaster 78 x 33 x 98.8

S2   **Leopard and the Golden Pheasant**
Plaster 77 x 45.7 x 94

S3   **Lion Feeding**
Plaster 18.5 x 35 x 12
Signed

S4   **Polar Bears Feeding on Mammoth**
Plaster 45 x 40 x 30.5
Signed

S5   **Polar Bears Wrestling (1914)**
Plaster 49 x 25 x 26
Signed, dated

S6   **Hunting Leopard**
Plaster 39.8 x 102 x 37

S7   **Leopard in Tree Top**
Plaster 45.5 x 174.8 x 47

S8   **Polar Bear Calling (1936)**
Plaster 22.5 x 17.5 x 10
Signed, dated

S9   **Leopard and Cub (1940)**
Plaster 26.5 x 11 x 10
Signed, dated

S10   **Leopard Resting**
Plaster 13 x 34 x 10

S11   **Polar Bears Mating**
Marble 29.5 x 56.5 x 18

S12   **Polar Bear on Ice-floe**
Plaster 23.5 x 32 x 14
Signed

Forty-five Drawings (1912-24)
Donated by Miss Rita Harding, 1966

N155.   Lion (1919)
A1   Pastel, charcoal on paper 22.5 x 29
Signed, dated

N155.   Young Lion
A2   Pastel, charcoal on paper 22.5 x 29.4
Signed

N155.   Tiger Eating (1919)
A3   Pastel, charcoal on paper 25 x 39
Signed, dated

N155.   Tiger Resting (1920)
A4   Pastel, charcoal on paper 22.8 x 30.6
Signed, dated

N155. **Lion Eating (1919)**
A5   Pastel, charcoal on paper 24 x 36
       Signed, dated

N155. **Lions**
A6   Pastel, charcoal on paper 27.5 x 36

N155. **Tiger Resting**
A7   Pastel, charcoal on paper 28 x 44.5

N155. **Lion Resting**
A8   Ink on paper 15 x 23

N155. **Lion (1919)** (Head only) *(Illus.p.353)*
A9   Pastel, charcoal on paper 22.8 x 18
       Signed, dated

N155. **Lion Resting (1920)**
A10   Pastel, charcoal on paper 24 x 29.3
       Signed, dated

N155. **Tiger Resting (1920)**
A11   Pastel, charcoal on paper 25.4 x 38.3
       Signed, dated

N155. **Polar Bear Calling (1912)**
A12   Pastel, charcoal on paper 28.3 x 38.5
       Signed, dated

N155. **Jaguar Resting (1924)** *(Illus.p.353)*
A13   Pastel, charcoal on paper 22.3 x 29.5
       Signed, dated

N155. **Leopard in a Tree** *(Illus.p.353)*
A14   Pastel, charcoal on paper 31 x 45.4
       Signed

N155. **Lion (1920)** (Head only)
A15   Pastel, charcoal on paper 38.1 x 25.3
       Signed, dated

N155. **Black Leopard**
A16   Pastel, charcoal on paper 23.1 x 29.3
       Signed

N155. **Lioness** (Head only)
A17   Pastel, charcoal on paper 12 x 16.8

N155. **Lion Snarling**
A18   Pastel, charcoal on paper 15.2 x 23.4

N155. **Leopards**
A19   Pastel, charcoal on paper 22 x 29.3

N155. **Lion Eating**
A20   Pastel, charcoal on paper 24.2 x 36.8

N155. **Leopard Resting**
A21   Pastel, charcoal on paper 30 x 18.5

N155. **Polar Bear Head**
A22   Pastel, charcoal on paper 28 x 38.5

N155. **Leopard** (Shoulder View)
A23   Pastel, charcoal on paper 31.8 x 16.9

N155. **Leopard on Slope**
A24   Pastel, charcoal on paper 28.2 x 40

N155. **Lion Stalking Snake**
A25   Pastel, charcoal on paper 21.5 x 29

N155. **Young Male Jaguar in Cave**
A26   Pastel, charcoal on paper 30.4 x 24

N155. **Lion Cub**
A27   Pastel, charcoal on paper 19 x 30.5

N155. **Lions**
A28   Pastel, charcoal on paper 25.2 x 32

N155. **Lion Head (1887)**
A29   Catalogued erroneously; is by John
       Macallen Swan 1847-1910

N155. **Head of Serval**
A30   Pastel, charcoal on paper 24.6 x 36

N155. **Panther**
A31   Pastel, charcoal on paper 19 x 30

N155. **Tiger Head**
A32   Pastel, charcoal on paper 19 x 30.5

N155. **Polar Bear Head**
A33   Pastel, charcoal on paper 15.5 x 23

N155. **Lion Feet**
A34   Pastel, charcoal on paper 15.6 x 23

N155. **Polar Bear Head**
A35   Pastel, charcoal on paper 26.5 x 27.8

N155. **Leopard Standing**
A36   Pastel, charcoal on paper 27.8 x 38.1

N155. **Polar Bear Head**
A37   Pastel, charcoal on paper 27.8 x 38.5

N155. **Leopard Sitting**
A38   Pastel, charcoal on paper 19 x 30.3

N155. **Lion Eating**
A39   Pastel, charcoal on paper 19.8 x 32.3

N155. **Lion Sleeping (1919)**
A40   Pastel, charcoal on paper 25.5 x 38 4
       Signed, dated

N155. **Leopard Eating (1919)**
A41   Pastel, charcoal on paper 26 x 38.7
       Signed, dated

N155. **Leopard Study**
A42   Pastel, charcoal on paper 32.3 x 25.4

N155. **Tiger Standing**
A43   Pastel, charcoal on paper 26.6 x 38.4

N155. **Lions and Lionesses Sleeping**
A44   Pastel, charcoal on paper 27.8 x 45.2

N155. **Lion Head**
A45   Pastel, charcoal on paper 17 x 30.5

N155. **Lioness and Two Cubs (1887)**
A46   Catalogued erroneously; is by John
       Macallen Swan 1847-1910

N155. **Jaguar (1919)**
A47   Pastel, charcoal on paper 20.4 x 33.5
       (sight)
       Signed, dated

N155. **Head of a Tiger**
A50   Catalogued previously as by George Elgar
       Hicks 1824-1914, Art dept. U1746
       Charcoal on paper 12.5 x 15.8
       Provenance unknown

HARRISON, John Cyril 1898-1985 (English)

N302   **Heron and Widgeon** *(Illus.p.353)*
       Watercolour on paper 55.6 x 77
       Signed
       Purchased 1971

N303   **Smews**
       Watercolour on paper 28.2 x 38.3 (sight)
       Signed
       Purchased 1971

N306   **Golden Pheasant** *(Illus.p.353)*
       Watercolour on paper 55.5 x 77 (sight)
       Signed
       Purchased 1971

HAY, Sylvia Baker 20th century (British)

N39   **Water Buffalo**
       Crayon on paper 26.8 x 36.8 (sight)
       Signed
       Purchased 1965

N40   **Baboon**
       Crayon on paper 32.5 x 21.8 (sight)
       Signed
       Purchased 1965

HILL, Robin b.1932 (Australian)

N45   **Jabiru Storks (1964)** *(Illus.p.353)*
       Watercolour on paper 58.7 x 43.8 (sight)
       Signed, dated
       Purchased 1966

N301   **Cuckoo and Chiffchaffs (1964)** *(Illus.p.)*
       Watercolour on paper 53.5 x 76
       Signed, dated
       Purchased 1971

HILLS, Robert 1769-1844 (British)

N233   **Stags in a Park** *(Illus.p.354)*
       Pencil, watercolour on paper 43 x 33.3
       Purchased 1968

HIRD, Elizabeth M. 20th century (Scottish)

N381   **Two Vultures Sitting**
       Charcoal on paper 37.5 x 51.8
       Signed
       Commissioned 1966

N382   **Vulture**
       Charcoal on paper 51.8 x 35
       Signed
       Commissioned 1966

HOLLYWOOD, William b.1923 (English,
worked in Ireland)

N273   **Guillemots on Muck Island (1969)**
       (Illus.p.354)
       Oil on canvas 59 x 43
       Signed, dated
       Purchased 1970

HURRELL, H. E. 20th century (British)

N267   **Pine Marten and Otter (1969)**
       Crayon on paper 42.3 x 53.5 (sight)
       Signed, dated
       Donated by the artist, 1969

N268   **Pine Marten Playing (1969)**
       Crayon on paper 49.5 x 51.8 (sight)
       Signed, dated
       Donated by the artist, 1969

HURST, Edward 1912-72 (British)

N365   **Longhi Lily** *(Illus.p.354)*
       Pastel on paper 52 x 37 (sight)
       Signed
       Purchased 1975

K

KELLY, Captain Richard Barrett Talbot 1896-1971 (English)

N25   **Redshank**
        Watercolour on paper 40 x 52.1
        Signed
        Purchased 1965

N44   **Heron Sunning Itself** *(Illus.p.354)*
        Watercolour, ink on paper 22 x 19.5
        Signed
        Purchased 1965

N48   **Lapwing in Flight**
        Watercolour on paper 31.8 x 32.6
        Signed
        Purchased 1966

N247   **Velvet Scoters**
        Watercolour on paper 28.6 x 38.8
        Signed
        Purchased 1968

N360   **Young Lapwing**
        Oil on board 29.2 x 28.8 (sight)
        Signed
        Purchased 1965

KENWORTHY, Jonathan 20th century (British)

S14   **Cheetah and Female Impala (1965)**
        (Illus.p.354)
        Sculpture, bronze 20.5 x 45 x 25.5
        Signed, dated
        Purchased 1966

KEULEMANS, John Gerrard 1842-1912 (British)

N231   **Goldfinches and Great Grey Shrike**
        (Illus.p.354)
        Watercolour on paper 30.6 x 26.4 (sight)
        Signed
        Purchased 1968

N232   **Kingfishers** *(Illus.p.354)*
        Watercolour on paper 31 x 26.5 (sight)
        Purchased 1968

KOSTER, David b.1926 (English)

N262   **Javan Fish Owls**
        Charcoal, wash on paper 55.3 x 36
        (sight)
        Signed
        Purchased 1969

N263   **Palm Cockatoos**
        Charcoal, wash on paper 55 x 37.1
        (sight)
        Signed
        Purchased 1969

N265   **Heron and Chicks**
        Pencil on paper 58.3 x 78.8
        Signed
        Purchased 1969

L

LANDSDOWNE, J. Fenwick b.1937 (British)

N37   **Cuckoo (1963)** *(Illus.p.354)*
        Watercolour on paper 55 x 45.2
        Signed, dated
        Purchased 1965

LANG, Wharton 20th century (British)

S13   **Great Northern Diver**
        Sculpture, wood 21 x 41 x 12
        Purchased 1966

S24   **Springtime Shags**
        Sculpture, wood 75 x 30 x 31
        Signed
        Purchased 1968

LAWS, R. M. 20th century (British?)

N22   **Spur-winged Plover (1963)** *(Illus.p.355)*
        Watercolour on paper 35.6 x 50.8
        Signed, dated
        Purchased 1965

LEVI, Peter John 20th century (British)

N51   **Magpie** *(Illus.p.355)*
        Watercolour on paper 27 x 38.7
        Signed
        Purchased 1966

LILJEFORD, Lindorm 20th century (Swedish)

N310   **Goldeneyes (1972)**
        Oil on board 40.9 x 56.2
        Signed, dated
        Purchased 1973

LODGE, George Edward 1860-1954 (British)

N19   **Gyrfalcon** *(Illus.p.355)*
        Watercolour on paper 37 x 49.6
        Signed
        Purchased 1965

N20   **Golden Eagle Soaring** *(Illus.p.355)*
        Watercolour on paper 35.5 x 52.1 (sight)
        Signed
        Purchased 1965

M

McMILLAN, John 20th century (British)

N313   **Robin (1972)** *(Illus.p.355)*
        Pencil on paper 29.8 x 21.1
        Signed, dated
        Purchased 1973

N314   **Pheasant (1972)**
        Pencil on paper 21.2 x 30.1
        Signed, dated
        Purchased 1973

MANDL, Anita 20th century (British?)

S25   **White Ermine**
        Sculpture, onyx 7 x 23 x 10
        Purchased 1970

MEE, Margaret b.1909 (British)

N391   **Aechmea mertensii** (Bromeliad)
        (Illus.p.355)
        Watercolour, pencil on paper 61.8 x 45.8
        (sight)

        Signed
        Purchased 1975

MÈNE, Pierre Jules 1810-79 (French)

S21   **Stag**
        Sculpture, metal 37.5 x 38.5 x 18
        Signed
        Provenance unknown

MILES, Louise 20th century (British?)

S26   **Preening Bird**
        Sculpture, stone 20 x 10 x 13
        Purchased 1968

MILLIKEN, Robert W. b.1920 (British)

N11   **Rathlin Revisited** *(Illus.p.355)*
        Watercolour on paper 67.2 x 92.3 (sight)
        Signed
        Purchased 1965

N151   **Teal in the Downpatrick Marshes**
        (Illus.p.355)
        Watercolour on paper 55.5 x 75.5
        Signed
        Purchased 1967

N

NEWMAN, Kenneth b.1924 (English)

N309   **African Fish Eagle (1972)** *(Illus.p.355)*
        Watercolour on paper 68.8 x 50.2 (sight)
        Signed, dated
        Purchased 1973

P

PARSONS, Joy b.1913 (English)

N184   **Toco Toucans** *(Illus.p.356)*
        Crayon on paper 37.4 x 51.8 (sight)
        Signed
        Purchased 1967

PEPPER, Hubert J. 20th century (British)

N50   **Roe Deer**
        Watercolour on paper 38.5 x 53.2
        Signed
        Purchased 1966

N280   **Common Seals in a Bay (1970)**
        (Illus.p.356)
        Oil on canvas 34.5 x 44.5 (sight)
        Signed, dated
        Purchased 1970

PETERSON, Roger Tory 20th century (?) (American)

N46   **King Vultures** *(Illus.p.356)*
        Watercolour on card 49 x 36 (sight)
        Signed
        Purchased 1966

PIPER, Raymond b.1923 (Irish)

N57   **Scented Evening Primrose (1966)**
        Pastel on paper 63.2 x 48.4
        Signed, dated

Purchased 1966

N58 **Rosebay Willowherb**
Pencil on paper 51.8 x 31.5
Signed
Purchased 1966

N59 **New Zealand Willowherb (1966)**
Pencil on paper 52.2 x 31.7
Signed, dated
Purchased 1966

N228 **Frog Orchid (Coeloglossum viride)
(1967)**
Watercolour, pencil on paper 38.3 x 28.2
Signed, dated
Purchased 1968

N229 **Irish Stoat (1968)**
Pencil on paper 38.2 x 28
Signed, dated
Purchased 1968

N376 **Dense Flowered Orchid (Neotinea
intacta)**
Watercolour, pencil on paper 51 x 31.8
Donated by the Friends of the Ulster
Museum, 1975

N377 **Lesser Twayblade (Listera cordata)
(1968)**
Watercolour, pencil on paper 50.8 x 31.6
Signed, dated
Donated by the Friends of the Ulster
Museum, 1977

N378 **Norman Carrothers (1970)**
Pencil on paper 51 x 31.5
Signed, dated
Purchased 1971

N380 **Marsh Helleborine Orchid (Epipactis
palustris)**
Watercolour on paper 49.5 x 31
Donated by the Friends of the Ulster
Museum, 1975

PRAEGER, Sophia Rosamond 1867-1954 (Irish)

N506 **Samuel Alexander Stewart, ALS, FBSE
1827-1910**
Commemorative plaque, plaster 55 x
37.7 (ellipse)
Donated by the Belfast Naturalists' Field
Club, 1918

R

REID-HENRY, David 1919-77 (British)

N9 **Gyrfalcon** *(Illus.p.356)*
Pencil on paper 25.5 x 20.3
Signed
Purchased 1964

N27 **Greenland Falcon** *(Illus.p.356)*
Watercolour on paper 25 x 23.7
Signed
Purchased 1965

N71 **Peregrine Falcon** *(Illus.p.356)*
Pencil on paper 26.6 x 20.1
Signed
Purchased 1966

RICKMAN, Philip Charles 1891-1982 (English)

N275 **Brown Leaves - Blue Tit and Great Tit
(1969)** *(Illus.p.356)*
Watercolour on card 41.3 x 27.8
Signed, dated
Purchased 1970

N356 **Bittern** *(Illus.p.356)*
Watercolour on paper 53.5 x 38.5 (sight)
Signed
Purchased 1972

ROOK, David 20th century (British)

N10 **Otter in a Stormy Sky** *(Illus.p.356)*
Oil on canvas 51 x 40.5
Purchased 1965

ROSEN, Count Bjourn van 20th century
(Swedish)

N88 **Vulture Eating (1946)**
Watercolour on paper 35 x 27.2
Signed, dated
Purchased 1966

S

SCOTT, Sir Peter 1909-89 (English)

N76 **King Eiders (1965)** *(Illus.p.357)*
Watercolour on paper 18 x 25 (sight)
Signed, dated
Purchased 1966

SEABY, Allen W. 1867-1953 (English)

N5 **Common Scoters and Velvet Scoters**
Gouache on silk 54.6 x 71.1
Signed
Purchased 1963

N6 **Pomarine Skua** *(Illus.p.357)*
Watercolour on paper 27.6 x 39.2
Signed
Purchased 1963

N7 **Long-tailed Skua**
Watercolour on paper 27.6 x 39
Signed
Purchased 1963

N8 **Purple Sandpipers**
Gouache on silk 28 x 41 (sight)
Signed
Purchased 1963

N18 **Gadwall**
Watercolour on paper 25.7 x 38.5
Signed
Donated by W. A. Seaby, 1954 (?)

N274 **Great Black-backed Gulls Disputing
Dead Mallard**
Watercolour on paper 45.3 x 64.8
Signed
Purchased 1963

SHACKLETON, Keith b.1923 (English)

N242 **Roseate Tern (1965)** *(Illus.p.357)*
Oil on board 60.5 x 45.3
Signed, dated
Purchased 1968

N244 **Auks**
Gouache on paper 47.5 x 36.6
Signed
Purchased 1968

N253 **Night Heron (1968)**
Ink on paper 25.2 x 20.3
Signed, dated
Purchased 1969

N259 **Brown Rat, Water Vole, Dolphin and
Porpoise (1966)**
Ink on board 25 x 30.5
Signed, dated
Purchased 1969

N264 **Peregrine Falcon (1966)**
Charcoal on paper 50.2 x 36.3
Signed, dated
Purchased 1969

N311 **Horses Drinking (1969)** *(Illus.p.357)*
Oil on board 74.5 x 49.2 (sight)
Signed, dated
Purchased 1973

SHEALS, Alfred 1856-1929 (British)

N357 **Kingfisher (1918)**
Watercolour on paper 29.8 x 22.3 (sight)
Signed, dated
Donated; year unknown

N385 **Kingfisher (1920)**
Watercolour on paper 30 x 21 (sight)
Signed, dated
Donated; year unknown

SHEPHERD, David b.1931 (English)

N93 **Elephants (1966)** *(Illus.p.357)*
Oil on canvas 60.7 x 91.5
Signed
Commissioned 1967

SHERIDAN, Vincent 20th century (Irish?)

N392 **Wildfowl over the Slobs**
Watercolour on paper 24.8 x 36 (sight)
Signed
Purchased 1973

SOPER, Eileen Alice 1905-90 (English)

N185 **Badger Twins** *(Illus.p.357)*
Watercolour, crayon on paper 36.7 x 53.5
(sight)
Signed
Purchased 1968

ST. OUEN, Michael de 20th century (African)

N192 **Caracas**
Pencil on paper 28 x 28 (sight)
Purchased 1968

STENDALL, Sidney 20th century (British)

N389 **Icelandic Gyrfalcon (1911)**
Ink, pencil, watercolour on paper 27.4 x
19.6 (sight)
Signed, dated
Provenance unknown

SUTTON, Elizabeth 20th century (British?)

S15 **Common Dolphin (Study)**

Sculpture, plaster; measurements
unknown
Purchased 1966

SWAN, John Macallen 1847-1910 (Irish)

N155.
A29   **Lion Head (1887)**
Pastel, charcoal on paper 38.2 x 32
Signed, dated
Provenance unknown
Catalogued previously as by Morris
Harding 1874-1964

N155.
A46   **Lioness and Two Cubs (1887)**
Pastel, charcoal on paper 26.5 x 39.4
Signed, dated
Provenance unknown
Catalogued previously as by Morris
Harding 1874-1964

N394
(a)   **Leopards**
Pastel, charcoal on paper 22.8 x 32.8
(sight)
Signed
Donated by Morris Harding, 1946

N394
(b)   **Leopard**
Pastel, charcoal on paper 15 x 30.8
Signed
Donated by Morris Harding, 1946

N395
(a)   **Lion and Leopard**
Pastel, charcoal on paper 18 x 29 (sight)
Signed
Donated by Morris Harding, 1946

N395
(b)   **Leopard**
Pastel, charcoal on paper 18.6 x 36
Signed
Donated by Morris Harding, 1946

T

THOMPSON, Murray G. J. 20th century (?)
(British)

N213   **Woodpigeon**
Watercolour on paper 26.7 x 38.5 (sight)
Signed
Purchased 1968

THOMPSON, Ralph 20th century (English)

N26   **Lar Gibbon (1965)** *(Illus.p.357)*
Charcoal on paper 28.4 x 36.8 (sight)
Signed
Purchased 1965

N34   **Porcupine** *(Illus.p.357)*
Charcoal on paper 37 x 29.8 (sight)
Signed
Purchased 1965

N35   **Cacomistle** *(Illus.p.357)*
Watercolour on paper 45.5 x 58.2 (sight)
Signed
Purchased 1965

N240   **Tiger Cub Stalking**
Watercolour on paper 27.5 x 37.5
Signed
Purchased 1968

THORBURN, Archibald 1860-1935 (English)

N21   **Woodcock (1897)** *(Illus.p.358)*
Watercolour on paper 38 x 55.2
Signed, dated
Purchased 1965

N38   **Heron (1918)**
Pencil on paper 13.8 x 9.5 (sight)
Signed, dated
Purchased 1965

N77   **Cock Blackbird in Distress (1876)**
(Illus.p.358)
Watercolour on paper 22.4 x 28
Signed, dated
Purchased 1967

N241   **Studies of Fieldfare (1912)**
Watercolour on paper 38.2 x 26.6
Signed, dated
Purchased 1968

N285   **Martial Eagles**
Pencil on paper 22.6 x 17.7
Signed
Purchased 1967

N350   **Osprey**
Pencil, watercolour, wash on paper 19.3 x
28 (sight)
Signed
Purchased 1982

TIMYM, William T. 1912-90 (Austrian)

N305   **Orang Study Sheet (1971)** *(Illus.p.358)*
Watercolour on paper 49.3 x 47.5
Signed, dated
Purchased 1972

N354   **Cheetahs (1971)**
Charcoal on paper 31.5 x 46.3
Signed, dated
Purchased 1971

N358   **Wild Boar Study Sheet (1970)**
Crayon on paper 52.8 x 75.2
Signed, dated
Purchased 1971

TRECHSLIN, Anna Maire 20th century (British)

N366   **Phalaenopsis** *(Illus.p.358)*
Watercolour, pencil on paper 50.2 x 36.4
Signed
Purchased 1975

TUNNICLIFFE, Charles Frederick 1901-79
(English)

N3   **Young Wings** *(Illus.p.358)*
Watercolour on paper 46.2 x 59
Signed
Purchased 1953

N238   **Whoopers Alighting** *(Illus.p.358)*
Watercolour on paper 40 x 66.3 (sight)
Signed
Purchased 1968

N300   **Hooded Lanner Falcon** *(Illus.p.358)*
Watercolour on paper 77.5 x 41.3
Signed
Purchased 1971

N307   **Black-tails Alighting** *(Illus.p.358)*
Watercolour on paper 49 x 76
Signed

Purchased 1973

U

UNKNOWN, 19th century

N503   **Snipe**
Watercolour, feathers on paper 17.8 x
22.3 (sight)
Donated by M. E. Paige Cox, 1953

N504   **Thrush**
Watercolour, feathers on paper 20 x 29.8
(sight)
Donated by M. E. Paige Cox, 1953

N505   **Seated Lion**
Sculpture, bronze 56.8 x 35.5 x 72
Provenance unknown

W

WARDLE, Arthur 1864-1949 (English)

N320   **Bengal Tiger** *(Illus.p.358)*
Oil on canvas 38 x 50.7
Signed
Purchased 1975

WARDLE, John C. 20th century (?) (British)

N183   **Lynx** *(Illus.p.359)*
Crayon on paper 21 x 36 (sight)
Signed
Purchased 1968

WATSON, Donald b.1918 (English)

N53   **Osprey on a May Morning (1966)**
(Illus.p.359)
Watercolour on paper 34.4 x 47.6
Signed, dated
Purchased 1966

N54   **Whitethroat (1966)** *(Illus.p.359)*
Watercolour on paper 35 x 25.5
Signed, dated
Purchased 1966

N55   **Adder (1966)** *(Illus.p.359)*
Watercolour on paper 30.4 x 15.4
Signed, dated
Purchased 1966

N248   **Oystercatchers in March** *(Illus.p.359)*
Watercolour on paper 13.3 x 26.1 (sight)
Signed
Purchased 1969

N260   **Long-tailed Drakes (1948)**
Watercolour on paper 21.5 x 22.5
Dated
Purchased 1969

N266   **Woodcock on Nest (1964)**
Pencil on paper 23.8 x 16.5
Signed, dated
Purchased 1969

WATSON, Raymond Cyril b.1935 (English)

N49   **Tern on the Shore** *(Illus.p.359)*
Bodycolour on paper 54.6 x 45.2

Signed
Purchased 1966

N156   **Magpies on a Birch Tree** *(Illus.p.359)*
Watercolour on paper 64.8 x 44.8 (sight)
Signed
Purchased 1967

N182   **Puffin over the Water** *(Illus.p.359)*
Bodycolour on paper 47.8 x 73
Signed
Purchased 1968

N269   **Avocets in Flight** *(Illus.p.359)*
Watercolour on paper 47 x 62.7
Signed
Purchased 1969

N370   **Red-breasted Geese** *(Illus.p.360)*
Watercolour on paper 46 x 78 (sight)
Signed
Purchased 1971

WEBB, Gwen L. 20th century (?) (British)

N15   **Sleeping Badger Cub**
Pencil on paper 22.8 x 17.8
Signed
Purchased 1965

WEIR, Douglas 20th century (British)

N52   **Iceland Falcon at Nest (1966)**
Watercolour on paper 37.8 x 52
Signed, dated
Purchased 1966

WILLIAMS, Ralph H. 20th century (British?)

S27   **Salmon**
Sculpture, wood 31 x 33.5 x 8
Purchased 1968

WILLIS, Ian Robert b.1944 (English)

N212   **Avocets (1968)**
Ink, gouache on paper 27.6 x 34.8
Signed, dated
Purchased 1968

N257   **Cock Brambling (1965)**
Watercolour on paper 21.5 x 13.2
Dated
Purchased 1969

WILSON, Maurice b.1914 (English)

N361   **Red Deer and Fawns (1972)** *(Illus.p.360)*
Watercolour on paper 39 x 28.8
Dated
Purchased 1972

N364   **Kingfisher** *(Illus.p.360)*
Watercolour on paper 35 x 27.4 (sight)
Purchased 1972

WOLF, Joseph 1820-99 (German, worked in Ireland)

N74   **Pallid Harriers** *(Illus.p.360)*
Watercolour, white on paper 58 x 47
Signed
Purchased 1966

N181   **Arctic Summer (1877)** *(Illus.p.360)*
Watercolour on paper 74.7 x 59.5 (sight)
Signed, dated

Purchased 1968

N351   **Peregrine Falcon Attacking Ducks Approaching at Lake Level**
Pencil, wash on paper 17.5 x 24.8
Signed
Purchased 1982

N352   **Black Cock at the Lake**
Pencil, wash, white on paper 20.2 x 25.3
Signed
Purchased 1982

N353   **Osprey at the Sanctuary**
Pencil on paper 17.5 x 24.8
Signed
Purchased 1982

drawings paintings & sculptures

the ulster museum
history
collection

A

ALLINGHAM, Helen 1848-1926 (English)

P246.1925 **William Allingham 1824-89 (1889)**
Pencil on paper 11.8 x 15.2
Signed, dated
Donated by the artist, 1925

ARNOLD, Phyllis b.1938 (Irish)

P46.1973 **Market Square, Tandragee, Co.
Armagh (1969)**
Pencil on paper 24.6 x 51.2
Signed, dated
Purchased 1969

P47.1973 **Armagh (1969)**
Watercolour on paper 36.6 x 25.3
Signed, dated
Purchased 1969

P48.1973 **Lower Main Street, Bangor, c.1910**
Ink, wash on paper 20.2 x 31.1
Signed
Purchased 1969

P49.1973 **Lisburn, c.1850**
Ink, wash on paper 19.1 x 27.8
Signed
Purchased 1969

AYRTON, Eileen fl.1927-76 (Irish)

P116.1945 **James Cumming Wynnes, OBE,
FRIBA 1875-1944 (1945)**
Chalk on paper 44.4 x 31.7
Signed, dated
Purchased 1945

P4.1986 **Martha McTier 1742-1837 (Copy)**
Pastel on paper 29.8 x 24.3
Donated by Miss S. M. Duffin, 1986

B

BAKER, Alfred Rawlings 1865-1939 (English,
worked in Ireland)

P14.1985 **Sub-Lieutenant Ian C. McCormick,
Royal Naval Division (c.1917-18)**
Oil on canvas 118 x 71.5
Signed
Donated by Dr. Pearl Young, 1969

BARRE, William James 1830-67 (Irish)

P366.1915 **Prince Consort Memorial, Belfast:
Architectural Perspective** (Albert
Memorial)
Watercolour on paper 71.6 x 49.3
Purchased 1915

P80.1984 **Interior of Ulster Hall, Belfast:
Architectural Perspective (1862)**
(Illus.p.362)
Watercolour on paper 47 x 59.9
Provenance unknown

BELLAIRS, W. J. 19th century (British)

P34.1973 **Downpatrick, Ireland**
Ink, wash on paper 17.2 x 24.7
Signed

Donated by Hugh Crawford, 1970

BÉRANGER, Gabriel 1729-1817 (French,
worked in Ireland) (attributed to)
The following works are as titled by the artist

P135.1973 **The Castle of Doe, Co. Donegal**
Watercolour on paper 16.5 x 24.1
Purchased 1965

P136.1973 **Lough a Doon Fort, Co. Donegal**
Watercolour on paper 18 x 22.8
(oval)
Purchased 1965

P137.1973 **Cromlechs on the Lands of Killcluny,
Co. Donegal**
Two watercolours on paper, each 14.9
x 30.1
Purchased 1965

P138.1973 **Castle Blayney, Co. Monaghan**
Watercolour on paper 17.7 x 23
(oval)
Purchased 1965

P139.1973 **Portsory Castle, Co. Fermanagh**
Watercolour on paper 16 x 23.5
Purchased 1965

P140.1973 **Castle Crevenish, Co. Fermanagh**
(a) Watercolour on paper, diameter
14.6 (two on one sheet)
Purchased 1965

P140.1973 **Tcharman Castle, Co. Fermanagh**
(b) Watercolour on paper, diameter 14.6
(two on one sheet)
Purchased 1965

P141.1973 **Abbey at Omagh, Co. Tyrone**
(a) Watercolour on paper, diameter 14.6
(two on one sheet)
Purchased 1965

P141.1973 **Castle near Newtown-Stewart,**
(b) **Co. Tyrone**
Watercolour on paper, diameter 14.6
(two on one sheet)
Purchased 1965

P142.1973 **The Castle of Carlingford**
Watercolour on paper 18.8 x 27.9
Purchased 1965

P143.1973 **Narrow-Water Castle, Co. Down**
(a) Watercolour on paper, diameter 14.6
(two on one sheet)
Purchased 1965

P143.1973 **Cromlech near Rosstrevor, Co. Down**
(b) Watercolour on paper, diameter 14.6
(two on one sheet)
Purchased 1965

BETTS, S. 19th century (British)

P352.1927 **Venerable Archdeacon Spence, DD
(1848)**
Silhouette, gouache, gum, white on
paper 34.1 x 23.4
Signed, dated
Purchased 1927

BLAIR, Doris Violet fl.1940s-'80s (Irish)

P281.1947 **Sam Hanna Bell 1909-90 (c.1943)**

Pencil on paper 16.8 x 13.8
Signed
Donated anonymously, 1947

P1.1984 **Belfast Blitzed Scene: Bridge Street**
Watercolour on paper 26.9 x 37
Purchased 1984

P2.1984 **Belfast Blitzed Scene: High Street**
Watercolour on paper 37.7 x 27.7
Signed
Purchased 1984

P3.1984 **Blitzed Building**
Watercolour on paper 36.9 x 27.3
Signed
Purchased 1984

P4.1984 **Blitzed Houses**
Watercolour on paper 26.1 x 36.8
Signed
Purchased 1984

P5.1984 **Devastation**
Watercolour on paper 28 x 38.1
Purchased 1984

P6.1984 **American Field Kitchen**
Watercolour on paper 27.8 x 38.3
Signed
Purchased 1984

P7.1984 **American Infantry Man at Rest**
Watercolour on paper 38.4 x 27.8
Signed
Purchased 1984

P8.1984 **Arc Welding**
Watercolour on paper 38 x 27.6
Signed
Purchased 1984

P9.1984 **Armoured Car Driver**
Watercolour on paper 38.1 x 27.7
Signed
Purchased 1984

P10.1984 **ATS Operators, AA Battery**
Watercolour on paper 28 x 38.5
Signed
Purchased 1984

P11.1984 **Copper Banding**
Watercolour on paper 27.9 x 38.4
Signed
Purchased 1984

P12.1984 **Despatch Rider, ATS**
Watercolour on paper 27.7 x 38.4
Signed
Purchased 1984

P13.1984 **Driver in Armoured Car**
Watercolour on paper 27.2 x 38.3
Signed
Purchased 1984

P14.1984 **The Erection of a Stirling**
(Illus.p.362)
Watercolour on paper 28.8 x 40.1
Purchased 1984

P15.1984 **Gas Test, Control Tower**
Watercolour on paper 28.1 x 38.4
Signed
Purchased 1984

P16.1984 **The Hangar Queen**

Watercolour on paper 28.6 x 37.7
Signed
Purchased 1984

P17.1984 **Havocs**
Watercolour on paper 27.9 x 38.5
Purchased 1984

P18.1984 **Height Takers ATS**
Watercolour on paper 27.8 x 38.6
Signed
Purchased 1984

P19.1984 **Infantry Howitzer Firing**
Watercolour on paper 27.9 x 38.2
Signed
Purchased 1984

P20.1984 **Infantry Howitzer on the Move**
Watercolour on paper 27 x 38.2
Signed
Purchased 1984

P21.1984 **In the Cookhouse**
Watercolour on paper 27.7 x 38
Signed
Purchased 1984

P22.1984 **Machining and Inspecting Parachutes
for Flares and Towing Targets**
Watercolour on paper 28.5 x 38.2
Purchased 1984

P23.1984 **Manufacturing Small Arms
Ammunition**
Watercolour on paper 28.6 x 38.2
Signed
Purchased 1984

P24.1984 **Marauder Pilot**
Watercolour on paper 27.9 x 38.4
Signed
Purchased 1984

P25.1984 **Marauders**
Watercolour on paper 28 x 38
Signed
Purchased 1984

P26.1984 **Off Duty**
Watercolour on paper 22.1 x 28.6
Signed
Purchased 1984

P27.1984 **Oxy-acetylene Welder**
Watercolour on paper 27.6 x 38.1
Signed
Purchased 1984

P28.1984 **The Paint Sprayer** *(Illus.p.362)*
Watercolour on paper 37.9 x 28.1
Signed
Purchased 1984

P29.1984 **Platoon Vehicle Inspection**
Watercolour on paper 27.7 x 38.2
Signed
Purchased 1984

P30.1984 **The Record Breaker** *(Illus.p.362)*
Watercolour on paper 38.3 x 27.7
Signed
Purchased 1984

P31.1984 **Sighting the Target**
Watercolour on paper 27.5 x 37.6
Signed
Purchased 1984

P32.1984 **Signals Exchange, Military HQ**
Watercolour on paper 27.4 x 38.5
Signed
Purchased 1984

P33.1984 **Sunderland Erection Bay**
Watercolour on paper 28 x 38.3
Signed
Purchased 1984

P34.1984 **Truck Driver, ATS**
Watercolour on paper 27.8 x 38.2
Signed
Purchased 1984

P35.1984 **Blood Transfusion, British Military
Hospital**
Watercolour on paper 27.6 x 38.5
Signed
Purchased 1984

P36.1984 **Eye Test by Army MO**
Watercolour on paper 27.8 x 38.1
Signed
Purchased 1984

P37.1984 **Nurse Tending Patient in Traction,
Military Field Hospital**
Watercolour on paper 27.5 x 38.2
Purchased 1984

P38.1984 **Surgical Operation, Military Field
Hospital**
Watercolour on paper 25.8 x 39.5
Signed
Purchased 1984

P39.1984 **Surgical Operation, Military Base
Hospital**
Watercolour on paper 28.1 x 38.4
Signed
Purchased 1984

P40.1984 **Air Sea Rescue - the Search**
(Illus.p.362)
Watercolour on paper 38.3 x 27.3
Signed
Purchased 1984

P41.1984 **Flight Sergeant T. Grimshaw, Air Sea
Rescue**
Watercolour on paper 38.1 x 23.7
Signed
Purchased 1984

P42.1984 **Captain Pilot W. J. Bither, US Army
Air Force**
Watercolour on paper 23.5 x 19
Signed
Purchased 1984

P43.1984 **Staff Sergeant O. W. Rutzen, Crew
Chief in Hangar**
Watercolour on paper 38.7 x 27.6
Signed
Purchased 1984

P44.1984 **Lieutenant Bombardier E. Sholley,
USAAF**
Watercolour on paper 29 x 25.5
Signed
Purchased 1984

P45.1984 **Plotting the Flight. W. E. Weylandt,
Bombardier Navigator**
Watercolour on paper 38.3 x 27.5
Signed

Purchased 1984

P46.1984 **British Army Corporal**
Watercolour on paper 27.5 x 19
Signed
Purchased 1984

P47.1984 **ATS Lieutenant**
Watercolour on paper 26 x 25.5
Signed
Purchased 1984

P48.1984 **ATS Private**
Watercolour on paper 38.2 x 26.8
Signed
Purchased 1984

P49.1984 **Second Lieutenant Bombardier,
USAAF**
Watercolour on paper 27.8 x 23
Signed
Purchased 1984

P50.1984 **American Serviceman**
Watercolour on paper 38.7 x 27.6
Purchased 1984

P51.1984 **Infantry Officer, US Army**
Watercolour on paper 37.5 x 25.5
Signed
Purchased 1984

P52.1984 **Servicewoman**
Watercolour on paper 31 x 26.8
Signed
Purchased 1984

P53.1984 **Lieutenant H. Aitkens, US Army
Nursing Corps**
Watercolour on paper 38 x 27.6
Purchased 1984

P54.1984 **Second Lieutenant Edith Dorell, US
Army Nursing Corps**
Watercolour on paper 27 x 33
Signed
Purchased 1984

P55.1984 **Second Lieutenant Fitzgerald, US
Army Nursing Corps**
Watercolour on paper 34 x 26.5
Purchased 1984

P56.1984 **Nurse Hussey, US Army Nursing
Corps**
Watercolour on paper 38 x 25
Purchased 1984

P57.1984 **Second Lieutenant Kazmanick, US
Army Nursing Corps**
Watercolour on paper 37.6 x 27.6
Signed
Purchased 1984

P58.1984 **Second Lieutenant Kleysteuber, US
Army Nursing Corps**
Watercolour on paper 24 x 33
Purchased 1984

P59.1984 **Nurse McKee, US Army Nursing
Corps**
Watercolour on paper 32 x 25
Purchased 1984

P60.1984 **Second Lieutenant McNeill, US Army
Nursing Corps**
Watercolour on paper 25 x 17.5
Signed

Purchased 1984

P61.1984   **Second Lieutenant Powers, US Army
Nursing Corps**
Watercolour on paper 38 x 20.5
Signed
Purchased 1984

P62.1984   **Second Lieutenant Sinks, US Army
Nursing Corps**
Watercolour on paper 37 x 27
Signed
Purchased 1984

P63.1984   **Second Lieutenant F. Theil, US Army
Nursing Corps**
Watercolour on paper 30.5 x 21
Signed
Purchased 1984

P64.1984   **Lieutenant Tierney, US Army
Nursing Corps**
Watercolour on paper 32 x 25
Signed
Purchased 1984

P65.1984   **Second Lieutenant, US Army
Nursing Corps, Knitting**
Watercolour on paper 32 x 22
Signed
Purchased 1984

P66.1984   **Second Lieutenant, US Army
Nursing Corps, in Pink Uniform**
Watercolour on paper 34 x 27
Purchased 1984

P67.1984   **Miss Irene Boyce, American Red
Cross**
Watercolour on paper 31 x 21.5
Signed
Purchased 1984

P68.1984   **Mrs. Cook, American Red Cross**
Watercolour on paper 19 x 16
Purchased 1984

P69.1984   **Welfare Officer, American Red Cross,
Seated at Desk**
Watercolour on paper 22.5 x 19.5
Signed
Purchased 1984

P70.1984   **Welfare Worker, American Red
Cross, Seated at Desk**
Watercolour on paper 26 x 25
Signed
Purchased 1984

P71.1984   **Welfare Worker, American Red
Cross, Seated**
Watercolour on paper 30 x 19.5
Signed
Purchased 1984

P72.1984   **Welfare Worker, American Red
Cross, Standing**
Watercolour on paper 37 x 24
Signed
Purchased 1984

P73.1984   **Rose of the Sperrins**
Watercolour on paper 27.6 x 18.8
Signed
Purchased 1984

P74.1984   **Staff Sergeant M. L. Smith, Nebraska**

Ink on paper 24 x 20
Purchased 1984

P75.1984   **Private Ed. Dunn, US Army**
Ink on paper 20 x 16
Purchased 1984

P76.1984   **PFC Driver Salvador Palacios, Texas**
Pencil on paper 30 x 22.5
Signed
Purchased 1984

P77.1984   **American Nurse (Second Lieutenant
F. Theil, USANC)**
Oil on canvas 76.2 x 61
Purchased 1984

P78.1984   **Miss Irene Boyce, American Red
Cross**
Oil on canvas 75.7 x 60.5
Purchased 1984

P23.1985   **Belfast Blitzed Scene: St. James's
Parish Schools, Antrim Road (1941)**
Watercolour on paper 27 x 36.7
Signed
Donated by the artist, 1985

BRANNON, Philip 19th century (British)

P498.1922 **Commercial Buildings, etc., Belfast
(1841)** *(Illus.p.362)*
Watercolour on paper 19.1 x 24
Signed, dated
Donated by Thomas McGowan, 1922

BRODERICK, Herbert (Hubert?) E. fl.1951-71
(Irish)

P407.1951 **Falls Road, Belfast**
Watercolour on paper 25.9 x 36
Signed
Purchased 1951

P408.1951 **Donegal House, Belfast** *(Illus.p.362)*
Watercolour on paper 22.1 x 27.7
Signed
Purchased 1951

P409.1951 **Mistletoe Café, Belfast** *(Illus.p.362)*
Watercolour on paper 27.6 x 22.1
Signed
Purchased 1951

P412.1951 **Kelly's Shop, Corner of Brown Street
and Millfield**
Watercolour on paper 22.2 x 27.7
Signed
Purchased 1951

P643.1963 **The Lighting Station**
Watercolour on paper 37.2 x 26.6
Signed
Purchased 1963

BUNTING, Robert J. fl.c.1914-27 (Irish)

P79.1973   **Carrick Castle, Town and Harbour
(1917)**
Watercolour on paper 21.7 x 32.1
Signed, dated
Purchased 1966

P80.1973   **Carrickfergus Castle, 1832 (1917)**
Watercolour on paper 21 x 31.2
Signed, dated
Purchased 1966

P81.1973   **Carrickfergus Castle and Old
Harbour, Year 1878 (1927)**
Watercolour on paper 14.5 x 22.1
Signed, dated
Purchased 1966

P82.1973   **Carrickfergus Castle and Old
Harbour (1920)**
Watercolour on paper 38.8 x 55.6
Signed, dated
Purchased 1966

P83.1973   **Carrick Castle and Independent
Church, Quay Gate, Carrickfergus,
Year 1878 (1918)**
Watercolour on card 27.5 x 48
Signed, dated
Purchased 1966

P84.1973   **St. Nicholas' RC Church,
Carrickfergus (1921)**
Watercolour on paper 21.9 x 29.9
Signed, dated
Purchased 1966

P85.1973   **Methodist Church, Carrickfergus
(1921)**
Watercolour on paper 24 x 34.3
Signed, dated
Purchased 1966

P86.1973   **Unitarian Church, 1836,
Carrickfergus (1917)** *(Illus.p.362)*
Watercolour on paper 20.1 x 35.6
Signed, dated
Purchased 1966

P87.1973   **Barnett's Quay and Shipyard,
Carrickfergus**
Watercolour on paper 30.8 x 48.5
Signed
Purchased 1966

P88.1973   **Scotch Quarter Quay, Carrickfergus,
Year 1920**
Watercolour on paper 22.2 x 36.5
Signed, dated
Purchased 1966

P89.1973   **Coffee's Square, Scotch Quarter,
Carrickfergus (1918)**
Watercolour on paper 19.3 x 34.4
Signed, dated
Purchased 1966

P90.1973   **North Gate, Carrickfergus when
Peace was Proclaimed, 11 Nov. 1918
(1918)**
Watercolour on paper 19.6 x 26.1
Signed, dated
Purchased 1966

P91.1973   **Illuminations from Sunnyland Camp,
11 Nov. 1918 (1918)**
Watercolour on paper 19.7 x 26.3
Signed, dated
Purchased 1966

P92.1973   **Bonn-fire, North Gate, Carrickfergus,
11 Nov. 1918 (1918)** (Bonfire)
Watercolour on paper 19.7 x 26.2
Signed, dated
Purchased 1966

P93.1973   **Carrickfergus Castle (1920)**
Watercolour on paper 33 x 53.4
Signed, dated

Purchased 1966

P94.1973 **Carrick Castle and Old Harbour, 1880 (1922)**
Watercolour on paper 16.6 x 24.2
Signed, dated
Purchased 1966

P95.1973 **Carrickfergus Castle and Woodwork, Year 1877 (1927)**
Watercolour on paper 19.7 x 50.2
Signed, dated
Purchased 1966

P96.1973 **Shipyard, Belfast Road, Carrickfergus, Year 1880 (1925)** *(Illus.p.363)*
Watercolour on paper 19.1 x 44.1
Signed, dated
Purchased 1966

P97.1973 **Scotch Quarter Quay, Carrickfergus, Year 1920 (1925)**
Watercolour on paper 15.4 x 25.6
Signed, dated
Purchased 1966

P98.1973 **Old Independent Meeting House and Quay Gate, Carrickfergus, 1880 (1918)**
Watercolour on paper 28.7 x 34.4
Signed, dated
Purchased 1966

P99.1973 **St. Nicholas' Church, Carrickfergus, Year 1918: North View (1922)** *(Illus.p.363)*
Watercolour on paper 27.2 x 37.2
Signed, dated
Purchased 1966

P100.1973 **St. Nicholas' Church, Carrickfergus: East View (1922)** *(Illus.p.363)*
Watercolour on paper 27 x 37.1
Signed, dated
Purchased 1966

P101.1973 **Old Spire, St. Nicholas' Church, Carrickfergus (1921)**
Watercolour on paper 38.5 x 18.4
Signed, dated
Purchased 1966

P102.1973 **War Memorial Bell Tower, St. Nicholas' Church, Carrickfergus (1921)**
Watercolour on paper 23.6 x 11.9
Signed, dated
Purchased 1966

P103.1973 **First Presbyterian Church, North Street, Carrickfergus (1923)**
Watercolour on paper 26.1 x 33
Signed, dated
Purchased 1966

P104.1973 **First Presbyterian Church and Old North Gate, Carrickfergus**
Watercolour on paper 18.3 x 24.7
Signed
Purchased 1966

P105.1973 **North Street Presbyterian Church, Carrickfergus and War Memorial Tablet: Placing the Last Stone (1920)**
Watercolour on paper 40.7 x 56.2
Signed, dated

Purchased 1966

P106.1973 **War Memorial Tablet, North Street Church, Carrickfergus (1921)**
Watercolour on paper 28.3 x 18.6
Signed, dated
Purchased 1966

P107.1973 **Bronze Plate (Introductory), War Memorial Tablet, North Street Church, Carrickfergus (1921)**
Watercolour on paper 27.8 x 19.7
Signed, dated
Purchased 1966

P108.1973 **Bronze Plate (Navy and Nursing Service), War Memorial Tablet, North Street Church, Carrickfergus (1921)**
Watercolour on paper 27.8 x 19.7
Signed, dated
Purchased 1966

P109.1973 **Bronze Plate (Army I), War Memorial Tablet, North Street Church, Carrickfergus (1921)**
Watercolour on paper 27.8 x 19.6
Signed, dated
Purchased 1966

P110.1973 **Bronze Plate (Army II), War Memorial Tablet, North Street Church, Carrickfergus (1921)**
Watercolour on paper 27.9 x 19.7
Signed, dated
Purchased 1966

P111.1973 **Memorial Fountain in Park, Belfast Road, Carrickfergus (1926)**
Watercolour on paper 55.6 x 38.5
Signed, dated
Purchased 1966

P112.1973 **Kilroot Orange Hall, 1896, Eden, near Carrickfergus (1922)**
Watercolour on paper 25 x 35.1
Signed, dated
Purchased 1966

P113.1973 **Landscape with Cattle near Carrickfergus (1919)**
Watercolour on paper 20.8 x 31
Signed, dated
Purchased 1966

P114.1973 **Hamilton's Row, Woodburn Road, near Carrickfergus (1921)** *(Illus.p.363)*
Watercolour on paper 14 x 39.5
Signed, dated
Purchased 1966

P115.1973 **Fairview, near Hamilton's Row, Woodburn Road (1921)** *(Illus.p.363)*
Watercolour on paper 14 x 39.5
Signed, dated
Purchased 1966

P116.1973 **Duncrue Mill or the Old Burnt Mill, Woodburn, near Carrickfergus (1917)**
Watercolour on paper 33.1 x 50.8
Signed, dated
Purchased 1966

P117.1973 **Dunn's Planting from Duncrue Bridge, Woodburn (1918)**
Watercolour on paper 27.8 x 35.5

Signed, dated
Purchased 1966

P118.1973 **Barn Mill and Fairymount from Buskyburn, North Road, Carrickfergus (1922)**
Watercolour on paper 24.3 x 49.7
Signed, dated
Purchased 1966

P119.1973 **Knocka Hills from West Road, Upper Woodburn, near Carrickfergus (1918)**
Watercolour on paper 29.6 x 49.4
Signed, dated
Purchased 1966

P120.1973 **The Telegraph Boy (1926)**
Watercolour on paper 25.5 x 16.6
Signed, dated
Purchased 1966

P121.1973 **Sword and Mace (1925)**
Ink on paper 26.9 x 19.1
Signed, dated
Purchased 1966

P122.1973 **Old Thatched House, Lancasterian Street, Carrickfergus (1914)**
Oil on canvas 30.4 x 40.7
Signed, dated
Purchased 1966

P158.1973 **Presbyterian Church, Ballynure (1927)** *(Illus.p.363)*
Watercolour on paper 13.9 x 21.3
Signed, dated
Purchased 1966

P4.1999 **A Cottage Scene**
Watercolour on paper 17.5 x 25
Purchased 1966

P7.1999 **Gateway to India**
Watercolour on paper 32.5 x 47
Purchased 1966

P9.1999 **Gabes-Djara (Tunis), Arab Quarters**
Watercolour on board 24.5 x 12
Signed
Purchased 1966

P10.1999 **Oasis at Bishra (Algeria) at Eventide (1924)**
Watercolour on paper 12.5 x 25
Signed, dated
Purchased 1966

P11.1999 **Traders and their Camels; The Mohamed Ali Mosque with its Dome and Minarets (1924)**
Watercolour on paper 12 x 35
Signed, dated
Purchased 1966

P12.1999 **The Wanderer's Return (1915)**
Watercolour on paper 28 x 42.5
Signed, dated
Purchased 1966

P13.1999 **Tomb of Imram-esh-Shafih**
Watercolour on paper 12 x 35
Signed
Purchased 1966

P14.1999 **The Village Street (1922)**
Watercolour on paper 22 x 34.5

Signed
Purchased 1966

P15.1999 **A Summer Day**
Watercolour on paper 22 x 34.5
Signed
Purchased 1966

BUNTING, T. 20th century (Irish)

P8.1999 **The Sphinx**
Watercolour on paper 29 x 22
Signed
Purchased 1966

BURGESS, James Howard c.1810-90 (Irish)

P178.1909 **River Lagan, Showing Molly Ward's
Cottage (1885)** *(Illus.p.363)*
Watercolour on paper 33.2 x 50.9
Signed, dated
Purchased 1909

P59.1951 **Belfast Harbour** *(Illus.p.363)*
Pencil, wash on paper 25.3 x 36.8
Purchased 1951

P359.1952 **Bryansford, Co. Down (1842)**
(Illus.p.363)
Pencil on paper 9.2 x 13.9 (sight)
Signed
Purchased 1952

P16.1980 **Sketrick Castle, Co. Down**
Watercolour on paper 26.9 x 44.1
Purchased 1980

P32.1980 **Waterfoot, Co. Antrim**
Watercolour on paper 32 x 48.9
Signed
Purchased 1980

P14.1981 **Newcastle, Co. Down** *(Illus.p.364)*
Watercolour on paper 29.4 x 44.1
Purchased 1981

P1.1982 **Village of Killyleagh and Castle, Co.
Down**
Watercolour on paper 27.2 x 47.9
Signed
Purchased 1982

P18.1985 **Hyde Park Bleach Works**
Pencil, white, sepia wash on paper
26.6 x 37.7
Purchased 1985

C

CAMPBELL, Arthur M. d.1994 (Irish)

P356.1952 **Pond in Botanic Gardens**
Charcoal, gouache on paper;
measurements unknown
Signed
Purchased 1952

P357.1952 **College Place North** *(Illus.p.364)*
Watercolour on paper 45 x 29.1
Signed
Purchased 1952

P358.1952 **Street at Whitehouse, Belfast**
Watercolour on paper 34.1 x 25
Signed

Purchased 1952

CAMPBELL, John Henry c.1757-1828 (Irish)

P17.1980 **Laurel Hill on the Bann near
Colerain** (Coleraine)
Watercolour on paper 17.1 x 23.9
Purchased 1980

CAREY, John and **Joseph William** 1861-1943 and
1859-1937 (Irish)

P25.1974 **Burning of Belfast Castle, 1708
(1895)**
Ink, white on paper 20.2 x 27.1
Signed, dated
Purchased 1974

CAREY, John 1861-1943 (Irish)

P106.1917 **Castle Lane, Belfast (1917)**
Watercolour on paper 50.6 x 38.4
Signed, dated
Donated by Thomas McGowan, 1917

P32.1973 **The Belfast Boat Club** *(Illus.p.364)*
Watercolour on paper 18.7 x 30
Signed
Purchased 1970

P19.1974 **The Covenanters Tearing their
Colours, Belfast, 1644 (1895)**
Ink, white on paper 17.2 x 21.2
Signed, dated
Purchased 1974

P23.1974 **The Belfast Corporation Address to
King William, 1690 (1895)**
Ink, white on paper 19.9 x 26.2
Signed, dated
Purchased 1974

P24.1974 **Thomas McCabe Denouncing
Waddell Cunningham's Proposed
Slaveship Company in the Old
Exchange, 1786 (1895)**
Ink, white on paper 18.9 x 24.6
Signed, dated
Purchased 1974

CAREY, Joseph William 1859-1937 (Irish)

P105.1908 **The Lodge, Cliftonville, Belfast
(1908)**
Sepia, pencil on paper 16.1 x 22.9
Signed, dated
Donated by John Horner,1908

P106.1910 **'Cranmore', Malone (1910)**
Sepia, pencil on paper 16.1 x 21.7
Signed, dated
Donated by A. Basil Wilson, 1910

P628.1932 **White Linen Hall, Belfast (1900)**
(Illus.p.364)
Watercolour on paper 28 x 34.8
Signed, dated
Donated by R. J. Welch, 1932

P9.1974 **The Keeper in Portmore Woods, 1666
(1895)**
Ink, white on paper 22.4 x 37.9
Signed, dated
Purchased 1974

P10.1974 **Enclosing the Deer Park, Cave Hill**

(1895)
Ink, white on paper 26.5 x 39.5
Signed, dated
Purchased 1974

P11.1974 **The Battle of Antrim (1895)**
Ink, white on paper 21.1 x 25.9
Signed, dated
Purchased 1974

P12.1974 **New Forge: Lock-Keeper's House on
the Lagan (1895)**
Ink, white on paper 26.4 x 42.3
Dated
Purchased 1974

P13.1974 **Mourne Mountains from Castlereagh
(1895)**
Ink, white on paper 20.9 x 33.9
Signed, dated
Purchased 1974

P14.1974 **Benburb Castle (1895)**
Ink, white on paper 20.7 x 34.2
Signed, dated
Purchased 1974

P15.1974 **Old Belfast Castle in 1690 (1895)**
Ink on paper 21.2 x 32.4
Signed, dated
Purchased 1974

P16.1974 **Old Waterworks, Stranmillis (1895)**
Ink on paper 10.3 x 24.8
Signed, dated
Purchased 1974

P17.1974 **The Conversion of the Old Church
in High Street into the 'Grand
Citadel', 1651 (1894)**
Ink, white on paper 21.6 x 36.5
Signed, dated
Purchased 1974

P20.1974 **Schomberg's Troops Crossing the
Long Bridge, Belfast, 1689**
Ink, white on paper 18.2 x 27
Purchased 1974

P21.1974 **The Ancient Gallows Called 'The
Three Sisters', Carrickfergus**
Ink, white on paper 18.6 x 34.1
Purchased 1974

P22.1974 **Hillsborough Fort**
Ink, white on paper 18.2 x 21
Purchased 1974

P37.1980 **Belfast Home Defence Corps (1915)**
(Illus.p.364)
Watercolour on paper 29 x 54.1
Signed, dated
Purchased 1980

CARR, Tom 1909-99 (Irish)

P283.1947 **R. V. Williams ('Richard Rowley')
1877-1947 (1947)**
Crayon on paper 25.2 x 20.2
Signed
Donated anonymously, 1947

P1.1999 **Edenderry House**
Oil on canvas 49 x 75 (sight)
Signed
Purchased 1993

P6.1999   Henrietta Street (1946-47)
           Watercolour on paper 25 x 34.5
           Signed
           Purchased 1999

CARRUTHERS, George A. 19th century (Irish)

P84.1984   The 'Great Britain', Dundrum Bay, 20
           July 1847 (Illus.p.364)
           Watercolour on paper 20.6 x 29.9
           Provenance unknown

CARRUTHERS, Rose 19th century (Irish)

P163.1921 Parish Church of Knock-Breda at the
           Newtown-Breda, Co. Down (1860)
           (Knockbreda, Newtownbreda)
           (Illus.p.364)
           Watercolour on paper 17.4 x 30.4
           Signed, dated
           Donated by T. Edens Osborne, 1921

P358.1927 Old Houses, High Street, Belfast
           (Illus.p.364)
           Watercolour on paper 18.1 x 25.1
           Signed
           Purchased 1927

CHIPP, Herbert fl.1877-98 (English)

P50.1973   Newcastle, Co. Down (1878)
           Watercolour on paper 31.1 x 55.5
           Signed, dated
           Purchased 1968

P51.1973   River Lagan at Belvoir
           Watercolour on paper; measurements
           unknown
           Purchased 1968

P52.1973   The Salmon House, Portrush
           (Illus.p.364)
           Watercolour on paper 25.1 x 53.5
           Signed
           Purchased 1968

P53.1973   River and Footbridge
           Watercolour on paper 15.4 x 31.6
           Signed
           Purchased 1968

CONOR, William 1881-1968 (Irish)

P234.1924 Lieutenant-General Rt. Hon. Sir
           James Craig, PC, DL, JP 1871-1940
           (later 1st Viscount Craigavon)(1916)
           Chalk on paper 70 x 44.4
           Signed, dated
           Donated by the artist, 1924

P235.1924 Major Robert E. McLean, MA (1916)
           Chalk on paper 55.6 x 34.5
           Signed, dated
           Donated by the artist, 1924

P236.1924 Major Peter Kerr Kerr-Smiley (1916)
           Chalk on paper 70 x 44.3
           Signed, dated
           Donated by the artist, 1924

P237.1924 Brigadier-General Sir George William
           Hacket Pain, KBE, CB 1855-1924
           (1916)
           Chalk on paper 69.8 x 44.3
           Signed, dated
           Donated by the artist, 1924

P238.1924 Colonel Rt. Hon. Robert Hugh
           Wallace, PC, CB, CBE (1916)
           Chalk on paper 69.8 x 44.3
           Signed, dated
           Donated by the artist, 1924

P239.1924 Sir Crawford McCullagh, MP, JP
           1868-1948 (1916)
           Chalk on paper 69.7 x 44.3
           Signed, dated
           Donated by the artist, 1924

P240.1924 Major William G. Forde, DL (1916)
           Chalk on paper 69.6 x 44.3
           Signed, dated
           Donated by the artist, 1924

P241.1924 Lieutenant-General Sir George
           Richardson, KCB (1916)
           Chalk on paper 69.8 x 44.3
           Signed, dated
           Donated by the artist, 1924

P242.1924 Lieutenant-Colonel T. V. P.
           McCammon (1916)
           Chalk on paper 69.8 x 44.3
           Signed, dated
           Donated by the artist, 1924

P328.1933 William Hunter Malcolm 1812-99
           Chalk on paper 54.2 x 44
           Signed
           Donated by Miss S. Malcolm, 1933

P4.1958   Barrack Street, Belfast (1914)
           Crayon on paper 34.7 x 48
           Signed, dated
           Donated by the artist, 1958

COTTAM, A. C. 20th century (Irish)

P56.1974   The Old Mill, Carr's Glen (1950)
           Pencil, watercolour on paper 13 x
           22.5
           Signed, dated
           Purchased 1974

P57.1974   The Cottages, Sunningdale (1950)
           Pencil, watercolour on paper 13.2 x
           20.6
           Signed, dated
           Purchased 1974

P58.1974   Kirkwood's Cottage, Ballysillen Road
           (1950) (Ballysillan)
           Pencil, watercolour on paper 94 x
           19.8
           Signed, dated
           Purchased 1974

CRAWFORD, M. 19th century (Irish?)

P113.1977 Antrim Round Tower (1885)
           (Illus.p.365)
           Oil on canvas 68.5 x 45.6
           Signed, dated
           Donated by Miss Bessie Maconachie,
           1977

CURZON, R. 19th century (Irish?)

P91.1984   Holywood Old Church and
           Graveyard (1885) (Illus.p.365)
           Watercolour on paper 22.6 x 35.1
           Signed, dated
           Purchased 1960

D

DAWSON, Robert 19th century (British)

P19.1976   Derry from the South (1833)
           Pencil on paper 18.6 x 23.9
           Dated
           Donated by Mrs. A. Whittaker, 1976

P20.1976   View on Walls of Derry (1833)
           Pencil on paper 19.9 x 24
           Dated
           Donated by Mrs. A. Whittaker, 1976

P21.1976   Walker's Testimonial (1833)
           Pencil on paper 17.5 x 34.1
           Dated
           Donated by Mrs. A. Whittaker, 1976

P22.1976   View down River Foyle from Walls of
           Derry (1833)
           Pencil on paper 17.5 x 25.2
           Dated
           Donated by Mrs. A. Whittaker, 1976

P23.1976   Birdstown, Donegal (1833)
           Pencil on paper 15.7 x 27.4
           Dated
           Donated by Mrs. A. Whittaker, 1976

P24.1976   Birdstown (1833)
           Pencil on paper 16.8 x 30.4
           Dated
           Donated by Mrs. A. Whittaker, 1976

P25.1976   View of Ballykelly from the North
           (1833)
           Pencil on paper 18.4 x 23.9
           Donated by Mrs. A. Whittaker, 1976

P26.1976   From Somerset, Coleraine (1833)
           Pencil on paper 14.9 x 22.1
           Dated
           Donated by Mrs. A. Whittaker, 1976

P27.1976   Somerset - from the Cuts (1833)
           Pencil on paper 14.2 x 21.8
           Dated
           Donated by Mrs. A. Whittaker, 1976

P28.1976   Kill-Owen, Coleraine, from Ship,
           Henry's Hotel (1833)
           Pencil on paper 14 x 21.9
           Dated
           Donated by Mrs. A. Whittaker, 1976

P29.1976   Cromore (1833)
           Pencil on paper 15.9 x 21
           Dated
           Donated by Mrs. A. Whittaker, 1976

P30.1976   Portstewart (1833)
           Pencil on paper 19 x 24
           Dated
           Donated by Mrs. A. Whittaker, 1976

P31.1976   Crescent, Portstewart (1833)
           Pencil on paper 13.6 x 21.8
           Dated
           Donated by Mrs. A. Whittaker, 1976

P32.1976   View of O'Hara Castle and North
           Derry Coast from Portstewart (1833)
           Pencil on paper 15.5 x 41.8
           Dated
           Donated by Mrs. A. Whittaker, 1976

**P33.1976 View of O'Hara Castle from South
West (1833)**
Pencil on paper 15.9 x 21
Dated
Donated by Mrs. A. Whittaker, 1976

P34.1976 View of Portrush from West (1833)
Pencil on paper 15.8 x 20.7
Dated
Donated by Mrs. A. Whittaker, 1976

P35.1976 White Rocks, Dunluce (1833)
Pencil on paper 18.2 x 23.6
Dated
Donated by Mrs. A. Whittaker, 1976

**P36.1976 Dunluce Castle, County Antrim
(1833)**
Pencil on paper 14 x 22
Dated
Donated by Mrs. A. Whittaker, 1976

P37.1976 Dunluce Castle (1833) (View from
West Side)
Pencil on paper 14.1 x 22
Dated
Donated by Mrs. A. Whittaker, 1976

P38.1976 Dunluce Castle (1833) (Interior
View)
Pencil on paper 14 x 22
Dated
Donated by Mrs. A. Whittaker, 1976

DE BURGH, Coralie b.1924 (Irish)

P144.1973 Glenariff
Oil on canvas 49.4 x 74.5
Signed
Purchased 1965

DOUGLAS, Harry R. 1862-1934 (Irish)

**P457.1925 Alderman George Augustus Doran,
JP d.1918 (1913)**
Charcoal on paper 69.4 x 56.4
Signed, dated
Donated by Miss Doran, 1925

**P352.1952 View of Molly Ward's Cottage, River
Lagan (1913)**
Oil on canvas 29.3 x 44.5
Signed, dated
Donated by Miss Ethne Maclaine,
1952

DRAKE, Cecil 20th century (English)

P14.1973 Sir James Martin
Oil on canvas 44.4 x 37.3
Signed
Purchased 1972

**DUFFERIN, Lord (later 1st Marquess of
Dufferin and Ava) 1826-1902** (Irish) (attributed
to)

**P26.1999 The Yacht 'Foam' at Stockholm in
1854**
Watercolour, gouache, gum on paper
22 x 35.5
Purchased 1994

E

ENTWISTLE, James 19th century (Irish?)

**P71.1973 Brandon Towers, Sydenham Park,
Belfast (1860)**
Ink, watercolour on paper 29.3 x 41.9
Dated
Purchased 1967

F

FIRTH, William A. fl.1893-1912 (Irish)

P186.1953 Carrickfergus Castle (1912)
Watercolour on paper 12.7 x 17.8
Signed, dated
Donated by J. A. S. Stendall, 1953

FOLEY, G. M. 19th century (?) (British)

P96.1984 Donaghadee
Watercolour on paper 23 x 36
Signed
Provenance unknown

FORD, B. 19th century (British)

P72.1973 Echlinville, Co. Down (1865)
Watercolour on paper 46.1 x 68.2
Signed, dated
Purchased 1967

FRAZER, Hugh fl.1813-61 (Irish)

P69.1922 View of Holywood
Oil on canvas 29.1 x 40
Bequeathed by H. Musgrave, 1922

P107.1947 Molly Ward's Cottage, River Lagan
Oil on canvas 44.7 x 59.5
Donated by J. St. Clair Boyd, 1946

P62.1973 Belvoir
Oil on canvas 44.9 x 60.1
Purchased 1968

P35.1980 View of Jennymount Mill, Belfast
(Illus.p.365)
Oil on canvas 47 x 58.8
Purchased 1980

P5.1981 Waringstown, Co. Down (1849)
(Illus.p.365)
Oil on canvas 63 x 76
Purchased 1981

P101.1984 Lilliput House, Belfast
Oil on panel 23.9 x 34.3
Purchased 1954

P5.1985 Scene on the River Lagan
Oil on canvas 48.9 x 65.1
Provenance unknown

**P8.1985 Joy's Paper Mill and River Blackstaff,
Belfast**
Oil on canvas 44.6 x 57.4
Provenance unknown

P13.1985 Scene on the River Lagan near Belfast
Oil on canvas 39.3 x 56.7
Purchased 1985

P1.1989 A Roadside Inn: View on the

Carrickfergus Road *(Illus.p.365)*
Oil on panel 29.5 x 45.9 (sight)
Purchased 1990

**P2.1990 View of Belvoir House from the
South, with the River Lagan in the
Foreground** *(Illus.p.365)*
Oil on panel 29.8 x 44.6
Donated by Dr. Terence Fulton, 1990

FRAZER, Hugh fl.1813-61 (Irish) (attributed to)

**P3.1983 View of River Lagan and Halfpenny
Bridge (c.1835-40)**
Oil on canvas 62.6 x 100.3
Purchased 1983

FRY, William Arthur 1865-1936 (English, worked
in Ireland)

P231.1910 'Macedon', Whitehouse, Co. Antrim
(Illus.p.365)
Sepia, pencil on paper 14.9 x 22.3
Donated by W. H. McLaughlin, 1910

P392.1914 'Parkmount', Shore Road (1914)
Sepia, pencil on paper 15.5 x 21.6
Signed, dated
Donated by Sir Robert Anderson, Bt.,
1914

**P242.1920 Side View of the Royal Hotel, Belfast
(1920)** *(Illus.p.365)*
Watercolour on paper 24.9 x 33.9
Signed, dated
Donated by Thomas McGowan, 1920

**P243.1920 Cranmore House, Malone, Belfast
(1920)**
Watercolour on paper 25 x 33.7
Signed, dated
Donated by Thomas McGowan, 1920

**P376.1926 William Hugh Patterson, MRIA 1835-
1918**
Watercolour on paper 34.4 x 27.8
Signed
Donated by the sitter's sons, 1926

**P556.1926 Alderman Sir James Henderson, DL,
MA 1848-1914**
Watercolour on paper 34.8 x 27.8
Signed
Donated by the Henderson family,
1926

P307.1927 Francis Joseph Bigger 1863-1926
(Illus.p.365)
Watercolour on paper 43.9 x 35.2
Signed
Donated by the sitter's executors,
1927

G

GIBSON, Colin b.1948 (Irish)

P35.1973 Belfast Rooftops (1969) *(Illus.p.366)*
Ink on paper 30.4 x 22.7
Signed, dated
Purchased 1970

**P8.1986 Maguire Castle and West End
Bridges, Enniskillen**
Pencil on paper 20 x 27.7

Signed
Donated by Fermanagh District
Council, 1986

GIBSON, H. 20th century (Irish)

P27.1973 **The Gate House of the Botanic
Gardens at University Road, Belfast
(1965)**
Oil on board 29.7 x 39.7
Signed, dated
Donated by the artist, 1971

P28.1973 **Great Northern Railway Terminus,
Belfast (1969)**
Oil on board 33.1 x 47.9
Signed, dated
Donated by the artist, 1971

P29.1973 **Public Baths, Peter's Hill, Belfast
(1970)**
Oil on board 33 x 44.1
Signed, dated
Donated by the artist, 1971

GORDON, W. R. 1872-1955 (Irish)

P230.1928 **David Manson 1726-92 (1928)**
Watercolour on paper 41.7 x 33.9
Signed, dated
Donated by Thomas McGowan, 1928

P244.1928 **James Sheridan Knowles 1784-1862
(1928)**
Watercolour on paper 41.6 x 34.2
Signed, dated
Donated by Thomas McGowan, 1928

P474.1929 **Fred W. Warden 1860-1929 (1928)**
Watercolour on paper 46 x 34.1
Signed, dated
Donated by Thomas McGowan, 1929

P125.1955 **Saul, Co. Down** *(Illus.p.366)*
Watercolour on paper 24 x 33.5
Signed
Purchased 1955

P126.1955 **Martin's Farmyard, Upper Malone**
(Illus.p.366)
Watercolour on paper 26.3 x 20.5
Signed
Purchased 1955

P128.1955 **St. Thomas's Church, Eglantine
Avenue, Belfast**
Watercolour on paper 20 x 26
Signed
Purchased 1955

GRACEY, Theo. J. 1895-1959 (Irish)

P576.1916 **Castle Market, Belfast (1916)**
(Illus.p.366)
Watercolour on paper 32 x 29.4
Dated
Donated by Thomas McGowan, 1916

P107.1917 **White Linen Hall, Belfast: View of
Front** *(Illus.p.366)*
Watercolour on paper 24.1 x 33
Signed
Donated by Thomas McGowan, 1917

P108.1917 **White Linen Hall, Belfast: View of
Quadrangle (1917)**
Watercolour on paper 23 x 32.7

Signed, dated
Donated by Thomas McGowan, 1917

P116.1917 **Ormeau** *(Illus.p.366)*
Watercolour on paper 20.9 x 42.9
Donated by Thomas McGowan, 1917

P164.1917 **Malone Toll House about 1820**
(Illus.p.366)
Watercolour on paper 25.9 x 38.4
Signed
Donated by Thomas McGowan, 1917

P38.1918 **Corner of Chichester Street and
Great Edward Street (1915)**
Watercolour on paper 24.7 x 33.6
Signed
Donated by Thomas McGowan, 1918

P39.1918 **Great Edward Street, Belfast**
Watercolour on paper 24.4 x 33.3
Signed
Donated by Thomas McGowan, 1918

P40.1918 **Old Morgue, Victoria Square, Belfast**
Watercolour on paper 24.5 x 33.7
Signed
Donated by Thomas McGowan, 1918

P68.1918 **The Pottinger Arms and Weighbridge**
Watercolour on paper 24.5 x 32.8
Signed
Donated by Thomas McGowan, 1918

P216.1918 **Donegall Street, Belfast, in the Early
19th Century**
Watercolour on paper 24.4 x 32.6
Donated by Thomas McGowan, 1918

P217.1918 **Brown Linen Hall, Donegall Street,
Belfast: Exterior View**
Watercolour on paper 24.5 x 33
Signed
Donated by Thomas McGowan, 1918

P218.1918 **Brown Linen Hall, Donegall Street,
Belfast: Interior View**
Watercolour on paper 24.4 x 32.7
Signed
Donated by Thomas McGowan, 1918

P937.1918 **A Bit of Old Ballymacarrett about
1900** *(Illus.p.366)*
Watercolour on paper 24.5 x 33.2
Signed
Donated by Thomas McGowan, 1918

P938.1918 **A Bit of Old Police Square in 1918**
Watercolour on paper 24.7 x 33.1
Signed
Donated by Thomas McGowan, 1918

P939.1918 **Hercules Place and Hercules Street**
(Illus.p.366)
Watercolour on paper 24.6 x 33
Signed
Donated by Thomas McGowan, 1918

P940.1918 **Old St. Anne's Church, Belfast**
Watercolour on paper 36.8 x 23.7
Signed
Donated by Thomas McGowan, 1918

P941.1918 **Old Fisherwick Place Presbyterian
Church**
Watercolour on paper 24.9 x 33.3
Signed

Donated by Thomas McGowan, 1918

P973.1918 **'Black Maria' Waiting for Prisoners in
Townhall Street, Belfast (1918)**
Watercolour on paper 23.9 x 23
Signed, dated
Donated by Thomas McGowan, 1918

P180.1919 **Last Houses in Mill Street, Belfast
(1919)**
Watercolour on paper 24.5 x 33
Signed, dated
Donated by Thomas McGowan, 1919

P211.1920 **Thatched Houses in Frederick Street,
Belfast (1919)**
Watercolour on paper 24.7 x 33.4
Signed, dated
Donated by Thomas McGowan, 1920

GREENLEES, William 19th century (British)

P7.1981 **Ballymoya Church near Portmorris,
County Armagh (1838)**
Watercolour on paper 9.6 x 17.2
Signed, dated
Purchased 1981

P8.1981 **View in the Domain, Mourne Park,
County Down (1838)**
Watercolour on paper 10.1 x 17.5
Signed, dated
Purchased 1981

P9.1981 **At Carlingford, County Louth (1838)**
Watercolour on paper 9.9 x 17.2
Signed, dated
Purchased 1981

P10.1981 **Mellefont Abbey, near Drogheda
(1838)**
Watercolour on paper 10 x 17.3
Signed, dated
Purchased 1981

GREER, A. 19th-20th century (Irish)

P6.1974 **Cartoon Portrait (probably of R. M.
Young 1851-1925) (c.1912)**
Ink, wash on paper 30.6 x 22.8
Signed
Purchased 1974

GREY, Charles 1808-92 (Scottish, worked in
Ireland)

P102.1953 **Andrew Nicholl 1804-86 (1840)**
Charcoal, white on paper 44.7 x 33.6
(oval)
Signed, dated
Donated by Miss Nicholl, 1953

GRIMSHAW, S. M. 19th century (Irish)
(attributed to)

P4.1974 **View of Cavehill (c.1822-24).
'Longwood', Robert Grimshaw's
House, in Foreground**
Pencil on paper 23 x 29
Signed, dated
Purchased 1974

H

HANFORD, Ernest fl.1886-99 (Irish)

P915.1896 **Old Bangor (1890)** *(Illus.p.367)*
Watercolour on paper 33.6 x 26.9
Signed, dated
Donated by James F. Johnson, 1896

P169.1906 **Pottinger's Entry: View towards Ann
(a) Street (1892)**
Watercolour on paper 31.3 x 20.3
Signed, dated
Donated by W. T. Braithwaite, 1906

P169.1906 **Pottinger's Entry: View towards High
(b) Street (1892)**
Watercolour on paper 31 x 20.4
Signed, dated
Donated by W. T. Braithwaite, 1906

P195.1906 **Old Paper Mill on Blackstaff River,
Belfast, before 1882**
Watercolour on paper 48.1 x 36.1
Signed, dated
Donated by W. T. Braithwaite, 1906

P82.1928 **Chapel Lane, Belfast (1894)**
Watercolour on paper 33.9 x 25.2
Signed, dated
Donated by Thomas McGowan, 1928

P136.1951 **Pottinger's Entry: View towards High
Street (1892)** *(Illus.p.367)*
Watercolour on paper 31.2 x 20.3
Signed
Donated by James R. Young, 1951

P137.1951 **Cul-de-sac off Pottinger's Entry
(1892)**
Watercolour on paper 31.2 x 20.2
Signed
Donated by James R. Young, 1951

P138.1951 **Pottinger's Entry: View towards Ann
Street (1892)**
Watercolour on paper 31.2 x 20.2
Signed
Donated by James R. Young, 1951

P139.1951 **Sugarhouse Entry: View towards
High Street, Showing Arch at
Bambridge Hotel (1892)**
Watercolour on paper 31.2 x 20.2
Signed
Donated by James R. Young, 1951

P140.1951 **Winecellar Entry: View towards
Rosemary Street, Showing Arch at
Duffy's Public House (1892)**
(Illus.p.367)
Watercolour on paper 31.2 x 20.2
Signed, dated
Donated by James R. Young, 1951

P141.1951 **Winecellar Entry: View towards
Waring Street (1892)**
Watercolour on paper 31.2 x 20.2
Signed
Donated by James R. Young, 1951

P142.1951 **Crown Entry: View towards High
Street (1892)**
Watercolour on paper 31.2 x 20.2
Signed, dated
Donated by James R. Young, 1951

P143.1951 **Crown Entry: View towards Ann
Street (1892)**
Watercolour on paper 31.1 x 20.3
Signed, dated
Donated by James R. Young, 1951

P144.1951 **Joy's Entry: View towards High Street
(1892)**
Watercolour on paper 31.1 x 20.3
Signed, dated
Donated by James R. Young, 1951

P145.1951 **In Crown Entry (1892)**
Watercolour on paper 30.4 x 20.3
Signed
Donated by James R. Young, 1951

P146.1951 **Wilson's Court: View towards Ann
Street (1892)**
Watercolour on paper 31.1 x 20.3
Donated by James R. Young, 1951

P147.1951 **Bigger's Entry: View Northwards
(1892)**
Watercolour on paper 31 x 20.3
Signed, dated
Donated by James R. Young, 1951

P148.1951 **Belfast Entry (1892)**
Watercolour on paper 31 x 20.3
Signed, dated
Donated by James R. Young, 1951

P149.1951 **Belfast Entry (1892)**
Watercolour on paper 31.2 x 20.3
Signed
Donated by James R. Young, 1951

P36.1973 **In Ormeau Park**
Watercolour on paper 21.9 x 33.3
Signed
Purchased 1969

P9.1979 **Misty Morning, First Lock, Lagan**
Watercolour on paper 17.4 x 37
Signed
Purchased 1979

HARLAND, Mary 19th century (English)

P21.1985 **A Part of Belfast Lough (c.1878-86)**
Watercolour on paper 12.7 x 17.5
Donated by Neville Harland, 1954

P22.1985 **Belfast Ship Yard from a Distance
(c.1878-86)**
Watercolour on paper 12.7 x 17.6
Donated by Neville Harland, 1954

HOBDAY, E. 19th–20th century (British)

P144.1944 **Royal Irish Constabulary Dress
Uniforms of Deputy Inspector-
General, Private Secretary and
Assistant Inspector-General (1904)**
Watercolour on paper 23.5 x 29.6
Signed, dated
Donated by Lady Ingram, 1944

HOOKE, Richard 1820-1908 (Irish)

P6.1985 **William Darragh (1869)**
Oil on panel 38 x 29.9
Signed, dated
Provenance unknown

HOME, Robert 1752-1834 (English, worked in
Ireland) (attributed to)

P3.1986 **William Drennan, MD 1754-1820**
Oil on canvas 75.2 x 62.5 (sight)
Donated by Miss S.M. Duffin,
1986

HOWARD, Ken b.1932 (English)

P47.1978 **Checking the Wheelbarrow - Army
Technical Officer, Belfast City Centre
(1978)** *(Illus.p.367)*
Watercolour on paper 37.5 x 54.5
Signed, dated
Purchased 1978

HUNTER, R. 19th century (Irish?)(attributed to)

P696.1927 **Rev. Samuel McComb 1836-91**
Charcoal on paper 51.7 x 40.1
Signed
Donated by Miss McComb, 1927

K

KERR, S. S. or **L. L.** 19th century (Irish?)

P102.1984 **Elizabeth Batt (1850)**
Silhouette, wash on paper 31.4 x 21.7
Signed, dated
Provenance unknown

KINNAIRD, Elizabeth Holmes fl.1920-38 (Irish)

P41.1976 **The Old Brickworks, Annadale**
Oil on canvas 49.2 x 59.3
Signed
Purchased 1975

L

LAWSON, Miss 19th century (Irish?)

P12.1980 **View of Bangor Bay from the
Harbour Beach** *(Illus.p.367)*
Watercolour on paper 17.2 x 24.6
Bequeathed by the estate of Miss
Margaret Mitchell, 1980

LOCKWOOD, F. W. fl.1886-96 (Irish)

P358.1914 **Cave Hill from above Newtownbreda
(1887)**
Watercolour on paper 11.1 x 17
Signed, dated
Donated by R. Welch, 1914

LODGE, F. G. 20th century (Irish?)

P376.1935 **Ulster Club, Castle Place, Belfast
(1933)** *(Illus.p.367)*
Ink, wash, white on paper 28.6 x 21.8
Signed, dated
Purchased 1935

LYNAS, John Langtry 1879-1956 (Irish)

P114.1977 **Nathaniel Carrothers 1853-1932
(1925)**
Oil on canvas 44.3 x 33.3
Dated
Donated by E. Norman Carrothers,
1973

LYNCH, William fl.1888-91 (Irish)

P40.1983 **Pottinger's Entry, Belfast (1891)**
(a) Pencil on paper 17.1 x 9.1
Signed, dated
Provenance unknown

P40.1983 **Wilson's Court, High Street (1891)**
(b) Pencil on paper 17.1 x 9.1
Signed, dated
Provenance unknown

P40.1983 **Crown Entry, Belfast (1891)**
(c) Pencil on paper 17.1 x 9.1
Signed, dated
Provenance unknown

P40.1983 **Orr's Entry, High Street (1891)**
(d) Pencil on paper 17.1 x 9.1
Signed, dated
Provenance unknown

P40.1983 **Sugar House Entry, High Street**
(e) **(1891)**
Pencil on paper 17.1 x 9.1
Signed, dated
Provenance unknown

P40.1983 **Commercial Court, Donegall Street**
(f) **(1891)**
Pencil on paper 17.1 x 9.1
Signed, dated
Provenance unknown

LYNN, William Henry 1829-1915 (Irish)

P216.1916 **Proposed Albert Memorial Clock
Tower, Belfast (c.1869)** *(Illus.p.367)*
Watercolour on paper 50.3 x 42.8
Donated by Miss E. M. Cooper, 1916

P224.1916 **Lurigedan, Cushendall** (Lurigethan)
Watercolour on paper; measurements
unknown
Donated by Miss E. M. Cooper, 1916

P39.1976 **Old Glass House, Ballycastle**
(Illus.p.367)
Watercolour on paper 24.6 x 35
Purchased 1976

LYNN, William Henry 1829-1915 (Irish)
(attributed to)

P6.1956 **County Antrim Courthouse, Crumlin
Road, Belfast** *(Illus.p.367)*
Watercolour on paper; measurements
unknown
Purchased 1956

LYTLE, Andrew fl.1886-1911 (Irish)

P386.1921 **Albert Bridge, Belfast (1886)**
(Illus.p.368)
Watercolour on paper 20 x 30.8
Signed
Provenance unknown

M

McBLAIN, Margaret fl.1892-1909, d.c.1910
(Irish)

P114.1910 **St. James's Church, Belfast (c.1900)**
Watercolour on paper 44.6 x 33.4

Signed
Bequeathed by the artist, 1910

McBURNEY, John 1877-1917 (Irish)

P106.1984 **On the Antrim Road**
Oil on board 24.4 x 18.1
Signed
Donated by F. W. Hull, 1950

McCLUGHIN, W. J. 1900-71 (Irish)

P633.1954 **Wooden Footbridge over Connswater**
(a) **(1930)**
Pencil on paper 21.3 x 31.5
Signed, dated
Donated by John Hewitt, 1954

P633.1954 **Wooden Footbridge over Connswater**
(b) **(1930)**
Pencil on paper 21.5 x 31.6
Signed, dated
Donated by John Hewitt, 1954

McCOY, Bernard J. fl.1886-1905 (Irish)

P695.1935 **St. Malachy's RC Church, Belfast
(c.1882)**
Watercolour on paper 16.5 x 24
Signed
Donated by the artist's family, 1935

McDADE, William fl.1891-1921, d.1946 (Irish)

P167.1921 **Old Belfast Water Cart (1921)**
(Illus.p.368)
Watercolour on paper 24.4 x 31.6
Signed, dated
Donated by Thomas McGowan, 1921

P168.1921 **Old Manual Fire Engine Passing the
House of Correction, Belfast (1921)**
(Illus.p.368)
Watercolour on paper 24.9 x 32.8
Signed, dated
Donated by Thomas McGowan, 1921

P475.1923 **Jaunting Car on Car Stand, St.
George's Church, Belfast (1923)**
Watercolour on paper 25.1 x 33.7
Signed, dated
Donated by Thomas McGowan, 1923

P162.1931 **Corner of North Queen Street and
Lancaster Street about 1856 (1930)**
Watercolour on paper 25.1 x 35.4
Signed, dated
Donated by Thomas McGowan, 1931

P93.1946 **The Penny Tram, York Street (The
Changes)**
Watercolour on paper 24.8 x 34
Signed
Purchased 1946

P129.1958 **The Penny Tram - Queen's Hotel
and Northern Counties Railway
(c.1890)**
Watercolour on paper 24 x 33.3
Signed
Purchased 1958

MacINTYRE, James b.1926 (Irish)

P469.1954 **Belfast Tramcar (1954?)** *(Illus.p.368)*
Watercolour on paper 32.2 x 46

Purchased 1954

McKELVEY, Frank 1895-1974 (Irish)

P108.1920 **Interior of Old St. Anne's Church,
Belfast (1920)**
Watercolour on paper 25.1 x 34
Signed, dated
Donated by Thomas McGowan, 1920

P116.1920 **Old St. Patrick's RC Church, Belfast
(1920)**
Watercolour on paper 24.8 x 33.8
Signed, dated
Donated by Thomas McGowan, 1920

P124.1920 **Annadale Hall (1920)**
Sepia on paper 16 x 20.9
Signed, dated
Donated by Thomas McGowan, 1920

P132.1920 **Temporary Building Erected for
Ulster Unionist Convention, 1892
(1920)**
Watercolour on paper 24.7 x 33.6
Signed, dated
Donated by Thomas McGowan, 1920

P133.1920 **Barrack Street, Belfast in 1920**
Watercolour on paper 25.2 x 34.1
Signed, dated
Donated by Thomas McGowan, 1920

P134.1920 **Castle Place, Belfast, in the 17th
Century (1920)**
Watercolour on paper 24.8 x 33.8
Signed, dated
Donated by Thomas McGowan, 1920

P135.1920 **Victoria Square, Belfast, c.1900
(1920)**
Watercolour on paper 25.1 x 33.7
Signed, dated
Donated by Thomas McGowan, 1920

P136.1920 **College Square East, Belfast (1920)**
Watercolour on paper 24.7 x 33.5
Signed, dated
Donated by Thomas McGowan, 1920

P152.1920 **Royal Visit to Belfast, 11 August
1849: Procession Entering White
Linen Hall (1920)**
Watercolour on paper 24.7 x 33.4
Signed, dated
Donated by Thomas McGowan, 1920

P153.1920 **Police Square (later Victoria Square)
at Church Lane c.1878 (1920)**
Watercolour on paper 24.5 x 33.6
Signed, dated
Donated by Thomas McGowan, 1920

P154.1920 **Street Scene with Children, Belfast
(1920)**
Watercolour on board 26.6 x 36.4
Signed, dated
Donated by Thomas McGowan, 1920

P155.1920 **Forster Green and Co. Ltd: 'The
Golden Canister' in 1920 (1920)**
Watercolour on paper 24.7 x 33.6
Signed, dated
Donated by Thomas McGowan, 1920

P187.1920 **Old Ballynafeigh Inn, 1920 (1920)**
Watercolour on paper 24.7 x 33.4

Signed, dated
Donated by Thomas McGowan, 1920

P207.1920 Corn Market, Belfast in 1910 (1920)
Watercolour on paper 24.9 x 33.4
Signed, dated
Donated by Thomas McGowan, 1920

**P208.1920 Grain and Meal Market, Belfast
(1920)**
Watercolour on paper 24.8 x 34
Signed, dated
Donated by Thomas McGowan, 1920

P209.1920 Bank Street, Belfast (1920)
Watercolour on paper 25.1 x 34.2
Signed, dated
Donated by Thomas McGowan, 1920

**P210.1920 Old Coal Offices, Queen's Quay,
Belfast, 1920**
Watercolour on paper 25 x 34.1
Signed
Donated by Thomas McGowan, 1920

**P216.1920 Linen Arch, Donegall Place, Belfast.
Erected for Royal Visit of 1885
(1920)**
Watercolour on paper 24.8 x 33.7
Signed
Donated by Thomas McGowan, 1920

**P244.1920 The Old Stag's Head, Corner of
North Street and Rosemary Street
(1920)**
Watercolour on paper 25.3 x 34
Signed
Donated by Thomas McGowan, 1920

**P245.1920 Buildings at Corner of May Street
and Cromac Street, Removed c.1918
(1920)**
Watercolour on paper 25.4 x 34.1
Signed, dated
Donated by Thomas McGowan, 1920

**P246.1920 Buildings in May Street between
Verner Street and Cromac Street,
Removed c.1918 (1920)**
Watercolour on paper 25.3 x 34.1
Signed, dated
Donated by Thomas McGowan, 1920

**P327.1920 Pepper Hill Steps, formerly
Connecting Carrick Hill and Stephen
Street (1920)**
Watercolour on paper 25.2 x 33.3
Signed, dated
Donated by Thomas McGowan, 1920

**P328.1920 Arthur Street, Showing Birthplace of
Belfast Evening Telegraph (1920)**
Watercolour on paper 25 x 33.2
Signed, dated
Donated by Thomas McGowan, 1920

**P329.1920 Lower Peter's Hill, Looking towards
North Street, c.1895 (1920)**
(Illus.p.368)
Watercolour on paper 25.1 x 33.3
Signed, dated
Donated by Thomas McGowan, 1920

**P330.1920 Corner of Donegall Place and Castle
Street, c.1890 (1920)**
Watercolour on paper 25.3 x 33.4
Signed, dated

Donated by Thomas McGowan, 1920

**P331.1920 Corner of Newtownards Road and
Old Scotch Row, c.1895**
Watercolour on paper 25.1 x 33.3
Donated by Thomas McGowan, 1920

**P332.1920 Old Ballymacarrett Parish Church,
Removed 1893 (1920)**
Watercolour on paper 33.3 x 24.9
Signed, dated
Donated by Thomas McGowan, 1920

P333.1920 Old Theatre Royal, Belfast (1920)
Watercolour on paper 25.2 x 33.2
Signed
Donated by Thomas McGowan, 1920

P346.1920 Berry Street, Belfast, c.1900 (1920)
Watercolour on paper 24.7 x 33.5
Donated by Thomas McGowan, 1920

P347.1920 Millfield, Belfast, c.1895 (1920)
(Illus.p.368)
Watercolour on paper 25.1 x 33.8
Signed, dated
Donated by Thomas McGowan, 1920

P348.1920 Carrick Hill, Belfast, c.1895 (1920)
Watercolour on paper 24.9 x 33.7
Signed, dated
Donated by Thomas McGowan, 1920

**P349.1920 Corner of Donegall Square West and
Wellington Place before 1897 (1920)**
Watercolour on paper 29.3 x 36.9
Signed
Donated by Thomas McGowan, 1920

**P416.1920 Old House, Corner of Ann Street and
Arthur Square, before 1868 (1920)**
Watercolour on paper 24.9 x 33.9
Signed, dated
Donated by Thomas McGowan, 1920

**P417.1920 Residential House formerly Situated
at Corner of Chichester Steet and
Callender Street (1920)**
Watercolour on paper 24.9 x 33.8
Signed, dated
Donated by Thomas McGowan, 1920

**P418.1920 Castle Street between Chapel Lane
and King Street (1920)**
Watercolour on paper 25 x 33.8
Signed, dated
Donated by Thomas McGowan, 1920

**P419.1920 The Lisburn Carriers Passing
Magdalene School House, Dublin
Road (1920)**
Watercolour on paper 25.2 x 33.9
Signed, dated
Donated by Thomas McGowan, 1920

**P437.1920 Bedeque House, Crumlin Road,
Belfast (1920)** *(Illus.p.368)*
Watercolour on paper 25 x 33.4
Signed, dated
Donated by Thomas McGowan, 1920

**P438.1920 College Square North, Belfast in
1920**
Watercolour on paper 25 x 34.5
Signed, dated
Donated by Thomas McGowan, 1920

P2.1921 Arthur Square, Belfast, c.1900 (1920)
Watercolour on paper 25 x 33.8
Signed, dated
Donated by Thomas McGowan, 1921

**P7.1921 The Royal Belfast Academical
Institution (1920)**
Watercolour on paper 24 x 33.2
Signed, dated
Donated by Thomas McGowan, 1921

**P8.1921 Old Shops in High Steet, Belfast,
c.1880 (1920)**
Watercolour on paper 24.6 x 33.4
Signed, dated
Donated by Thomas McGowan, 1921

**P19.1921 The Old Bank Buildings, Belfast in
1853 (1920)**
Watercolour on paper 24.9 x 33
Signed, dated
Donated by Thomas McGowan, 1921

P20.1921 Theatre Tavern (1920)
Watercolour on paper 24.9 x 32.5
Signed
Donated by Thomas McGowan, 1920

**P27.1921 Property Adjoining Site of Northern
Bank, Victoria Street, Belfast (1921?)**
Watercolour on paper 26.3 x 44.7
Donated by Thomas McGowan, 1920

**P30.1921 Laying the First Stone of St. Anne's
Cathedral, Belfast, 6 September 1899
(1921)**
Watercolour on paper 27.7 x 35.2
Signed, dated
Donated by Thomas McGowan, 1921

P153.1921 Lagan Village, c.1885 (1920)
Watercolour on paper 25.2 x 41
Signed, dated
Donated by Thomas McGowan, 1920

**P166.1921 Royal Visit to Belfast, 22 June 1921:
Their Majesties Approaching the City
Hall to Open the First Parliament of
Northern Ireland (1921)**
Watercolour on paper 35.1 x 26.3
Signed, dated
Donated by Thomas McGowan, 1920

**P289.1922 Donegall Square East, Belfast in 1922
(1922)**
Watercolour on paper 25 x 33.9
Signed
Donated by Thomas McGowan, 1922

P290.1922 Ann Street, Belfast in 1904 (1922)
Watercolour on paper 25 x 33.9
Signed
Donated by Thomas McGowan, 1922

**P503.1922 Ulster Special Constabulary Outpost
at Rosetta, Belfast, Spring 1922
(1922)**
Watercolour on paper 25.2 x 34.9
Signed, dated
Donated by Thomas McGowan, 1922

**P85.1923 Thatched Shops in Waring Street,
Demolished for the Erection of the
Commercial Buildings in 1820**
Watercolour on paper 25.1 x 34.1
Signed
Donated by Thomas McGowan, 1923

P86.1923 **Belfast Model School, Divis Street (1921)**
Watercolour on paper 25.2 x 34.1
Signed, dated
Donated by Thomas McGowan, 1923

P157.1923 **House and Garden of John F. Ferguson, Donegall Place, Belfast**
Watercolour on paper 25.2 x 33.9
Signed
Donated by Thomas McGowan, 1923

P158.1923 **Castle Market, Belfast (1922)**
Watercolour on paper 22.3 x 30.7
Signed, dated
Donated by Thomas McGowan, 1923

P168.1923 **First State Entrance into Belfast of the First Governor of Northern Ireland, His Grace the Duke of Abercorn, KP, 26 February 1923 (1923)**
Watercolour on paper 25.4 x 34.1
Signed, dated
Donated by Thomas McGowan, 1923

P240.1923 **Smithfield Square, 1923: South and West Views (1923)**
Watercolour on paper 25.2 x 34
Signed, dated
Donated by Thomas McGowan, 1923

P241.1923 **Smithfield Square, 1923: South and East Views (1923)**
Watercolour on paper 24.6 x 32
Signed, dated
Donated by Thomas McGowan, 1923

P242.1923 **Smithfield Square, 1923: East and North Views (1923)**
Watercolour on paper 25 x 33.8
Signed, dated
Donated by Thomas McGowan, 1923

P243.1923 **Smithfield Square, 1923: North and West Views (1923)**
Watercolour on paper 25 x 33.9
Signed, dated
Donated by Thomas McGowan, 1923

P244.1923 **Smithfield Market, 1923: Extended View towards One of the Winetavern Street Entrances (1923)**
Watercolour on paper 25.2 x 33.8
Donated by Thomas McGowan, 1923

P245.1923 **Smithfield Market, 1923: View from the Centre towards One of the Winetavern Street Entrances (1923)** *(Illus.p.368)*
Watercolour on paper 25.3 x 34.1
Signed, dated
Donated by Thomas McGowan, 1923

P246.1923 **Smithfield Market, 1923: One of the Winetavern Street Entrances (1923)**
Watercolour on paper 25.9 x 34.7
Signed, dated
Donated by Thomas McGowan, 1923

P247.1923 **Smithfield, at the Corner of Berry Street, c.1909 (1923)**
Watercolour on paper 25.8 x 34.7
Signed, dated
Donated by Thomas McGowan, 1923

P255.1923 **Smithfield Market: View towards**

Marquis Street, Showing the Sale of Old Clothes that formerly Took Place beside the Gateway (1923)
Watercolour on paper 33.7 x 25
Signed, dated
Donated by Thomas McGowan, 1923

P354.1923 **Temporary Cenotaph Unveiled on Peace Day, 9 August 1919, at the Corner of Chichester Street and Donegall Square East (1922)**
Watercolour on paper 35.8 x 26.4
Signed, dated
Donated by Thomas McGowan, 1923

P374.1923 **Balloon Ascent at the Easter Monday Sports, Royal Botanic Gardens, Belfast, 1893**
Watercolour on paper 25.1 x 33.9
Signed
Donated by Thomas McGowan, 1923

P472.1923 **Butter Market, Great Patrick Steet: Exterior and Interior (1923)**
Two watercolours on paper 11.2 x 17.1; 11.9 x 17.1
Signed, dated
Donated by Thomas McGowan, 1923

P6.1924 **Cottages at the Junction of Ormeau Road and Ravenhill Road, Belfast (1924)**
Watercolour on paper 25.1 x 33.9
Signed, dated
Donated by Thomas McGowan, 1924

P144.1924 **A Bit of King Street, Belfast (1924)**
Watercolour on paper 25.1 x 33.3
Signed, dated
Donated by Thomas McGowan, 1924

P167.1924 **The Swan Inn, Wheeler's Place, Newtownards Road, Belfast, c.1877**
Watercolour on paper 25.2 x 33.9
Signed
Donated by Thomas McGowan, 1924

P322.1924 **Ulster Unionist Convention, Belfast, 17 June 1892 (1924)**
Watercolour on paper 15.2 x 38.5
Signed, dated
Donated by Thomas McGowan, 1924

P370.1924 **The Old Asylum, Grosvenor Road, Belfast (1924)**
Watercolour on paper 24.9 x 33.4
Signed, dated
Donated by Thomas McGowan, 1924

P529.1924 **Queen's Quay, Belfast, c.1880** *(Illus.p.368)*
Watercolour on paper 25.5 x 34.7
Signed
Donated by Thomas McGowan, 1924

P655.1924 **The Artillery Barracks, North Queen Street, Belfast**
Watercolour on paper 25.2 x 33.3
Signed
Donated by Thomas McGowan, 1924

P695.1924 **James McQuitty (1922)**
Oil on canvas 70.7 x 63.2
Signed, dated
Donated by the Belfast Printing Trades Employers' Association, 1924

Formerly Art dept. U1979

P57.1925 **The Old Belfast Ballast Office**
Watercolour on paper 25.3 x 34.1
Signed
Donated by Thomas McGowan, 1924

P58.1925 **High Street, Belfast, c.1830**
Watercolour on paper 25.3 x 34.1
Signed
Donated by Thomas McGowan, 1925

P214.1925 **Entrance to the Old Artillery Barracks, Barrack Street, Belfast, 1925 (1925)**
Watercolour on paper 25.1 x 34.3
Signed
Donated by Thomas McGowan, 1925

P244.1925 **The 'Gin Palace', Belfast, 1914 (1924)** *(Illus.p.369)*
Watercolour on paper 25.2 x 33.9
Signed, dated
Donated by Thomas McGowan, 1925

P377.1925 **Block of Houses in Chichester Street, Belfast, between Arthur Street and Donegall Square East (1925)**
Watercolour on paper 24.9 x 33.3
Signed
Donated by Thomas McGowan, 1925

P378.1925 **Sinclair's Shops in Royal Avenue, Belfast (1925)**
Watercolour on paper 25.1 x 34
Signed, dated
Donated by Thomas McGowan, 1925

P379.1925 **Belfast at the End of the 18th Century (1925)**
Watercolour on paper 25.2 x 34.4
Signed, dated
Donated by Thomas McGowan, 1925

P380.1925 **High Street, Belfast, between Lombard Street and Bridge Street, c.1860**
Watercolour on paper 25.3 x 33.2
Signed
Donated by Thomas McGowan, 1925

P395.1925 **Chichester Memorial, St. Nicholas' Church, Carrickfergus**
Watercolour on paper 52.8 x 37.5
Signed
Donated by Thomas McGowan, 1925

P83.1926 **Four-Wheelers or 'Growlers', Great Northern Railway Station, Belfast, 1926 (1926)**
Watercolour on paper 25.1 x 33.9
Signed, dated
Donated by Thomas McGowan, 1926

P377.1926 **Valentine Jones the First 1711-1805**
Watercolour on paper 34.9 x 26.6
Signed
Purchased 1926

P533.1926 **George Hall Elliott 1856-1917**
Watercolour on paper 35.6 x 26.6
Signed, dated
Donated by F. Adens Heron, 1926

P534.1926 **Corner of Rosemary Street and Hercules Street, c.1865 (1926)**
Watercolour on paper 25.3 x 33.7

Signed, dated
Donated by Thomas McGowan, 1926

P549.1926 **The Rt. Hon. H. M. Pollock, DL, MP (1925)**
Watercolour on paper 33.3 x 26.2
Signed, dated
Donated by Rt. Hon. S. Cunningham, 1926

P578.1926 **Robert Magill Young, JP, MA, MRIA, FRIBA 1851-1925 (1926)**
Watercolour on paper 32.1 x 25.1
Signed, dated
Donated by subscribers, 1926

P591.1926 **Andrew William Stewart, FJI 1862-1924 (1926)**
Watercolour on paper 35 x 25.5
Signed, dated
Donated by Sir Robert Baird, 1926

P598.1926 **Sir Robert Baird, KBE, DL 1855-1934**
Watercolour on paper 33.4 x 25.8
Signed
Donated by Thomas McGowan, 1926

P599.1926 **Sir Robert Lynn, MP**
Watercolour on paper 33 x 25.4
Signed
Donated by Thomas McGowan, 1926

P601.1926 **James Cunningham 1857-1924, of Glencairn, Belfast (1925)**
Watercolour on paper 33.6 x 26.6
Signed, dated
Donated by Thomas McGowan, 1926

P603.1926 **Alexander Finlay 1827-1918**
Watercolour on paper 34.4 x 26.9
Signed
Donated by the sitter's sons,1926

P619.1926 **William S. Baird, JP 1824-86**
Watercolour on paper 35.4 x 26.8
Signed
Donated by Sir Robert Baird and Major William Baird, 1926

P620.1926 **George Baird 1833-75**
Watercolour on paper 35.2 x 26.8
Signed
Donated by Sir Robert Baird and Major William Baird, 1926

P664.1926 **Sir Robert Hart, Bt., GCMG, MA, LLD 1835-1911**
Watercolour on paper 34 x 26
Signed
Donated by Thomas McGowan, 1926

P788.1926 **James McConnell, JP 1840-1926 (1926)**
Watercolour on paper 34 x 26.1
Signed, dated
Donated by Thomas McGowan, 1926

P863.1926 **Louis Crommelin 1652-1727**
Watercolour on paper 33.3 x 25.7
Signed
Donated by Thomas McGowan, 1926

P864.1926 **Old Houses, Clarendon Place, May Street, Belfast**
Watercolour on paper 25.7 x 34.5
Signed

Donated by Thomas McGowan, 1926

P865.1926 **Crystal Palace, Queen's Island, Belfast**
Watercolour on paper 31.4 x 25.1
Signed
Donated by Thomas McGowan, 1926

P979.1926 **The Rt. Hon. Thomas Sinclair, DL, JP, MA, DLitt 1838-1914 (1926)**
Watercolour on paper 37.9 x 26.8
Signed, dated
Donated by Kenneth D. Sinclair, 1926

P980.1926 **General Hospital, Frederick Street, Belfast (1926)**
Watercolour on paper 25.4 x 33.3
Signed, dated
Donated by Thomas McGowan, 1926

P981.1926 **Baron Kelvin of Largs, OM, GCVO 1824-1907**
Watercolour on paper 35.8 x 26.2
Signed
Donated by Thomas McGowan, 1926

P983.1926 **Vere Foster 1819-1900**
Watercolour on paper 34.9 x 26.7
Signed
Donated by subscribers, 1926

P66.1927 **Old Ballymacarrett Methodist Church, Newtownards Road**
Watercolour on paper 25.3 x 33.9
Signed
Donated by Thomas McGowan, 1926

P67.1927 **Beaver Hall, Ballymacarrett**
Watercolour on paper 25.2 x 33.5
Signed
Donated by Thomas McGowan, 1926

P190.1927 **Sir Thomas Johnstone Lipton, Bt., KCVO 1850-1931**
Watercolour on paper 36.4 x 26.1
Signed, dated
Donated by Thomas McGowan, 1926

P242.1927 **Buildings in Cromac Street between Little May Street and May Street (1927)**
Watercolour on paper 25.3 x 34
Signed, dated
Donated by Thomas McGowan, 1927

P308.1927 **Sir John Newell Jordan, KCB, KCMG 1852-1925**
Watercolour on paper 36.3 x 26.3
Signed
Donated by Thomas McGowan, 1927

P309.1927 **Field-Marshal Sir Henry Wilson, Bt., GCB, DSO 1864-1922 (1927)**
Watercolour on paper 34.4 x 26.2
Signed, dated
Donated by Thomas McGowan, 1927

P354.1927 **Sir Samuel Ferguson 1810-86**
Pencil on paper 35.3 x 27.2
Signed
Donated by Thomas McGowan, 1927

P688.1927 **Sedan Chairs and Bearers, Belfast**
Sepia on paper 26 x 35.5
Signed
Donated by Thomas McGowan, 1927

P769.1927 **The Rt. Hon. Robert Graham Glendinning, DL 1844-1928**
Watercolour on paper 35.5 x 26.6
Signed
Donated by the sitter's family, 1927

P770.1927 **Robert J. Welch, MSc, MRIA 1859-1936**
Watercolour on paper 35 x 25.8
Signed, dated
Donated by Thomas McGowan, 1927

P11.1928 **Sir Hans Sloane, MD, FRS 1660-1753**
Sepia on paper 32.5 x 26
Signed
Donated by Thomas McGowan, 1928

P12.1928 **Sir Almroth Edward Wright, KBE, CB, MD, FRS (b.1861)**
Watercolour on paper 35.3 x 26.3
Signed
Donated by Thomas McGowan, 1928

P83.1928 **Shops and Offices in Chichester Street on Site of Law Courts (1928)**
Watercolour on paper 25.8 x 34.3
Signed, dated
Donated by Thomas McGowan, 1928

P85.1928 **Major-General Rollo Gillespie, KCB 1766-1814**
Watercolour on paper 34.7 x 27.2
Signed
Donated by Thomas McGowan, 1928

P89.1928 **The Rt. Hon. Lord O'Hagan 1812-85, Lord Chancellor of Ireland**
Watercolour on paper 36.1 x 26.2
Signed
Donated by Thomas McGowan, 1928

P90.1928 **Josias Cunningham 1819-95**
Watercolour on paper 32.6 x 26.2
Signed
Donated by Thomas McGowan, 1928

P91.1928 **Lord Lawrence 1811-79 (1927)**
Watercolour on paper 35.5 x 27.9
Signed, dated
Donated by Thomas McGowan, 1928

P92.1928 **Charles Wilson 1817-96 (1928)**
Watercolour on paper 33.8 x 25.6
Signed, dated
Donated by John C. Craig, 1928

P93.1928 **Sir Samuel Wilson 1832-95**
Watercolour on paper 36.2 x 27.2
Donated by John C. Craig, 1928

P94.1928 **John Cleaver 1841-1926 (1926)**
Watercolour on paper 37.8 x 26.7
Signed, dated
Donated by Sir Frederick Cleaver, 1928

P108.1928 **Sir Samuel McCaughey 1835-1919 (1928)**
Watercolour on paper 36.5 x 25.6
Signed, dated
Donated by John C. Craig, 1928

P119.1928 **Henry Shaw Ferguson, MD, FRCSE 1815-90** *(Illus.p.369)*
Watercolour on paper 32.1 x 25.3
Signed
Donated by the sitter's family, 1928

P177.1928 **Sir Henry Montgomery Lawrence, KCB 1806-57**
Watercolour on paper 35.6 x 26.6
Signed
Donated by Thomas McGowan, 1928

P178.1928 **Frederick Lane, Belfast (1928)**
Watercolour on paper 25.2 x 33.9
Signed, dated
Donated by Thomas McGowan, 1928

P179.1928 **Sir John de Courcy, Earl of Ulster d.c.1219 (1927)**
Watercolour on paper 32.7 x 25
Signed, dated
Donated by Thomas McGowan, 1928

P199.1928 **Shops between Junction of Albertbridge Road and Madrid Street (1928)**
Watercolour on paper 25.2 x 33.9
Signed, dated
Donated by Thomas McGowan, 1928

P200.1928 **Part of Victoria Street between Gloucester Street and Chichester Street (1928)**
Watercolour on paper 25.3 x 34
Signed, dated
Donated by Thomas McGowan, 1928

P201.1928 **Robert Bruce Mantell 1854-1928 (1928)**
Watercolour on paper 31.5 x 25.1
Signed, dated
Donated by Thomas McGowan, 1928

P223.1928 **Part of North Queen Street between Lancaster Street and Great George's Street (1928)**
Watercolour on paper 25.2 x 34
Signed, dated
Donated by Thomas McGowan, 1928

P231.1928 **Lord Carson of Duncairn 1854-1935**
Watercolour on paper 51.2 x 37.9
Signed
Donated by Thomas McGowan, 1928

P247.1928 **General Francis Rawdon Chesney 1789-1872**
Watercolour on paper 32.1 x 25.1
Signed
Donated by John J. C. Craig, 1928

P315.1928 **Sir Denis Stanislaus Henry, PC, DL 1864-1925**
Watercolour on paper 48 x 37.1
Signed
Donated by Thomas McGowan, 1928
Formerly Art dept. U1980

P318.1928 **Sir Richard Whieldon Barnett, MA, MP 1863-1930**
Watercolour on paper 33.5 x 26
Signed
Donated by the Rt. Hon. S. Cunningham, 1928

P319.1928 **James, Viscount Bryce 1838-1922 (1927)**
Sepia on paper 35.8 x 27.3
Signed, dated
Donated by Thomas McGowan, 1928

P320.1928 **The Rt. Hon. William Moore 1864-1944 (1928)**

Watercolour on paper 43.3 x 35
Signed, dated
Donated by Thomas McGowan, 1928

P321.1928 **Judge Henry Hanna (b.1872)**
Watercolour on paper 34.1 x 26.9
Signed
Donated by the sitter, 1928

P323.1928 **F. Adens Heron, DL, JP 1848-1939 (1926)**
Watercolour on paper 34.9 x 26.8
Signed, dated
Donated by the Heron family, 1928

P325.1928 **George Canning 1770-1827**
Watercolour on paper 35.7 x 26.8
Signed
Donated by the Rt. Hon. S. Cunningham, 1928

P326.1928 **Major Eldred Pottinger 1811-43 (1927)**
Watercolour on paper 32.8 x 25.8
Signed, dated
Donated by Thomas McGowan, 1928

P332.1928 **Old Town Hall, Victoria Square, Belfast (1923)**
Watercolour on paper 25.8 x 36.3
Signed, dated
Donated by Thomas McGowan, 1928

P79.1929 **Dr. John Smyth Crone, JP, MRIA 1858-1945**
Watercolour on paper 37.3 x 27
Signed
Donated by Thomas McGowan, 1929

P80.1929 **Lord Russell of Killowen 1832-1900**
Watercolour on paper 44.5 x 34
Signed
Donated by Thomas McGowan, 1929

P137.1929 **The Rt. Hon. Samuel Cunningham 1862-1946**
Watercolour on paper 50.6 x 36.6
Signed
Donated by Thomas McGowan, 1929

P157.1929 **Ulster Volunteer Force Hospital, Queen's University, Belfast**
Watercolour on paper 29.1 x 48.2
Signed
Donated by Thomas McGowan, 1929

P159.1929 **Metropole Hotel, York Street, Belfast (1929)**
Watercolour on paper 25.7 x 34.7
Signed
Donated by Thomas McGowan, 1929

P161.1929 **Donegall Street Presbyterian Church, Belfast**
Watercolour on paper 24.8 x 33.9
Signed
Donated by Thomas McGowan, 1929

P163.1929 **William Ferguson Massey 1856-1925**
Pencil, watercolour on paper 33.3 x 24.5
Signed
Donated by Thomas McGowan, 1929

P356.1929 **Thomas McMullan 1835-1905**
Watercolour on paper 37.5 x 28.5
Signed

Donated by Sir Thomas McMullan, 1929

P444.1929 **The Rt. Rev. George Walker, Bishop of Derry 1618-90**
Sepia on paper 37.5 x 26.7
Signed
Donated by Thomas McGowan, 1929

P467.1929 **Colonel Alexander Lawrence 1764-1835 (1927)**
Pencil on paper 35.5 x 27
Signed, dated
Donated by Thomas McGowan, 1929

P468.1929 **Miss A. Marjorie Robinson, ARMS 1858-1924 (1927)**
Pencil on paper 31.2 x 24.1
Signed, dated
Donated by Thomas McGowan, 1929

P475.1929 **Field-Marshal Sir George Stuart White, VC, OM 1835-1912**
Watercolour on paper 43.5 x 31.7
Signed
Donated by Thomas McGowan, 1929

P476.1929 **The Rt. Hon. Andrew Bonar Law 1858-1923**
Watercolour on paper 46 x 37
Signed
Donated by the Rt. Hon. S. Cunningham, 1929
Formerly Art dept. U1488

P477.1929 **The Venerable Robert Henry Charles, MA, DD, LLD 1855-1931, Archdeacon of Westminster (1919)**
Watercolour on paper 37.3 x 30.3
Signed
Donated by John J. C. Craig, 1929

P484.1929 **The Rt. Hon. Arthur Chichester, 1st Earl of Donegall 1606-75**
Ink on paper 32.1 x 25.2
Donated by Thomas McGowan, 1929

P153.1930 **John Boyd Dunlop, MRCVS 1839-1921 (1929)**
Pencil on paper 39.8 x 32.1
Signed, dated
Donated by Thomas McGowan, 1929

P442.1930 **House in Gloucester Street where John Boyd Dunlop Invented the Pneumatic Tyre, 1888**
Watercolour on paper 26.5 x 32
Signed
Donated by Thomas McGowan, 1930

P443.1930 **Cole's Alley, Belfast (Church Lane to Ann Street) (1929)**
Watercolour on paper 33.8 x 25.2
Signed, dated
Donated by Thomas McGowan, 1930

P159.1931 **Castle Place, Belfast, 1843**
Watercolour on paper 25 x 34.5
Signed
Donated by Thomas McGowan, 1931

P160.1931 **Corner of Donegall Place and Castle Place, Belfast, 1880**
Watercolour on paper 26.2 x 36.8
Signed
Donated by Thomas McGowan, 1931

P161.1931 **Corner of Ann Street and Church Lane, Belfast (1930)**
Watercolour on paper 25.2 x 32.3
Signed, dated
Donated by Thomas McGowan, 1931

P232.1931 **Barrack Street, Belfast, Showing Horses from Artillery Barracks Entering Stables in Kennedy's Court**
Watercolour on paper 26.1 x 36.5
Signed
Donated by Thomas McGowan, 1931

P358.1931 **John Adams 1735-1826, Second President of the USA**
Pencil on paper 32.8 x 25.2
Signed
Donated by Thomas McGowan, 1931

P359.1931 **Andrew Jackson 1767-1845, Seventh President of the USA (1930)**
Pencil, watercolour on paper 32.2 x 25.2
Signed, dated
Donated by Thomas McGowan, 1931

P360.1931 **James Knox Polk 1795-1849, Eleventh President of the USA**
Pencil on paper 32.2 x 25.2
Signed
Donated by Thomas McGowan, 1931

P361.1931 **James Buchanan 1791-1868, Fifteenth President of the USA (1930)**
Pencil, watercolour on paper 32.2 x 25.3
Signed, dated
Donated by Thomas McGowan, 1931

P362.1931 **Andrew Johnson 1808-75, Seventeenth President of the USA**
Pencil, ink, watercolour on paper 32.3 x 25.2
Signed
Donated by Thomas McGowan, 1931

P363.1931 **Ulysses S. Grant 1822-85, Eighteenth President of the USA**
Pencil on paper 32.2 x 25.2
Signed
Donated by Thomas McGowan, 1931

P364.1931 **Chester A. Arthur 1830-86, Twenty-first President of the USA**
Pencil on paper 32.3 x 25.2
Signed
Donated by Thomas McGowan, 1931

P365.1931 **Grover Cleveland 1837-1908, Twenty-second President of the USA**
Pencil on paper 32.2 x 25.2
Signed
Donated by Thomas McGowan, 1931

P366.1931 **Benjamin Harrison 1833-1901, Twenty-third President of the USA**
Pencil on paper 32.2 x 25.2
Signed
Donated by Thomas McGowan, 1931

P367.1931 **William McKinley 1843-1901, Twenty-fifth President of the USA**
Pencil on paper 32.2 x 25.2
Signed

Donated by Thomas McGowan, 1931

P368.1931 **Theodore Roosevelt 1858-1919, Twenty-sixth President of the USA**
Pencil on paper 32.2 x 25.2
Signed
Donated by Thomas McGowan, 1931

P369.1931 **Woodrow Wilson 1856-1924, Twenty-eighth President of the USA**
Charcoal, white, chalk, wash on paper 32.1 x 25.2
Signed
Donated by Thomas McGowan, 1931

P370.1931 **Alexander Hamilton 1757-1804, American Statesman and Soldier**
Pencil, watercolour, white on paper 34 x 25.8
Signed
Donated by Thomas McGowan, 1931

P1.1932 **James Monroe 1758-1831, Fifth President of the USA**
Pencil, watercolour on paper 34.6 x 26.3
Signed
Donated by Thomas McGowan, 1931

P76.1932 **Connswater Bridge, 1603**
Watercolour on paper 25.1 x 33.9
Signed
Donated by Thomas McGowan, 1932

P77.1932 **Gihon's Shop Front, Castle Street, Belfast, 1790**
Watercolour on paper 25.2 x 33.9
Donated by Thomas McGowan, 1932

P78.1932 **Glass House of Benjamin Edwards, Jnr., Ballymacarrett**
Watercolour on paper 25.2 x 34
Signed
Donated by Thomas McGowan, 1932

P157.1932 **Donegall Street Congregational Church, Belfast**
Watercolour on paper 25.4 x 34
Signed
Donated by Thomas McGowan, 1932

P471.1932 **Ann Street, Belfast, between Victoria Street and Queen's Bridge (1932)**
Watercolour on paper 25.3 x 34
Signed
Donated by Thomas McGowan, 1932

P412.1933 **Opening of the Royal Courts of Justice, Belfast, 31 May 1933 (1933)**
Watercolour on paper 53.4 x 75.7
Signed
Donated by Thomas McGowan, 1933

P582.1934 **Old Cottages in Dundonald Village (1934)**
Watercolour on paper 25.9 x 37.1
Signed, dated
Donated by Thomas McGowan, 1934

P628.1934 **Robert Bell 1864-1934 (1934)**
Charcoal on paper 53.2 x 42.8
Signed, dated
Donated by Belfast Naturalists' Field Club subscribers, 1924

P259.1935 **Murray's Terrace, Belfast** *(Illus.p.369)*
Watercolour on paper 25.8 x 37.2

Signed
Donated by Thomas McGowan, 1935

P260.1935 **Fisherwick Place, Belfast**
Watercolour on paper 26.5 x 37.7
Signed
Donated by Thomas McGowan, 1931

P696.1935 **Half-way House**
Watercolour on paper 26 x 35.3
Signed
Donated by Thomas McGowan, 1935

P52.1937 **St. John's Church, Laganbank Road, Belfast (1936)**
Watercolour on paper 26.3 x 35.7
Signed, dated
Donated by Thomas McGowan, 1937

P31.1938 **Corner of Linenhall Street West and Ormeau Avenue, Belfast (1938)**
Watercolour on paper 26.5 x 37.6
Signed, dated
Donated by Thomas McGowan, 1938

P32.1938 **The 'Rose and Crown' and 'Shakespeare Bar', William Street South, Belfast (1938)**
Watercolour on paper 26.5 x 37.6
Signed, dated
Donated by Thomas McGowan, 1938

P149.1938 **Newtownbreda Village (1921)** *(Illus.p.369)*
Watercolour on paper 27.2 x 40.3
Signed, dated
Bequeathed by Thomas McGowan, 1938

P150.1938 **Knockbreda Parish Church (1921)**
Watercolour on paper 27.3 x 40.2
Signed, dated
Bequeathed by Thomas McGowan, 1938

P116.1944 **The Rt. Hon. Robert Young 1822-1917 (1920)** *(Illus.p.369)*
Watercolour on paper 27.3 x 16.7
Signed, dated
Donated by Miss Minnie G. Graham, 1944

P9.1985 **Henry Riddell, ME, MIMechE 1851-1923 (1923)**
Watercolour on paper 32.7 x 26
Signed, dated
Donated by members of the Belfast Natural History and Philosophical Society, 1923

P18.1999 **Thomas Lorimer Corbett 1854-1910, MP for North Down 1900-10**
Watercolour on paper 15 x 10.5 (sight)
Signed
Provenance unrecorded

P19.1999 **Portrait of a Man**
Watercolour on paper 15 x 10.5 (sight)
Signed
Provenance unrecorded

P29.1999 **The *Belfast Telegraph* Boy**
Pencil on paper 26.5 x 20
Signed
Donated by Mervyn Solomon, 1993

McKINSTRY, Robert b.1925 (Irish)

P5.1988   Suggested Coronation Decorations
           for the City Hall, Belfast (1953)
           Watercolour on paper 30.4 x 48.5
           Signed, dated
           Donated by the artist, 1988

McLAUGHLIN, C. 19th-20th century (Irish?)

P18.1948   Glass Island, Ballycastle
           MDCCCLXX (1910)
           Pencil on paper 54 x 73
           Signed, dated
           Donated by Hugh Alexander Boyd,
           1948

McMILLEN 19th century (Irish)

P90.1984   The Sailing Ship 'Queen's Island'
           (1891)
           Watercolour on paper 27.8 x 49.4
           Signed, dated
           Donated by C. H. Matthews, 1957

MAGENIS, H. 19th century (Irish)

P446.1954 Owen O'Cork Flax Spinning Mill
           (James Steen and Co.)(1864)
           Pencil on paper 17.1 x 27.9
           Signed, dated
           Purchased 1954

MAGUIRE, William Henry fl.c.1820-40 (Irish)

P359.1927 Academical Institution, Belfast
           (1820-30)
           Oil on metal 19.2 x 29.8
           Purchased 1927

P360.1927 Commercial Buildings and
           Exchange, Belfast (1820-30)
           Oil on metal 19.3 x 29.7
           Purchased 1927

P807.1931 Bridges on the River Lagan (1835)
           Oil on canvas 21 x 32.7
           Purchased 1931

MOFFAT, G. 19th-20th century (Irish)

P85.1984   White Star Liner 'Titanic' (1913)
           Oil on panel 33.3 x 48.2
           Signed, dated
           Donated by Miss Ethel Bartlett, 1984

MOLLOY, Joseph 1798-1877 (Irish)

P821a.1893 Ballyleidy - Seat of Right Hon.
           Lord Dufferin (1830)
           Pencil, wash on paper 14.8 x 21.3
           Signed, dated
           Provenance unknown

P821b.1893 Belvoir - Seat of Sir Robert
           Bateson, Bt., MP (1830)
           Pencil, wash on paper 14.8 x 21.3
           Signed, dated
           Provenance unknown

P821c.1893 Bangor Castle - Seat of Edward
           Southwell Ward, Esq. (1830)
           Pencil, wash on paper 14.8 x 21.3
           Signed, dated
           Provenance unknown

P821d.1893 Crawford's Burn - Seat of Sharman
           Crawford, Esq. (1830)
           Pencil, wash on paper 14.8 x 21.3
           Signed, dated
           Provenance unknown

P821e.1893 Purdy's Burn - Seat of Narcissus
           Batt, Esq. (1830)
           Pencil, wash, white on paper 14.8 x
           21.3
           Signed, dated
           Provenance unknown

P821f.1893 Suffolk - Seat of John McCance,
           Esq. (1830)
           Ink, wash on paper 14.8 x 21.3
           Signed, dated
           Provenance unknown

P821g.1893 Derramore - Seat of Lawson
           Annesley, Esq. (1830)
           Ink, wash on paper 14.8 x 21.3
           Signed, dated
           Provenance unknown

P821h.1893 Old Park - Seat of Henry Lyons,
           Esq. (1830)
           Pencil, wash on paper 14.8 x 21.3
           Signed, dated
           Provenance unknown

P821i.1893 Wheatfield - Seat of James Blair
           Esq. (1830)
           Pencil, wash, white on paper 14.8 x
           21.3
           Signed, dated
           Provenance unknown

P821j.1893 Cultra - Seat of Hugh Kennedy,
           Esq. (1830)
           Pencil, wash on paper 14.8 x 19.8
           Signed, dated
           Provenance unknown

P821k.1893 Lismoyne - Seat of Robert Callwell,
           Esq. (1830) (Illus.p.369)
           Pencil, wash on paper 14.8 x 21.3
           Signed, dated
           Provenance unknown

P821l.1893 Jennymount - Seat of Robert
           Thompson, Esq. (1830)
           (Illus.p.369)
           Pencil, wash on paper 14.8 x 21.3
           Signed, dated
           Provenance unknown

P821m.1893 Lakefield - Seat of Miss Richison
           (1830)
           Pencil, wash on paper 14.8 x 21.3
           Signed, dated
           Provenance unknown

P821n.1893 Lambeg House - Seat of Robert
           Williamson, Esq. (1830)
           Pencil, wash on paper 14.8 x 21.3
           Signed, dated
           Provenance unknown

P821o.1893 Seymour Hill - Seat of William
           Charley, Esq. (1830)
           Pencil, wash on paper 14.8 x 21.3
           Signed, dated
           Provenance unknown

P821p.1893 Richmond - Seat of Francis
           Turnley, Esq. (1830)
           Pencil, wash on paper 14.8 x 21.3
           Signed, dated
           Provenance unknown

P821q.1893 Glenburne - Seat of Edward
           Curtiss, Esq. (1830)
           Pencil, wash on paper 14.8 x 21.3
           Signed, dated
           Provenance unknown

P821r.1893 Drum House - Seat of William
           Hunter, Esq. (1830)
           Pencil, wash on paper 14.8 x 21.3
           Signed, dated
           Provenance unknown

P821s.1893 Rathgael House - Seat of James R.
           Clealand, Esq. (1830)
           Pencil, wash on paper 14.8 x 20.9
           Signed, dated
           Provenance unknown

P821t.1893 Ligoniel - Seat of Alexander
           Stewart, Esq. (1831) (Illus.p.369)
           Pencil, wash on paper 14.8 x 21.3
           Signed, dated
           Provenance unknown

P821u.1893 Sea View - Seat of James Boomer,
           Esq. (1831)
           Pencil, wash on paper 14.8 x 21.3
           Signed, dated
           Provenance unknown

P821v.1893 White House - Seat of Edmund
           Grimshaw, Esq. (1831)
           Pencil, wash on paper 14.8 x 21.3
           Signed, dated
           Provenance unknown

P821w.1893 Orangefield House (1831)(Seat of
           John H. Houston, Esq.)
           Pencil, wash on paper 14.8 x 21.3
           Provenance unknown

MORRISON, Robert Boyd 1896-1969 (Irish)

P23.1957   R. V. Williams ('Richard Rowley')
           1877-1947 (1929)
           Chalk on paper 44.2 x 33.5
           Signed, dated
           Purchased 1956

N

NICHOLL, Andrew 1804-86 (Irish)

P129.1960 Waterloo Bridge, Clifden,
           Connemara (1836) (Illus.p.369)
           Pencil, wash, white on paper 21 x
           42.3
           Dated
           Donated by J. E. Robson, 1960

P130.1960 Pontoon Bridge, Lough Conn
           Pencil, wash, white on paper 16.8 x
           25.1
           Donated by J. E. Robson, 1960

P131.1960 Steaming Cauldron with Kegs and
           Tubs (1835)
           Pencil, wash, white on paper 12.3

x 17.7
Dated
Donated by J. E. Robson, 1960

P132.1960 Coast Scene (1835)
Pencil, wash, white on paper 16.3 x
23.9
Dated
Donated by J. E. Robson, 1960

P1.1973 Shore Road, Belfast
Oil on canvas 24.4 x 34.9
Donated by H. B. McCance, 1962

P3.1973 Bay with Pier
Watercolour on paper 23.3 x 33.5
Signed
Purchased 1963

P6.1973 Upper Lake, Killarney (formerly
'Lower Lake, Killarney')
Pencil, watercolour, white on paper
16.7 x 24.8
Signed
Purchased 1965

P10.1973 Red Bay, Co. Antrim *(Illus.p.370)*
Oil on canvas 45 x 66.3
Purchased 1966

P5.1983 View of Holywood, Co. Down
Watercolour on board 26.9 x 51.5
Signed
Purchased 1983

P37.1983 Lord Dufferin's Ho. [use]
Pencil, wash, white on paper 15.6 x
23.8
Purchased 1983

P5.1999 Salmon Leap (1835)
Pencil, white on paper 17 x 25.5
Signed, dated
Provenance unknown

NICHOLL, William 1794-1840 (Irish)

P23.1982 The Hermitage, Tollymore Park
Watercolour on paper 24.9 x 35.4
Signed
Purchased 1982

NIXON, John c.1750-1818 (English)
The following works are as titled by the artist

P396.1925 Belfast (c.1790)
Watercolour on paper 10.8 x 16.4
Purchased 1925

**P59.1974 The White House near the Cave
Hills, Belfast**
Watercolour on paper 11.5 x 17.7
Purchased 1974

P1.1980 Hillsborough Church and Castle
Ink, watercolour on paper 15.2 x 22.7
Purchased 1980

**P2.1980 Mr. Stewart's Ballroom near Lisburn
(1785)** *(Illus.p.370)*
Ink, watercolour on paper 11.5 x 18
Signed, dated
Purchased 1980

**P3.1980 Down Hill, the Seat of the Earl of
Bristol** *(Illus.p.370)*
Watercolour on paper 14.5 x 22

Purchased 1980

P4.1980 Londonderry
Watercolour on paper 14.4 x 21.9
Purchased 1980

P13.1980 Colrain (1785) (Coleraine)
(Illus.p.370)
Watercolour on paper 11.5 x 17.7
Signed, dated
Purchased 1980

**P14.1980 View of the White Rocks near
Portrush**
Watercolour on paper 13.9 x 22.2
Purchased 1980

P15.1980 Rocks near Portrush (1782)
Watercolour on paper 14.3 x 22.1
Signed, dated
Purchased 1980

P36.1980 Glenarm, Co. Antrim (c.1780-1800)
Ink, wash, on paper 10.8 x 18.4
Purchased 1980

**P24.1982 Carrickfergus Taken from the Larne
Road to Belfast (1783)**
Watercolour on paper 15.6 x 22.4
Signed, dated
Purchased 1982

P25.1982 Larne Harbour, Co. Antrim (1785)
Watercolour on paper 17.7 x 27.3
Signed, dated
Purchased 1982

P1.1983 Belfast Poor House (c.1785-90)
(Illus.p.370)
Watercolour on paper 10.9 x 17.4
Signed
Purchased 1983

P38.1983 View of Ballycastle from Bon-a-Margy
(Bonamargy)
Watercolour on paper 10.1 x 17.4
Purchased 1983

**P17.1985 A Cabin in Rt. Stewart's Boat, Belfast
(1785)** (Robert)
Watercolour on paper 11.3 x 18.1
Dated
Purchased 1985

O

O'RAMSEY, J. J. 19th-20th century (Irish?)

**P73.1973 Greencastle, Co. Donegal:
Northburgh (1909)**
Ink on paper 18 x 29.5
Signed, dated
Donated by W. S. Ferguson, 1967

P

P., J. or T. [J. P. or T. P.] 19th century (Irish?)

P4.1983 Newry, Ireland (1812) *(Illus.p.370)*
Ink, wash on paper 18 x 22.9
Signed (monogram), dated
Purchased 1983
Formerly by Unknown

PATON, W. M. 19th-20th century (Irish?)

**P331.1928 Old Houses, Prince's Street, Belfast
(1913)**
Ink on paper 26.5 x 22.4
Signed, dated
Donated by Adam Millin, 1928

PATTERSON, William Hugh 1835-1918 (Irish)

**P95.1984 Cross at Mevagh, Co. Donegal
(1893)**
Watercolour on paper 17.5 x 25
Signed, dated
Provenance unknown

PENDER, D. Eugene 19th century (?) (Irish?)

P86.1984 St. Mary's Chapel, Belfast, Built 1783
Ink, wash on paper 16.6 x 20
Provenance unknown

PETRIE, George 1790-1866 (Irish)

P1.1974 The Long Bridge, Belfast (1829)
Watercolour on paper 14.4 x 26.9
Dated
Purchased 1984

PHILLIPS, J. J. d.c.1936 (Irish)

**P983.1937 Belfast Castle Looking towards Cave
Hill (1874)**
Watercolour on paper 37.3 x 64.6
Signed, dated
Bequeathed by the artist, 1936

**P984.1937 Belfast Castle Looking towards the
City**
Watercolour on paper 32.1 x 57.3
Signed
Bequeathed by the artist, 1936

P145.1973 Entrance Gate and Lodge, Belfast
(a) Castle (c.1870)
Ink, sepia wash, white on paper 25.6
x 51.2
Signed
Donated by Michael and Robert
Hogg, 1965

P145.1973 Entrance Lodge, Methodist College,
(b) Belfast (c.1870)
Ink, sepia wash, white on paper 21.6
x 26.2
Signed
Donated by Michael and Robert
Hogg, 1965

P145.1973 Entrance Lodge, Glenavna,
(c) Whiteabbey
Ink, sepia wash, white on paper 21.6
x 25.7
Donated by Michael and Robert
Hogg, 1965

**P87.1984 Grey Abbey - Co. Down - Ireland
(1874)**
Ink, charcoal, white on paper 25 x
41.1
Signed, dated
Bequeathed by the artist, 1936

P107.1984 Olderfleet Castle, Larne (1897)
Watercolour on paper 24.5 x 34.9
Signed, dated

Provenance unknown

PICCIONI, Felice M. fl.1830-42 (Italian)

P550.1926 **John Galt Smith III**
Charcoal on paper 33 x 24.8
Donated by Miss Frances McTear,
1926

P551.1926 **Frank Smith**
Charcoal on paper 43.5 x 35.5
Donated by Miss Frances McTear,
1926

P552.1926 **George K. Smith and his Nephew,
John Smith McTear (1847)**
Charcoal on paper 53.3 x 41
Donated by Miss Frances McTear,
1926

P554.1926 **Mrs. Samuel B. Smith, née Mary
Bryan 1820-78**
Charcoal on paper 42 x 35.3
Donated by Miss Frances McTear,
1926

P555.1926 **Charlotte Smith 1816-76 and Mrs.
George McTear 1808-61**
Charcoal on paper 55.2 x 43.2
Donated by Miss Frances McTear,
1926

P382.1939 **Henry Nicholl (1839)**
Charcoal on paper 25.3 x 20.3
Purchased 1939

P383.1939 **Mrs. Henry Nicholl**
Charcoal on paper 25.3 x 20.3
Purchased 1939

P384.1939 **William Nicholl 1794-1840 (1839)**
Charcoal on paper 25.3 x 20.3
Signed, dated
Purchased 1939

P385.1939 **James Nicholl (1839)**
Charcoal on paper 25.3 x 20.2
Signed
Purchased 1939

P386.1939 **Mrs. James Nicholl and Daughter
(1839)**
Charcoal on paper 25.4 x 20.3
Signed
Purchased 1939

P103.1953 **Andrew Nicholl 1804-86**
Charcoal on paper 38.3 x 25.7
Donated by Miss Nicholl, 1953

PINKERTON, Thomas G. fl.1894-1927 (Irish)

P188.1928 **Cavehill Bridge, Belfast (1927)**
(Illus.p.370)
Watercolour on paper 25.8 x 35.9
Signed, dated
Purchased 1928

PIPER, Raymond b.1923 (English, works in
Ireland)

P90.1951 **Theatre Royal, Belfast (1951)**
Pencil on paper 35.5 x 26.2
Signed, dated
Purchased 1951

P555.1951 **Castle Arcade, Belfast (1951)**

Pencil on paper 36 x 25.7
Signed, dated
Purchased 1951

P246.1953 **Nos. 168 and 170 York Street, Belfast
(1952)**
Pencil on paper 36 x 26.6
Signed, dated
Purchased 1953

P247.1953 **College Place North, Belfast (1951)**
(Illus.p.370)
Pencil on paper 37 x 27.4
Signed, dated
Purchased 1953

P248.1953 **Hercules Place, Belfast (1952)**
(Torrens Market)
Pencil on paper 27.4 x 37.4
Signed, dated
Purchased 1953

P19.1980 **View of Victoria Square, Belfast**
Pencil on paper 37.1 x 26.8
Signed
Purchased 1966

P20.1980 **Orangemen Returning from the
Field, Nearing the Old Toll House at
Bradbury Place, Belfast, 12 July 1957
(1957)**
Pencil on paper 25.9 x 36.3
Signed, dated
Purchased 1966

P21.1980 **Old Rosemary Street Church, Belfast
- the 2nd Presbyterian Church,
Rosemary Street (1954)**
Pencil on paper 36.4 x 28.1
Signed, dated
Purchased 1966

P22.1980 **Elmwood Presbyterian Church,
Belfast (1966)**
Pencil on paper 51.9 x 31.7
Signed, dated
Purchased 1966

P23.1980 **C. A. Arthur House, Cullybackey
(1965)**
Pencil on paper 28.2 x 38.1
Signed, dated
Purchased 1966

P24.1980 **McKinley's Cottage, Dervock (1965)**
Pencil on paper 28.1 x 38.1
Signed, dated
Purchased 1966

P25.1980 **The Wilson House, Dergalt, Strabane
(1965)** *(Illus.p.370)*
Pencil on paper 28.1 x 38.3
Signed, dated
Purchased 1966

P26.1980 **Gray's Printing Shop, Strabane; Kevin
the 'Buroo-man' (1965)** *(Illus.p.371)*
Pencil on paper 28 x 38.2
Signed, dated
Purchased 1966

P10.1985 **McMahon's Spade-making Factory,
(a)   Lacky Bridge, near Rosslea,
Co.Fermanagh: The Bellows with
Extended Nozzle to Forge (1955)**
Pencil on paper 37.2 x 26.3
Signed, dated

Purchased 1955

P10.1985 **McMahon's Spade-making Factory,
(b)   Lacky Bridge, near Rosslea, Co.
Fermanagh: The Drop Hammer and
Main Shaft to Water-wheel (1955)**
Pencil on paper 37.2 x 26.5
Signed, dated
Purchased 1955

P19.1985 **View of Barbour's Mill, Whitehouse
(1955)**
Pencil on paper 24.7 x 37.5
Signed, dated
Purchased 1985

P20.1985 **The Old National School,
Carnmoney: Glebe Road**
Pencil on paper 23.9 x 32.9
Purchased 1985

R

R., M. [M. R.] 19th century (Irish?)

P147.1973 **View of Elmwood Presbyterian
Church and Queen's Elms**
Watercolour on paper 32.7 x 26
Signed (monogram)
Purchased 1964

RAMSAY, Sinclair 19th century (Irish?)

P79.1917 **Old Houses in High Street, Belfast
(1888)**
Oil on canvas 29.1 x 39.3
Dated
Purchased 1917

P80.1917 **Cooney's Court, Ann Street, Belfast
(1893)**
Oil on canvas 24.4 x 34.5
Signed, dated
Purchased 1917

P81.1917 **Building Known as 'The Castle' in a
Court off Castle Place (1893)**
Oil on canvas 24.4 x 34.5
Signed, dated
Purchased 1917

P82.1917 **Artillery Barracks, Belfast, on Old
Dublin Road**
Oil on canvas 28.1 x 44.3
Purchased 1917

REED, Edward Tennyson fl.1885-92 (British)

P8.1989 **'Wrop in Myst'ry' (c.1908)**
(Caricature of Lord Arthur Hill 1846-
1931)
Pencil on paper 19.5 x 10.3
Purchased 1989

RICH, Alfred William 1856-1921 (English)

P497.1954 **Lisburn**
Watercolour on paper 14.9 x 38
Signed
Purchased 1954

ROBINSON, Thomas d.1810 (English, worked in
Ireland)

P2.1983 **View in Dr. Thomas Percy's Demesne**

(a)   at Dromore, Co. Down:
Upper Cascade in the Glen with the
Lower Waterfall Adjoining (1803)
Ink, wash on paper 10.9 x 15.8
Purchased 1983

P2.1983   View in Dr. Thomas Percy's Demesne
(b)   at Dromore, Co. Down: The
Painted Wooden Obelisk (1803)
Ink, wash on paper 13.8 x 10.9
Purchased 1983

P2.1983   View in Dr. Thomas Percy's Demesne
(c)   at Dromore, Co. Down: The Glen
(1803)
Ink, wash on paper 12.8 x 16.1
Signed, dated
Purchased 1983

S

SANDFORD, Matt 20th century (Irish?)
(attributed to)

P28.1999   William Conor and Fellow
Apprentices at D. Allen's (David
Allen's Printing and Publishing Firm)
Pencil, charcoal on paper;
measurements unknown
Purchased 1992

SCOTT-SMITH, Jessie fl.1883-1903 (English)

P485.1929   Mrs. King-Kerr
Pastel on paper 64.6 x 49.4
Donated by Miss Frances McTear,
1929

SEMPLE, Thomas 19th century (Irish)

P3.1985   The Late William Dougherty's Fowl
Stores (1869) (Illus.p.371)
Oil on canvas 59.3 x 89
Signed, dated
Donated by Miss M. A. Magowan,
1959

SLOAN, Garnet 20th century (Irish?)

P579.1926   Buttermilk Loaney, Shore Road
Oil on canvas 16 x 23.4
Donated by Miss Frances McTear,
1926

SMITH, Sidney 1912-82 (Irish)

P24.1950   Sir Orme Rowan-Hamilton 1877-
1949 (1943)
Chalk on paper 35.3 x 33.2
Signed, dated
Donated by H. Rowan Hamilton,
1950

SMYTH, J. B. 19th century (Irish?)

P273.1913   View of the Giant's Causeway from
the East (1874)
Watercolour on paper 15.5 x 24.5
Signed, dated
Purchased 1913

P274.1913   Dunluce Castle (1876)
Watercolour on paper 24.5 x 34.8
Signed, dated

Purchased 1913

SPEED, Harold 1872-1957 (English)

P33.1999   Sir Frederick Moneypenny, CVO,
CBE 1859-1932 (c.1929)
(Illus.p.371)
Oil on canvas 104.2 x 63.5
Signed
Provenance unknown

STAFFORD, A. G. 19th century (Irish?)

P45.1978   View on River Lagan (1892)
(Illus.p.371)
Watercolour on paper 31.8 x 40.6
Signed, dated
Purchased 1978

STANNUS, Anthony Carey 1830-1919 (Irish)

P20.1907   Belfast High Street, Looking East
(c.1851) (Illus.p.371)
Watercolour on paper 34.8 x 47.9
Signed
Donated by Edward C. Clarke, 1907

P7.1974   Bawn at Bellahill, near Carrickfergus
(Illus.p.371)
Pencil on paper 22.5 x 31.5
Signed
Purchased 1974

STEWART, D. fl.1805-12 (Irish?)

P603.1888   Belfast Shipyard, 1812: View from
the River Lagan
Watercolour on paper 23.9 x 62.4
Donated by A. MacLaine, 1888

P604.1888   Belfast Shipyard, 1812: View from
the Landward Side
Watercolour on paper 23.6 x 62.9
Donated by A. MacLaine, 1888

P246.1947   Ritchie's Dock, Belfast, 1805
Watercolour on paper 36.4 x 52.7
Purchased 1947

STRONG, W. J. 20th century (Irish)

P27.1999   Laganside (1994)
Watercolour, acrylic on paper 48 x 62
Signed
Purchased 1994

SUMNER, John fl.1884-96 (Irish)

P69.1945   Belfast Harbour Scene (1884)
Oil on canvas 22.6 x 32.8
Signed, dated
Donated by T. C. Sumner, 1945

P26.1947   Rugby Road, Belfast (1890)
Watercolour on paper 20.9 x 34
Signed, dated
Purchased 1947

P81.1984   The Old Bridge, Newcastle, Co.
Down (1890) (Illus.p.371)
Watercolour on paper 24.4 x 37.2
Signed, dated
Provenance unknown

P82.1984   View of Dundrum Castle (1890)
Watercolour on paper 28.1 x 38.3
Signed, dated

Provenance unknown

P98.1984   The Bloody Bridge, near Newcastle,
Co. Down (1890)
Watercolour on paper 38.1 x 56.4
Signed, dated
Provenance unknown

T

THOMPSON, M. E. 19th century (Irish?)

P46.1978   Garron Tower (1853) (Illus.p.371)
Oil on canvas 68.2 x 98.8
Signed, dated
Purchased 1978

THOMSON, Hugh 1860-1920 (Irish)

P785.1937   Ormeau Road, Belfast, Looking
towards the City from South of the
Ormeau Bridge (c.1880) (Illus.p.371)
Watercolour on paper 16.9 x 23.2
Donated by J. H. McKisack, 1937

TONE, Catherine Sampson 18th-19th century
(Irish) (attributed to)

P23.1999   Theobald Wolfe Tone 1763-98
Miniature, watercolour on ivory 11 x
9.2 (sight)
Purchased 1994

TROBRIDGE, George 1856-1909 (English,
worked in Ireland)

P111.1908   Cooney's Court, Ann Street, Belfast
(1880) (Illus.p.372)
Watercolour on paper 24.8 x 35.9
Signed, dated
Purchased 1908

P112.1908   Queen's Bridge, Belfast (1884)
Watercolour on paper 36.7 x 54.1
Signed, dated
Purchased 1908

TURNER, John b.1916 (Irish)

P195.1955   Samuel Somerset Keith, Esq. 1859-
1955 (1945)
Pastel on paper 42.6 x 33.2
Signed, dated
Bequeathed by the sitter, 1955

U

UNKNOWN 18th century

P803.1922   Lieutenant John McBride
Gouache on paper 97 x 7.5
Donated by Mrs. Andrew Morrow,
1922

P321.1927   William Brown, Belfast Battalion
Watercolour on paper 16.8 x 13.8
Purchased 1927

P322.1927   William Bruce, DD 1757-1841,
Belfast Volunteers
Watercolour on paper 16.8 x 13.6
Purchased 1927

P323.1927 **William Dawson 1759-1834, Belfast Volunteer Company**
Watercolour on paper 16.8 x 13.5
Purchased 1927

P324.1927 **James Hope 1764-1847, Roughfort Volunteers**
Watercolour on paper 16.8 x 13.6
Purchased 1927

P325.1927 **James McCleery, Ards Battalion**
Watercolour on paper 17.6 x 14.8
Purchased 1927

P326.1927 **James Thompson, Belfast Merchants' Corps**
Watercolour on paper 16.7 x 13.7
Purchased 1927

P8.1949 **Walter (Watty) Graham**
Pencil, wash on paper 9.2 x 6.9
Donated by George G. Grahame, 1949

P82.1966 **John Reilly of Scarva, Co. Down (1750)**
Oil on canvas 75.5 x 62.9
Purchased 1966

P1.1986 **Rev. Thomas Drennan 1696-1768**
Oil on canvas 75.5 x 63
Donated by Miss S. M. Duffin, 1986

P2.1986 **Anne Lennox 1719-1806, Wife of Rev. Thomas Drennan**
Oil on canvas 75.4 x 62.8
Donated by Miss S. M. Duffin, 1986

P2.1987 **View of City of Londonderry from East Bank of River Foyle**
Oil on canvas 81.8 x 133.3
Purchased 1987

UNKNOWN 18th century (?)

P105.1984 **John Getty 1770-1832, in Uniform of Belfast Volunteers**
Pastel on paper 32.6 x 26.7 (oval)
Donated by C. H. Murray, 1958

UNKNOWN 18th-19th century (?)

P100.1984 **The Rev. Samuel Barber 1738-1811**
Pastel on paper 39.8 x 23.5 (oval)
Provenance unknown

UNKNOWN 19th century

P229.1910 **John Bates, Town Clerk of Belfast 1842-55 (1861)**
Ink on paper 18.5 x 11.9
Dated
Donated by Miss L'Estrange, 1910

P540.1914 **William Ritchie's Shipbuilding Yard, Belfast, c.1810**
Watercolour on paper 33.7 x 49.3
Bequeathed by Arthur Dudgeon, 1914

P173.1924 **Glenarm, Co. Antrim (c.1841)**
Details unknown
Purchased 1924

P328.1927 **Patrick Murney (1839)**
Watercolour on paper 21.3 x 15.5
Dated
Purchased 1927

P339.1927 **Henry MacCormac, MD 1800-86**
Crayon on paper 40.5 x 30
Purchased 1927

P357.1927 **The Old Queen's Bridge (1843)**
Watercolour on paper 15 x 26
Dated
Purchased 1927

P255.1932 **Belfast from Lagan Village, 1767** *(Illus.p.372)*
Watercolour, gum on paper 42.6 x 51.7
Signed as by G. Morland (?), dated (forged signature and date?)
Donated by Miss D. M. Agnew, 1932

P355.1936 **Frederick Richard Chichester, Earl of Belfast 1827-53 (1852)**
Crayon on paper 46.1 x 35.5 (oval)
Signed illegibly, dated
Donated by the Duffin family, 1936

P88.1937 **Sir James Hamilton 1815-82, Chairman of the Belfast Harbour Commissioners 1867-75**
Charcoal on paper 25 x 19.7
Donated by A. S. Megaw, 1937

P166.1937 **Ormeau Castle (c.1830)**
Watercolour on paper 28.7 x 41.5
Purchased 1937

P2269. 1942 **Miss Margaret Smith 1774-1884**
Oil on canvas 60.8 x 45.8
Donated by Mrs. E. M. Sinclair, 1942

P74.1951 **Old Annadale House, Belfast (c.1870)**
Watercolour on paper 23.7 x 34.8
Bequeathed by Mrs. Annie Greer, 1951

P122.1958 **William Getty 1791-1843 (1828)**
Pencil, watercolour on paper 8.9 x 5.8
Dated
Donated by C. H. Murray, 1957

P123.1958 **Samuel Gibson Getty 1817-77 (1828)**
Pencil, watercolour on paper 8.9 x 5.8
Dated
Donated by C. H. Murray, 1957

P124.1958 **Robert Getty 1820-41 (1828)**
Pencil, watercolour on paper 9.4 x 6.3
Dated
Donated by C. H. Murray, 1957

P125.1958 **Margaret Getty 1816-37**
Pencil, watercolour on paper 8.8 x 5.8
Dated
Donated by C. H. Murray, 1957

P126.1958 **Mary Getty 1819-93 (1828)**
Pencil, watercolour on paper 8.9 x 5.8
Dated
Donated by C. H. Murray, 1957

P127.1958 **Agnes Getty d.1844 (1828)**
Pencil, watercolour on paper 8.9 x 5.8
Dated
Donated by C. H. Murray, 1957

P383.1961 **Oldpark Printworks and Village (c.1860)** *(Illus.p.372)*
Watercolour on paper 30.9 x 48.7

Donated by John Blair, 1961

P21.1973 **Bessbrook Mill (c.1860)** *(Illus.p.372)*
Watercolour on paper 32.2 x 50.6
Purchased 1971

P33.1973 **Launch of the 'Jane Porter' at the Queen's Island, 1860**
Watercolour on paper 70.8 x 103.9
Purchased 1970

P76.1973 **View of Buildings in Donegall Street at Academy Street (c.1890)**
Watercolour on paper 35 x 24.5
Purchased 1966

P156.1973 **View of River Lagan and Halfpenny Bridge (c.1835)**
Oil on canvas 40.7 x 59.1
Provenance unknown

P157.1973 **View of Belfast from Cave Hill (c.1835)**
Oil on canvas 67.3 x 101.3
Provenance unknown

P3.1974 **View of Belfast Academical Institution from College Square North (c.1850)**
Ink on paper 13.9 x 22.5
Purchased 1974

P5.1974 **Carved Stone Block from the Long Bridge, Belfast (1840)**
Pencil, wash on paper 13.8 x 9.7
Dated
Purchased 1974

P8.1974 **Black Sam (Belfast Street Character) (c.1830)**
Watercolour on card 35 x 27.9
Purchased 1974

P49.1974 **Robert Shipboy McAdam (?) 1808-95 (1837)**
Silhouette, gouache, ink, gum on paper 10 x 7.5
Dated
Purchased 1974

P55.1974 **Armorial Bearings of the Rt. Hon. Arthur Magenis, 2nd Viscount Iveagh**
Watercolour on paper 31.8 x 19.5
Purchased 1974

P48.1978 **John Montgomery of Ballydrain 1832-76**
Oil on canvas 54.5 x 44.5
Donated by C. H. Crawford, 1978

P4.1981 **View of 'The Bunch of Grapes' Public House, Beersbridge Road, Belfast (1866)**
Watercolour on paper 28.2 x 44.5
Dated
Bequeathed by Sir Thomas Brown, 1981

P4.1983 **Newry, Ireland (1812)** *(Illus.p.370)*
Now by J. P. or T. P.

P88.1984 **Sketrick Castle, Co. Down (1869)**
Watercolour on paper 17.5 x 25.3
Purchased 1955

P97.1984 **Francis Dalzell Finlay d.1857?**
Oil on canvas 76.3 x 64.1
Donated by the Public Record Office

of Northern Ireland, 1971

P104.1984 Mary Anne Nicholl
Pencil, wash on paper 19.4 x 15.1
(oval)
Provenance unknown

**P1.1985 View of Joy's Paper Mill, Belfast
(c.1830-40)**
Oil on canvas 61.5 x 74.4
Purchased 1966

**P12.1985 View of Arthur Square, Belfast
(1860)**
Watercolour on paper 16.4 x 26.4
Provenance unknown

P15.1985 William Gibson, Belfast Jeweller
Oil; support and measurements
unknown
Donated by Gladys Skelton, 1974

**P24.1985 'Dundonald' of Belfast: Four-masted
Barque in Full Sail**
Oil on panel 26.1 x 47.3
Purchased 1985

**P8.1990 Panoramic View of the Harbour of
Larne, Co. Antrim (1833)**
Watercolour on card 11.5 x 93.4
Dated
Donated by Col. P. H. Hordern, 1990

P2.1999 Sirocco Engineering Works
Watercolour on paper 32.5 x 45.5
Provenance unknown

P16.1999 Arthur Square, Belfast, 1860
Watercolour on paper 16.3 x 26.2
Provenance unknown

P17.1999 A Special Constable (Cartoon)
Ink on paper 30.5 x 22
Provenance unknown

**P24.1999 The Drawing Room at Tyrella: Mrs.
Montgomery Reading by the Fire
(1831-43)** *(Illus.p.372)*
Watercolour on paper 23 x 35
Purchased 1993

**P25.1999 View of the Ruins of the Church at
Greyabbey**
Watercolour on paper 21.8 x 30.6
Purchased 1993

**P31.1999 Princess Victoria 1840-1901, Aged
Eight** (Copy of an Original by
'Florian')
Watercolour on paper 23 x 18 (sight)
Donated by Miss K. M. Ferris, 1998

UNKNOWN 19th century (?)

**P253.1910 View of Carrickfergus Castle from
the Sea**
Watercolour on paper 33.3 x 50.7
Donated by Miss L'Estrange, 1910

P85.1917 The Old Long Bridge, Belfast
Oil on canvas 15.8 x 29.9
Donated by the Misses McBride, 1917

P167.1937 Carrickfergus Castle (c.1860)
Watercolour on paper 15.6 x 21.4
Purchased 1937

P26.1941 Shaw's Bridge, River Lagan
Oil on canvas 36.9 x 53.4
Donated by William Ewart and Sons,
1941

P27.1941 Joy's Paper Mill, Belfast
Oil on canvas 36.1 x 53.6
Donated by William Ewart and Sons,
1941

**P146.1973 View of Farmhouse, Corner of
Malone and Stranmillis Roads**
(Illus.p.372)
Watercolour on paper 34.5 x 45.7
Donated by Miss M. Cunningham,
1964

P83.1984 Carrickfergus Castle
Pencil, white on paper 21.3 x 28.1
Provenance unknown

P94.1984 Carrickfergus
Pencil, wash, white on paper 19 x
27.4
Provenance unknown

P99.1984 Kilclief Castle, Strangford
Crayon, white on paper 26 x 33
Provenance unknown

P103.1984 Alexander MacKay 1764-1844
Silhouette, gouache, gum on paper
25.1 x 17.1
Donated by the Misses MacKay, 1898

**P11.1985 View of Cottage among Trees beside
Bend in River (possibly the Lagan)**
Oil on canvas 40.2 x 54.1
Provenance unknown

P5.1990 View of Orange Hall, Omagh
Watercolour on paper 33.1 x 42
Purchased 1990

UNKNOWN 19th-20th century

P2.1988 Passenger Ship 'Britannic'
Oil on canvas 76.1 x 55.7
Purchased 1987

**P4.1990 Redburn Square, Holywood, Co.
Down, Showing Holywood Orange
Hall**
Watercolour on paper 22.8 x 40
Purchased 1990

UNKNOWN 20th century

**P609.1923 First Presbyterian Church, Lisburn:
View of the Pulpit, Musgrave Organ
and Choir Box, with the Musgrave
Memorial Window and Barbour
Memorial Window (post 1918)**
Watercolour on paper 43.4 x 60
Bequeathed by H. Musgrave, 1923

**P314.1924 Campbell Inn (Denny Liddy's Inn)
and Ballroom, Malone Road, Belfast
(c.1875)**
Watercolour on paper 18 x 27.3
Donated by Thomas McGowan, 1924

**P60.1973 Laburnum Cottage, Knock Road,
Belfast (1944)**
Watercolour on paper 28.5 x 39.3
Dated
Purchased 1968

P61.1973 Groomsport (1946)
Watercolour on paper 28.3 x 18.4
Dated
Purchased 1968

P123.1973 View of Carrickfergus Castle (1909)
Oil on canvas 31.5 x 44.5
Dated
Purchased 1966

P124.1973 Old Holywood Road, Belfast (1935)
(Illus.p.372)
Watercolour on paper 18.7 x 23.7
Signed illegibly, dated
Donated by W. Denny, 1966

**P16.1985 Alexander R. Hogg 1870-1939
(1924)**
Gouache on paper 13.1 x 8.2
Dated
Provenance unknown

P9.1989 Alexander Buchanan d.1941
Oil on panel 58.7 x 48.6
Donated by Mrs. M. Turner, 1989

P7.1990 Robert Patterson
Oil on panel 36.9 x 30.3
Provenance unknown

P3.1999 Drawing of Stained Glass Windows
Watercolour on paper 43.5 x 60
Provenance unknown

P32.1999 Balloon over Dundonald Hills
(a) Oil on board 31.5 x 38
Donated by Mrs. McClelland, 1991

P32.1999 Aeroplane Searchlights
(b) Oil on canvas 29 x 45 (sight)
Donated by Mrs. McClelland, 1991

P32.1999 Three Men Aloft a Factory Chimney
(c) Oil on canvas 55.5 x 44.5 (sight)
Donated by Mrs. McClelland, 1991

UNKNOWN 20th century (?)

**P39.1983 Memorial Window, 1st Presbyterian
Church, Rosemary Street, Belfast**
Watercolour on paper 61.8 x 36.8
Provenance unknown

P4.1985 William III on Horseback
Oil on canvas 73 x 52.6
Purchased 1961

**P7.1985 View of Old Toll House, Dublin
Road, Belfast**
Oil on canvas 30.2 x 35.2
Provenance unknown

V

VINYCOMB, John Knox 1833-1928 (English,
worked in Ireland)

P198.1909 'Maryville', Malone (1909)
Sepia, pencil on paper 17.1 x 21.6
Signed, dated
Donated by A. Basil Wilson, 1909

**P118.1910 Old Ormeau Bridge from near
Stranmillis (1860)** *(Illus.p.372)*
Watercolour on paper 18.3 x 25.9
Signed, dated

Donated by the artist, 1910

P66.1911   Brookvale House, Belfast (1911)
Sepia, pencil on paper 15.1 x 22.7
Signed, dated
Donated by the Rt. Hon. Thomas
Sinclair, 1911

P67.1911   Hopefield House, Belfast (1911)
Sepia, pencil on paper 15.1 x 22.7
Signed, dated
Donated by the Rt. Hon. Thomas
Sinclair,1911

P92.1984   Dunseverick Castle (formerly
'Coastal Scene with Ruined Building:
Kinbane Castle?')
Watercolour on paper 14.2 x 30.5
Signed
Provenance unknown

**P25.1985   The Valley of the Lagan from the
Castlereagh Hills, Belfast (1892)**
Ink, wash, white on paper 10.4 x
111.5
Signed, dated
Donated by Angus McDonald, 1964

Pencil on paper 29.5 x 23
Dated
Provenance unrecorded

P21.1999   Stanway Hall (1923)
Pencil on paper 24 x 18
Dated
Provenance unrecorded

P22.1999   Sketch of a House
Pencil on paper 29.5 x 23
Provenance unrecorded

YOUNG, Robert 1822-1917 (Irish)

P2.1974   John Bates (1857)
Pencil on paper 18.9 x 13.7
Signed, dated
Purchased 1974

W

WAKEMAN, Thomas 1820-76 (English)

P365.1915   High Street, Belfast, 1780
Gouache on paper 51 x 76.6
Signed
Purchased 1915

WALTER, J. fl.1834-49 (British)

**P30.1999   SS 'Great Britain' Aground at
Dundrum Bay (1847)**
Watercolour on paper 58 x 91.5
Signed, dated
Purchased 1995

WEIR, Margaret 19th century (Irish)

**P18.1973   View of Old Cottage at Shaw's
Bridge, Belfast**
Sepia on paper 17.2 x 24.7
Donated by Miss Margaret C. Weir,
1972

WHITE, J. 19th-20th century (Irish?)

P89.1984   Ballykinlar, Dundrum Bay (1905)
Watercolour on paper 19 x 51.9
Signed, dated
Purchased 1955

WILSON, James Glen 1827-63 (Irish)

**P1.1988   View of the Cathedral and Mall,
Downpatrick (1850)** *(Illus.p.372)*
Oil on canvas 22.8 x 30.9
Signed, dated
Purchased 1988

Y

Y., J. R. [J.R.Y.] 20th century (Irish?)

P20.1999   Evesham (1923)

drawings paintings & sculptures

the
armagh county
museum

A

ALLEN, Barbara b.1959 (Irish)

3.1990 **Gateway in Moy (1989)**
Watercolour on paper 28.1 x 16.5
(sight)
Signed, dated
Purchased 1990

ARMSTRONG, C. D. 20th century (Irish)

35.1964 **Portadown Bridge (1964), from the
Original of 1820**
Sepia on paper 22.8 x 38.8 (sight)
Purchased 1964

B

B., J. D. [J. D. B.] 19th century (Irish)

50.1960 **Miss Dorothy Gervais (1895)**
(Illus.p.374)
Pencil, crayon, pastel on paper 24.2 x
18.6 (oval)
Signed, dated
Donated by Mrs. D. Rhodes, 1960

BAINBRIGGE, Philip 19th century (Irish)

3.1968 **View of Armagh (1834)**
Sepia wash on paper 18.3 x 40.2
(sight)
Donated by T. G. F. Paterson, 1968

BEATTIE, R. D. 20th century (Irish)

81.1982 **Market Street, Armagh in 1910
(1982)** *(Illus.p.374)*
Ink, wash on paper 27.4 x 37.4 (sight)
Signed
Purchased 1982

BELL, G. P. 20th century (Irish?)

73.1986 **Canal Barge Selling Coal**
Pencil on paper 13.5 x 22.2 (sight)
Donated by Mrs. M. A. Bell, 1986

BERESFORD, Kathleen M. 20th century (Irish)

276.1988 **Bluebells in the Glen, Castledillon**
Watercolour on paper 8 x 13 (sight)
Signed
Donated by Miss L. E. N. Reid, 1988

BEVINGTON, Geoffrey 19th century (Irish)

6.1945 **Portrush (1870)** *(Illus.p.374)*
Watercolour on paper 18 x 34.5
(sight)
Signed, dated
Donated by Captain C. H. Ensor, 1945

BICKERSTAFF, Renée 1909-84 (Irish)

20.1977 **Teasels (1977)**
Oil on board 49 x 39 (sight)
Signed
Purchased 1977

BLACK, James d.1829 (Irish)

92.1937 **City of Armagh (1811)**

Ink, wash on paper 54.7 x 86
Donated by Mrs. N. Smith, 1937

25.1950 **Armagh City (1819)**
Ink, wash on paper 53 x 83.5 (sight)
Donated by the Very Rev. Dean Forde-
Tichbourne, 1950

156.1958 **City of Armagh (1810)** *(Illus.p.374)*
Oil on canvas 92.2 x 132.3 (sight)
Donated by the Armagh Natural
History and Philosophical Society,
1958

BLACKER, Stewart 1813-81 (Irish)

8.1948 **Album of Twenty-eight Drawings
(1827-31)**
Pencil, watercolour, ink, wash on paper
23.3 x 18.2 (page size)
Signed, dated (some)
Donated by Major W. D. Blacker, 1948

13.1948 **Scrapbook of Two Hundred and
Eighteen Sketches (1819-41); also
Three Architectural Plans by an
Unknown Artist**
Pencil, watercolour, ink, wash, crayon
on paper 23.3 x 18.2 (page size)
Signed, dated (several)
Donated by Major W. D. Blacker, 1948

BLAIR, Thomas 20th century (Irish)

1.1973 **Portrait of T. G. F. Paterson 1888-1971
(1972)**
Watercolour on paper 34.5 x 28.4
(sight)
Signed
Purchased 1973

BOURKE, Michael J. 1913-85
See under Micheál J. de Burca

BOWDEN, John 19th century (?) (Irish)

8.1958 **Plan and Elevation of Church of
Tullamaine in the Diocese of Cashel**
Ink, wash on paper 58.4 x 47.7
Signed
Donated by Sir Albert Richardson,
1958

9.1958 **Plan and Elevation for Fenner Church
in the Diocese of Cashel**
Ink, wash on paper 55.9 x 42.6
Signed
Donated by Sir Albert Richardson,
1958

BRANDT, Muriel 1909-81 (Irish)

113.1967 **Macha's Height (1964)** *(Illus.p.374)*
Watercolour on paper 39.4 x 24.8
(sight)
Signed
Donated by T. G. F. Paterson, 1967

BROWN, Mary 20th century (Irish)

8.1982 **Hollyhocks** *(Illus.p.374)*
Watercolour on paper 96 x 60.3
(sight)
Donated by Miss A. G. C. Brown, 1982

58.1981 **Moneypenny's Lock on the Newry**

**Canal near Portadown around the
Turn of the Century** *(Illus.p.374)*
Watercolour on paper 17.1 x 26.1
Donated by J. Daniel Thompson, 1981

BUCK, Adam 1759-1833 (Irish) (attributed to)

77.1996 **Archbishop the Hon. William Stuart
of Armagh 1755-1822** *(Illus.p.374)*
Pastel on paper 25 x 22.5
Purchased 1996

BURGESS, James Howard c.1810-90 (Irish)

143.1964 **Carlingford Lough**
Pencil, chalk, wash on paper 25 x 36.3
(sight)
Donated by E. N. Carrothers, 1964

C

CAMPBELL, Charlotte 19th century (Irish)

5.1953 **View of Armagh Cathedral (1834)**
Ink, wash on paper 18 x 22.2 (sight)
Dated
Donated by Rev. D. R. Tarleton, 1953

CAMPBELL, Christopher 1908-72 (Irish)
(attributed to)

149.1957 **Jonathan Seaver, FGS, FRCS 1853-
1927** *(Illus.p.374)*
Oil on board 28.9 x 23 (sight)
Donated by the Very Rev. G. Seaver,
1957
Formerly by Unknown

CAREY, Joseph William 1859-1937 (Irish)

101.1975 **An Irish Farm Interior**
Ink, wash on paper 12.6 x 19
Signed
Purchased 1975

102.1975 **Kelp Burning on the Antrim Coast**
Ink, wash on paper 12.2 x 18.5
Purchased 1975

103.1975 **Bleach Green**
Ink, wash on card 21.7 x 33
Purchased 1975

CARR, Tom 1909-99 (Irish)

79.1987 **Oil Lamp and Stuffed Canary (1971)**
(Illus.p.375)
Ink, wash on paper 23.3 x 26.5 (sight)
Signed
Bequeathed by W. A. N. MacGeogh
Bond, 1987

80.1987 **McAuley's Lake (1971)** *(Illus.p.375)*
Watercolour on paper 57.5 x 76
(sight)
Signed
Bequeathed by W. A. N. MacGeogh
Bond, 1987

CARROLL, J. Rawson fl.1861-88 (Irish)

7.1973 **Garden Elevation, Elm Park, Killylea,
Co. Armagh**
Ink, wash on paper 45.4 x 68.3 (sight)

Signed by stamp
Donated anonymously, 1973

CARTER, Vernon b.1945 (Irish)

50.1979   **Overlooking Lough Neagh No. 4**
Oil on board 36.5 x 26.4 (sight)
Purchased 1979

CAULFEILD, K. A. 19th-20th century (Irish)

2.1984   **Drumcairne Formal Garden (1914)**
(Illus.p.375)
Watercolour on paper 34.8 x 27.3
(sight)
Dated
Donated by Robert McKinstry, 1984

9.1984   **Lough Neagh from Drumcairne
(1914)**
Watercolour on paper 21.6 x 29
(sight)
Dated
Donated by Robert McKinstry, 1984

CHAMBERS, Henrietta L. fl.1827-48 (Irish)

112.1975   **Old Kilcullen Round Tower**
Ink, wash on paper 26 x 18
Signed
Purchased 1975

113.1975   **Cross at Castledermot (1827)**
Pencil on paper 13 x 20
Signed
Purchased 1975

114.1975   **Cross Shaft and Head, Castledermot
(1848)**
Pencil on paper 13 x 21
Signed, dated
Purchased 1975

CHAMBERS, Henrietta L. fl.1827-48 (Irish)
(attributed to)
The following works were formerly by Unknown

116.1975   **Our Lady's Chapel, Glendalough
from West; A Short Ring Cross;
Doorway of Our Lady's Chapel
Looking West**
Pencil on paper 22.7 x 31.7
Purchased 1975

117.1975   **Cross and Base, Kildare Church;
Tablet in Kildare Churchyard (1846)**
Pencil on paper 22.7 x 31.7
Dated
Purchased 1975

118.1975   **Cross at Moone Abbey near
Castledermot**
Pencil on paper 22.7 x 31.7
Purchased 1975

119.1975   **Castledermot Round Tower and Cross
from the West**
Pencil on paper 22.7 x 31.7
Purchased 1975

120.1975   **Old Kilcullen Church, Cross Shaft**
Pencil on paper 22.7 x 31.7
Purchased 1975

121.1975   **Round Tower at Killahea, Kildare;
Cross on Bishop's Tomb, Glendalough**
Pencil on paper 22.7 x 31.7

Purchased 1975

122.1975   **Ram's Island from the West; Dungiven
Church Window; Armagh Cross**
Pencil on paper 26.5 x 37
Purchased 1975

123.1975   **Ardboe Cross, Co. Tyrone**
Pencil on paper 26.5 x 37
Purchased 1975

124.1975   **Antrim Round Tower from West
South West**
Pencil on paper 26.5 x 37
Purchased 1975

125.1975   **Entrance to Newgrange Cave near
Drogheda; A Cell for Waking the
Clergy in Cashel Cathedral**
Pencil on paper 26.5 x 37
Purchased 1975

126.1975   **The Lesser Cross at St. Patrick's,
Monasterboice, Co. Louth, from the
West**
Pencil on paper 26.5 x 37
Purchased 1975

127.1975   **Round Tower and Crosses,
Monasterboice, Co. Louth, from the
East**
Pencil on paper 26.5 x 37
Purchased 1975

128.1975   **Kells Town Cross, East Side**
Pencil on paper 26.5 x 37
Purchased 1975

129.1975   **Kells Town Cross, West Side**
Pencil on paper 26.5 x 37
Purchased 1975

130.1975   **Kells Churchyard Cross**
Pencil on paper 26.5 x 37
Purchased 1975

131.1975   **An Ancient Cross at Tuam; The
Smallest Cross at Monasterboice (St.
Patrick's), Co. Louth**
Pencil on paper 26.5 x 37
Purchased 1975

COLEMAN, Simon b.1916 (Irish)

1.1957   **The Pond, Stephen's Green, Dublin**
(Illus.p.375)
Oil on canvas 51 x 61.1
Signed
Donated by the Thomas Haverty Trust,
1957

COLVILL, Helen 1856-1953 (Irish)

5.1995   **The Mall, Armagh** *(Illus.p.375)*
Watercolour on paper 40.1 x 49.8
Signed
Purchased 1994

CONOR, William 1881-1968 (Irish)

7.1953   **T. G. F. Paterson 1888-1971**
Oil on canvas 75 x 62.8 (sight)
Signed
Donated by the City of Armagh Field
Club, 1953

12.1972   **Wayside Chat**

Crayon on paper 47.2 x 31 (sight)
Signed
Donated by Dr. Charlotte Warner,
1972

13.1972   **Belfast Children (1918)** *(Illus.p.375)*
Crayon on paper 29.8 x 23.5 (sight)
Signed, dated
Donated by Dr. Charlotte Warner,
1972

39.1973   **Thomas A. Montgomery, DL, JP**
Oil on canvas 89 x 69.4 (sight)
Signed
Donated by Armagh County Council,
1973

82.1987   **The Jockey (1965)**
Crayon on paper 46.5 x 32.5 (sight)
Signed
Bequeathed by W. A. N. MacGeogh
Bond, 1987

COOKE-COLLIS, Sylvia 1900-73 (Irish)

67.1973   **A Whirlpool**
Gouache on paper 21.8 x 33.5 (sight)
Signed
Bequeathed by Sylvia Cooke-Collis
(per the Friends of the National
Collections of Ireland), 1973

COOPER, Wilfred 20th century (Irish)

4.1984   **Ardmore Bay, Lough Neagh (1983)**
Watercolour on paper 27 x 37 (sight)
Signed, dated
Purchased 1984

COURTNEY, J. 19th century (Irish)

58.1960   **A Gentleman (1833)**
Miniature, oil on panel 10.3 x 8.2
(sight)
Signed, dated
Donated by Mrs. D. Rhodes, 1960

COWDY, Diana b.1918 (Irish)

45.1971   **Interior (1968)** *(Illus.p.375)*
Oil on board 32 x 30.5
Signed, dated
Donated by the Very Rev. J. T. F.
Paterson, 1971

1.1975   **The Palace, Armagh (1974)**
Oil on board 39 x 49.1 (sight)
Signed, dated
Purchased 1974

63.1979   **Grazing Horse beneath Two Trees**
Cut-out silhouette on card 10.8 x 13
(sight)
Donated by the artist, 1979

5.1991   **The Black Bank in Armagh (1973)**
(Illus.p.375)
Oil on board 38.6 x 50.4
Signed, dated
Donated by Miss N. Dawson, 1991

6.1991   **The Borough - Derryscollop (1975)**
Oil on board 34 x 47.8 (sight)
Signed, dated
Donated by Miss N. Dawson, 1991

CRAIG, James Humbert 1877-1944 (Irish)

140.1957 **In County Galway** *(Illus.p.375)*
Oil on board 38 x 50.5 (sight)
Signed
Purchased 1957

CREGAN, Martin 1788-1870 (Irish)

157.1958 **Leonard Dobbin, MP for the Borough of Armagh 1833-38** *(Illus.p.376)*
Oil on canvas 91.2 x 71
Donated by the Armagh Natural History and Philosophical Society, 1958

50.1962 **Lieutenant-Colonel Sir William Verner, Bt. 1782-1871**
Oil on canvas 124.5 x 98.3 (sight)
Donated by Sir E. D. W. Verner, Bt., 1962

CRESWICK, Thomas 1811-69 (English)

14.1982 **Charlemont Fort, Co. Armagh, from the River** *(Illus.p.376)*
Oil on board 22.8 x 17.1
Signed
Purchased 1982

CROOKSHANK, T. C. 19th century (Irish)

42.1968 **Castlecaulfield (1846)** *(Illus.p.376)*
Pencil on paper 22.2 x 29
Signed, dated
Purchased 1968

CUCKSON, George 20th century (Irish)

86.1980 **The White Walk, Armagh** *(Illus.p.376)*
Watercolour on paper 40.5 x 50.6 (sight)
Signed
Purchased 1980

D

DE BURCA, Micheál J. (Michael J. Bourke) 1913-85 (Irish)

100.1960 **Summer Evening, Achill** *(Illus.p.376)*
Oil on board 45.5 x 50.5
Signed
Donated by the Thomas Haverty Trust, 1960

DE BURGH, Lydia b.1923 (Irish)

68.1975 **The Black Causeway, Strangford**
Watercolour on paper 40.1 x 50.1
Signed
Purchased 1975

35.1993 **South Armagh near Forkhill (1983)** *(Illus.p.376)*
Watercolour on paper 39 x 48.5 (sight)
Signed, dated
Purchased 1993

DEWART, J. 20th century (Irish)

96.1973 **The Primate's Palace, Armagh, North Elevation (1972)**

Ink on paper 59.7 x 89.5 (sight)
Signed, dated
Donated by the artist, 1973

97.1973 **The Primate's Palace, Armagh, East Elevation (1972)**
Ink on paper 59 x 91.5 (sight)
Signed, dated
Donated by the artist, 1973

DICKSEE, John Robert 1817-1905 (English)

21.1951 **Brigadier-General John Nicholson 1821-57 (1867)**
Oil on canvas 97 x 76.3
Donated by Miss H. K. Seymour, 1951

DONNELLY, Robert 19th century (Irish)

66.1943 **A Pictorial View of Eden Hall**
Ink, wash on paper 64.4 x 54.5
Signed
Donated by P. Kelly, 1943

119.1963 **Moyallon House** *(Illus.p.376)*
Ink, wash on paper 53 x 65
Donated by J. S. W. Richardson, 1963

DOUGLAS, Ena fl.1930-63 (Irish)

83.1976 **Cashel Bay**
Oil on board 30.2 x 40.5
Signed
Purchased 1976

DOUGLAS, Harry R. 1862-1934 (Irish)

35.1973 **Joseph Atkinson, DL, JP**
Oil on canvas 106.7 x 83.8 (sight)
Signed
Donated by Armagh County Council, 1973

36.1973 **R. G. McCrum, DL, JP 1829-1915 (1909)**
Oil on canvas 106.7 x 85.1 (sight)
Signed, dated
Donated by Armagh County Council, 1973

2.1985 **Judith Paul (1897)**
Oil on canvas 110.5 x 85 (sight)
Signed, dated
Donated by Mrs. A. D. K. Miller, 1985

4.1985 **Harriet McCrum (1899)**
Oil on canvas 111.8 x 76.2
Signed, dated
Donated by Mrs. A. D. K. Miller, 1985

DU NOYER, George Victor 1817-69 (Irish)
The following works are as titled by the artist

105.1975 **Crosses on Aran, Co. Galway (1847)**
Pencil on paper 26.5 x 37.2
Signed, dated
Purchased 1975

106.1975 **Cross, Church of St. Kieran, Isle of Aran, Co. Galway (1847)**
Pencil on paper 24.2 x 19
Signed, dated
Purchased 1975

107.1975 **Granite Crosses, Tullagh, Co. Dublin (1848)** (Tallaght?)

Pencil on paper 26.8 x 37.1
Signed, dated
Purchased 1975

108.1975 **Cross of St. Nen, Innish Mac-Saint, Fermanagh, Looking North West (1847)** (Inishmacsaint)
Pencil on paper 25.6 x 35.3
Signed, dated
Purchased 1975

109.1975 **From the Graveyard of the Old Church of Kilbride, Co. Dublin**
Pencil on paper 27 x 17.5
Purchased 1975

110.1975 **Granite Crosses, Killary and Lissknock, Co. Meath (1847)**
Pencil on paper 26.7 x 37.9
Signed, dated
Purchased 1975

111.1975 **Detail of Donaghmore Round Tower and Monasterboice Cross (1848)**
Pencil on card 25 x 33
Signed, dated
Purchased 1975

DUNLOP, Doveton 19th-20th century (Irish)

51.1961 **The Rt. Hon. Mr. Justice Ross 1854-1934 (1905)**
Sculpture, plaster bust, ht. 64.7
Signed, dated
Donated by Mrs. Corry, 1961

E

EDOUART, Augustin Amant Constant Fidèle 1789-1861 (French)

15.1982 **The Verner Family at Churchill (1834)**
Series of cut-out silhouettes on paper 40 x 98
Signed, dated
Bequeathed by Miss R. Verner, 1982

ELLIS, E. K. 19th-20th century (Irish)

34.1960 **Dorothy, Daughter of Francis Peter Gervais of Cecil Manor (1910)**
Watercolour on paper 15.2 x 9.8 (sight)
Signed, dated
Donated by Mrs. D. Rhodes, 1960

F

FISHER, Jonathan d.1809 (Irish) (attributed to)

153.1958 **Castledillon, Co. Armagh (c.1782)**
Oil on canvas 79.4 x 127 (sight)
Donated by Armagh County Council, 1958
Formerly by Unknown

3.1965 **Castledillon from across the Lake (c.1782)**
Oil on canvas 79.3 x 126 (sight)
Donated by J. McLaughlan, 1965
Formerly by Unknown

FLACK, Rev. James Hall 20th century (Irish)

19.1977   **Mourne Farmhouse**
Watercolour on paper 27.5 x 37.6 (sight)
Signed
Purchased 1977

49.1979   **Camlough Lake**
Watercolour on paper 29.2 x 41 (sight)
Signed
Purchased 1979

42.1981   **Farm Buildings at Bolton Hill**
Watercolour on paper 37.5 x 54.8 (sight)
Signed
Purchased 1981

3.1984   **Mountain Farmstead near Slieve Gullion** *(Illus.p.376)*
Watercolour on paper 26.8 x 37.2 (sight)
Signed
Purchased 1984

FLANAGAN, Terence Philip b.1929 (Irish)

81.1987   **Blue Shore** *(Illus.p.376)*
Acrylic on board 63.4 x 76.4
Signed
Bequeathed by W. A. N. MacGeogh Bond, 1987

FRENCH, Percy 1854-1920 (Irish)

3.1943   **Album of Twelve Sketches, Each Illustrating a Printed Poem**
Donated by Miss Gwen Tupper, 1943

1. **Snatches of Song**
Watercolour on paper 12.7 x 17.5

2. **The Fairies' Lough**
Watercolour on paper 13 x 17.5

3. **Morning**
Watercolour on paper 12.5 x 17.5

4. **Evening**
Watercolour on paper 13.5 x 17.5

5. **In the Studio**
Watercolour on paper 13 x 17.6

6. **The Kindly Welcome**
Watercolour on paper 12.7 x 17.5

7. **To E. R.** *(Illus.p.377)*
Watercolour on paper 12.7 x 17.5

8. **To the Dark Rosaleen**
Watercolour on paper 13 x 17.5

9. **Gortnamona**
Watercolour on paper 12.8 x 17.5

10. **To the West**
Watercolour on paper 13 x 17

11. **L'Envoi**
Watercolour on paper 12.6 x 17.6

12. **The End of the Holiday**
Watercolour on paper 12.6 x 18

FRY, E. E. 19th-20th century (Irish)

29.1954   **Charles Seaver, DD 1820-1907 (1903)**
Oil on canvas 110.5 x 85.1 (sight)
Signed, dated
Donated by the Very Rev. G. Seaver, 1954

FRIERS, Rowel Boyd 1920-98 (Irish)

23.1987   **This Little Piggy Went to Market (1986)**
Ink on paper 49.4 x 74.8 (sight)
Signed, dated
Donated by the artist, 1987

G

GLENAVY, Lady Beatrice 1883-1968 (Irish)

99.1966   **From the Sea** *(Illus.p.377)*
Oil on board 41.3 x 47.3
Signed
Donated by the Thomas Haverty Trust, 1966

GORDON, J. D. 20th century (Irish)

69.1966   **'Light and Blight': Houses in High Street, Lurgan** *(Illus.p.377)*
Watercolour on paper 26.5 x 38.1
Donated by T. G. F. Paterson, 1966

GORDON, W. R. 1872-1955 (Irish)

5.1945   **Knocknacarry, near Cushendun** *(Illus.p.377)*
Ink, watercolour on paper 34.2 x 49.3 (sight)
Signed
Donated by the Thomas Haverty Trust, 1945

65.1957   **Cushendun Bridge, Co. Antrim** *(Illus.p.377)*
Watercolour on paper 22 x 28.2 (sight)
Signed
Donated by John Hewitt, 1957

GRAHAM, Carol b.1951 (Irish)

3.1978   **Black Bear in the Clearing (1976)**
Pencil on paper 31.7 x 24.4
Signed
Purchased 1977

GREENLEES, William 19th century (British)

73.1979   **Market Street, Armagh (1838)** *(Illus.p.377   )*
Ink, wash on paper 11.2 x 17.2
Signed, dated
Purchased 1979

2.1983   **Greencastle, Co. Down (1838)**
Watercolour on paper 11.2 x 17.5 (sight)
Signed, dated
Purchased 1983

H

HANKEY, David G. 20th century (Irish)

69.1975   **Moira Parish Church** *(Illus.p.377)*
Oil on canvas 45 x 76
Signed
Purchased 1975

21.1977   **Patterstown Farm, Moira**
Oil on canvas 59.7 x 75.5 (sight)
Purchased 1977

28.1980   **Greenhouse Glory**
Oil on board 122 x 91.4
Signed
Purchased 1980

116.1983   **Canna Orchids**
Oil on canvas on board 90.6 x 121.5
Signed
Donated by the artist, 1983

HANLON, Rev. Jack Paul 1913-68 (Irish)

78.1969   **Strange Fruit (1964)**
Watercolour on paper 55.8 x 77.4 (sight)
Signed, dated
Donated by the Friends of the National Collections of Ireland, 1969

HARKNESS, Harriette A. 19th century (English, worked in Ireland)

58.1956   **Album of One Hundred and Twenty-three Sketches of Ireland from Nature and One Watercolour (1844-45)**
Purchased 1956
Most of the following works are as titled by the artist

1. **Dunluce Castle**
Pencil, wash on paper 12 x 17.5

2. **Cliffs near Dunluce**
Pencil, wash on paper 16.8 x 11.7

3. **Near the Giant's Causeway from the Hotel (June 1844)**
Pencil, wash on paper 12.4 x 17.5

4. **Ruins at Ballycastle (June 1844)**
Pencil, wash on paper 12.4 x 17.6

5. **Ruins at Ballycarry (June 1844)**
Pencil, wash on paper 12.3 x 17.5

6. **Bridge at Bunamargey (June 1844)** (Bonamargy)
Pencil, chalk on paper 12.3 x 17.5

7. **Viaduct at Glen Dunn (June 1844)** (Glendun)
Pencil, wash on paper 12.3 x 17.5

8. **Cushendall (June 1844)**
Pencil on paper 12.2 x 17.4

9. **Drumnasole (June 1844)**
Pencil, wash on paper 12.2 x 17

10. **Carrickfergus Castle (June 1844)**
Pencil, wash on paper 12.2 x 17.5

11. **Dungannon (30 November 1844)**
Pencil, wash on paper 12.8 x 18

12. **Dungannon Castle (June 1844)**
Pencil on paper 12.2 x 17.5

13. **Charlemont Fort (April 1844)**

Watercolour on paper 15.1 x 23.7

14. **Charlemont Fort and the Bridge over the Blackwater (May 1844)**
Pencil, wash, white on paper 12.4 x 17.5

15. **Charlemont Fort (November 1844)**
Pencil, wash on paper 12.8 x 18

16. **Leaguer Hill (May 1844)** (Legar Hill)
Pencil, wash on paper 12.3 x 17.5

17. **From Leaguer Hill (23 November 1844)**
Pencil, wash on paper 12.8 x 18

18. **Moy from the Banks of the Blackwater (May 1844)**
Pencil, white on paper 12 x 17.5

19. **Near Moy (27 November 1844)**
Pencil, wash on paper 12.7 x 18

20. **Roxburgh Castle, the Seat of Lord Charlemont (4 November 1844)** (Roxborough)
Pencil on paper 13 x 18

21. **Near Moy (April 1844)**
Pencil, wash, white on paper 12.2 x 17.4

22. **Moy from the Marshes (November 1844)**
Pencil, wash on paper 12.9 x 18

23. **Moy and Charlemont from the Marshes (November 1844)**
Pencil, wash on paper 12.7 x 18

24. **Garrison Chapel at Charlemont (28 November 1844)**
Pencil, wash on paper 13 x 18

25. **Catholic Chapel at Moy (29 November 1844)**
Pencil, wash on paper 12.7 x 18

26. **Benburb**
Pencil, wash on paper 13 x 21.6

27. **Benburb**
Pencil, white on paper 16 x 23.3

28. **The River Blackwater and the Marshes near Moy (November 1844)**
Pencil, wash on paper 12.8 x 18

29. **Bridges across the Ulster Canal at Charlemont (4 November 1844)**
Pencil, wash on paper 12.8 x 18

30. **Moy Church from the Graveyard (November 1844)**
Pencil, wash on paper 12.8 x 18

31. **Roxburgh Castle from the Graveyard at Moy (16 November 1844)** (Roxborough)
Pencil, wash on paper 12.8 x 18

32. **The Tomb of Wm. Francis Longden Needham at Moy (16 November 1844)**
Pencil, wash on paper 18 x 12.8

33. **Cathedral, Armagh from the Mall (November 1844)**
Pencil, wash on paper 12.8 x 18

34. **Moy**
Pencil, wash on paper 12.8 x 18

35. **The Diamond at Moy and Charlemont Fort (27 November 1844)**
Pencil, wash on paper 12.8 x 18

36. **Moy Church**
Pencil, wash on paper 13 x 18

37. **The Diamond at Moy (November 1844)**
Pencil, wash on paper 12.7 x 18

38. **From Coney Island, Lough Neagh (8 November 1844)**
Pencil, wash on paper 12.8 x 18

39. **Ruins on Coney Island (8 November 1844)**
Pencil, wash on paper 12.8 x 18

40. **Coney Island (8 November 1844)**
Pencil, wash on paper 12.8 x 18

41. **On the Banks of Lough Neagh (8 November 1844)**
Pencil, wash on paper 12.7 x 18

42. **Near the Red Forge, Grange near Moy**
Pencil, wash on paper 18 x 12.6

43. **Near the Grange**
Pencil, wash on paper 12.8 x 18

44. **Ross Trevor** (Rostrevor)
Pencil, wash on paper 12.9 x 18

45. **Ross Trevor**
Pencil, wash on paper 12.8 x 18

46. **Ballincollig Castle, County Cork (31 May 1845)**
Pencil, wash, white on paper 11.7 x 16.5

47. **Ballincollig Castle (30 May 1845)**
Pencil on paper 12.5 x 17.6

48. **Junction of the Rivers Lee and Awbeg near Ballincollig (27 May 1845)**
Pencil, wash on paper 12.7 x 18

49. **Ballincollig (30 May 1845)**
Pencil, wash on paper 12.5 x 17

50. **Lodge Gate, at the Barracks, Ballincollig, from the Interior**
Pencil on paper 11.2 x 17.5

51. **Powder Mills, Ballincollig (24 October 1845)**
Pencil, wash on paper 12.5 x 17.5

52. **In the Grounds of the Powder Mills (26 May 1845)**
Pencil, wash on paper 12.6 x 18

53. **Carrigrohan Castle, County Cork (25 May 1845)**
Pencil, wash on paper 12.6 x 18

54. **River Lee at Carrigrohan (25 May 1845)**
Pencil, wash on paper 12.8 x 18

55. **Carrigrohan (27 May 1845)**
Pencil, wash on paper 12.8 x 18

56. **Carrigrohan (27 May 1845)**
Pencil, wash on paper 12.8 x 18

57. **Village of Carrigrohan (10 June 1845)**
Pencil, wash on paper 11.7 x 16.5

58. **Near Carrigrohan, Junction of Rivers Lee and Awbeg**
Pencil, white on paper 11.5 x 17.9

59. **Ruins of a Powder Mill, Hely's Bridge, River Awbeg near Blarney (2 June 1845)**
Pencil, white on paper 12.2 x 17.8

60. **Ruins of the Mill at Hely's Bridge (15 November 1845)**
Pencil, wash, white on paper 11.5 x 17.4

61. **Hely's Bridge (2 June 1845)**
Pencil, wash, white on paper 11.8 x 16.8

62. **The Groves of Blarney (2 June 1845)**
Pencil, white on paper 11.6 x 17

63. **Blarney Castle (2 June 1845)**
Pencil on paper 12.2 x 17.8

64. **Blarney Castle (2 June 1845)**
Pencil on paper 12.3 x 17.5

65. **Inniscarra Church (9 June 1845)**
Pencil, wash on paper 11.7 x 16.7

66. **Inniscarra Church (9 June 1845)**
Pencil, wash, white on paper 11.5 x 17.7

67. **Inniscarra, Junction of Rivers Bride and Lee (27 September 1845)**
Pencil, white on paper 11.9 x 17.6

68. **Inniscarra (1 June 1845)**
Pencil, wash, white on paper 11.7 x 16

69. **Inniscarra Bridge (4 June 1845)**
Pencil, wash on paper 12.5 x 17.6

70. **Inniscarra (26 May 1845)**
Pencil, wash on paper 12.8 x 18

71. **Ovens, River Bride (1 June 1845)**
Pencil, wash, white on paper 11.6 x 17

72. **Ovens (1 June 1845)**
Pencil, white on paper 12 x 17

73. **Road between Inniscarra and Ovens (1 June 1845)**
Pencil, wash, white on paper 12.2 x 17.3

74. **The River Lee at Ardrum (4 June 1845)**
Pencil, wash, white on paper 11.7 x 16.2

75. **River Lee between Inniscarra and Ardrum (4 June 1845)**
Pencil, wash, white on paper 11.8 x 16.6

76. **River Lee at Ardrum (9 June 1845)**
Pencil, wash, white on paper 11.8 x 17.4

77. **Castle Inch between Ardrum and Dripsey (13 June 1845)**
Pencil, wash, white on paper 12 x 17.8

78. **Castle Inch (18 October 1845)**
Pencil, wash, white on paper 11.8 x 17.5

79. **From the Lake at Michelstown (13 June 1845)** (Mitchelstown)
Pencil on paper 11.7 x 17.1

80. **Dripsey Castle (13 June 1845)**
Pencil on paper 11.6 x 17

81. **Dripsey Castle (18 November 1845)**
Pencil, wash, white on paper 11.6 x 17.3

82. **Dripsey Castle (18 November 1845)**
Pencil, wash on paper 11.4 x 18

83. **Kilcrea Abbey (11 June 1845)**
Pencil, wash, white on paper 11.8 x 17

84. **Kilcrea Abbey (11 June 1845)**
Pencil, wash on paper 11.8 x 17.6

85. **Kilcrea Abbey (11 June 1845)**
Pencil, wash on paper 11.7 x 16.8

86. **Kilcrea (11 June 1845)**
Pencil, white on paper 11.7 x 17

87. **Canal and Powder Mills, Ballincollig (31 May 1845)**
Pencil, wash, white on paper 12.5 x 17.6

88. **The Canal and Powder Mills, Ballincollig**
Pencil on paper 12.3 x 17.5

89. **Haulbowline Island, Cove of Cork**
Pencil, wash, white on paper 11.8 x 17.5

90. **Castle More, Rye Court (31 October 1845)**
Pencil on paper 12.5 x 17.5

91. **Bridge at Adragol (18 September 1845)** (Adrigole)
Pencil, wash on paper 12.6 x 17.4

92. **Carriganass Castle, River Ouvaune** (Owvane)
Pencil, wash on paper 12.5 x 17.5

93. **Carrignacurra Castle, Inchageela** (Inchigeelagh)
Pencil, wash on paper 12.5 x 17.5

94. **The Pass of Keim-an-eigh** (Keamaneigh)
Pencil, wash on paper 12.6 x 17.5

95. **Gougaune Barra (15 September 1845)** (Gougane Barra)
Pencil, wash on paper 12.6 x 17.5

96. **Hermitage of St. Finbar, Gougaune Barra (15 September 1845)**
Pencil, wash on paper 12.6 x 17.5

97. **Cromwell's Bridge, Glengariff (16 September 1845)**
Pencil, wash on paper 12.7 x 17.5

98. **Bridge in Lord Bantry's Grounds, Glengariff (19 September 1845)**
Pencil, wash on paper 12.5 x 17.5

99. **Road between Glengariff and Beerhaven (18 September 1845)** (Castletown Bearhaven)
Pencil, wash on paper 12.6 x 17.5

100. **Near Glengariff (17 September 1845)**
Pencil, wash on paper 12.6 x 17.5

101. **Cascade at Hungry Hill (18 September 1845)**
Pencil, wash, white on paper 12.6 x 17.5

102. **Bridge of Bally-lickey between Bantry and Glengariff (19 September 1845)** (Ballylickey)
Pencil, wash on paper 12.6 x 17.5

103. **Falls of Dunamark (19 September 1845)**
Pencil, wash , white on paper 12.7 x 17.5

104. **Dallan, near Bantry Bay (19 September 1845)**
Pencil, wash on paper 11.6 x 17.3

105. **Dunloe Castle from the Road near Agadoe (17 June 1845)** (Aghadoe)
Pencil, wash on paper 12.5 x 17.5

106. **Ross Castle and the O'Donague's Prison from Innisfallen, Lower Lake, Killarney**

Pencil, wash on paper 12.5 x 17.5

107. **Black Lake, Gap of Dunloe, Looking towards Agadoe (17 June 1845)**
Pencil on paper 12.5 x 17.4

108. **Entrance to the Gap of Dunloe (17 June 1845)**
Pencil on paper 12.5 x 17.4

109. **The Eagle's Nest, Killarney**
Pencil, wash on paper 12.5 x 17.5

110. **The Anger Lake and Turnpike Stones, Gap of Dunloe. Looking towards Agadoe (17 June 1845)**
Pencil, wash on paper 12.5 x 17.4

111. **Killarney, O'Sullivan's Cascade (17 June 1845)**
Pencil, wash on paper 17.5 x 12.5

112. **Killarney. Part of Turk Cascade (20 June 1845)** (Torc Cascade)
Pencil, white on paper 17.5 x 12.4

113. **View from the Victoria Hotel, Killarney (20 June 1845)**
Pencil on paper 12.2 x 17.4

114. **Agadoe Church and Round Tower (18 June 1845)**
Pencil, wash on paper 12.5 x 17.5

115. **Old Weir Bridge, Killarney (20 June 1845)**
Pencil on paper 12.6 x 17.5

116. **Mucross Abbey (20 June 1845)** (Muckross)
Pencil on paper 12.5 x 17.4

117. **Mucross from the Park, Killarney (21 June 1845)**
Pencil on paper 12.6 x 17.4

118. **Beginning of the Ascent to Mangerton (21 June 1845)**
Pencil, wash on paper 12.5 x 17.5

119. **The Horses' Glen, Killarney (21 June 1845)**
Pencil, wash on paper 12.5 x 17.4

120. **The Devil's Punch Bowl (21 June 1845)**
Pencil, wash, white on paper 12.5 x 17.5

121. **Untitled Sketch of Bridge in Glen**
Pencil on paper 12.6 x 17.5

122. **Untitled Sketch of Lakeside Road**
Pencil on paper 12.5 x 17.5

123. **From the Road from Killarney to Kenmare (22 June 1845)**
Pencil, wash on paper 12.7 x 17.5

124. **Blackrock River, Lough Carrig (22 June 1845)**
Pencil, wash on paper 12.6 x 17.4

HAWKSETT, Samuel 1801-59 (Irish)

3.1985   **Martha Wentworth (1846)**
Signed, dated
Donated by Mrs. A. D. K. Miller, 1985
Formerly by Unknown

HEANEY, Aidan 20th century (Irish)

19.1976   **Cottages on Achill**
Oil on canvas 38.6 x 64.2 (sight)

Signed
Purchased 1976

HEMMINGWAY, Dr. Douglas L. 1894-1968 (Irish)

84.1976   **Cottages at Glen Mona, Isle of Man (1938)** *(Illus.p.377)*
Watercolour on paper 27.3 x 37.8 (sight)
Signed, dated
Purchased 1976

85.1976   **Near Hamiltonsbawn, September (1941)**
Watercolour on paper 37.5 x 26.7 (sight)
Signed, dated
Purchased 1976

86.1976   **Curraghs**
Watercolour on paper 27 x 37.8 (sight)
Signed
Purchased 1976

87.1976   **On Slieve Gullion**
Watercolour on paper 26.8 x 37.7 (sight)
Purchased 1976

88.1976   **Near Loughgall, Co. Armagh**
Ink on paper 22.2 x 17 (sight)
Purchased 1976

HEWSON, Edith fl.1914-32 (Irish)

98.1973   **Armagh Cathedral and Mall**
Watercolour on paper 21.6 x 13 (sight)
Donated by M. H. Armstrong, 1973

HUGHES, Nigel 20th century (Irish)

51.1979   **Out to Sea over Dundrum, Co. Down**
Watercolour on paper 25.5 x 35.4 (sight)
Signed
Purchased 1979

HUNTER, John Frederick 1893-1951 (Irish)

27.1987   **Street in Dungannon** *(Illus.p.377)*
Watercolour on board 37.8 x 48
Signed
Purchased 1987

HYNES, Joseph 20th century (Irish?)

42.1989   **Nasturtiums (c.1988)** *(Illus.p.378)*
Watercolour on paper 38.2 x 46.8 (sight)
Signed
Purchased 1988

I

IRWIN, Clara 1853-1921 (Irish)

1.1953   **Armagh from the Keady Road (1910)**
Watercolour on paper 20.7 x 35.2 (sight)
Signed
Donated by the Friends of Armagh

County Museum, 1953

2.1953 **Ballinahone, Armagh (1900)**
Watercolour on paper 20.3 x 32.7
(sight)
Signed
Donated by the Friends of Armagh
County Museum, 1953

3.1953 **Scotch Street, Armagh (c.1910)**
(Illus.p.378)
Watercolour on paper 34.2 x 25
(sight)
Donated by the Friends of Armagh
County Museum, 1953

4.1953 **Market Street, Armagh (c.1920)**
(Illus.p.378)
Watercolour on paper 33.2 x 52.3
(sight)
Signed
Donated by the Friends of Armagh
County Museum, 1953

4.1959 **College Street, Armagh (1920)**
(Illus.p.378)
Watercolour on paper 14.5 x 14.3
Donated by Mrs. Houston, 1959

ITEN, Hans 1874-1930 (Swiss, worked in Ireland)

59.1960 **Belvoir Park** *(Illus.p.378)*
Charcoal, pencil on paper 35.4 x 43.6
(sight)
Donated by W. Heaney, 1960

16.1977 **Sunset, Belvoir Park**
Oil on board 14.6 x 20.8 (sight)
Signed
Donated by R. P. Smyth, 1977

17.1977 **The Old Beech Tree, July**
Oil on canvas 16 x 22.5
Signed
Donated by R. P. Smyth, 1977

J

JELLETT, Mainie 1897-1944 (Irish)

66.1973 **Coast Scene (1935)**(Dooagh, Achill
Island)*(Illus.p.378)*
Gouache on paper 25.2 x 35.3 (sight)
Signed, dated
Bequeathed by Sylvia Cooke-Collis
(per the Friends of the National
Collections of Ireland), 1973

JOHNSTON, Francis 1760-1829 (Irish)

116.1968 **West Elevation of Armagh Cathedral
in its Present State (1785)**
Ink, wash on paper 35.6 x 28 (sight)
Dated
Purchased 1968

K

KEATING, Séan 1889-1977 (Irish)

98.1966 **Life Class** *(Illus.p.378)*
Sepia on paper 50.5 x 72.2 (sight)
Signed

Donated by the Thomas Haverty Trust,
1966

KIRKWOOD, Harriet 1880-1953 (Irish)

2.1946 **Tea in the Studio** *(Illus.p.378)*
Oil on canvas 50.7 x 61.2
Donated by the Thomas Haverty Trust,
1946

KNOX, Harry Cooke fl.1931-78 (Irish)

59.1977 **Major P. Terris (1968)**
Pencil on paper 19.7 x 14.3 (sight)
Signed, dated
Donated by the artist, 1977

KYLE, Georgina Moutray 1865-1950 (Irish)

1.1946 **The End of the Dyke, Volendam**
(Illus.p.378)
Oil on canvas 44 x 34.4
Donated by the artist, 1946

L

LAMB, Charles 1893-1964 (Irish)

134.1947 **Taking in the Lobster Pots** *(Illus.p.379)*
Oil on canvas 49 x 59 (sight)
Signed
Purchased 1947

9.1990 **A Connemara Lake** *(Illus.p.379)*
Oil on board 33.2 x 40.7
Signed
Purchased 1990

LARGEY, Hugh d.1992 (Irish)

2.1982 **Haymaking at Maghera, Co. Donegal**
Oil on canvas 30.5 x 40.6
Signed
Purchased 1982

8.1993 **The Hostage**
Oil on board 90.2 x 59.8 (sight)
Signed
Donated by Mrs. A. Largey, 1993

9.1993 **After Interrogation**
Oil on board 74.6 x 64.5 (sight)
Signed
Donated by Mrs. A. Largey, 1993

LENNOX, A. 19th-20th century (Irish)

43.1981 **At Ballinahone (1915)**
Watercolour on paper 20.2 x 27.8
(sight)
Signed, dated
Donated by J. D. Thompson, 1981

LESLIE, Sir John, Bt. fl.1865-80 (Irish)

1.1966 **Tynan Hunt (1880)** *(Illus.p.379)*
Watercolour on paper 25.5 x 33.1
Bequeathed by C. E. Huston, 1966

LIVESAY, Richard 1753-c.1823 (English)

51.1960 **Francis Gervais d.1849**
Oil on canvas 22.8 x 19.8 (sight)
Donated by Mrs. D. Rhodes, 1960

LODER, James fl.1820-57 (English)

154.1958 **Mare, Castledillon Stables (1831)**
(Illus.p.379)
Oil on canvas 58.6 x 76
Signed, dated
Donated by Armagh County Council,
1958

LUKE, John 1906-75 (Irish)

2.1945 **The Old Callan Bridge (1945)**
(Illus.p.379)
Oil, tempera on board 55.4 x 77.5
Signed, dated
Commissioned 1945

42.1980 **Judith and Holofernes** *(Illus.p.379)*
Oil on canvas 50 x 60.5
Signed
Purchased 1980

LYNAS, John Langtry 1879-1956 (Irish)

69.1957 **Creation of Man**
Pastel on paper 34.8 x 23.8 (sight)
Donated by John Hewitt, 1957

M

MacCANN, George Galway 1909-67 (Irish)

115.1973 **George Paterson of Armagh 1888-
1971 (c.1938)**(T. G. F. Paterson)
Chalk on paper 35 x 24.2 (sight)
Signed
Donated by Mrs. Mercy MacCann,
1973

1.1984 **Mercy Hunter 1910-89 (1931)**
Sculpture, plaster head, ht. 36.2; base
12.7
Donated by the sitter (Mrs. Mercy
MacCann), 1984

77.1986 **Head of Christ**
Gouache on paper 55 x 37.2 (sight)
Signed
Donated by Robert McKinstry, 1986

McCLUGHIN, W. J. 1900-71 (Irish)

66.1957 **Ballyduff Brae (1932)**
Watercolour on paper 20.8 x 29.5
(sight)
Signed, dated
Donated by John Hewitt, 1957

68.1957 **The Circle in the Italian Garden,
Mountstewart, Co. Down (1926)**
Pastel on paper 32.6 x 50.4 (sight)
Signed, dated
Donated by John Hewitt, 1957

MacCRACKEN, Raymond 20th century (Irish)

27.1980 **Barn Owl (1978)**
Watercolour on paper 35.1 x 23.7
(sight)
Signed, dated
Purchased 1980

McENDOO, Lesley 20th century (Irish?)

60.1990 **Kenneth MacQueen Hamilton**

Oil on board 44.5 x 35 (sight)
Bequeathed by the sitter, 1990

MacGONIGAL, Maurice 1900-79 (Irish)

4.1945   **Fishing Boats, Clogher Head, Co.**
       Louth *(Illus.p.379)*
       Oil on board 29.8 x 39.8 (sight)
       Signed
       Donated by the Thomas Haverty Trust,
       1945

MacMANUS, Henry c.1810-78 (Irish)

87.1937   **The Court House, Armagh (1830)**
       Watercolour, white on paper 16 x 24.2
       (sight)
       Donated by the Hon. Mrs. H. C.
       Alexander, 1937

MACKIE, Miss Isa 1869-1958 (Irish)

1.1942   **Chin Angles, or How the Poets Passed**
       (Cartoon)
       Ink, wash on paper 27 x 35.7 (sight)
       Signed
       Donated by Mrs. Verschoyle, 1942

MAGUIRE, Cecil b.1930 (Irish)

16.1992   **Long Walk from Claddagh Quay,**
       Galway (1987) *(Illus.p.379)*
       Oil on board 61 x 45.5
       Signed, dated
       Purchased 1992

MALLON, Charles 20th century (Irish)

18.1977   **Flowers for St. Bridget at Genoa**
       (1959)
       Oil on board 26.4 x 19.2 (sight)
       Signed, dated
       Donated by E. N. Carrothers, 1977

MEE, Anne c.1775-1851 (English, worked in
Ireland)

67.1975   **Joseph Mee d.1849, of Mount Anna,**
       Co. Armagh
       Watercolour on paper 17.3 x 13.2
       (sight)
       Purchased 1975

MILLER, John 19th century (Irish?)

1.1990   **A View of the Principal Front of**
       Gosford Castle, Armagh *(Illus.p.379)*
       Ink, wash on paper 64.7 x 98.7
       Purchased 1990

MORROW, Michael fl.1949-54 (Irish)

2.1957   **Chloe** *(Illus.p.380)*
       Oil on board 39.8 x 30.5
       Donated by the Thomas Haverty Trust,
       1957

N

NICHOLL, Andrew 1804-86 (Irish) (attributed
to)

100.1975   **Narrow Water Castle** *(Illus.p.380)*
       Watercolour on paper 23.5 x 35

(sight)
Purchased 1975
Formerly by Unknown

NICHOLSON, Thomas 20th century (Irish)

51.1969   **The Broken Link, Brackagh Lock**
       (Illus.p.380)
       Oil on canvas 40 x 50.6 (sight)
       Signed
       Purchased 1969

NIXON, John c.1750-1818 (English)

96.1980   **Narrow Water, near Newry (1787)**
       (Illus.p.380)
       Ink, wash on paper 15.8 x 23.2
       Signed, dated
       Purchased 1980

97.1980   **Rostrevor, Seven Miles from Newry**
       (Illus.p.380)
       Ink, wash on paper 16.2 x 23.3
       Purchased 1980

98.1980   **Fathom, near Newry** *(Illus.p.380)*
       Ink, wash on paper 15.9 x 23
       Purchased 1980

99.1980   **The Collector's House and Canal near**
       Newry *(Illus.p.380)*
       Watercolour, ink, wash on paper 16.2
       x 22.3
       Purchased 1980

O

O'MURNAGHAN, Art 1872-1954 (Irish)

28.1946   **Irish Book of the Resurrection: Four**
       Sketches (1924-26)
       Donated by the artist, 1946

1.   **Prophecy of Malachy (1926)**
    Pencil on paper 31.5 x 26.4
    Signed, dated

2.   **Celtic Design (1924)**
    Pencil on paper 30.8 x 30.6
    Signed

3.   **Celtic Design**
    Pencil on paper 23 x 19.7
    Signed

4.   **Celtic Design**
    Pencil on paper 23 x 19.5
    Signed

ORPEN, Bea 1913-80 (Irish)

3.1957   **Harbour Master's House, Aberdeen**
       (1950) *(Illus. p. 380)*
       Watercolour on paper 16 x 23 (sight)
       Signed, dated
       Donated by the Thomas Haverty Trust,
       1957

OSBORNE, Jean 1926-65 (Irish)

91.1967   **Grief**
       Oil on board 46.7 x 61 (sight)
       Signed
       Purchased 1967

P

PINGRET, Edouard Henri Théophile 1788-1875
(French)

9.1965   **Colonel Dawson Kelly, CB (1818)**
       Oil on canvas 22.3 x 17 (sight)
       Signed, dated
       Donated by Mrs. W. M. Tate, 1965

PIPER, Raymond b.1923 (English, works in
Ireland)

43.1991   **George Galway MacCann 1909-67**
       and Mercy MacCann, née Hunter
       1910-89 (1953)
       Pencil on paper 35.8 x 26.8 (sight)
       Donated by Robert McKinstry, 1991

PITT-TAYLOR, Lady Daphne 1889-1945 (Irish)

3.1954   **The Island Cross, Tynan** *(Illus.p.380)*
       Watercolour on paper 30.4 x 22.2
       Donated by Miss Jessie Stronge, 1954

137.1959   **Linenhall Street, Armagh (c.1935)**
       (Illus.p.381)
       Watercolour on paper 28.1 x 38.2
       Signed
       Donated by T. G. F. Paterson, 1959

138.1959   **Beech Trees, Tynan (1939)**
       Watercolour on paper 35.3 x 27
       (sight)
       Signed, dated
       Donated by T. G. F. Paterson, 1959

104.1960   **Totaria Woods, New Zealand**
       Watercolour on paper 24.8 x 34.6
       (sight)
       Donated by T. G. F. Paterson, 1960

POWER, G. 19th century (Irish?)

14.1997   **The Moy** *(Illus.p.381)*
       Watercolour on paper 23 x 33.1
       Signed
       Purchased 1997

R

RANKEN, William Bruce Ellis 1881-1941
(English)

6.1946   **The Yellow Tree** *(Illus.p.381)*
       Oil on canvas 75.6 x 63.5
       Signed
       Donated by Mrs. E. Thesiger, 1946

READE, Kate 20th century (Irish)

47.1977   **Blue Tits on Hemmellis**
       Watercolour on paper 40.7 x 34.7
       (sight)
       Signed
       Purchased 1977

REID, B. 20th century (Irish?)

274.1988   **Ballinahone**
       Oil on canvas 30.6 x 40.5
       Donated by Miss L. E. M. Reid, 1988

REID, Henrietta Roberta 1875-1957 (Irish)

26.1981   **Armagh from the Golf Links (1918)**
(Illus.p.381)
Watercolour on paper 27.2 x 37.8
Signed, dated
Purchased 1981

RIBOULET, Eugène 1883-1972 (French, worked in Ireland)

71.1957   **June in the Cevennes** *(Illus.p.381)*
Oil on canvas 64.7 x 49.5
Signed
Donated by John Hewitt, 1957

ROBINSON, Thomas d.1810 (English, worked in Ireland)

1.1979   **Thomas Romney Robinson 1792-1882**
(Illus.p.381)
Oil on canvas 121.8 x 102.4
Purchased 1979

RUSSELL, George William ('AE') 1867-1935 (Irish)
Most of the following works are as titled by the artist

39.1940   **Sketch in Oils** *(Illus.p.381)*
Oil on canvas 23 x 28.2
Donated by Mrs. A. M. Maude, 1940

50.1940   **Girls in a Wood**
Oil on canvas 41 x 53.5
Signed
Donated by Dermod O'Brien, 1940

52.1940   **Sunset** *(Illus.p.381)*
Oil on board 22 x 31.4
Signed
Purchased 1940

5.1943   **Lady with a Lamp**
Pastel on paper 37.3 x 20 (sight)
Donated by Mrs. A. M. Maude, 1943

9.1944   **In County Donegal**
Oil on canvas 53 x 82
Signed
Purchased 1944

4.1946   **Girls by the Sea**
Oil on canvas 47.7 x 76.8 (sight)
Signed
Donated by Lady Pitt-Taylor, 1946

5.1946   **The Traveller** *(Illus.p.381)*
Ink, wash on paper 36.3 x 25.4 (sight)
Signed
Donated by Monk Gibbon, 1946

1.1948   **A Warrior of the Sidhe**
Pastel on paper 30.4 x 20.3 (sight)
Donated by Miss Ella Young, 1948

2.1948   **The Stolen Child**
Pastel on paper 23 x 33 (sight)
Donated by Miss Ella Young, 1948

1.1949   **The Potato Gatherers** *(Illus.p.382)*
Oil on canvas 50.7 x 61
Donated by the representatives of Miss Lily Yeats, 1949

2.1950   **Women on Hillside** *(Illus.p.382)*
Oil on canvas 53.5 x 81.4
Signed
Donated by the Hon. Miss E.

McNaghten, 1950

14.1954   **Self-Portrait (1903)** *(Illus.p.382)*
Pastel on paper 37.3 x 27.3
Signed
Donated by Mrs. V. D. Franklin, 1954

42.1957   **The Prince of Tir-na-nog** (Tír na nÓg)
Pastel on paper 26.5 x 21.2 (sight)
Signed
Donated by the Theosophical Society, 1957

43.1957   **Come Away**
Pastel on paper 21.5 x 26.8 (sight)
Signed
Donated by the Theosophical Society, 1957

146.1957   **Portrait of C. A. Weekes (1891)**
Ink on paper 10.2 x 11.4
Signed, dated
Donated by Mrs. C. A. Weekes, 1957

13.1958   **The Spirit of the Pool**
Oil on canvas 49 x 66.8 (sight)
Signed
Purchased 1958

110.1963   **On the Beach** *(Illus.p.382)*
Oil on canvas 53.4 x 81.4
Signed
Donated by the Rt. Hon. the Viscountess Simon, 1963

109.1965   **Miss Elizabeth Young**
Oil on canvas 59.6 x 47 (sight)
Signed
Bequeathed by the sitter, 1965

110.1965   **Deirdre at the Door of her Dun**
Oil on canvas 47 x 59.6 (sight)
Signed
Bequeathed by Miss Elizabeth Young, 1965

111.1965   **Cuchulan at the Ford** (Cuchúlainn)
(Illus.p.382)
Oil on card 22.5 x 34.1
Bequeathed by Miss Elizabeth Young, 1965

128.1965   **Eventide**
Oil on canvas 53.4 x 81.4
Signed
Purchased 1965

90.1980   **Parent and Child**
Ink on paper 15 x 12 (sight)
Donated anonymously, 1980

24.1986   **Holyhead Excursion (1884)** (Sixteen Sketches on Page)
Ink on paper 74.5 x 54.6 (sight)
Signed, dated
Donated by the Friends of Armagh County Museum, 1986

25.1986   **Intermediate Examination** (Seven Sketches on Page)
Ink on paper 53.2 x 49.8 (sight)
Signed
Donated by the Friends of Armagh County Museum, 1986

S

SKENE, H. 20th century (Irish)

115.1983   **The Mall, Armagh (1971)**
Oil on canvas on board 39.5 x 64.8 (sight)
Signed
Purchased 1983

SLAUGHTER, Stephen 1697-1765 (English, worked in Ireland)

30.1987   **John Hoadly 1678-1746, Archbishop of Armagh and Primate of All Ireland (1744)** *(Illus.p.382)*
Oil on canvas 126 x 101
Signed, dated
Purchased 1987

SLEATOR, James Sinton 1885-1950 (Irish)

1.1950   **Still Life**
Oil on canvas 74.5 x 61.8 (sight)
Donated by the Thomas Haverty Trust, 1950

134.1956   **Jenny King**
Oil on board 56.5 x 41.5 (sight)
Signed
Purchased 1956

101.1960   **Self-Portrait** *(Illus.p.382)*
Oil on board 58.2 x 43.3
Purchased 1960

60.1966   **Mrs. MacNamara** *(Illus.p.382)*
Oil on canvas 122.5 x 91.7
Signed
Purchased 1966

90.1969   **Daffodils**
Oil on canvas 50.7 x 60.6
Signed
Bequeathed by Miss Ethel Sleator, 1969

37.1973   **Rt. Hon. Henry Bruce Armstrong, DL, JP 1844-1943**
Oil on canvas 89.6 x 69.8 (sight)
Donated by Armagh County Council, 1973

38.1973   **John Compton, DL, JP**
Oil on canvas 76 x 63.5
Donated by Armagh County Council, 1973

SMITH, Sidney 1912-82 (Irish)

76.1957   **John Hewitt, BA 1907-87 (1943)**
Pencil on paper 37 x 25
Signed, dated
Donated by the sitter, 1957

50.1990   **George Galway MacCann 1909-67**
Oil on canvas 63.8 x 48.3 (sight)
Signed
Purchased 1990

STAPLES, Sir Robert Ponsonby, Bt. 1853-1943 (Irish)

7.1942   **Field-Marshal Lord Kitchener 1850-1916 (1916)**
Watercolour on paper 37.8 x 28.8

(sight)
Signed, dated
Donated by the Rev. W. E. R. Scott,
1942

STEVENSON, Patric 1909-83 (Irish)

77.1987   **Knockchree and the Mournes from
           Greencastle, Co. Down (1968)**
           (Illus.p.382   )
           Oil on board 17.4 x 25.5
           Signed
           Bequeathed by W. A. N. MacGeogh
           Bond, 1987

STEWART, D. fl.c.1810 (Irish)
The following works are as titled by the artist

75.1975   **Augher Castle, Co. Tyrone**
           Ink, wash on paper 20.2 x 25.8
           Purchased 1975

76.1975   **Downpatrick**
           Ink, wash on paper 20.2 x 25.8
           Purchased 1975

77.1975   **Newcastle near Tullamore, Co. Down**
           ('Tollymore?')
           Ink, wash on paper 20.2 x 25.8
           Purchased 1975

78.1975   **Grey Abbey, Co. Down** (Greyabbey)
           Ink, wash on paper 20.2 x 25.8
           Purchased 1975

79.1975   **Old Mansion of Dundrum, Co. Down**
           Ink, wash on paper 20.2 x 25.8
           Purchased 1975

80.1975   **Newark Castle, Co. Down**
           Ink, wash on paper 20.2 x 25.8
           Purchased 1975

81.1975   **Isle of Devenish, Co. Fermanagh**
           (Ledwich's *Antiquities*) *(Illus.p.383)*
           Ink, wash on paper 20.2 x 25.8
           Purchased 1975

82.1975   **Devenish Island, Co. Fermanagh**
           Ink, wash on paper 20.2 x 25.8
           Purchased 1975

83.1975   **Old Church Tower, Dundalk, Co.
           Louth**
           Ink, wash on paper 20.2 x 25.8
           Purchased 1975

84.1975   **Carlingford Castle, Co. Louth**
           Ink, wash on paper 20.2 x 25.8
           Purchased 1975

85.1975   **Carlingford Abbey, Co. Louth**
           Ink, wash on paper 20.2 x 25.8
           Purchased 1975

86.1975   **Roche Castle, Co. Louth**
           Ink, wash on paper 20.2 x 25.8
           Purchased 1975

87.1975   **Castletown Castle, Co. Louth**
           Ink, wash on paper 20.2 x 25.8
           Purchased 1975

88.1975   **Priory of Drumlane, Co. Cavan**
           Ink, wash on paper 20.2 x 25.8
           Purchased 1975

89.1975   **Dromahaire Castle, Co. Leitrim**

Ink, wash on paper 20.2 x 25.8
Purchased 1975

90.1975   **Abbey of Dromahaire, Co. Leitrim**
           Ink, wash on paper 20.2 x 25.8
           Purchased 1975

91.1975   **O'Rourke's Hall, Co. Leitrim**
           Ink, wash on paper 20.2 x 25.8
           Purchased 1975

92.1975   **Salmon Leap, Ballyshn** (Ballyshannon)
           Ink, wash on paper 20.2 x 25.8
           Purchased 1975

93.1975   **Carrickarede, Co. Antrim** (Carrick-a-
           Rede)
           Ink, wash on paper 20.2 x 25.8
           Purchased 1975

94.1975   **The Pleaskin, Co. Antrim**
           Ink, wash on paper 20.2 x 25.8
           Purchased 1975

95.1975   **West View of the Giant's Causeway**
           Ink, wash on paper 20.2 x 25.8
           Purchased 1975

96.1975   **The East Prospect of the Giant's
           Causeway**
           Ink, wash on paper 20.2 x 25.8
           Purchased 1975

97.1975   **Benmore or Fair Head in the Co.
           Antrim**
           Ink, wash on paper 20.2 x 25.8
           Purchased 1975

98.1975   **Dunluce Castle, Co. Antrim**
           Ink, wash on paper 20.2 x 25.8
           Purchased 1975

99.1975   **Dunluce Castle**
           Ink, wash on paper 20.2 x 25.8
           Signed
           Purchased 1975

STOREY, Harold 20th century (Irish)

20.1976   **Greer's Cottage, Lurgan** *(Illus.p.383)*
           Oil on canvas 49.6 x 59.8 (sight)
           Signed
           Purchased 1976

T

TAYLOR, Dr. James. 19th century (Irish)

144.1964   **Demonstration in Tandragee (c.1886)**
           Watercolour on paper 24.4 x 34.4
           (sight)
           Donated by A. McClelland, 1964

THOMPSON, J. H. S. 20th century (Irish)

94.1983   **HM Prison, Armagh (1982)**
           Watercolour on paper 18.9 x 29
           (sight)
           Signed, dated
           Purchased 1983

THOMSON, Richard 19th-20th century and
Joseph William CAREY 1859-1937 (Irish)

23.1969   **Presentation Album with Illuminated
           Address Containing Seven Sketches**

and Vignettes by Carey (1915)
Watercolour on board 38.1 x 30.5
Signed
Donated by Rev. J. W. McMiller, 1969

THORNTON, W. R. 20th century (Irish?)

59.1981   **Front Elevation, Carrickblacker
           House, Co. Armagh**
           Ink on paper 56 x 81 (sight)
           Signed
           Donated by the artist, 1981

TURNER, John b.1916 (Irish)

70.1957   **Castlerock, Co. Londonderry (1943)**
           Oil on canvas 35.7 x 40
           Signed, dated
           Donated by John Hewitt, 1957

U

UNKNOWN, 17th century

27.1953   **Sir Thomas Molyneux, Bt., FRS 1661-
           1733**
           Oil on canvas 128 x 101.4
           Donated by Armagh County Council,
           1953

35.1954   **Woman with a Gold Chain**
           Oil on canvas 75.8 x 63.5
           Donated by Armagh County Council,
           1954

100.1955   **Susanna Johnston**
           Oil on canvas 72.2 x 62.5
           Purchased 1955

4.1960   **Daniel Gervais, Gentleman Usher to
           the Duke of Shrewsbury**
           Miniature, watercolour on ivory 5.7 x
           4.7 (oval)
           Donated by Mrs. D. Rhodes, 1960

6.1960   **Jean Gervais**
           Miniature, carved ivory 9.3 x 7.3
           (oval)
           Donated by Mrs. D. Rhodes, 1960

17.1961   **Young Man in a Blue Coat**
           Oil on canvas 76 x 63
           Donated by Armagh County Council,
           1961

19.1961   **Gentleman in a Red Cloak**
           Oil on canvas 74 x 61 (sight)
           Donated by Armagh County Council,
           1961

1.1963   **Wilhelmina Molyneux**
           Oil on canvas 135 x 107
           Donated by the representatives of the
           late T. E. Reid, 1963

103.1990   **The Jacobean Child** *(Illus.p.383)*
           Oil on canvas 94 x 76
           Bequeathed by Mrs. D. Rhodes, 1960

UNKNOWN, 18th century

7.1945   **Michael Boyle, DD, Archbishop of
           Armagh 1678-1702**
           Oil on canvas 74.5 x 62.3 (sight)
           Donated by the Hon. Mrs. H. C.

Alexander, 1945

30.1954 **Joseph Addison 1672-1719**
Oil on canvas 125.1 x 101.6 (sight)
Donated by Armagh County Council,
1954

31.1954 **Portrait of a Clergyman** (Style of
James Latham 1696-1747)
(Illus.p.383)
Oil on canvas 66 x 55
Donated by Armagh County Council,
1954

32.1954 **General John Adlercron (1758)**
Oil on canvas 74.2 x 62.5
Dated
Donated by Armagh County Council,
1954

33.1954 **Dr. Garnet, Bishop of Clogher 1758-
82**
Oil on canvas 63 x 52 (sight)
Donated by Armagh County Council,
1954

34.1954 **Dorothea Molyneux (1766)**
Oil on canvas 108 x 125.6 (sight)
Dated
Donated by Armagh County Council,
1954

151.1957 **Jonathan Seaver 1760-1841 (c.1781)**
Oil on board 59.5 x 48.8 (sight)
Donated by the Very Rev. G. Seaver,
1957

150.1958 **Most Rev. and Hon. William Stuart,
DD, d.1822, Archbishop of Armagh**
Oil on canvas 127.2 x 100.3 (sight)
Donated by the Armagh Natural
History and Philosophical
Society, 1958

151.1958 **Mina Molyneux** (Style of Stephen
Slaughter 1697-1765) *(Illus.p.383)*
Oil on canvas 127 x 101
Donated by Armagh County Council,
1958

153.1958 **Castledillon, Co. Armagh (c.1782)**
Now attributed to Jonathan Fisher
d.1809

158.1958 **Thomas Ogle, Sovereign of Armagh**
Oil on canvas 125.1 x 99.1 (sight)
Donated by the Armagh Natural
History and Philosophical
Society, 1958

7.1960 **A Lady of the Gervais Family**
Miniature, watercolour on ivory 9.3 x
7.3 (sight)
Donated by Mrs D. Rhodes, 1960

52.1960 **Peter Gervais 1722-1800**
Oil on canvas 30.5 x 24.5 (sight)
Donated by Mrs. D. Rhodes, 1960

53.1960 **Mrs. Peter Gervais d.1800 (c.1770)**
Oil on canvas 30.4 x 24.8 (sight)
Donated by Mrs. D. Rhodes, 1960

54.1960 **Mr. Blennerhasset**
Pastel on paper 24 x 18.6 (sight)
Donated by Mrs D. Rhodes, 1960

55.1960 **Mr. Blennerhasset**

Pastel on paper 24 x 18.6 (sight)
Donated by Mrs D. Rhodes, 1960

18.1961 **Gentleman in a Red Coat** (Style of
James Latham 1696-1747)
(Illus.p.383)
Oil on canvas 76 x 63.4
Donated by Armagh County Council,
1961

20.1961 **Sir Capel Molyneux 1717-97**
Oil on canvas 74.5 x 61 (sight)
Donated by Armagh County Council,
1961

30.1961 **Captain Nicholas Gay (1782)**
Oil on canvas 74.7 x 62.8 (sight)
Dated
Donated by Armagh County Council,
1961

53.1961 **'Glad Buckle': A Lady of the
Molyneux Family**
Oil on canvas 76 x 64.2
Donated by Armagh County Council,
1961

2.1963 **Rev. William Lodge, DD 1742-1813
(c.1758)** (Style of Stephen Slaughter
1697-1765) *(Illus.p.383)*
Oil on canvas 127.8 x 101.3
Purchased 1963

3.1965 **Castledillon from across the Lake
(c.1782)**
Now attributed to Jonathan Fisher
d.1809

4.1965 **Lake Scene** (Style of Jonathan Fisher
d.1809)
Oil on canvas 81.8 x 128
Donated by J. McLaughlan, 1965

UNKNOWN, 19th century

82.1937 **William McWilliams of the Armagh
Yeomanry, d.1840**
Oil on canvas 62.8 x 48.9 (sight)
Donated by A. Davidson, 1937

30.1941 **Mrs. Mason**
Silhouette, ink, wash on paper 26.7 x
17.5 (sight)
Donated by Miss J. Weir, 1941

31.1941 **Mr. Mason**
Silhouette, ink, wash on paper 26.7 x
17.5 (sight)
Donated by Miss J. Weir, 1941

6.1942 **Armagh (c.1850-60)**
Oil on canvas 46 x 87.6 (sight)
Donated by Col. W. F. Templer, 1942

11.1943 **Gentleman Facing Left**
Silhouette, ink on paper 28.6 x 18.7
(sight)
Donated by A. E. Greer, 1943

12.1943 **Gentleman Facing Right with a Book**
Silhouette, ink on paper 28.5 x 19
(sight)
Bequeathed by A. E. Greer, 1943

13.1943 **Lady Facing Right with a Book**
Silhouette, ink on paper 28.6 x 18.7
(sight)
Donated by A. E. Greer, 1943

14.1943 **Lady Facing Left with a Book**
Silhouette, ink on paper 28.5 x 19
(sight)
Bequeathed by A. E. Greer, 1943

15.1943 **Child with a Cat**
Silhouette, ink, wash on paper 19.1 x
13.3 (sight)
Bequeathed by A. E. Greer, 1943

23.1944 **Lieutenant-Colonel Charles H. Knox
1808-64 (1831)**
Pencil on paper 22.3 x 17 (sight)
Donated by J. St. Clair Boyd, 1944

18.1951 **Charlemont Fort, Co. Armagh**
(Illus.p.383)
Pencil, wash on paper 13.4 x 20.8
Purchased 1951

6.1953 **Toulerton Lutton 1771-1854 (1812)**
Oil on canvas 55 x 44 (sight)
Donated by J. Bryson, 1953

29.1957 **St. Patrick's Cathedral, Exterior by
(a)   Moonlight**
Watercolour on paper 8.2 x 10.8
Donated by the Linen Hall Library,
1957

29.1957 **St. Patrick's Cathedral, Interior**
(b)
Watercolour on paper 8.2 x 10.8
Donated by the Linen Hall Library,
1957

125.1957 **Joseph Seaver 1798-1874**
Oil on board 54 x 44
Donated by the Very Rev. G. Seaver,
1957

126.1957 **Commander Charles Seaver 1799-
1862, RN**
Oil on canvas 59 x 51.5 (sight)
Donated by the Very Rev. G. Seaver,
1957

127.1957 **Bridget Seaver, Wife of Sackville
Hatch Lovett**
Oil on canvas 63.8 x 49.5 (sight)
Donated by the Very Rev. G. Seaver,
1957

128.1957 **Maria Nicholina Seaver 1821-83**
Oil on canvas 61 x 51
Donated by the Very Rev. G. Seaver,
1957

148.1957 **Thomas Seaver 1825-1900, of Heath
Hall, Co. Armagh**
Oil on board 54 x 45.5
Donated by the Very Rev. G. Seaver,
1957

149.1957 **Jonathan Seaver, FGS, FRCS 1853-
1927** *(Illus.p.374)*
Now attributed to Christopher
Campbell 1908-72

150.1957 **Jonathan Seaver 1760-1841, of Heath
Hall, Co. Armagh**
Crayon, wash on paper 49.5 x 39.4
(sight)
Donated by the Very Rev. G. Seaver,
1957

152.1957 **Thomas Seaver 1789-1848, of Heath
Hall, Co. Armagh**

Oil on board 56.6 x 46.6 (sight)
Donated by the Very Rev. G. Seaver,
1957

153.1957 **Lieutenant Jonathan P. Seaver 1790-
1822, 15th Foot** *(Illus.p.383)*
Oil on board 60.5 x 49.5
Donated by the Very Rev. G. Seaver,
1957

10.1958 **Plan and Elevation of Entrance Gates
on the Road to Rathangan**
Ink, wash on paper 37.5 x 48.3
Donated by Sir Albert Richardson,
1958

148.1958 **Sir George K. A. Molyneux, Bt., on
'Pantaloon'** *(Illus.p.384)*
Oil on canvas 58.8 x 76.2
Donated by Armagh County Council,
1958

149.1958 **Lieutenant-General Sir Thomas
Molyneux, Bt., on 'Masterpiece'**
(Illus.p.384)
Oil on canvas 58.8 x 76
Donated by Armagh County Council,
1958

152.1958 **Lieutenant-General Sir Thomas
Molyneux, Bt., d.1841**
Oil on canvas 75 x 62 (sight)
Donated by Armagh County Council,
1958

155.1958 **Sir George K. A. Molyneux, Bt.
(1826)** *(Illus.p.384)*
Oil on canvas 91.7 x 71
Dated
Donated by Armagh County Council,
1958

128.1959 **James Lougheed**
Watercolour on paper 26.7 x 16.5
(sight)
Donated by Miss C. Lockhart, 1959

14.1960 **Georgina Frances Dalrymple Gervais
(c.1886)**
Watercolour on paper 12.2 x 9.8
(sight)
Donated by Mrs. D. Rhodes, 1960

49.1960 **The Misses Catherine and Fanny
Gervais (c.1830)**
Ink, wash on paper 18.1 x 15.5 (sight)
Donated by Mrs. D. Rhodes, 1960

96.1960 **John Francis Gervais 1818-82**
(Illus.p.384)
Oil on canvas 42.1 x 34.2
Donated by Mrs. E. M. Stuart, 1960

97.1960 **Mrs. F. P. Gervais**
Oil on board 53.2 x 43
Donated by Mrs E. M. Stuart, 1960

99.1960 **Captain Richard Maunsell, 7th
Fusiliers** *(Illus.p.384)*
Oil on canvas 76.5 x 60.7
Donated by Mrs. C. Maunsell-Eyre,
1960

102.1960 **George Corry of Armagh**
Silhouette, ink on paper 26.7 x 15.5
(sight)
Donated by T. G. F. Paterson, 1960

103.1960 **Robert Jocelyn, 3rd Earl of Roden
1788-1870**
Silhouette, ink on paper 28 x 20.3
(sight)
Donated by T. G. F. Paterson, 1960

75.1962 **William Lodge Kidd**
Cut-out silhouette on paper 27 x 12
(sight)
Donated by Miss E. Kidd, 1962

130.1962 **The Paymaster** *(Illus.p.384)*
Oil on board 36.5 x 30.7
Donated anonymously, 1962

34.1963 **Pastoral Scene**
Pencil on paper 13.4 x 18.7 (sight)
Donated by Miss L. Shields, 1963

60.1963 **Heath Hall, Co. Armagh (1852)**
Pencil on paper 21 x 36.8 (sight)
Donated by the Very Rev. G. Seaver,
1963

117.1965 **Marcus Beresford 1801-85,
Archbishop of Armagh**
Miniature, watercolour on ivory 8.3 x
6 (sight)
Purchased 1965

92.1967 **Acton House, Co. Armagh**
Watercolour on paper 25 x 35.6
(sight)
Donated by J. Vitty, 1967

97.1967 **Great Northern Railway Locomotive
No. 26, 'Armagh' (1880)**
Pencil, wash on paper 30.5 x 83.8
(sight)
Donated by K. M. Clendinning, 1967

98.1967 **Drumbanagher House from the Lake
(c.1850)**
Pencil on paper 19.5 x 27.2 (sight)
Donated by D. H. Gillman, 1967

1.1969 **Castleraw**
Oil on board 27.5 x 46.7 (sight)
Donated by Field-Marshal Sir Gerald
Templer, 1969

100.1975 **Narrow Water Castle** *(Illus.p.380)*
Now attributed to Andrew Nicholl
1804-86

115.1975 **Cairn Ban, near Newry (1830)**
Pencil on card 22 x 14.3
Dated
Purchased 1975

116.1975- Now attributed to Henrietta L.
131.1975 Chambers fl.1827-48

34.1978 **Killeavy Castle** *(Illus.p.384)*
Ink, wash on paper 38.9 x 50.3 (sight)
Purchased 1978

178.1978 **A Lady of the Johnston Family**
Silhouette, ink, wash, gold on paper
11.3 x 8.6 (sight) (oval)
Bequeathed by Mrs. G. N. Wallace,
1978

179.1978 **Sophiah Johnston, neé Cheney**
Silhouette, ink on card 7.5 x 6 (sight)
(oval)
Bequeathed by Mrs. G. N. Wallace,
1978

180.1978 **Mrs. Anne Johnston, née Barnes 1769-
1841**
Silhouette, ink, wash on card 9 x 7.2
(sight) (oval)
Bequeathed by Mrs. G. N. Wallace,
1978

181.1978 **Mrs. Gregg, Wife of the Dean of
Armagh**
Silhouette, ink, wash on card 7.7 x 6.3
(sight) (oval)
Bequeathed by Mrs G. N. Wallace,
1978

182.1978 **Francis Johnston 1760-1829**
Silhouette, ink, wash on card 9 x 7.3
(sight) (oval)
Bequeathed by Mrs G. N. Wallace,
1978

183.1978 **Andrew Johnston 1770-1833**
Silhouette, ink on card 7.7 x 6.4
(sight) (oval)
Bequeathed by Mrs G. N. Wallace,
1978

184.1978 **George Barnes**
Silhouette, ink, wash on card 9 x 7.4
(sight) (oval)
Bequeathed by Mrs G. N. Wallace,
1978

185.1978 **Francis G. Johnston 1811-68 (c.1830)**
Silhouette, ink, wash on card 7.6 x 6.4
(sight) (oval)
Bequeathed by Mrs G. N. Wallace,
1978

186.1978 **William Johnston 1813-89 (c.1825)**
Silhouette, ink, wash on card 7.8 x 6.2
(sight) (oval)
Bequeathed by Mrs G. N. Wallace,
1978

187.1978 **George Johnston 1814-89 (c.1824)**
Silhouette, ink, wash on card 6.8 x 5.6
(sight) (oval)
Bequeathed by Mrs G. N. Wallace,
1978

188.1978 **Richard Johnston 1816-1907 (c.1830)**
Silhouette, ink, wash on card 6.7 x 5.5
(sight) (oval)
Bequeathed by Mrs G. N. Wallace,
1978

189.1978 **Andrew Johnston 1819-38 (c.1830)**
Silhouette, ink, wash on card 6.7 x 5.5
(sight) (oval)
Bequeathed by Mrs G. N. Wallace,
1978

190.1978 **Robert Johnston 1822-1901 (c.1832)**
Silhouette, ink, wash on card 6.5 x 5.4
(sight) (oval)
Bequeathed by Mrs G. N. Wallace,
1978

1.1983 **Armagh Courthouse (1810)**
(Illus.p.384)
Watercolour on paper 28.9 x 40.2
Purchased 1983

1.1985 **Stampede at Schechem (1888)**
Watercolour on paper 29.2 x 43.6
(sight)
Purchased 1985

3.1985   **Martha Wentworth (1846)**
Now by Samuel Hawksett 1801-59

49.1986   **The Black Lady (Sarah or Sally
Peebles) 1797-1852**
Silhouette, watercolour on paper 72.1
x 39.5 (sight)
Donated by W. P. Williamson, 1986

17.1987   **Armagh from the East (1836)**
Pencil on paper 10.3 x 16.7 (sight)
Donated by Dr. and Mrs. E. Duffy,
1987

121.1998   **Conolly and the Armagh Harriers
(1841)**
Pencil, wash on paper 19.4 x 30.6
Purchased 1998

53.1999   **Gentleman Facing Right**
Silhouette, ink, wash, gold on paper 28
x 14 (sight)
Provenance unknown

UNKNOWN, 20th century

67.1936   **Market Street, Armagh (c.1927)**
Watercolour on paper 17.5 x 23.3
(sight)
Donated by the representatives of the
Gibson family, 1936

95.1960   **F. P. Gervais (c.1905-15)**
Oil on board 29.4 x 37.6
Donated by Mrs. E. M. Stuart, 1960

V

VALLELY, John B. b.1941 (Irish)

32.1985   **The Red Fiddle (1984)**
Oil on canvas 101 x 126.3 (sight)
Signed
Donated by the Friends of Armagh
County Museum, 1985

78.1987   **Untitled**
Ink on paper 24.5 x 33.5 (sight)
Bequeathed by W. A. N. MacGeogh
Bond, 1987

VALLELY, Dara b.1946 (Irish)

13.1992   **Musicians**
Oil on canvas 152.3 x 125.4
Signed
Purchased 1992

VARLEY, Cornelius 1781-1873 (English)

33.1937   **Mullabrack Church, Co. Armagh,
from Drapiers' Hall (1808)**
Pencil on paper 21 x 36.3 (sight)
Signed
Purchased 1937

34.1937   **Gosford Manor, Markethill, Co.
Armagh, (1808)**
Pencil on paper 20.6 x 38.4 (sight)
Purchased 1937

35.1937   **Armagh Cathedral from the West
(1808)**
Pencil on paper 20.6 x 38.4 (sight)
Donated by Sir H. McAnally, 1937

3.1946   **Markethill, Co. Armagh (1800)**
Pencil on paper 29.8 x 46.6 (sight)
Donated by Sir H. McAnally, 1946

8.1973   **Market Street, Armagh**
Pencil on paper 26.8 x 51.8 (sight)
Donated by the T. G. F. Paterson
Memorial Fund, 1973

9.1973   **Woman Spinning in a Doorway
(1808)**
Pencil on paper 33.8 x 24.2 (sight)
Donated by the T. G. F. Paterson
Memorial Fund, 1973

10.1973   **Interior of a House**
Pencil on paper 35.5 x 32.3 (sight)
Signed
Donated by the T. G. F. Paterson
Memorial Fund, 1973

11.1973   **Cottage, Ireland**
Pencil on paper 12.2 x 19
Donated by the T. G. F. Paterson
Memorial Fund, 1973

12.1973   **Markethill, Co. Armagh (1808)**
Pencil on paper 12.2 x 19
Signed, dated
Donated by the T. G. F. Paterson
Memorial Fund, 1973

13.1973   **The Kennel near Markethill, Co.
Armagh (1808)**
Pencil on paper 12 x 18.5 (sight)
Signed, dated
Donated by the T. G. F. Paterson
Memorial Fund, 1973

W

WALKER, David Bond 1891-1977 (Irish)

7.1946   **The Hon. R. H. Henderson, CMG,
b.1862**
Oil on canvas 62.5 x 49 (sight)
Signed
Donated by T. E. Reid, 1946

WALLER, Colonel C. D. 19th century (English)

86.1937   **Charlemont Fort, Co. Armagh
(c.1820)**
Watercolour on paper 17.8 x 25.4
(sight)
Donated by Miss C. V. Trench, 1937

WILKS, Maurice C. 1910-84 (Irish)

67.1957   **The Mournes from Portaferry, Co.
Down (1912)**
Watercolour on paper 18.2 x 25.6
(sight)
Signed
Donated by John Hewitt, 1957

136.1959   **Winter, Cushendun** *(Illus.p.384)*
Oil on canvas 40.7 x 51.7
Signed
Donated by T. G. F. Paterson, 1959

WILLIAMS, Alexander 1846-1930 (Irish)

64.1957   **The White Rocks, Portrush, Co.
Antrim**

Watercolour on paper 23 x 35 (sight)
Signed
Donated by John Hewitt, 1957

WILSON, Joseph fl.c.1766-93, d.1793 (Irish)

3.1945   **Alexander Stewart, d.c.1802, of Acton
House, Co. Armagh (1789)**
Oil on canvas 33.7 x 25.4 (sight)
(oval)
Signed, dated
Purchased 1945

105.1960   **Mrs. Stewart of Acton House, Co.
Armagh (1789)**
Pastel on paper 22.8 x 18.4 (sight)
(oval)
Donated by T. G. F. Paterson, 1960

WOOD, Shakspere 1827-86 (English)

129.1965   **Coventry Patmore 1823-96 (1865)**
Sculpture, marble bust, ht. 77.5
Signed, dated
Donated by St. Patrick's College,
Armagh, 1965

WRAY, Margaret L. F. 19th century (Irish)

**49.1936
(a)**   **Cathedral from Market Square
(c.1868)**
Watercolour on paper 16 x 11.7
(sight)
Donated by Miss C. V. Trench, 1936

**49.1936
(b)**   **Folly Lake (c.1868)**
Watercolour on paper 16 x 11.7
(sight)
Donated by Miss C. V. Trench, 1936

**49.1936
(c)**   **Cathedral from Observatory Hill
(c.1868)**
Watercolour on paper 16 x 11.7
(sight)
Donated by Miss C. V. Trench, 1936

74.1936   **City of Armagh (c.1868)**
Watercolour on paper 12.4 x 32.7
Donated by Miss C. V. Trench, 1936

3.1939   **Folly Lake (1868)**
Watercolour on paper 18.8 x 23.8
(sight)
Donated by T. G. F. Paterson, 1939

drawings paintings & sculptures

the ulster folk and transport museum

A

ADAMS, Margaretta (Mrs. Robert Dunlop) 19th century (Irish)

1334.2000 **Basket of Flowers (1865-70)**
Watercolour on paper 13.5 x 18 (sight)
Provenance unknown

1335.2000 **Flowerpiece (1865-70)**
Watercolour on paper 13.5 x 18 (sight)
Provenance unknown

1336.2000 **Flowerpiece (1865-70)**
Watercolour on paper 20.5 x 15.5 (sight)
Provenance unknown

1337.2000 **Flowerpiece (1865-70)**
Watercolour on paper 20.5 x 15.5 (sight)
Provenance unknown

1338.2000 **Flowerpiece (1865-70)**
Watercolour on paper 13.5 x 18.5 (sight)
Provenance unknown

1339.2000 **Flowerpiece (1865-70)**
Watercolour on paper 17.5 x 21.5 (sight)
Provenance unknown

1340.2000 **Flowerpiece**
Watercolour on paper 20.5 x 15.5 (sight)
Provenance unknown

1341.2000 **Flowerpiece**
Watercolour on paper 20.5 x 15.5 (sight)
Provenance unknown

1342.2000 **Flowerpiece**
Watercolour on paper 18.5 x 13.5 (sight)
Provenance unknown

ARCHIBALD, Mrs. S. A. 19th century (Irish?)

1343.2000 **Ross Castle, Killarney (?)**
Oil on canvas 15.5 x 20
Signed
Provenance unknown

B

B., F. [F. B.] 19th century (British?)

1344.2000 **Portrait of a Disraelian Gentleman (1874)**
Oil on canvas 34 x 29 (sight)
Signed, dated
Provenance unknown

BENINGTON, M. 20th century (Irish?)

1345.2000 **Ploughing with Two Horses**
Oil on canvas 40.5 x 55.5
Signed
Provenance unknown

BION, Cyril Walter 1889-1976 (English, worked in Ireland)

1346.2000 **Thatched Cottage Overlooking a Lough**
Oil on canvas 51 x 61
Signed
Provenance unknown

BLAIR, Doris Violet fl.1940s-'80s (Irish)

271.1982 **Lock on the Lagan Canal** (Newforge)
(Illus.p.386)
Oil on board 34 x 47
Donated by Mr. and Mrs. James Lloyd MacQuitty, 1982

BOTH, Jan c.1618-52 (Dutch) (attributed to)

8094.1942 **An Italian Landscape with Peasants Driving Cattle at Evening**
Oil on canvas 63 x 76
Provenance unknown

BROWN, C. 20th century (British?)

1311.1988 **The Arrival of 'Olympic', White Star Line, Rounding West Bramble**
Watercolour on paper 36 x 52.5 (sight)
Purchased 1988

BUCHANAN, A. 20th century (Irish?)

1347.2000 **Cultra Manor**
Watercolour on paper 22 x 39.5
Signed
Provenance unknown

1348.2000 **Town Area, Folk Museum**
Watercolour on paper 24 x 39.5
Provenance unknown

C

CAREY, John 1861-1943 (Irish)

1349.2000 **Waiting for a Fare** (Jaunting Car Driver)
Oil on panel 16 x 12
Signed
Donated by Miss T. D. Hamilton, 1962

1350.2000 **Study of a Girl with a Red Skirt**
Watercolour on card 15 x 9
Provenance unknown

1351.2000 **Three Studies of Irish Peasants**
Ink on paper 11.5 x 7.5
Provenance unknown

1352.2000 **Farmer Leading a Pig**
Watercolour on paper 8.5 x 7
Provenance unknown

1353.2000 **Woman Spinning**
Watercolour on card 16 x 11
Provenance unknown

1354.2000 **Girl Selling Whiskey at the Giant's Well at the Causeway**
(Advertisement for Bushmill's Whiskey?)

Watercolour on card 12 x 8.5
Provenance unknown

1355.2000 **Irish Peasant at a Cottage Door**
Watercolour on paper 11 x 8
Provenance unknown

1356.2000 **Irish Peasant** (Man at Prayer?)
Watercolour on paper 11 x 8.5
Provenance unknown

1357.2000 **Family of Shepherds** (Vignette)
Watercolour on paper 11 x 13.5
Provenance unknown

1358.2000 **Girl Spinning**
Watercolour on card 13 x 10.5
Provenance unknown

1359.2000 **Amorous Couple**
Ink on card 12 x 10
Provenance unknown

1360.2000 **High Street, Saturday Night**
(Humorous Sketch: High Street Seen through the Eyes of a Drunk))
Ink, wash, white on paper 22.5 x 17
Provenance unknown

1361.2000 **Journey's End: The Climax of a Life of Unrewarded Toil** (Old Horses Being Shipped to Belgium)
Bodycolour on card 20.5 x 17
Provenance unknown

1362.2000 **Master Joyce**
Watercolour on paper 19 x 10.5
Provenance unknown

1363.2000 **Robert Burns Ploughing**
Ink on paper 15.5 x 20.5
Provenance unknown

1364.2000 **Girl with a Red Hood** (Red Riding Hood?)
Watercolour on paper 19 x 16
Provenance unknown

1365.2000 **Girl with a Red Hood** (Red Riding Hood?)
Watercolour on card 13 x 13
Provenance unknown

1366.2000 **Sketches of Ships and Boats at Ilfracombe**
Pencil, watercolour on paper 21 x 25.5
Provenance unknown

1367.2000 **Parish Meeting** (Book Jacket Design for *Sons of the Sod* by W. G. Lyttle of Bangor)
Watercolour on paper 22 x 15
Provenance unknown

1368.2000 **Old Woman Threading a Needle**
Watercolour on card 18.5 x 14.5
Provenance unknown

1369.2000 **Amorous Couple**
Ink, wash on card 27 x 16
Provenance unknown

1370.2000 **Sketch - a Private Still** (Poteen)
Ink, watercolour on paper 11.5 x 24.5
Provenance unknown

1371.2000 **Woman Wearing a Kimono**

Pencil, watercolour on paper 46 x
24.5
Provenance unknown

1372.2000 **Amorous Couple**
Pencil on paper 16.5 x 12
Provenance unknown

1373.2000 **Amorous Couple**
Pencil on paper 16.5 x 13
Provenance unknown

1374.2000 **Couple Irish Dancing**
Pencil on paper 12 x 10
Provenance unknown

1375.2000 **Whiskey Seller**
Pencil on paper 14 x 9 (irregular)
Provenance unknown

1376.2000 **Sketches for Illustrations to Moore's**
Irish Melodies
Pencil on paper 20 x 17.5 (irregular);
drawn on both sides
Provenance unknown

1377.2000 **Erin go Bragh** (Spinner and a Harp)
Pencil on paper 21.5 x 14
Provenance unknown

1378.2000 **Amorous Couple**
Pencil on paper 18.5 x 11.5
Provenance unknown

1379.2000 **Irishman Standing in front of a**
Cottage
Pencil on paper 22 x 17.5
Provenance unknown

1380.2000 **Faction Fight with Shillelaghs**
Pencil on paper 20.5 x 17.5
Provenance unknown

1382.2000 **Irish Dance**
Pencil on paper 18.5 x 18.5
Provenance unknown

1383.2000 **Lettering Layouts (1930)**
Pencil, ink on paper 25.5 x 20 (Back
of Letter to Carey from British Red
Cross Society, Belfast and Co. Antrim
Branch, City Hall, Belfast, 6 October
1930)
Provenance unknown

1384.2000 **A Colleen and a Chapter Heading**
Pencil on paper 23.5 x 16
Provenance unknown

1385.2000 **Scene in a Shop**
Pencil on paper 24 x 15
Provenance unknown

1386.2000 **Two Men Arguing on a Country**
Road
Pencil on paper 26 x 21.5 (Back of
Sale of Work Programme in Aid of
University Road Moravian Church)
Provenance unknown

1387.2000 **A Coat of Arms** (Motto 'Tutamen
Pulchris')
Pencil on paper 29 x 27
Provenance unknown

1388.2000 **Fishwives Bargaining**
Pencil on paper 35 x 25 (squared)
Provenance unknown

1389.2000 **Emigrants on the Deck of a Ship**
Pencil on paper 28 x 32
Provenance unknown

1390.2000 **A Landlord in a Carriage Guarded**
by Militia
Pencil on paper 21.5 x 27.5
Provenance unknown

1391.2000 **Two Drawings of a Girl Dancing**
Pencil on paper 28.5 x 26
Provenance unknown

1392.2000 **Thumbnail Sketches of Four**
Fishermen
Pencil on paper 8 x 4
Provenance unknown

1393.2000 **An Irish Toper**
Pencil on paper 50 x 32.5 (Back of
The Moravian Church Almanac)
Provenance unknown

1394.2000 **The Long Car**
Ink, watercolour, white on paper 26 x
43.5 (sight)
Signed
Provenance unknown

1395.2000 **The Long Car**
Ink, wash, white on paper 12.5 x 19.5
(sight)
Signed
Provenance unknown

1396.2000 **Jaunting Car Driver** (in Dublin?)
Ink, wash, white on paper 28 x 22
(sight)
Signed
Provenance unknown

1397.2000 **Race between Jaunting Car and**
Donkey Cart
Ink, wash, white on paper 12.5 x 19.5
(sight)
Signed
Provenance unknown

CAREY, Joseph William 1859-1937 (Irish)

502.1977 **Fanad Head, Co. Donegal (1922)**
Watercolour on paper 25 x 38 (sight)
Signed, dated
Provenance unknown

92.1996 **Cultra Glen Waterfall, Kennedy**
Estate (1910)
Watercolour on paper 28 x 21.5
(sight)
Signed, dated
Donated by Peter Burke Murphy (per
Mrs. R. Strachan), 1996

1398.2000 **Cultra Manor (1910)**
Watercolour on paper 19 x 33 (sight)
Signed, dated
Provenance unknown

1399.2000 **Steam Coaster 'Clandeboye' (1929)**
Watercolour on paper 35 x 50 (sight)
Signed, dated
Provenance unknown

CARVILL, J. F. 20th century (Irish?)

821.1974 **TSS 'Oceanic' (1908)** (White Star
Line)

Watercolour on paper 25 x 75 (sight)
Signed, dated
Donated by John Gilmore, 1974

822.1974 **TSS 'Celtic' (1905)** (Starboard
Profile)
Watercolour, white on paper 25 x 72
(sight)
Donated by John Gilmore, 1974

CAUGHEY, William S. 19th century (Irish)

1400.2000 **Vallée de la Menage (1888)** (Vallée
du Ménage)
Pencil, white on paper 29 x 40
Donated by Thomas Watson Caughey,
1969

CHAPPELL, Reuben 1870-1940 (English)

1401.2000 **Steam Coaster 'Glencregagh' (1920-**
27) *(Illus.p.386)*
Watercolour on paper 34.5 x 53.5
(sight)
Signed
Provenance unknown

COCKERHAM, C. 20th century (British?)

272.1984 **'Monaleen' (1921)**
Oil on canvas 50 x 75.5 (sight)
Signed, dated
Purchased 1984

273.1984 **SS 'Brideen' (1921)**
Oil on canvas 50 x 75 (sight)
Signed, dated
Purchased 1984

COLEMAN, William Stephen 1829-1904
(English)

1506.2000 **An English Cottage Garden**
Watercolour on paper 16.5 x 22.5
(sight)
Signed
Provenance unknown

CONOR, William 1881-1968 (Irish)

104.2000 **Edna Helen (c.1930)** (Girl in a Green
(C1)   Suit)
Oil on canvas 91 x 69
Signed
Purchased 1982

105.2000 **For Us! (1916)**
(C2)   Pencil, watercolour on paper
39.5 x 26 (sight)
Signed, dated
Purchased 1982

107.2000 **Within the Lights of Belfast (1908)**
(C4)   Pencil, crayon on paper 24.5 x 15
(sight)
Signed
Purchased 1982

108.2000 **River Lagan Bridge** (Minnowburn)
(C5)   Watercolour on paper 13 x 20
(sight)
Signed
Purchased 1982

109.2000 **The Politician (1925)**
(C6)   Oil on canvas 44 x 34 (sight)

Signed
Purchased 1982

110.2000 (C7) **The Two of Us** (Woman with a Cat)
Oil on panel 37 x 29 (sight)
Purchased 1982

111.2000 (C8) **The Passing Stranger (1908)** (Old Lodge Road, Belfast)
Crayon on paper 29 x 33 (sight)
Acquired 1961

112.2000 (C9) **Group of Mill Girls (1906)** (Belfast)
Ink, crayon on paper 25.5 x 19.5 (sight)
Signed, dated
Purchased 1982

113.2000 (C10) **Weavers** (Preparatory Drawing for 'Weaving', Ulster Museum U2322)
Crayon on paper 42 x 26.5 (sight)
Signed
Acquired 1961

114.2000 (C11) **Four Figure Studies:**
Seated Woman
Ink on paper 18.5 x 15 (sight)
Seated Woman
Crayon, ink on paper 25 x 21 (sight)
Man Playing a Melodeon
Crayon, ink on paper 17 x 12.5 (sight)
Woman Wearing a Hat
Ink on paper 17 x 12.5 (sight)
Purchased 1982

116.2000 (C13) **Roses**
Watercolour on paper 33.5 x 26 (sight)
Signed
Purchased 1982

117.2000 (C14) **Four Crayon Studies (c.1910)**
All on paper 19.5 x 14.5 (sight)
Purchased 1982
Man Reading a Newspaper
Figures in Street
Woman Reading
Entrance to a Pub

118.2000 (C15) **The Reader (1939)**
Oil on canvas 44 x 34 (sight)
Signed
Acquired 1961

119.2000 (C16) **Robert Lynd 1879-1949**
Oil on canvas 74 x 62 (sight)
Signed
Purchased 1982

120.2000 (C17) **Women of the Field (1948)**
Oil on canvas 49 x 39 (sight)
Purchased 1982

121.2000 (C18) **Trees and Water**
Watercolour on paper 24 x 16 (sight)
Signed
Purchased 1982

122.2000 (C19) **Cronies (1907)**
Ink, crayon on paper 20 x 13.5 (sight)
Signed

Acquired 1961

123.2000 (C20) **The Twelfth (1918)** (Wellington Place, Belfast)*(Illus.p.386)*
Oil on canvas 71.2 x 91.2
Signed
Acquired 1961

124.2000 (C21) **Woman Washing her Hair, 15 March '08**
Pencil on paper 22.5 x 13.5 (squared)
Signed
Purchased 1982

125.2000 (C22) **Girl Reading in a Kitchen** (or 'Girl Drying her Hair')
Pencil on paper 21 x 13.5
Purchased 1982

126.2000 (C23) **Sketches of Bugler's Uniform**
Pencil on paper 22 x 16 (squared)
Purchased 1982

127.2000 (C24) **Old Man Seated in a Kitchen, 10 April**
Pencil on paper 12.6 x 18.5 (squared)
Purchased 1982

128.2000 (C25) **Fireside, 6 Jan. '10** (A Kitchen Range)
Pencil on paper 18.5 x 13
Purchased 1982

129.2000 (C26) **The Sonsy Boy (1909)**
Ink, crayon on paper 18 x 12
Signed
Purchased 1982

130.2000 (C27) **York Street (1908)** (Figure Studies of Shawlies)
Ink, crayon on paper 18 x 24
Signed
Purchased 1982

131.2000 (C28) **Self-Portrait Sketch**
Pencil on card 12 x 7.5
Purchased 1982

132.2000 (C29) **Three Women Gossiping, 11 March**
Pencil on paper 18.5 x 12.5
Purchased 1982

133.2000 (C30) **Woman Scrubbing a Floor, 11 March '10**
Pencil on paper 18 x 12 (squared)
Purchased 1982

134.2000 (C31) **Woman Putting on a Shawl**
Watercolour on paper 13.5 x 8.5 (squared)
Purchased 1982

135.2000 (C32) **Standing Shawlie**
Pencil, charcoal, watercolour on card 25 x 15
Purchased 1982

136.2000 (C33) **Standing Woman in Profile**
Pencil, ink on paper 16.5 x 12
Purchased 1982

137.2000 (C34) **Caricature - French Revolutionaries**
Ink on paper 28.5 x 22.5
Signed

Purchased 1982

138.2000 (C35) **Armagh Cathedral and Courthouse from the Mall**
Pencil on paper 19 x 24 (squared)
Purchased 1982

141.2000 (C38) **Major Hall, Newcastle (1916)**
Pencil on paper 23 x 14
Signed
Purchased 1982

144.2000 (C41) **Seated Army Officer with a Pipe**
Pencil on paper 22.5 x 13.5
Purchased 1982

146.2000 (C43) **Getting Ready for Parade, RIR J. Telford**
Pencil on paper 23 x 14
Signed
Purchased 1982

147.2000 (C44) **Colonel Wallace, CO Newcastle Company (1916)**
Pencil on paper 23 x 14
Signed, dated
Purchased 1982

148.2000 (C45) **The Salute (1916)**
Pencil on paper 22 x 14
Signed, dated
Purchased 1982

149.2000 (C46) **Caricature: Self-Portrait**
Crayon on paper 26 x 17
Purchased 1982

150.2000 (C47) **Gerald Burns**
Chalk, crayon on paper 25 x 17.5
Signed
Purchased 1982

151.2000 (C48) **Dancing Couple**
Ink on paper 28.5 x 22
Purchased 1982

152.2000 (C49) **Dancing Couple**
Pencil on paper 28.5 x 21.5 (squared)
Purchased 1982

153.2000 (C50) **Street Urchins Fighting**
Pencil on paper 28 x 22
Signed
Purchased 1982

157.2000 (C54) **Man Asleep in a Chair, 8 Feb.** (Conor's Father?)
Pencil on paper 22 x 14
Signed
Purchased 1982

158.2000 (C55) **Seated Woman Reading a Newspaper (1907)** (Conor's Mother?)
Pencil on paper 22 x 13.5
Signed, dated
Purchased 1982

159.2000 (C56) **Seated Woman Reading, 29 Jan. '08**
Pencil on paper 22 x 14
Signed
Purchased 1982

160.2000 (C57) **Cleaning Windows** (World War I)
Pencil on paper 23 x 14
Purchased 1982

161.2000
(C58)
Having a Haircut *(Illus.p.386)*
Crayon on paper 45.5 x 34
Signed
Purchased 1982

162.2000
(C59)
Keep Fighting Fit
Crayon, watercolour on paper
44.5 x 35.5
Signed
Purchased 1982

164.2000
(C61)
Colonel Wallace's Son (1917)
Chalk on paper 47 x 31
(irregular)
Signed
Purchased 1982

165.2000
(C62)
Two Men Watching Lambeg Drummers
Pencil, crayon on paper 22.5 x 28
Signed
Purchased 1982

166.2000
(C63)
Two Head Studies of Women Wearing Hats (1908)
Pencil, crayon on paper 23 x 13.5, 23 Oct. '08
Signed
Pencil on paper 19 x 14 (irregular)
Purchased 1982

167.2000
(C64)
Cottages on the Lagan
Watercolour on paper 39 x 30
Purchased 1982

168.2000
(C65)
Mount Stewart
Watercolour on paper 39 x 28
Purchased 1982

169.2000
(C66)
Cottages
Pencil, crayon on paper 26.5 x 37
(squared)
Purchased 1982

170.2000
(C67)
Distant View of a Town
Watercolour on paper 28 x 40
Purchased 1982

171.2000
(C68)
Lagan Towpath
Crayon, watercolour on paper
30 x 39
Signed
Purchased 1982

172.2000
(C69)
Man Wearing a Deerstalker Cap
Crayon on paper 40 x 24
Purchased 1982

173.2000
(C70)
Belfast Mill Girl
Charcoal, crayon on paper 32 x 24
Signed
Acquired 1961

174.2000
(C72)
Village and Trees
Ink, watercolour on paper 23 x 33.5
Signed
Purchased 1982

175.2000
(C73)
Cottages on the Lagan (?)
Crayon, watercolour on paper
25 x 32.5
Signed
Purchased 1982

176.2000
(C74)
A Village Street
Pencil, crayon on paper 26.5 x 36

Purchased 1982

177.2000
(C75)
'Richard Rowley' (R. V. Williams 1877-1947)
Pencil on paper 28 x 22
Purchased 1982

178.2000
(C76)
Head of a Man, 18 March '09 (Self-Portrait?)
Chalk on paper 29 x 20.5
Signed
Purchased 1982

179.2000
(C71)
Cronies (1909)
Ink, crayon, watercolour on paper
31 x 25
Signed
Acquired 1961

180.2000
(C77)
Music in the Park (1947) (Botanic Gardens, Belfast) *(Illus.p.386)*
Oil on canvas 61 x 75 (sight)
Signed
Acquired 1961

181.2000
(C78)
My Aunt (1909)
Ink, crayon on paper 13 x 10 (sight)
Signed
Purchased 1982

182.2000
(C79)
Potato Harvest (1910) (Portadown, Co. Armagh)
Ink, crayon, watercolour on paper
27 x 21 (sight)
Signed
Acquired 1961

183.2000
(C80)
Girl over Jumps - the Huntress
Oil on panel 44 x 35 (sight)
Purchased 1982

184.2000
(C81)
Daffodils
Oil on canvas 50 x 39 (sight)
Signed
Purchased 1982

185.2000
(C82)
Taking his Steps (c.1920)
Oil on canvas 49 x 44 (sight)
Acquired 1961

186.2000
(C83)
Nine Male Figure Studies (1910-14)
Pencil on paper 18 x 10 (sight)
Purchased 1982

187.2000
(C84)
The Potato Diggers (1948) (Dromara, Co. Down)
Oil on canvas 39 x 49 (sight)
Signed
Acquired 1961

188.2000
(C85)
Lurigedan (Lurigethan, Cushendall?)
Oil on panel 34 x 44 (sight)
Signed
Purchased 1982

189.2000
(C86)
Parade Ring (1937) (Royal Dublin Society)
Crayon on paper 46.5 x 57 (sight)
Signed
Purchased 1982

190.2000
(C87)
Portrait of an RAF Officer
Oil on canvas 59 x 49 (sight)
Purchased 1982

191.2000
(C88)
Going to the Mills (1914) (Crumlin Road, Belfast)
Chalk on paper 120 x 90 (sight)

Signed
Acquired 1961

192.2000
(C89)
Carrying Potatoes (1939) (near Ballyclare, Co. Antrim)
Oil on canvas 49 x 62 (sight)
Signed
Purchased 1982

193.2000
(C90)
Fun of the Fair (1935) (Lammas Fair, Ballycastle, Co. Antrim)
Oil on canvas 74 x 62 (sight)
Signed
Acquired 1961

194.2000
(C91)
Open-air Market (1933) (Co. Antrim)
Oil on canvas 59 x 49 (sight)
Signed
Acquired 1961

195.2000
(C92)
Seaweed Gathering (1935) (Co. Donegal)
Oil on canvas 39 x 49 (sight)
Signed
Acquired 1961

196.2000
(C93)
Street Singers - Three Generations (1918)
Crayon on paper 70 x 46 (sight)
Signed
Acquired 1961

198.2000
(C95)
The Concertina Player (1930) (Ballyclare, Co. Antrim)
Oil on canvas 75 x 62 (sight)
Signed
Acquired 1961

199.2000
(C96)
Flitting
Crayon on paper 67 x 100 (sight)
Purchased 1982

201.2000
(C98)
Girl Drying her Hair
Oil on canvas 75 x 60 (sight)
Signed
Purchased 1982

202.2000
(C99)
The Hurley Players (1948) (Falls Park, Belfast) *(Illus.p.386)*
Crayon on paper 50.8 x 61 (sight)
Signed
Acquired 1961

203.2000
(C100)
Self-Portrait in an MA Gown (1957) *(Illus.p.386)*
Oil on canvas 75 x 59 (sight)
Purchased 1982

204.2000
(C101)
Girl in a Red Cardigan
Oil on canvas 90 x 70 (sight)
Signed
Purchased 1982

205.2000
(C102)
Late Self-Portrait
Crayon on paper 45 x 56.6
Signed
Purchased 1982

206.2000
(C103)
Portrait of a Red-haired Young Man
Oil on canvas 80 x 62 (sight)
Purchased 1982

207.2000
(C104)
The Artist's Mother
Oil on panel 90 x 70 (sight)
Signed
Acquired 1961

208.2000　**Blitz Dwelling - Antrim Road,**
(C105)　　**Belfast**
　　　　　Crayon on paper 31 x 41 (sight)
　　　　　Signed
　　　　　Purchased 1982

209.2000　**The Studio Dance** *(Illus.p.386)*
(C106)　　Oil on canvas 127 x 102
　　　　　Signed
　　　　　Purchased 1982

210.2000　**Child (1910)**
(C107)　　Oil on panel 70 x 57 (sight)
　　　　　Signed
　　　　　Purchased 1982

211.2000　**First American Ashore**
(C108)　　Crayon on paper 49 x 59 (sight)
　　　　　Signed
　　　　　Purchased 1982

212.2000　**The Turf Barrow (1920)** (Co. Antrim)
(C109)　　Oil on canvas 90 x 70 (sight)
　　　　　Signed
　　　　　Acquired 1961

213.2000　**Picture House Queue (1930-34)**
(C110)　　(Shankill Road, Belfast) *(Illus.p.386)*
　　　　　Oil on canvas 90 x 70 (sight)
　　　　　Signed
　　　　　Acquired 1961

214.2000　**Bomb-damaged Church**
(C60)　　Crayon on paper 45.5 x 35.5
　　　　　Signed
　　　　　Purchased 1982

216.2000　**The White Door, the Green Door**
(C113)　　Oil on canvas 92 x 71
　　　　　Signed
　　　　　Purchased 1982

217.2000　**Eleventh Night (1912)** (Shankill
(C114)　　Road, Belfast)
　　　　　Crayon on paper 37.5 x 27 (sight)
　　　　　Signed
　　　　　Acquired 1961

218.2000　**Mother and Child**
(C115)　　Crayon on paper 39 x 32 (sight)
　　　　　Signed
　　　　　Acquired 1961

219.2000　**Jaunting Car (1931)**
(C116)　　Ink, crayon on paper 29 x 22 (sight)
　　　　　Signed
　　　　　Purchased 1982

220.2000　**Saturday Morning (1906)**
(C117)　　Ink, crayon on paper 31 x 21 (sight)
　　　　　Signed, dated
　　　　　Acquired 1961

221.2000　**To the Mainland**
(C118)　　Crayon, watercolour on paper 38 x 50
　　　　　Signed
　　　　　Acquired 1961

222.2000　**Trees on the Lagan (1935)** (near
(C119)　　Shaw's Bridge) *(Illus.p.387)*
　　　　　Oil on canvas 50.8 x 40.6
　　　　　Signed
　　　　　Acquired 1961

223.2000　**Delph Woman (1912)**
(C120)　　Oil on canvas 54 x 39 (sight)
　　　　　Signed

Acquired 1961

224.2000　**The Minnowburn Bridge**
(C121)　　Crayon, watercolour on paper
　　　　　36 x 27 (sight)
　　　　　Purchased 1982

225.2000　**Lamp-post Swinging (1957)** (Belfast)
(C122)　　*(Illus.p.387)*
　　　　　Crayon on paper 37 x 49 (sight)
　　　　　Signed
　　　　　Acquired 1961

226.2000　**Gossiping (1910)** (Old Lodge Road,
(C123)　　Belfast)
　　　　　Pencil, crayon on paper 34.5 x 27
　　　　　(sight)
　　　　　Signed
　　　　　Acquired 1961

227.2000　**Potato Digging**
(C124)　　Crayon on paper 50 x 36.5 (sight)
　　　　　Signed
　　　　　Acquired 1961

228.2000　**The Hobby Horses (1951)** (Belfast)
(C125)　　Crayon on paper 50.8 x 40.6
　　　　　Signed
　　　　　Acquired 1961

229.2000　**Ardglass Fishergirls (1945)**
(C126)　　Crayon on paper 48.5 x 38
　　　　　Signed
　　　　　Acquired 1961

230.2000　**Sunday Morning (1911)** (Belfast)
(C127)　　Crayon on paper 35 x 27.5 (sight)
　　　　　Acquired 1961

231.2000　**At the Pump (1932)**
(C128)　　Crayon on paper 48.5 x 36.5
　　　　　(sight)
　　　　　Signed
　　　　　Purchased 1982

238.2000　**Sketches of Workmen**
(C1027)　　Pencil, crayon on paper 14 x 22
　　　　　(partly squared)
　　　　　Purchased 1982

239.2000　**Boy Fishing, 2 March '10**
(C1028)　　Pencil on paper 18 x 12 (squared)
　　　　　Signed
　　　　　Purchased 1982

240.2000　**Little Girl Eating an Apple**
(C1029)　　Pencil on paper 19 x 15.5 (squared)
　　　　　Purchased 1982

241.2000　**Two Sketches:**
(C1030)　　**Woman on Chaise-Longue, Reading,**
　　　　　23 April '09
　　　　　Face of Girl, Oct. '09
　　　　　Pencil on paper 20.5 x 13.5
　　　　　Purchased 1982

242.2000　**Four Studies of Man Digging**
(C1031)　　Pencil, crayon on paper 14 x 22
　　　　　Purchased 1982

243.2000　**Woodland Scene**
(C1032)　　Watercolour on paper 16 x 21
　　　　　(squared)
　　　　　Signed
　　　　　Purchased 1982

244.2000　**Sketches of Children on a Beach, 14**
(C1033)　　**June '09**

Pencil on paper 16 x 13
Purchased 1982

245.2000　**A Street Fight**
(C1034)　　Crayon on paper 15 x 17
　　　　　Signed
　　　　　Purchased 1982

246.2000　**Head of Boy**
(C1035)　　Pencil on paper 18 x 12
　　　　　Purchased 1982

247.2000　**Boy Flying a Kite, 12 March '10**
(C1036)　　Ink on paper 17.5 x 12
　　　　　Purchased 1982

248.2000　**Edenderry Village (?)**
(C1037)　　Watercolour on paper 14 x 22.5
　　　　　Signed
　　　　　Purchased 1982

249.2000　**Weir near River Lagan**
(C1038)　　Watercolour on paper 20.5 x13
　　　　　(sight)
　　　　　Purchased 1982

250.2000　**Three Sailing Boats**
(C1039)　　Pencil, watercolour on paper 22.5 x
　　　　　13.5
　　　　　Signed
　　　　　Purchased 1982

251.2000　**Harbour Scene**
(C1040)　　Watercolour on paper 22.5 x 14.5
　　　　　Signed
　　　　　Purchased 1982

252.2000　**Queen's Bridge**
(C1041)　　Watercolour on paper 14 x 22.5
　　　　　Purchased 1982

253.2000　**Heysham Steamers**
(C1042)　　Watercolour on paper 13 x 21
　　　　　(squared)
　　　　　Signed
　　　　　Purchased 1982

254.2000　**Italian Peasant Girl** (probably a
(C1043)　　Copy)
　　　　　Watercolour on paper 24 x 16
　　　　　Purchased 1982

255.2000　**Red Mill at Whitehouse, from the**
(C1044)　　**Mountain**
　　　　　Ink, watercolour on paper 23 x 31.5
　　　　　(squared)
　　　　　Purchased 1982

256.2000　**Off Durham Street - the Back**
(C1045)　　Watercolour on card 33 x 23
　　　　　Signed
　　　　　Purchased 1982

257.2000　**The Point**
(C1046)　　Watercolour on paper 19 x 28
　　　　　Purchased 1982

258.2000　**Study of Boat**
(C1047)　　Watercolour on card 13 x 20
　　　　　Purchased 1982

259.2000　**Mountain Cottages - Donegal?**
(C1048)　　Watercolour on paper 18.5 x 25.5
　　　　　Purchased 1982

260.2000　**Country Scene with Mountain**
(C1049)　　Pencil on paper 22 x 28.5
　　　　　Purchased 1982

261.2000
(C1050)
Village near the Sea
Watercolour on paper 25 x 31
Purchased 1982

262.2000
(C1051)
Queen's Bridge
Watercolour on paper 28.5 x 39
Purchased 1982

263.2000
(C1052)
Crane, Belfast Harbour
Watercolour on paper 34 x 44
Purchased 1982

264.2000
(C1053)
A Lagan Lighter Ashore
Watercolour on paper 28 x 40.5
Purchased 1982

265.2000
(C1054)
Head of Young Woman
Crayon on paper 37 x 26.5
Signed
Purchased 1982

266.2000
(C1055)
A Curragh
Pencil on paper 28 x 38
Purchased 1982

267.2000
(C1056)
A Suburban Avenue with Telegraph Poles
Pencil, watercolour on paper 39 x 39
Signed
Purchased 1982

268.2000
(C1057)
Cottages with Women at a Pump
Crayon, watercolour on paper 28 x 38
Purchased 1982

269.2000
(C1058)
Scrabo Tower
Crayon, watercolour on paper 34 x 44.5
Signed
Purchased 1982

270.2000
(C1059)
Trees on the Lagan (?)
Crayon, watercolour on paper 45 x 34
Purchased 1982

271.2000
(C1060)
Village (Co. Wicklow?)
Pencil, watercolour on paper 28 x 40
Purchased 1982

272.2000
(C1061)
Village with Tall Church Tower
Crayon, watercolour on paper 34 x 44.5
Purchased 1982

273.2000
(C1062)
Harbour with Mountain (Lurigethan, Cushendall?)
Crayon, watercolour on paper 17 x 43 (irregular)
Purchased 1982

274.2000
(C1063)
The Edge of the Wood
Watercolour on paper 44 x 38
Signed
Purchased 1982

275.2000
(C1064)
Drum Bridge Lock on the Lagan
Crayon, watercolour on paper 35 x 45
Signed
Purchased 1982

276.2000
(C1065)
Lighter on the Lagan in Central Belfast
Crayon, watercolour on paper 31.5 x 42.5
Purchased 1982

277.2000
(C1066)
A Village
Watercolour on paper 30 x 38

Signed
Purchased 1982

278.2000
(C1067)
Soldier Resting
Pencil on paper 14 x 22
Purchased 1982

279.2000
(C1068)
Soldier Sleeping in his Hut
Pencil on paper 14 x 23.5
Purchased 1982

280.2000
(C1069)
Officer Reading in an Armchair
Pencil on paper 14 x 22
Purchased 1982

281.2000
(C1069a)
Head of a Young Woman with an Arch Expression
Crayon on paper 35.5 x 26
Signed
Purchased 1982

282.2000
(C1070)
Study for 'Bugler, Ulster Division'
(Ulster Museum U1251)
Pencil on paper 22 x 14
Purchased 1982

283.2000
(C1071)
A Sergeant Filling his Pipe
Pencil on paper 22 x 14
Purchased 1982

284.2000
(C1072)
RIR Officer Seated (Royal Irish Rangers)
Pencil on paper 14.5 x 22
Signed
Purchased 1982

285.2000
(C1073)
Study of Military Uniform, with Colour-notes on Ribbons
Pencil on paper 22 x 14
Purchased 1982

286.2000
(C1074)
Study of Officer's Uniform, with Colour-notes on Ribbons (1916)
Pencil on paper 22.5 x 14
Signed
Purchased 1982

287.2000
(C1075)
RIR - Boys in the Gun
Pencil on paper 22.5 x 14
Signed
Purchased 1982

288.2000
(C1076)
Boys Playing Checker Board, 20th RIR
Pencil on paper 24 x 14
Purchased 1982

289.2000
(C1077)
At Training Corps, Newtownards, 1916, William Conor
Pencil on paper 22 x 14
Purchased 1982

290.2000
(C1078)
Types at Newcastle Camp, 1916
Pencil on paper 22 x 14
Purchased 1982

291.2000
(C1080)
Old Man with Hands in Pockets
Crayon, watercolour on paper 43.5 x 30.5
Purchased 1982

292.2000
(C1081)
Early Academic Study - Head of Boy
Charcoal on paper 44 x 30
Purchased 1982

293.2000
(C1082)
Head of Child (1910)
Crayon, watercolour on paper 26 x 26

(sight)
Purchased 1982

294.2000
(C1083)
A Village Street
Crayon, watercolour on paper 29 x 41
Signed
Purchased 1982

295.2000
(C1084)
Crowd in a Back Alley
Chalk on paper 44 x 32
Signed
Purchased 1982

296.2000
(C1085)
Ships and Cranes in a Harbour
Ink, watercolour on paper 26.5 x 34.5
Signed
Purchased 1982

297.2000
(C1086)
The Mournes (?)
Watercolour on paper 43.5 x 35
Purchased 1982

298.2000
(C1087)
Standing Female Nude
Verso, **River Scene** (Shaw's Bridge?)
Watercolour on paper (crayon, watercolour on verso) 39 x 29
Purchased 1982

299.2000
(C1088)
A Gate Lodge
Watercolour on paper 29 x 39.5
Signed
Purchased 1982

300.2000
(C1089)
Queen's Bridge (in a Fog?)
Crayon, watercolour on paper 26.5 x 36.5
Signed
Purchased 1982

301.2000
(C1090)
Cottages by a River (Lagan?)
Crayon, watercolour on paper 34 x 39
Signed
Purchased 1982

302.2000
(C1091)
Jug of Nasturtiums
Watercolour on paper 39 x 29
Purchased 1982

303.2000
(C1092)
The Blasket Island
Crayon, watercolour on paper 35.5 x 46.5
Purchased 1982

304.2000
(C1093)
Ships in a Harbour
Watercolour on paper 18.5 x 26.5
Purchased 1982

305.2000
(C1094)
Shaw's Bridge
Watercolour on paper 18 x 28
Signed
Purchased 1982

306.2000
(C1095)
Two Ladies on a Park Bench
Crayon, watercolour on paper 30.5 x 24
Purchased 1982

307.2000
(C1096)
Law Courts, Belfast, from the Lagan
Watercolour on paper 30 x 41
Signed
Purchased 1982

308.2000
(C1097)
Bomb Damage, Central Belfast
Crayon on paper 47 x 37
Signed
Purchased 1982

309.2000
Bombed Mill Buildings

(C1098) Crayon on paper 36.5 x 46
Signed
Purchased 1982

310.2000 **Glenties, Co. Wicklow**
(C1100) Signed
Verso, **Delgany, Co. Wicklow**
Crayon, watercolour on paper 37 x 41.5
Purchased 1982

311.2000 **Turf Cutting**
(C1101) Watercolour on paper 27.5 x 48.5
Purchased 1982

312.2000 **Carrying Potatoes**
(C1102) Pencil, watercolour on paper 50.5 x 38 (Back of Red Cross Poster)
Signed
Purchased 1982

313.2000 **Roulette Table**
(C1103) Crayon, chalk on paper 37.5 x 50
Signed
Purchased 1982

314.2000 **Stitching Room (1920)**
(C1104) Crayon, watercolour on paper 27.5 x 42
Signed
Purchased 1982

315.2000 **The Doorstep**
(C1105) Crayon, watercolour on paper 42 x 30.5
Signed
Purchased 1982

316.2000 **Portrait of a Man**
(C1106) Pencil, crayon on paper 45.5 x 38
Purchased 1982

317.2000 **St. John Ervine 1883-1971 (1928)**
(C1107) Pencil, crayon on paper 47.5 x 37.5
Signed, dated
Purchased 1982

318.2000 **Near Shaw's Bridge**
(C1108) Watercolour on paper 27 x 38
Signed
Purchased 1982

319.2000 **Vase of Carnations**
(C1109) Watercolour on paper 38.5 x 28
Purchased 1982

320.2000 **A Village** (Co. Wicklow?)
(C1110) Watercolour on paper 53 x 39
Purchased 1982

321.2000 **Landscape** (Donegal?)
(C1111) Watercolour on paper 48 x 40
Purchased 1982

322.2000 **Trees on the Lagan (?)**
(C1112) Crayon, watercolour on paper 49.5 x 38
Signed
Purchased 1982

323.2000 **Village in a Valley, beneath a Conical**
(C1114) **Peak** (Co. Wicklow?)
Crayon, watercolour on paper 39 x 46.5 (Back of French Ordnance Map)
Purchased 1982

324.2000 **Lisburn**
(C1115) Crayon, watercolour on paper 37 x 44
Purchased 1982

325.2000 **Study for 'Portrait of a Red-haired**
(C1116) **Young Man'** (206.2000)
Crayon on card 50 x 39
Signed
Purchased 1982

326.2000 **Open Air Meeting (?)**
(C1117) Pencil on paper 40.5 x 51 (squared)
Signed
Purchased 1982

327.2000 **Homewards, Co. Donegal (1925)**
(C1118) Crayon on paper 48 x 33
Signed
Purchased 1982

328.2000 **Trees and Cottages**
(C1119) Crayon, watercolour on paper 46.5 x 37.5
Signed
Purchased 1982

329.2000 **Young Woman in a Hat**
(C1120) Pencil on paper 19 x 14
Purchased 1982

330.2000 **Seated Woman Reading, 30 Nov. '08**
(C1121) Pencil on paper 21 x 13.5
Purchased 1982

331.2000 **Woman Reading**
(C1122) Pencil on paper 21 x 13
Purchased 1982

332.2000 **Woman in a Dutch Costume, 14 June**
(C1123) **'06**
Pencil on paper 21 x 13
Purchased 1982

333.2000 **Head of Young Woman, 14 Feb. '08**
(C1125) Pencil on paper 20 x 14.5
Signed
Purchased 1982

334.2000 **Young Woman Inserting a Hatpin**
(C1126) Pencil on paper 13 x 10.5
Purchased 1982

335.2000 **Head of Old Woman in Profile**
(C1127) Pencil on paper 13 x 10.5
Purchased 1982

336.2000 **Young Woman in a Hat**
(C1128) Pencil on paper 13 x 10.5
Purchased 1982

337.2000 **Seated Woman, 1 Feb. '09**
(C1129) Pencil on paper 20.5 x 13.5
Purchased 1982

338.2000 **Seated Woman**
(C1130) Pencil, crayon on paper 20.5 x 12
Purchased 1982

339.2000 **Seated Woman, Aug.-Sept. 28**
(C1131) Pencil on paper 18.5 x 12
Purchased 1982

340.2000 **Seated Woman**
(C1132) Pencil on paper 21 x 13.5
Purchased 1982

341.2000 **Seated Woman, Oct. '07**
(C1133) Pencil on paper 22.5 x 14

Signed
Purchased 1982

342.2000 **Head of Young Woman**
(C1134) Pencil, crayon on paper 24.5 x 19
Purchased 1982

343.2000 **Profile of Old Lady**
(C1135) Charcoal, crayon on paper 23.5 x 18.5 (oval)
Signed
Purchased 1982

344.2000 **Two Studies of Young Woman in a**
(C1136) **Hat, 9 Dec. '09**
Pencil on paper 18 x 12
(recto and verso)
Purchased 1982

345.2000 **Three Studies of Elderly Man with a**
(C1137) **Moustache, 21 Dec. '09**
Charcoal on paper 17 x 20
(two on recto, one on verso)
Purchased 1982

346.2000 **Three Shawlies**
(C1138) Pencil on paper 18 x 20 (squared)
Purchased 1982

347.2000 **Young Couple Dancing**
(C1142) Pencil on paper 28.5 x 22
Purchased 1982

348.2000 **Street Barrow** (Selling Shellfish?)
(C1143) Pencil on paper 25 x 14 (squared)
Purchased 1982

349.2000 **Man in a Bowler Hat**
(C1144) Pencil on paper 23 x 14.5
Purchased 1982

350.2000 **Cleaning Windows**
(C1145) Pencil on paper 23 x 13.5
Purchased 1982

351.2000 **Man Wearing a Cap**
(C1146) Pencil on paper 23 x 18.5 (squared)
Purchased 1982

352.2000 **A Shawlie and a Man**
(C1148) Pencil on paper 19 x 24.5 (squared)
Purchased 1982

353.2000 **Spectators at a Race Meeting**
(C1149) Pencil on paper 16 x 21
Purchased 1982

354.2000 **Courting Couple**
(C1150) Pencil on paper 23 x 13.5
Purchased 1982

355.2000 **Study of Young Man with a**
(C1151) **Moustache and Pipe, 12 Feb. '08**
Pencil on paper 24.4 x 15.5
Signed
Purchased 1982

356.2000 **Seated Woman**
(C1152) Verso, **Study of Same Woman and Fragment of Young Woman's Head**
Pencil on paper (crayon on verso) 22 x 17
Purchased 1982

357.2000 **Redcoat Soldier with a Musket**
(C1153) Verso, **Young Woman**
Crayon on paper 34 x 25.5
Purchased 1982

358.2000
(C1154)
Young Man
Pencil on paper 24 x 15.5
Purchased 1982

359.2000
(C1155)
Four Studies of Young Woman
Pencil on paper 23 x 15
Purchased 1982

360.2000
(C1156)
Horse and Cart with Driver
Pencil on paper 21 x 25.5 (squared)
Purchased 1982

361.2000
(C1157)
Hobby Horses
Pencil on paper 16.5 x 21.5 (squared)
Purchased 1982

362.2000
(C1158)
At Empire (1910)
Ink, crayon on paper 23.5 x 21
Signed
Purchased 1982

363.2000
(C1159)
Study for 'At Empire' (362.2000)
Pencil, ink on paper 26 x 21
Purchased 1982

364.2000
(C1160)
Young Woman with a Bucket,
Kneeling
Pencil, crayon on paper 14 x 23
Purchased 1982

365.2000
(C1161)
Woman at a Sewing Machine
Pencil on paper 18.5 x 21 (squared)
Purchased 1982

366.2000
(C1162)
Dog
Pencil on paper 14 x 24
Purchased 1982

367.2000
(C1163)
Mounted Huntsman with Foxhounds
(Outline only)
Pencil on paper 19.5 x 26.5
Purchased 1982

368.2000
(C1164)
Two Shawlies with Babies
Pencil on paper 29.9 x 23
Purchased 1982

369.2000
(C1165)
Man and Two Women at the Races
Pencil on paper 20.5 x 20 (squared)
Purchased 1982

370.2000
(C1166)
Crowd at Side Show (?)
Pencil on paper 14 x 25 (squared)
Purchased 1982

371.2000
(C1167)
Belfast Races, Refreshment Stall,
2 April '15
Pencil on paper 19 x 12 (squared)
Purchased 1982

372.2000
(C1168)
Crowd round a Chip Potatoes'
Cart, 16 Aug. '18
Pencil on paper 19 x 12 (squared)
Purchased 1982

373.2000
(C1169)
Alhambra, 26 Dec. '09
Pencil on paper 12 x 18
Purchased 1982

374.2000
(C1170)
Crowd Leaving the Dress Circle
Pencil on paper 23 x 25.5 (squared)
Purchased 1982

375.2000
(C1171)
Bar Room Doorway
Pencil on paper 23.5 x 17.5 (squared)
Purchased 1982

376.2000
(C1172)
Scrabo Tower
Pencil on paper 17 x 31

Purchased 1982

377.2000
(C1173)
Jaunting Car
Pencil on paper 20.5 x 23.5 (squared)
Purchased 1982

378.2000
(C1174)
Woman and Three Girls, 7 April '10
Pencil on paper 12.5 x 18
Purchased 1982

379.2000
(C1175)
Crowd in Street
Pencil, crayon on paper 19.5 x 25
(squared)
Purchased 1982

380.2000
(C1176)
Three Studies of a Woman, 6 Aug.
Pencil on paper 19 x 12.5
Purchased 1982

381.2000
(C1177)
Woman with a Headscarf
Pencil on paper 22.5 x 29.5
Purchased 1982

382.2000
(C1178)
Street Crowd Inspecting a Painting
on an Easel
Pencil on paper 19 x 21 (irregular)
Purchased 1982

383.2000
(C1179)
Man with a Melodeon
Ink on paper 23 x 18
Signed
Purchased 1982

384.2000
(C1180)
Fiddler (Outline only)
Pencil, ink on paper 18 x 22.5
Purchased 1982

385.2000
(C1181)
Two Studies of Men on High Stools
Pencil on paper 27 x 22.5
(recto and verso)
Purchased 1982

386.2000
(C1182)
Three Studies of a Man
Pencil on paper 22 x 27.5
(two on recto, one on verso)
Purchased 1982

387.2000
(C1183)
Bespectacled Man on a High Stool
Pencil on paper 27 x 13
Signed
Purchased 1982

388.2000
(C1184)
Girl Leaning over a Wall
Pencil on paper 21.5 x 18.5 (squared)
Purchased 1982

389.2000
(C1185)
Girl Leaning over a Wall
Pencil on paper 34.5 x 17.5 (squared)
Purchased 1982

390.2000
(C1186)
Top-hatted Man with Umbrella over
Shoulder
Crayon on paper 26 x 35.5
Purchased 1982

391.2000
(C1187)
Studies of Men Sitting on Stools
Pencil on paper 22 x 28.5
Purchased 1982

392.2000
(C1188)
Three Shawlies
Crayon on paper 16 x 20 (partly
squared)
Purchased 1982

393.2000
(C1189)
Copy of Academic Painting: Girl
Playing a Double-pipe (1897)
Pencil on paper 28.5 x 22
Signed, dated
Purchased 1982

394.2000
(C1191)
Two Cloth-capped Men and a
Shawlie
Pencil, crayon on paper 14 x 22
(partly squared)
Purchased 1982

395.2000
(C1192)
Three Men in Deck Chairs
Pencil on paper 13 x 21
Purchased 1982

396.2000
(C1193)
Man at a Door, Shaking Fist at
Grinning Boy
Pencil on paper 28 x 24 (squared)
Purchased 1982

397.2000
(C1194)
Study for 'At Empire' (362.2000)
Pencil on paper 21 x 22
Purchased 1982

398.2000
(C1195)
Sheet of Slight Sketches
Pencil on paper 29 x 20.5 (recto and
verso, both squared)
Purchased 1982

399.2000
(C1196)
Three Men Lounging on a Beach (?)
Pencil, crayon on paper 23 x 31
(squared)
Purchased 1982

400.2000
(C1198)
Studies of Men, Clothed
Pencil on paper 22 x 28.5
Purchased 1982

401.2000
(C1199)
Studies of Men Sitting on Stools
Pencil on paper 24 x 21
Purchased 1982

402.2000
(C1200)
Studies of Men Sitting on Stools
Pencil on paper 22 x 28.5
Purchased 1982

403.2000
(C1201)
Studies of Men, Clothed
Pencil on paper 22 x 28.5
Purchased 1982

404.2000
(C1202)
Studies of Men, Clothed
Pencil on paper 22 x 28.5
Purchased 1982

405.2000
(C1203)
Studies of Men, Clothed
Pencil on paper 22 x 28.5
Purchased 1982

406.2000
(C1204)
Studies of Men, Clothed
Pencil on paper 22 x 28.5
Purchased 1982

407.2000
(C1205)
Studies of Men, Clothed
Pencil on paper 22 x 28.5
Purchased 1982

408.2000
(C1206)
Studies of Men, Clothed
Pencil on paper 22 x 28.5
Purchased 1982

409.2000
(C1207)
Studies of Men, Clothed
Pencil on paper 22 x 28.5
Purchased 1982

410.2000
(C1208)
Studies of Men, Clothed
Pencil on paper 22 x 28.5
Purchased 1982

411.2000
(C1209)
Two Shawlies (Outline only)
Pencil on paper 25 x 20 (squared)
Purchased 1982

412.2000
(C1210)
Group of Art Students (?)
Pencil on paper 28.5 x 21.5 (squared)

Purchased 1982

413.2000
(C1211)
Snow on the Lagan
Crayon, watercolour on paper 29.5 x 43
Signed
Purchased 1982

414.2000
(C1212)
Tram Crossing Queen's Bridge
Watercolour on paper 28 x 38.5
Signed
Purchased 1982

415.2000
(C1213)
Boats, Harbour, Water
Watercolour on paper 28.5 x 39
Purchased 1982

416.2000
(C1214)
Shaw's Bridge
Watercolour on paper 19 x 27
Signed
Purchased 1982

417.2000
(C1256)
Country Scene
Watercolour on paper 13 x 19 (squared)
Purchased 1982

418.2000
(C1257)
Queen's Bridge
Watercolour on card 12 x 17
Purchased 1982

419.2000
(C1258)
Stitching Room
Crayon, watercolour on paper 39 x 49.5
Signed
Purchased 1982

420.2000
(C1259)
Jaunting Car (1933)
Oil on canvas 75 x 60 (sight)
Signed
Purchased 1982

421.2000
(C1260)
Portrait of a Youth
Oil on canvas 64 x 77
Signed
Purchased 1982

422.2000
(C1261)
Portrait of a Woman
Oil on canvas 91 x 71
Signed
Purchased 1982

423.2000
(C1262)
The Glorious Dead (Scene at Cenotaph)
Watercolour, crayon on paper 136 x 85
Provenance unknown

424.2000
(C1263)
Study for 'The Launch'
Charcoal on paper 136 x 90
Purchased 1982

425.2000
(C1264)
Mill Workers (Study for 'Ulster Past and Present', Ulster Museum U1934)
Charcoal on paper 80 x 137
Purchased 1982

439.2000
(C136)
Courthouse Polling; Shawlie, 20 Jan. '10
Verso, **Head of Soldier**
Pencil on paper 21 x 13
Purchased 1982

440.2000
(C137)
Terrace of Houses
Verso, **Cottage in Mountains**
Pencil on paper 18 x 12.5
Purchased 1982

441.2000
(C138)
Railway Bridge, Whitehouse
Verso, **Moonlight, 13 March '16**
Pencil on paper 17.5 x 12
Purchased 1982

442.2000
(C139)
Two Arches
Pencil on paper 21.5 x 13.5
Purchased 1982

443.2000
(C140)
Terrace of Houses with Shawlies
Pencil on paper 18 x 12.5 (squared)
Purchased 1982

444.2000
(C141)
Wooden Sheds
Verso, **Wooden Barn**
Pencil on paper 17.5 x 12
Purchased 1982

445.2000
(C142)
Repairing Gaol [Jail] Chimney, 3 July '10
Pencil on paper 18 x 13.5
Purchased 1982

446.2000
(C143)
Factory with Chimneys; Shawlie, 19 April '10
Verso, **Two Male Figure Studies**
Pencil on paper 12.5 x 18
Purchased 1982

447.2000
(C144)
Houses in an Entry
Pencil on paper 12.5 x 18 (squared)
Purchased 1982

448.2000
(C145)
Outside the Theatre (Grand Opera House?)
Pencil on paper 19 x 10.5
Purchased 1982

449.2000
(C146)
Terrace of Buildings
Verso, **Barrack** (Street?) (squared)
Pencil on paper 12.5 x 18.5
Purchased 1982

450.2000
(C147)
Ardoyne Village, 12 Jan. 1917
Pencil on paper 18 x 12 (squared)
Purchased 1982

451.2000
(C148)
Queen's Bridge with Trams
Verso, **Trams, Red**
Pencil on paper 21 x 14.5
Purchased 1982

452.2000
(C149)
View through French Windows into a Dining Room
Verso, **Ship**
Pencil on paper 21 x 13
Purchased 1982

453.2000
(C150)
Tumbledown Shed, 9 Dec. '11
Pencil on paper 13.5 x 20
Purchased 1982

454.2000
(C151)
Courtyard with Archway
Pencil on paper 19.5 x 13.5
Purchased 1982

455.2000
(C152)
View of Carrickfergus Showing Church Steeple, 17 July '09
Verso, **A Classical Doorway and Window**
Pencil on paper 20 x 13.5
Purchased 1982

456.2000
(C153)
Gateway, Saturday Morning, 11 June 1910
Verso, **Four Shawlies**
Pencil on paper 12.5 x 18.5
Purchased 1982

457.2000
(C154)
Cottage, Fence and Stonewall (Lagan Canal?)
Pencil on paper 18 x 12
Purchased 1982

458.2000
(C155)
Terrace of Buildings, 3 Oct. 1909
Verso, **Male Figure Sketch;**
Two Male Heads; Male Leg
Pencil on paper 12 x 17
Purchased 1982

459.2000
(C156)
Urban View of Terrace Buildings
Verso, **Two Male Figure Sketches**
Pencil, crayon on paper 18.5 x 13.5
Purchased 1982

460.2000
(C157)
View of Old-fashioned Lamp, Ligoniel, 29 Jan. 1910
Verso, **Landscape, Snow Scene, 30 Jan. 1910**
Pencil on paper 20.5 x 13
Purchased 1982

461.2000
(C158)
Elmwood Church, 9 Oct. 1916 (squared)
Verso, **Horse in Shafts**
Pencil on paper 20 x 13.5
Purchased 1982

462.2000
(C159)
A Street, 6 Aug. 1909
Pencil on paper 20.5 x 13.5
Purchased 1982

463.2000
(C160)
Windmill, Bangor
Verso, **Store**
Pencil on paper 20.5 x 13.5
Purchased 1982

464.2000
(C161)
Sketch of Doorway and Balcony above
Verso, **Sketch of Terrace House with Street Lamp**
Pencil on paper 20.5 x 13.5
Purchased 1982

465.2000
(C162)
Cottage, 7 Dec. 1910?
Verso, **Sketch of Doorway**
Pencil on paper 13.5 x 19
Purchased 1982

466.2000
(C163)
Classical Doorway with Steps, 27 Feb. 1910
Verso, **Wall with Building behind**
Pencil on paper 18 x 12
Purchased 1982

467.2000
(C164)
'Oh my Head Is Light. Dear, I Don't Think that Is possible'
(Sketch of house - pub? - on roadside)
Verso, **Farmhouse, 27 Dec. 1910**
Pencil on paper 12 x 18
Purchased 1982

468.2000
(C165)
Row of Thatched Houses with Spade and Buckets outside
Verso, **Male Figure Sketch**
Pencil on paper 12 x 18.5
Purchased 1982

469.2000
(C166)
A Street Preacher or Speaker
Verso, **Roman-style Letters**
Pencil on paper 20.9 x 14
Purchased 1982

470.2000
(C167)
Whitehouse by Moonlight, 13 March 1911
Pencil on paper 12 x 18

Purchased 1982

471.2000 (C168) Sketch of Town Buildings, 6 March 1910
Pencil on paper 15 x 12
Purchased 1982

472.2000 (C169) Ardoyne, Moonlight, Snow Scene, 16 Nov. 1910
Verso, Sketch of Houses, 16 Nov. 1910
Pencil on paper 15.5 x 12
Purchased 1982

473.2000 (C170) Ballysillan Road, 24 Dec. 1910
Verso, Sketch of House
Pencil on paper 18 x 12
Purchased 1982

474.2000 (C171) School House, Ballysillan Road, Moonlight, 26 Jan. 1910
Verso, Sketch of Arm and Hand
Pencil on paper 18.5 x 11.5
Purchased 1982

475.2000 (C172) Snow Scene, Ardoyne Village, 12 Jan. 1910
Verso, Snow Scene. View from the Back, 12 Jan. 1910
Pencil on paper 12 x 18.5
Purchased 1982

476.2000 (C173) Moonlight Snow Scene, Ardoyne, 16 Nov. '10
Pencil on paper 18 x 12.5
Purchased 1982

477.2000 (C174) Sketch of House (squared)
Verso, Castellated Wall on Top of Rocks
Pencil on paper 12.5 x 18.5
Purchased 1982

478.2000 (C175) House with Conservatory
Pencil on paper 17.5 x 12
Purchased 1982

479.2000 (C176) Carrickfergus Castle
Verso, View of Part of Carrickfergus, 11 July '09
Pencil on paper 13.5 x 21
Purchased 1982

480.2000 (C177) Election Scene, Court House, 26 Jan. '10
Pencil on paper 21 x 13.5 (squared)
Purchased 1982

481.2000 (C178) Terrace of Houses, 27 Dec. '10 (squared)
Verso, Cottage, Road
Pencil on paper 19.5 x 12
Purchased 1982

482.2000 (C179) Building with Stairs to First Floor Door, 27 Dec. '10
Verso, Sketch of First Floor Door, Going to Attic, 27 Dec. ('10?)
Pencil on paper 12 x 18
Purchased 1982

483.2000 (C180) Wooden Door
Verso, Landscape
Pencil on paper 12 x 18
Purchased 1982

484.2000 Old Cottage, Fireside

(C181) Verso, Interior View of Window
Pencil on paper 18 x 12
Purchased 1982

485.2000 (C182) Queen's Bridge, 11 July '10
Verso, Old Farmer (to Artist who Had just Had his Whole Sketching Apparatus Blown on top of him), 'Trying to Fly, are you?'
Pencil on paper 18.5 x 12.5
Purchased 1982

486.2000 (C183) Work in Progress near Bridge, Scaffolding, 7 July '10
Verso, Different Angle of Same View
Pencil on paper 18.5 x 12.5
Purchased 1982

487.2000 (C184) Detail of Balustrade, 11 July '09
Pencil on paper 21 x 14
Purchased 1982

488.2000 (C185) Queen's Bridge (squared)
Verso, Handwriting of Themes, e.g., Moonlight, Motherhood
Pencil on paper 12.5 x 18
Purchased 1982

489.2000 (C186) Queen's Bridge, Jetty, 5 March '10
Pencil on paper 18 x 23.5
Purchased 1982

490.2000 (C187) View of Castle Junction, 26 Dec. '09
Pencil on paper 18 x 12
Purchased 1982

491.2000 (C188) Sketches, Market, 10 June '10
Pencil on paper 18.5 x 12.5 (squared)
Purchased 1982

492.2000 (C189) Sketch of Wall and Pillar, 7 July '10
Verso, Figure Sketch
Pencil on paper 18.5 x 12.5
Purchased 1982

493.2000 (C190) Interior Stairs
Pencil on paper 18.5 x 13
Purchased 1982

494.2000 (C191) Armchair
Pencil on paper 18 x 12
Purchased 1982

495.2000 (C192) Passage, 6 March '10
Pencil on paper 18 x 12
Purchased 1982

496.2000 (C193) Sketch of Studio Skylight, 6 March '10
Pencil on paper 18 x 12
Purchased 1982

497.2000 (C194) Booking Office, Co. Down Railway, 27 Feb. '10
Pencil on paper 18 x 12 (squared)
Purchased 1982

498.2000 (C195) Sketch of Billiard Table, 25 Dec. '09
Pencil on paper 12 x 18
Purchased 1982

499.2000 (C196) Sketch of Grandfather Clock, Chair and Potted Plant
Pencil on paper 14 x 20.5
Purchased 1982

500.2000 (C197) Wall Clock
Pencil on paper 17.5 x 11

Purchased 1982

501.2000 (C198) Fireplace and Table or Chest
Verso, Door, Cradle and Shawlie
Pencil, crayon on paper 12 x 18
Purchased 1982

502.2000 (C199) Bottom of Staircase Showing First Stair Post
Verso, Three Figure Sketches (Father, Mother, Child) (squared)
Pencil on paper 22 x 14
Purchased 1982

503.2000 (C200) Fireplace
Pencil on paper 12 x 18
Purchased 1982

504.2000 (C201) Wooden Armchair
Verso, Calculations
Pencil on paper 19 x 12
Purchased 1982

505.2000 (C202) Wooden Chair
Pencil on card 12.5 x 10
Purchased 1982

506.2000 (C203) Studio Door, March ('10?)
Pencil on paper 18 x 12.5
Purchased 1982

507.2000 (C204) Stairs Leading to Studio Door?
Verso, View of Studio through Open Door
Pencil on paper 18 x 12
Purchased 1982

508.2000 (C205) Stairs Leading to Door, April '10
Pencil on paper 18 x 12.5
Purchased 1982

509.2000 (C206) Sketch of Artist's Studio
Pencil on paper 12 x 18
Purchased 1982

510.2000 (C207) View of Allen's Artist Room, Looking down towards Office, 14 Jan. '10
Verso, Sketch of a Radiator
Pencil on paper 22 x 14
Purchased 1982

511.2000 (C208) View of Artist Room, 13 Jan. '10
Pencil on paper 14 x 22.5
Purchased 1982

512.2000 (C209) Store, Belfast Art Society Rooms
Pencil on paper 21 x 14
Purchased 1982

513.2000 (C210) Reading Room, Central Library, 10 Jan. '19
Verso, Male Figure Sketch from Memory
Pencil on paper 18 x 12
Purchased 1982

514.2000 (C211) Library Reading Room
Pencil on paper 22 x 14
Purchased 1982

515.2000 (C212) Library Reading Room, 27 Dec. '19
Verso, Female Figure Sketch; Male Figure Sketch
Pencil on paper 13.5 x 21.5
Purchased 1982

516.2000 (C213) Theatre Royal, View in the Pit, 27 Dec. '09 (squared)

Verso, **Theatre Royal Balcony Sketch, 29 Dec. '09**
Pencil on paper 12 x 18
Purchased 1982

517.2000
(C214)
Looking into a Public House, 26 Dec. '09 (squared)
Verso, **Two Male Head Studies**
Pencil on paper 18 x 12
Purchased 1982

518.2000
(C215)
Cultra Regatta, 14 June '09
Verso, **Cultra Regatta**
Pencil on paper 15 x 13.5
Purchased 1982

519.2000
(C216)
Sketches of Yachts, 14 June '09
Verso, **Sketch of Yacht**
Pencil on paper 20.5 x 13.5
Purchased 1982

520.2000
(C217)
Sketch of Yacht, 14 June '09
Verso, **Sketch of Yacht**
Pencil on paper 20 x 13.5
Purchased 1982

521.2000
(C218)
Sketch of Rowing Boat and Shoreline, 14 June '09
Pencil on paper 20.5 x 13
Purchased 1982

522.2000
(C219)
Sketch of Boats, 11 June '09
Pencil on paper 13.5 x 20
Purchased 1982

523.2000
(C220)
Sketch of Steamer, 11 July '09 (Copy)
Pencil on paper 21 x 13.5
Purchased 1982

524.2000
(C221)
Sketch of Sailing Boat, 11 July '09
Pencil on paper 21 x 13.5
Purchased 1982

525.2000
(C222)
Sketch of Barge (Tiller)
Pencil on paper 18 x 12
Purchased 1982

526.2000
(C223)
Sketch of Barge (Stern and Tiller)
Pencil on paper 18 x 12
Purchased 1982

527.2000
(C224)
Sketch of Barge (Stern and Tiller)
Crayon on paper 19 x 13.5
Purchased 1982

528.2000
(C225)
Rowing Boats
Verso, **Boats**
Pencil on paper 21 x 14
Purchased 1982

529.2000
(C226)
Steamer
Pencil on paper 19.5 x 13
Purchased 1982

530.2000
(C227)
Deck of Boat
Pencil on paper 12 x 18
Purchased 1982

531.2000
(C228)
Boat
Pencil on paper 21 x 13.5
Purchased 1982

532.2000
(C229)
Boat
Crayon on paper 20 x 11
Purchased 1982

533.2000
(C230)
Bridge on the Ballysillan Road
Verso, **Moonlight. Snow on Hill**

Pencil on paper 12 x 18.5
Purchased 1982

534.2000
(C231)
Sketch of Houses in Landscape
Verso, **Landscape**
Pencil on paper 18 x 12
Purchased 1982

535.2000
(C232)
View of Whitehead, 4 July '09
Pencil on paper 20 x 13.5
Purchased 1982

536.2000
(C233)
View of Bobbies, 24 Dec. '09 (Fairground Roundabout)
Pencil on paper 12 x 17
Purchased 1982

537.2000
(C234)
Skating Rink, 28 Dec. '09
Pencil on paper 21.5 x 13
Purchased 1982

538.2000
(C235)
Skating Rink, 28 Dec. '09
Pencil on paper 13.5 x 18.5
Purchased 1982

539.2000
(C236)
Cavehill by Moonlight
Pencil on paper 13 x 21.5
Purchased 1982

540.2000
(C237)
Snow Scene, 12 Jan. '10
Pencil on paper 18 x 12
Purchased 1982

541.2000
(C238)
Snow Scene. View from the Mountains, Ardoyne, 12 Jan. '10
Pencil on paper 12 x 18
Purchased 1982

542.2000
(C239)
Snow Scene, Cavehill, 12 Jan. '10
Pencil on paper 12 x 18
Purchased 1982

543.2000
(C240)
Snow Scene before you Come to the Cavehill
Pencil on paper 12 x 18
Purchased 1982

544.2000
(C241)
Top of Oldpark Road, 26 Jan. '10
Verso, **Snow and Hills, Moonlight**
Pencil on paper 12 x 18
Purchased 1982

545.2000
(C242)
Snow Scene with Cottage, 29 Jan. '10
Pencil on paper 13 x 20.5
Purchased 1982

546.2000
(C243)
Cavehill, Snow Scene, 30 Jan. '10
Pencil on paper 14 x 21
Purchased 1982

547.2000
(C244)
Rocky Coast, 23 Feb. '10
Pencil on paper 19 x 13
Purchased 1982

548.2000
(C245)
Sketch of Newcastle, Aug. '10
Pencil on paper 18 x 12
Purchased 1982

549.2000
(C246)
View of Merry-Go-Round, Bangor, 8 Aug. '09
Pencil on paper 13 x 20
Purchased 1982

550.2000
(C247)
Landscape with Trees
Verso, **Snow on Cavehill in Moonlight**
Pencil on paper 18 x 12
Purchased 1982

551.2000
(C248)
Moonlight on the River Lagan, 16 Nov. '10
Verso, **Cart**
Pencil on paper 18 x 12
Purchased 1982

552.2000
(C249)
River Landscape, 16 Nov. '10
Verso, **Moonlit Lagan, 16 Nov. '10**
Pencil on paper 18 x 12
Purchased 1982

553.2000
(C250)
Landscape with Trees. Moonlight on Lagan, 16 Nov. '10
Verso, **Landscape with Path, 16 Nov. '10**
Pencil on paper 18 x 12
Purchased 1982

554.2000
(C251)
Bridge, Ballysillan Road, 24 Dec. '10
Verso, **Landscape with Buildings, 24 Dec. '10**
Pencil on paper 18 x 12
Purchased 1982

555.2000
(C252)
Sketch, Ballysillan Road, 24 Dec. '10
Pencil on paper 18 x 12
Purchased 1982

556.2000
(C253)
Winter Trees, 11 Jan. '11
Verso, **Public Hall, 11 Jan. '11**
Pencil on paper 18 x 12
Purchased 1982

557.2000
(C254)
Landscape with Cottages, 12 Jan. '11
Verso, **Moonlight in Yard, 12 Jan. '11**
Pencil on paper 18 x 12
Purchased 1982

558.2000
(C255)
Moonlight, Lagan, 12 Jan. '11
Verso, **Lagan, Moonlight, 14 Jan. '11**
Pencil on paper 14 x 12.5
Purchased 1982

559.2000
(C256)
Moonlight, Whitehouse, 13 Mar. '11
Pencil on paper 12 x 18
Purchased 1982

560.2000
(C257)
Scene with Street Lamp (squared)
Verso, **Carts**
Pencil on paper 20 x 13.5
Purchased 1982

561.2000
(C258)
Sketch of Tree
Verso, **Sketches of Faces and Hands**
Pencil on paper 21 x 14
Purchased 1982

562.2000
(C259)
Bangor, 18 Aug. '15
Pencil on paper 12 x 18
Purchased 1982

563.2000
(C260)
Couple in Bed, Being Disturbed by Singers outside (Cartoon)
Pencil on paper 9 x 14
Purchased 1982

564.2000
(C261)
Theatre Box
Verso, **Lions in Cage at Fairground**
Pencil on paper 18 x 12.5
Purchased 1982

565.2000
(C262)
First Class Railway Carriage
Verso, **Two Male Figure Studies**
Pencil on paper 13.5 x 20.5
Purchased 1982

566.2000
(C263)
Fairground Organ with Punch and Judy Show, 26 Dec. '07?

Pencil on paper 18.5 x 12
Purchased 1982

567.2000 **Merry-Go-Round**
(C264) Pencil on paper 12 x 18.5
Purchased 1982

568.2000 **Fairground Sideshow - Living**
(C265) **Pictures**
Pencil on paper 12 x 18
Purchased 1982

569.2000 **Gipsy Caravan, 8 Aug. '09**
(C266) Verso, **Fairground Swings, 8 Aug. '09**
Pencil on paper 20.5 x 13.5
Purchased 1982

570.2000 **Open Newspaper**
(C267) Pencil on paper 20 x 12.5
Purchased 1982

571.2000 **Ford Model T, 13 June '09**
(C268) Verso, **Tree, 13 June '09**
Pencil on paper 20 x 13.5
Purchased 1982

572.2000 **Taxi**
(C269) Pencil on paper 18 x 12
Purchased 1982

573.2000 **Sketch of Machinery, 5 Aug. '10**
(C270) Pencil on paper 12.5 x 18
Purchased 1982

574.2000 **Horse Studies**
(C271) Verso, **Human Head Studies**
Pencil on paper 15 x 9.5
Purchased 1982

575.2000 **Horse Studies**
(C272) Verso, **Male Figure Studies**
Pencil on paper 18.5 x 12
Purchased 1982

576.2000 **Horse and Human Figure Studies**
(C273) Verso, **Horse Studies**
Pencil on paper 19 x 12
Purchased 1982

577.2000 **Horse Studies and One Male Head**
(C274) Verso, **Human Anatomical Studies**
Pencil on paper 19 x 11
Purchased 1982

578.2000 **Studies of a Horse's Head**
(C275) Verso, **Human Figure Studies**
Pencil on paper 19 x 11
Purchased 1982

579.2000 **Horse Studies**
(C276) Verso, **Horse Studies**
Pencil on paper 20.5 x 13
Purchased 1982

580.2000 **Horse Studies** (one squared)
(C277) Verso, **Horse Studies**
Pencil on paper 21 x 13.5
Purchased 1982

581.2000 **Horse Studies**
(C278) Pencil on paper 15 x 10.5
Purchased 1982

582.2000 **Horse Study**
(C279) Verso, **Horse Studies**
Pencil on paper 11 x 15
Purchased 1982

583.2000 **Horse Studies**

(C280) Verso, **Male Figure Studies**
Pencil on paper 21 x 13.5
Purchased 1982

584.2000 **Horse Study; Clown Costume**
(C281) **Study**
Pencil on paper 18.5 x 12
Purchased 1982

585.2000 **Horse Studies**
(C282) Verso, **Male Figure Study**
Pencil on paper 13 x 21
Purchased 1982

586.2000 **Cavalryman on Horseback** (squared);
(C283) **Female Figure in Cape**
Verso, **Shawlies**
Pencil on paper 13.5 x 20
Purchased 1982

587.2000 **Plough Horses, 11 Feb. '10**
(C284) Pencil on paper 13.5 x 21 (squared)
Purchased 1982

588.2000 **Horses Ploughing**
(C285) Pencil on paper 14 x 21.5
Purchased 1982

589.2000 **Horse Feeding from Nose Bag, 12**
(C286) **Oct. '10; Male Figure Sketch**
Verso, **Male Figure Studies**
Pencil on paper 13.5 x 20
Purchased 1982

590.2000 **Polo Players on Horseback** (squared)
(C287) Verso, **Horse Study**
Pencil on paper 13.5 x 21
Purchased 1982

591.2000 **Polo Players on Horseback, 12 Feb.**
(C288) **'10**
Verso, **Polo Players on Horseback**
Pencil on paper 14 x 21
Purchased 1982

592.2000 **Polo Player on Horseback, 12 Feb. '10**
(C289) Verso, **Polo Player on Horseback**
Pencil on paper 14 x 21
Purchased 1982

593.2000 **Hunter on Horseback; Hound**
(C290) **Sketches**
Verso, **Man on Horseback, 27 Dec.**
'09
Pencil on paper 12 x 18
Purchased 1982

594.2000 **Four-wheeler Cab, 14 March '09**
(C291) Pencil on paper 13.5 x 21
Purchased 1982

595.2000 **Horse Pulling Passenger Carriage, 11**
(C292) **July '09**
Verso, **Two Figure Studies of Young**
Girls
Pencil on paper 13.5 x 20
Purchased 1982

596.2000 **Horse and Jaunting Car; Male Figure**
(C293) **Sketch, 17 April '09** (squared)
Verso, **Male and Female Figure**
Sketches
Pencil on paper 14 x 21
Purchased 1982

597.2000 **Country Cart**
(C294) Verso, **Male Figure Using Shears;**

Wooden Trestle
Pencil on paper 18.5 x 12
Purchased 1982

598.2000 **Horse and Cart**
(C295) Verso, **Two Male and One Female**
Figure Sketches
Pencil on paper 20 x 13.5
Purchased 1982

599.2000 **Donkey and Cart**
(C296) Pencil on paper 12 x 18
Purchased 1982

600.2000 **Horse and Cart**
(C297) Pencil on paper 14 x 22 (squared)
Purchased 1982

601.2000 **Hound Study; Male Leg Studies**
(C298) Verso, **Male Anatomical Studies**
Pencil on paper 22 x 14
Purchased 1982

602.2000 **Study of a Puppy; Study of a Woman**
(C299) Verso, **Study of a Man in 18th**
Century Costume
Pencil on paper 21 x 14
Purchased 1982

603.2000 **Dog Studies, July '08**
(C300) Verso, **Dog Studies; Male and Female**
Head Studies
Pencil on paper 21 x 13.5
Purchased 1982

604.2000 **Study of a Lioness?**
(C301) Pencil on paper 11 x 15
Purchased 1982

605.2000 **Cattle Studies**
(C302) Verso, **Cattle Studies**
Pencil on paper 13 x 20
Purchased 1982

606.2000 **Cattle Sketches**
(C303) Verso, **Three Male Figure Studies**
Pencil on paper 21.5 x 14
Purchased 1982

607.2000 **'Shure, 'tis the Mother with the**
(C304) **Bonnet on', 20 June '09** (Studies of
Ducks)
Pencil on paper 17 x 12
Purchased 1982

608.2000 **Lion Studies, 9 March '10**
(C305) Verso, **Female Figure Study**
Pencil on paper 21 x 14
Purchased 1982

609.2000 **Horse Studies**
(C306) Verso, **Horse Studies**
Pencil on paper 15 x 12
Purchased 1982

610.2000 **Horse Studies**
(C307) Verso, **Horse Studies**
Pencil on paper 19 x 11.5
Purchased 1982

611.2000 **Study of a Child Drinking from a**
(C308) **Mug**
Pencil on paper 17.5 x 13
Purchased 1982

612.2000 **Three Studies of a Boy with a Cap**
(C309) Verso, **Shawlies**
Pencil on paper 21 x 13.5

Purchased 1982

613.2000
(C310)
Matthew Connor: Portrait Study of
Crossed Legs
Verso, **Male Head Study**
Pencil on paper 21.5 x 13.5
Purchased 1982

614.2000
(C311)
Study of a Baby, 11 Feb. '10
Verso, **Study of a Baby**
Pencil on paper 13.5 x 10.5
Purchased 1982

615.2000
(C312)
Head of a Young Baby
Verso, **Six Male Head Studies; Torso
Study**
Pencil on paper 18 x 12
Purchased 1982

616.2000
(C313)
Matt O'Connor, 2 Feb. '09; Study of
Male Figure Bending Over
Verso, **Study of a Man and Woman**
Pencil on paper 21 x 13.5
Purchased 1982

617.2000
(C314)
Head of a Young Boy, 28 Jan. '09
Verso, **Three Heads of Young
Boys, Jan. '09**
Pencil on paper 21 x 13.5
Purchased 1982

618.2000
(C315)
Two Heads of Young Boys, 21 Jan.
1909
Verso, **Two Heads of Young Boys;
Sketch of Woman's Skirt**
Pencil on paper 21 x 14
Purchased 1982

619.2000
(C316)
Four Male Heads
Verso, **Two Male Heads; One Male
Figure Study**
Pencil on paper 14 x 22
Purchased 1982

620.2000
(C317)
Three Portrait Studies
Pencil on paper 18 x 12
Purchased 1982

621.2000
(C318)
Male Portrait - Self-Portrait?
Verso, **Study of Man Sleeping; Side
Outline of Man's Face**
Pencil on paper 21 x 13.5
Purchased 1982

622.2000
(C319)
Two Male Heads
Verso, **Two Male Heads**
Pencil on paper 13 x 8
Purchased 1982

623.2000
(C320)
Two Male Portraits; Sketches of an
Eye and an Ear
Verso, **Sketches of a Face and a Jacket**
Pencil on paper 21 x 14
Purchased 1982

624.2000
(C321)
Head of Sleeping Man
Pencil on paper 18 x 11.5
Purchased 1982

625.2000
(C322)
Two Male Head Studies
Pencil on paper 22 x 12.5
Purchased 1982

626.2000
(C323)
Three Male Head Studies
Verso, **Male Head Study; Study of
Person Sitting on a Chair**
Pencil on paper 18 x 12

Purchased 1982

627.2000
(C324)
Study of Man Smoking a Pipe
Verso, **Study of Man Smoking a Pipe**
Pencil on paper 14.5 x 22
Purchased 1982

628.2000
(C325)
Male Portrait Study
Pencil on paper 12 x 18
Purchased 1982

629.2000
(C326)
Head of a Young Man with a Cap
Verso, **Outline Sketches**
Pencil on paper 18.5 x 12
Purchased 1982

630.2000
(C327)
Two Male Head Studies
Verso, **Male Figure Studies**
Pencil on paper 14 x 21.5
Purchased 1982

631.2000
(C328)
Fourteen Male Head Studies
Verso, **Three Male Head Studies**
Pencil on paper 14 x 21.5
Purchased 1982

632.2000
(C329)
Male Portrait Study
Pencil on paper 21 x 13.5
Purchased 1982

633.2000
(C330)
Four Male Head Studies
Verso, **Three Male Head Studies**
Pencil on paper 15 x 13.5
Purchased 1982

634.2000
(C331)
Three Male Head Studies (Self-
caricatures?)
Verso, **Four Male Head Studies**
Pencil on paper (pencil, ink on verso)
21 x 14
Purchased 1982

635.2000
(C332)
Four Male Head Studies, 18 Oct. '09
Signed
Verso, **Three Male Head Studies**
Pencil on paper 21 x 13.5
Purchased 1982

636.2000
(C333)
Two Male Head Studies
Verso, **Male Head Study**
Pencil on paper 21 x 14
Purchased 1982

637.2000
(C334)
Two Male Portrait Studies
Verso, **Four Male Head Studies**
Pencil on paper 21.5 x 14
Purchased 1982

638.2000
(C335)
Male Head Study
Pencil on paper 16.5 x 13.5
Purchased 1982

639.2000
(C336)
Male Portrait Study
Verso, **Male Head Study**
Pencil on paper 22 x 13.5
Purchased 1982

640.2000
(C337)
Three Male Head Studies
Verso, **Female Head Study**
Pencil on paper 22 x 13.5
Purchased 1982

641.2000
(C338)
Six Male Head Studies
Verso, **Five Male Head Studies**
Pencil on paper 21 x 13.5
Purchased 1982

642.2000   Two Male Head Studies

(C339)
Pencil on paper 14 x 22
Purchased 1982

643.2000
(C340)
Male Head and Arm Study
Pencil on paper 22.5 x 14.5
Purchased 1982

644.2000
(C341)
Male Portrait
Pencil on paper 15 x 13.5
Purchased 1982

645.2000
(C342)
Five Studies from the Antique
Pencil on paper 20 x 14
Purchased 1982

646.2000
(C343)
Female Portrait Study
Verso, **Female Head Study; Head
Study of Soldier Wearing a Shako**
Pencil on paper 21 x 14
Purchased 1982

647.2000
(C344)
Female Head Study; Female Costume
Study
Verso, **Seated Female Costume Study**
Pencil on paper 21 x 14
Purchased 1982

648.2000
(C345)
Three Female Head and Face Studies;
Study of Female Arms
Verso, **Four Female Face Studies**
Pencil on paper 21.5 x 14
Purchased 1982

649.2000
(C346)
Female Portrait Study
Pencil on paper 18.5 x 12
Purchased 1982

650.2000
(C347)
Female Portrait Study
Pencil on paper 10 x 12.5
Purchased 1982

651.2000
(C348)
Two Female Head Studies
Verso, **Female Anatomical Studies**
Pencil on paper 20 x 11.5
Purchased 1982

652.2000
(C349)
Two Female Portrait Studies, 8 Nov.
'09
Pencil on paper 21 x 14
Purchased 1982

653.2000
(C350)
Two Female Head Studies, 8 Nov. '09
Verso, **Female Head Study**
Pencil on paper 22 x 14
Purchased 1982

654.2000
(C351)
Two Female Portrait Studies, 8 March
'09
Pencil on paper 21.5 x 13.5
Purchased 1982

655.2000
(C352)
Old Woman with Spectacles, 1 Oct.
'08
Pencil on paper 14 x 8
Signed
Purchased 1982

656.2000
(C353)
Male Head Study
Verso, **Two Male and One
Female Head Studies**
Pencil on paper 22 x 14
Purchased 1982

657.2000
(C354)
Female Head Study; Sketch of a Face
Verso, **Kettle**
Pencil on paper 22.5 x 14
Purchased 1982

658.2000
(C355)
Three Female Face Sketches
Verso, Seated Male Costume Study
Pencil on paper 22 x 13.5
Purchased 1982

659.2000
(C356)
Five Male Head Studies; Head Study
Verso, Studies of a Dog; Two Female Torsos; Two Faces
Pencil on paper 22 x 14
Purchased 1982

660.2000
(C357)
Three Female Head Studies
Verso, Five Face Studies; Study of a Man in a Top Hat; Female Costume Study
Pencil on paper 21.5 x 14
Purchased 1982

661.2000
(C358)
Two Female Head Studies
Verso, Three Male Head Studies (Caricatures)
Pencil on paper 21.5 x 13.5
Purchased 1982

662.2000
(C359)
Two Male and One Female Head Studies; Female Costume Study
Verso, Two Male Figure Studies; Male Head Study
Pencil on paper 22 x 14
Purchased 1982

663.2000
(C360)
Two Face Studies
Verso, Male Figure Study
Pencil on paper 21.5 x 13.5
Purchased 1982

664.2000
(C361)
Five Male Face Studies
Verso, One Male and One Female Figure Study (squared)
Pencil on paper 22 x 13.5
Purchased 1982

665.2000
(C362)
One Male and One Female Head Study
Verso, Female Costume Study
Pencil on paper 21.5 x 13.5
Purchased 1982

666.2000
(C363)
Two Female and One Male Head Studies
Verso, Four Male Face Studies
Pencil on paper 21.5 x 14
Purchased 1982

667.2000
(C364)
Three Male Face Studies
Verso, Three Male Costume Studies
Pencil on paper 14 x 22
Purchased 1982

668.2000
(C365)
Female Portrait Study
Verso, Male Figure Study
Pencil on paper 21.5 x 13.5
Purchased 1982

669.2000
(C366)
Two Female Head Studies, 30 Sept. '08
Signed
Verso, Male Figure Study (Tin Whistle Player) (squared)
Pencil on paper 21 x 13
Purchased 1982

670.2000
(C367)
Two Female and One Male Head Studies
Verso, Three Male Head Studies, 16 Oct. '09
Pencil on paper 12 x 18

Purchased 1982

671.2000
(C368)
Four Male Face Studies
Verso, Two Male Face Studies
Pencil on paper 22 x 14
Purchased 1982

672.2000
(C369)
Female Head Study
Verso, Three Male Head Studies
Pencil on paper 19 x 13
Purchased 1982

673.2000
(C370)
Two Female Head Studies, 30 Sept. '08
Verso, Three Male Head Studies
Pencil on paper 21 x 13
Purchased 1982

674.2000
(C371)
Two Head Studies
Verso, Two Face Profiles
Pencil on paper 21.5 x 13.5
Purchased 1982

675.2000
(C372)
Male Head Study; Bowler Hat
Verso, Female Figure Study
Pencil on paper 21 x 14
Purchased 1982

676.2000
(C373)
Male Head Study
Verso, Two Male Figure Studies
Pencil on paper 21.5 x 13.5
Purchased 1982

677.2000
(C374)
Three Female Face Studies
Verso, Female Face Study; Two Male Figure Studies
Pencil on paper 14 x 22
Purchased 1982

678.2000
(C375)
Portrait of a Woman
Verso, Male Figure Study
Pencil on paper 22 x 14
Purchased 1982

679.2000
(C376)
Two Female Head Studies
Verso, Two Male Figure Studies
Pencil on paper 21 x 13.5
Purchased 1982

680.2000
(C377)
Five Female Face Studies
Verso, Head Study of a Soldier; Two Male Figure Studies
Pencil on paper 14 x 22
Purchased 1982

681.2000
(C378)
Portrait of a Young Girl, 28 Jan. '09
Verso, Figure Study of a Boy Wearing a Coat
Pencil on paper 21 x 14
Purchased 1982

682.2000
(C379)
Two Female Head Studies; Female Costume Study
Verso, Figure Study of a Child
Pencil on paper 13.5 x 21
Purchased 1982

683.2000
(C380)
Two Figure Sketches of a Sleeping Woman
Verso, Male Figure Sketch
Pencil on paper 21 x 13
Purchased 1982

684.2000
(C381)
Two Male and One Female Figure Sketches
Verso, Two Female Figure Sketches
Pencil, crayon on paper 12 x 18.5

Purchased 1982

685.2000
(C382)
Male and Female Figure Sketch, 22 Aug. '15
Pastel on paper 11 x 18 (squared)
(Back of Foreword by John Hewitt, William Conor Retrospective Exhibition Catalogue)
Purchased 1982

686.2000
(C383)
Female Figure Sketch (squared); Male Head Study
Verso, Two Female Figure Studies; Female Head Study
Pencil on paper 13.5 x 20.5
Purchased 1982

687.2000
(C384)
Three Female Figure Studies (squared)
Verso, Two Male Figure Studies
Pencil on paper 12 x 18
Purchased 1982

688.2000
(C385)
Three Female Figure Sketches
Verso, Two Male and One Female Figure Studies
Pencil on paper 12.5 x 18.5
Purchased 1982

689.2000
(C386)
Female Costume Study
Verso, Male Costume Study
Pencil on paper 22 x 13.5
Purchased 1982

690.2000
(C387)
Four Male Figure Studies
Verso, Male Figure Study; Female Figure Study
Pencil, crayon on paper 14 x 22
Purchased 1982

691.2000
(C388)
Sleeping Male Figure Sketch
Verso, One Male and One Female Costume Sketch
Pencil on paper 14 x 22
Purchased 1982

692.2000
(C389)
Male Figure Study; Male Torso Study
Verso, Male Figure Study; Female Figure Study
Pencil on paper 22 x 13.5
Purchased 1982

693.2000
(C390)
Four Female Figure Studies
Verso, Three Male Figure Studies
Pencil on paper 21.5 x 14
Purchased 1982

694.2000
(C391)
Two Male and Two Female Figure Studies
Verso, Male Figure Study; Shawlie
Pencil on paper 12.5 x 18.5
Purchased 1982

695.2000
(C392)
One Female and Two Male Figure Studies (squared)
Verso, Three Female Figure Studies
Pencil, crayon on paper (pencil only on verso) 14 x 21.5
Purchased 1982

696.2000
(C393)
Seated Female Figure Study; Male Figure Study
Pencil on paper 12.5 x 18.5
Purchased 1982

697.2000
(C394)
Seated Male Figure Study
Verso, One Female and One Male

Figure Study
Pencil on paper 21 x 14
Purchased 1982

698.2000
(C395)
Two Male and One Female Figure Studies (squared)
Verso, Study of a One-legged Man on Crutches
Pencil on paper 12 x 18
Purchased 1982

699.2000
(C396)
Three Female Figure Studies; Three Female Head Studies
Verso, Four Male Figure Studies
Pencil on paper 14 x 22
Purchased 1982

700.2000
(C397)
Female Figure Study
Verso, Male Figure Study
Pencil on paper 18 x 12
Purchased 1982

701.2000
(C398)
Two Male Figure Studies
Verso, Female Figure Study; Six Sketches of Ladies' Hats
Pencil on paper 14 x 22
Purchased 1982

702.2000
(C399)
Female Figure Study (squared)
Verso, Three Male Head Studies
Pencil on paper 21 x 13.5
Purchased 1982

703.2000
(C400)
Female Figure in Theatrical Dress
Verso, Male Figure in Theatrical Dress
Pencil on paper 21 x 14
Purchased 1982

704.2000
(C401)
Female Figure Study
Verso, One Male and One Female Figure Study
Pencil on paper 21.5 x 13.5
Purchased 1982

705.2000
(C402)
Two Female Figure Studies
Dated indistinctly
Verso, One Male and One Female Figure Study
Pencil on paper 12 x 19
Purchased 1982

706.2000
(C403)
Three Male Figure Studies; Figure Study of a Child
Verso, One Male and One Female Figure Study
Pencil on paper 14 x 22
Purchased 1982

707.2000
(C404)
Portrait of a Woman; Female Face Study; Male Figure Study
Verso, Three Male Figure Studies
Pencil, crayon on paper 14.5 x 22
Purchased 1982

708.2000
(C405)
Female Head Study; Three Male Figure Studies
Verso, Three Male Figure Sketches
Pencil on paper 14.5 x 22
Purchased 1982

709.2000
(C406)
Female Head Study; Three Male Figure Studies
Verso, Twelve Studies of Men in Caps and Bowler Hats
Pencil on paper 14.5 x 22
Purchased 1982

710.2000
(C407)
Male Head Study; Male Figure Study
Verso, Male Figure Studies
Pencil on paper 14 x 23
Purchased 1982

711.2000
(C408)
Male and Female Head and Figure Studies
Verso, Male Figure Studies
Pencil on paper 14 x 23
Purchased 1982

712.2000
(C409)
Male Figure Studies (one squared)
Verso, Male Face Studies
Pencil on paper 14 x 22
Purchased 1982

713.2000
(C410)
Female Costume Studies; Scottish Soldier Figure Study (squared)
Verso, Male Figure Studies
Pencil on paper 14 x 22.5
Purchased 1982

714.2000
(C411)
Male Figure Studies
Verso, Male Figure Studies; Study of a Woman's Head
Pencil on paper 14 x 22
Purchased 1982

715.2000
(C412)
Male and Female Head Studies; Male Figure Study
Verso, Male Figure Studies
Pencil on paper 14 x 22
Purchased 1982

716.2000
(C413)
Male and Female Head Studies
Verso, Female Costume Study
Pencil on paper 21.5 x 13.5
Purchased 1982

717.2000
(C414)
Male and Female Head Studies; Male Figure Studies
Verso, Male Figure Studies
Pencil on paper 14 x 22
Purchased 1982

718.2000
(C415)
Male and Female Figure Studies
Verso, Male Head and Figure Studies
Pencil on paper 14 x 22
Purchased 1982

719.2000
(C416)
Male Figure Study
Verso, Head Studies
Pencil on paper 22 x 14
Purchased 1982

720.2000
(C417)
Male Figure Studies
Verso, Male and Female Figure Studies
Pencil on paper 14 x 22
Purchased 1982

721.2000
(C418)
Sketch of a Woman in Theatrical Dress
Verso, Sketch of a Man in Theatrical Dress
Pencil on paper 22 x 14
Purchased 1982

722.2000
(C419)
Male Figure Study
Verso, Female Head Study
Pencil on paper 21.5 x 13.5
Purchased 1982

723.2000
(C420)
Female Figure Study
Verso, Male Figure Study
Pencil on paper 12 x 18

Purchased 1982

724.2000
(C421)
Male and Female Figure Studies
Verso, Theatre Box
Pencil on paper 13.5 x 20
Purchased 1982

725.2000
(C422)
Male and Female Figure Studies
Verso, Studies of Hands and a Bucket
Pencil on paper 17.5 x 12.5
Purchased 1982

726.2000
(C423)
Male Figure Studies
Verso, Female Figure Studies
Pencil on paper 13.5 x 21.5
Purchased 1982

727.2000
(C424)
Male Figure Studies
Verso, Male and Female Figure Studies
Pencil on paper 14 x 21.5
Purchased 1982

728.2000
(C425)
Male and Female Figure Studies
Verso, Male and Female Figure Studies
Pencil on paper 13.5 x 18.5
Purchased 1982

729.2000
(C426)
Male and Female Figure Studies
Verso, Male Figure Studies
Pencil on paper 14 x 22
Purchased 1982

730.2000
(C427)
Male Figure Studies
Verso, Male and Female Figure Studies
Pencil on paper 21.5 x 14
Purchased 1982

731.2000
(C428)
Male Figure Studies
Verso, Female Figure Studies
Pencil, crayon on paper 14 x 22
Purchased 1982

732.2000
(C429)
Male and Female Figure Studies (squared)
Verso, Sketch of Colonel Sanders' Statue
Pencil on paper 12.5 x 18
Purchased 1982

733.2000
(C430)
Male and Female Figure Studies (squared)
Verso, Male Figure Study
Pencil on paper 12 x 17.5
Purchased 1982

734.2000
(C431)
Female Portrait Study, 12 Dec. 1907
Verso, Male Figure Sketches
Pencil on paper 21 x 14
Purchased 1982

735.2000
(C432)
Male Figure Sketch, 12 Dec. '07
Verso, Female Figure Sketch
Pencil on paper 14 x 21.5
Purchased 1982

736.2000
(C433)
Male Figure Sketch, 21 Feb. '08
Signed
Verso, Two Female Figure Studies (from the Antique?)
Pencil on paper 14 x 21
Purchased 1982

737.2000
Female Figure Study, 13 March '08

(C434)   Signed
Verso, **Male Figure Study**
Pencil on paper 21 x 13.5
Purchased 1982

738.2000   **Male Figure Studies, 8, 12 Aug. '08**
(C435)   Verso, **Male and Female Figure
Studies**
Pencil on paper 13.5 x 21
Purchased 1982

739.2000   **Study of a Man Sleeping in a Chair,**
(C436)   **10 Aug. '08**
Verso, **Male and Female Face Studies**
Pencil on paper 21 x 13.5
Purchased 1982

740.2000   **Male Figure Study, Sept. '08**
(C437)   Signed
Verso, **Female Figure Studies, Aug.
'08**
Pencil on paper 21 x 13.5
Purchased 1982

741.2000   **Male Figure Study**
(C438)   Verso, **Male and Female Figure
Studies, 15 Sept. '08**
Pencil on paper 21 x 13
Purchased 1982

742.2000   **Male and Female Figure Studies, 9**
(C439)   **Oct. '08** (squared)
Verso, **Female Figure Studies,
9 Oct. '08**
Pencil on paper 13.5 x 21.5
Purchased 1982

743.2000   **Male and Female Figure Study, 19**
(C440)   **Oct. '08**
Verso, **Female Figure Study**
Pencil on paper 13.5 x 21
Purchased 1982

744.2000   **Male Figure Studies, 13 Dec. 1908**
(C441)   Verso, **Female Figure Study**
Pencil on paper 13.5 x 21
Purchased 1982

745.2000   **Female Figure Study, 24 Jan. '09**
(C442)   (squared)
Verso, **Three Male Head Studies**
Pencil on paper 14 x 21
Purchased 1982

746.2000   **Female Figure Study, 1 Feb. '09**
(C443)   Verso, **Male Figure Study, 6 Feb. '09**
Pencil on paper 21 x 31.5
Purchased 1982

747.2000   **Female Figure Studies, 1 Feb. '09**
(C444)   Verso, **Male Figure Studies**
Pencil on paper 13.5 x 21
Purchased 1982

748.2000   **Male and Female Figure Studies, 7**
(C445)   **March '09**
Verso, **Male Figure Studies**
Pencil on paper 13.5 x 21.5
Purchased 1982

749.2000   **Male and Female Figure Studies**
(C446)   Verso, **Male Figure Studies, 3 April
'09**
Pencil on paper 13.5 x 21.5
Purchased 1982

750.2000   **Male Figure Studies, 4 April '09**

(C447)   Verso, **Female Figure Studies**
Pencil on paper 12 x 18
Purchased 1982

751.2000   **Male and Female Figure Studies, 16**
(C448)   **April '10**
Verso, **Female Figure Study**
Pencil on paper 12 x 18
Purchased 1982

752.2000   **Male Figure Studies, 17 April '09**
(C449)   Verso, **Male and Female Figure
Studies**
Pencil on paper 14 x 21
Purchased 1982

753.2000   **Male Figure Studies, 13 June '09**
(C450)   Verso, **Female Figure Studies**
Pencil on paper 18 x 12
Purchased 1982

754.2000   **Male and Female Figure Studies, 26**
(C459)   **Dec. '09**
Pencil on paper 12 x 18
Purchased 1982

755.2000   **Male and Female Figure Studies, 26**
(C460)   **Dec. '09**
Verso, **Male Figure Study**
Pencil on paper 12 x 18
Purchased 1982

756.2000   **Male and Female Figure Studies, 26**
(C461)   **Dec. '09**
Pencil on paper 12 x 18
Purchased 1982

757.2000   **Alhambra, 26 Dec. '09**
(C462)   Pencil on paper 12 x 18.5 (squared)
Purchased 1982

758.2000   **Woman Selling Oranges, 28 Dec. '09**
(C463)   Verso, **Male Figure Studies, 28 Dec.
'09**
Pencil on paper 12 x 19 (squared)
Purchased 1982

759.2000   **French Pesants 1870, 29 Dec. '09**
(C464)   (Peasants)
Verso, **German Costumes, 1870**
Pencil on paper 12 x 18.5
Purchased 1982

760.2000   **Polling in a School? 15 Jan. '10**
(C465)   Pencil on paper 13.5 x 18.5 (squared)
Purchased 1982

761.2000   **Crowd, Custom House, 23 Jan. '10**
(C466)   Pencil on paper 13.5 x 20 (squared)
Purchased 1982

762.2000   **Man Asleep in a Chair, 11 Feb. '10**
(C467)   Verso, **Female Head and Hand Study**
Pencil on paper 20 x 13.5
Purchased 1982

763.2000   **Girl; Boy in an Eton Collar and**
(C468)   **Mortar Board, 8 Feb. '10**
Verso, **Male and Female Figure
Studies**
Pencil on paper 15 x 21.5
Purchased 1982

764.2000   **Male Figure Studies**
(C469)   Verso, **Male and Female Figure
Studies, 21 Feb. '10**
Pencil on paper 14 x 22
Purchased 1982

765.2000   **Embracing Couple, 28 Feb. '10**
(C470)   Verso, **Male Figure Study**
Pencil on paper 18.5 x 12.5
Purchased 1982

766.2000   **Poulterer's Shop, 26 March '10**
(C471)   (squared)
Verso, **Male and Female Figure
Studies**
Pencil on paper 18.5 x 20.5
Purchased 1982

767.2000   **Male and Female Figure Studies, 21**
(C472)   **March '10** (squared)
Verso, **Male and Female Figure
Studies**
Pencil on paper 12 x 18
Purchased 1982

768.2000   **Male and Female Figure Studies,**
(C473)   **Portadown, 28 March '10**
Verso, **Male Figure Studies**
Pencil on paper 12.5 x 18
Purchased 1982

769.2000   **Watching the Race, Ballyhaft, 2 April**
(C474)   **'10** (squared)
Verso, **Male and Female Figure
Studies**
Pencil, crayon on paper 12.5 x 18
Purchased 1982

770.2000   **Watching the Race, 2 April '10**
(C475)   (squared)
Verso, **Male and Female Figure
Studies**
Pencil on paper 18.5 x 12.5
Purchased 1982

771.2000   **Woman Reading, 6 April '10**
(C476)   (squared)
Verso, **Male Facial Studies**
Pencil on paper 12.5 x 18
Purchased 1982

772.2000   **Lisnalinchy Races, 9 April '10**
(C477)   Verso, **Male and Female Figure
Studies**
Pencil on paper 17.5 x 12.5
Purchased 1982

773.2000   **Amorous Couple, 15 April '10**
(C478)   Verso, **Male and Female Figure
Studies**
Pencil on paper 18 x 12.5
Purchased 1982

774.2000   **Woman Walking a Dog, 18 April '10**
(C479)   Verso, **Male and Female Figure
Studies**
Pencil on paper 12.5 x 18
Purchased 1982

775.2000   **Female Figure Studies, 18 April '10**
(C480)   Verso, **Male and Female Figure
Studies**
Pencil on paper 12.5 x 18
Purchased 1982

776.2000   **Man Cleaning a Lamp, 18 April '10**
(C481)   (squared)
Verso, **Female Figure Studies, 18
April '10**
Pencil on paper 18 x 12.5
Purchased 1982

777.2000
(C482)
Male and Female Figure Studies, 18 April '10
Pencil on paper 12.5 x 17.5
Purchased 1982

778.2000
(C483)
Female Figure Studies, 18 April '10
Verso, **Male and Female Figure Studies**
Pencil on paper 12.5 x 18
Purchased 1982

779.2000
(C484)
Female Figure Studies, 19 April '10
Verso, **Male Figure Study**
Pencil on paper 12.5 x 18
Purchased 1982

780.2000
(C485)
Street Organ Player, 20 April '10
Verso, **Female Figure Studies, 23 April '10**
Pencil on paper (pencil, crayon on verso) 18 x 12.5
Purchased 1982

781.2000
(C486)
Male and Female Figure Studies, 22 April '10
Verso, **Male Figure Studies**
Pencil, crayon on paper 13.5 x 22
Purchased 1982

782.2000
(C487)
Male and Female Figure Studies, 22 April '10
Verso, **Male and Female Figure Studies**
Pencil on paper 14 x 22
Purchased 1982

783.2000
(C488)
Male Figure Studies, 26 April '10
Verso, **Male and Female Figure Studies**
Pencil on paper 14 x 21.5
Purchased 1982

784.2000
(C489)
Male and Female Figure Studies, 6 May '10
Verso, **Female Figure Studies, 6 May; A Cold Blowy Day**
Pencil on paper 12.5 x 18.5
Purchased 1982

785.2000
(C490)
Female Figure Studies, 11 May '10
Verso, **Male and Female Figure Studies**
Pencil on paper (pencil, crayon on verso) 12.5 x 18
Purchased 1982

786.2000
(C491)
Male and Female Figure Studies, 11 May '10
Verso, **Female Figure Studies, 11 May '10**
Pencil on paper 12.5 x 18.5
Purchased 1982

787.2000
(C492)
Man Carrying a Crate, 17 May '10
Verso, **Female Figure Studies**
Pencil on paper 12.5 x 18
Purchased 1982

788.2000
(C493)
Male and Female Figure Studies, 17 May '10
Verso, **Male Figure Studies**
Pencil, crayon on paper 14 x 22
Purchased 1982

789.2000
(C494)
Male and Female Figure Studies, 30 May '10

Verso, **Male and Female Figure Studies**
Pencil, crayon on paper 12.5 x 18.5
Purchased 1982

790.2000
(C495)
Male and Female Figure Studies, 2 June '10
Verso, **Male Figure Studies**
Pencil, crayon on paper 14 x 22
Purchased 1982

791.2000
(C496)
Male and Female Figure Studies, 3 June '10
Verso, **Male and Female Figure Studies**
Pencil on paper 12.5 x 18.5
Purchased 1982

792.2000
(C497)
Woman Carrying Golf Clubs, 3 June '10
Verso, **Male and Female Figure Studies**
Pencil, crayon on paper 14 x 22
Purchased 1982

793.2000
(C498)
Male and Female Figure Studies, 8 June '10 (squared)
Verso, **Female Figure Studies**
Pencil on paper (pencil, crayon on verso) 14.5 x 22
Purchased 1982

794.2000
(C499)
Male and Female Figure Studies, 16 June '10
Verso, **Male and Female Figure Studies**
Pencil on paper 14 x 22
Purchased 1982

795.2000
(C500)
Male Figure Studies, Agnes Street, Shankhill Road, 17 June '10
Verso, **Female Figure Studies**
Pencil on paper 12.5 x 18.5
Purchased 1982

796.200
(C501)
Male and Female Figure Studies, 17 June '10
Verso, **Male and Female Figure Studies**
Pencil on paper 14 x 22
Purchased 1982

797.2000
(C502)
Male Figure Studies, 10 July '10
Verso, **Female Figure Studies**
Pencil on paper 12.5 x 18.5
Purchased 1982

798.2000
(C503)
Male Figure Studies, 29 July '10
Verso, **Male and Female Figure Studies**
Pencil on paper 14 x 22
Purchased 1982

799.2000
(C504)
Male and Female Figure Studies, 16 Aug. '10
Verso, **Male Figure Studies**
Pencil on paper 12 x 18
Purchased 1982

800.2000
(C505)
Woman Scrubbing a Doorstep, 28 Aug. '10
Verso, **Male and Female Figure Studies**
Pencil on paper 12 x 18
Purchased 1982

801.2000
(C506)
Male and Female Figure Studies, 7 Oct. '10
Verso, **Male Figure Study**
Pencil on paper 14.5 x 22
Purchased 1982

802.2000
(C507)
Male Figure Studies, 24 Oct. '10
Verso, **Male and Female Figure Studies**
Pencil on paper 14 x 22
Purchased 1982

803.2000
(C508)
Cinema Show, Shankhill Road, 24 Dec. '10
Verso, **Male Figure Sketch**
Pencil on paper 12 x 18
Purchased 1982

804.2000
(C509)
Male and Female Studies, Portrush, '10
Pencil on paper 12.5 x 18.5 (squared)
Purchased 1982

805.2000
(C510)
Male and Female Figure Studies, June 14 (squared)
Verso, **Male and Female Figure Studies; Aberdeen Line from Australia**
Pencil on paper 12 x 17.5
Purchased 1982

806.2000
(C511)
Female Figure Study, 3 Dec. '04
Verso, **Male Figure Study**
Pencil on paper 20.5 x 13
Purchased 1982

807.2000
(C512)
Male and Female Figure Studies, 1 April '12
Verso, **Male Figure Studies**
Pencil on paper 13.5 x 21
Purchased 1982

808.2000
(C513)
Sketch of Carriage, 10 July '01
Verso, **Female Figure Studies**
Pencil on paper 13.5 x 20
Purchased 1982

809.2000
(C514)
Sketch of Boxing Ring
Pencil on paper 15 x 20
Purchased 1982

810.2000
(C515)
Sketch of Boxing Ring, 28 April; Boxing Match, Star Music Hall, 23 (?) April '10
Verso, **Sketch of Boxing Match**
Pencil on paper 14 x 22
Purchased 1982

811.2000
(C516)
Woman on a Couch
Verso, **Female Figure Study**
Pencil on paper 12.5 x 18
Purchased 1982

812.2000
(C517)
Male and Female Figure Studies
Pencil on paper 13 x 20
Purchased 1982

813.2000
(C518)
Female Figure and Head Study
Verso, **Female Head Study**
Pencil on paper 13.5 x 21
Purchased 1982

814.2000
(C519)
Female Figure Studies
Pencil on paper 18.5 x 15 (squared)
Purchased 1982

815.2000
(C520)
Female Figure Studies
Verso, **Sketch of Street Lamp**
Pencil on paper 13.5 x 21
Purchased 1982

816.2000
(C521)
Woman Sewing, Jan. 21 (squared)
Verso, **Female Figure Studies**
Pencil on paper 13.5 x 21
Purchased 1982

817.2000
(C522)
Female Figure Study
Verso, **Female Figure Study**
Pencil on paper 22 x 13
Purchased 1982

818.2000
(C523)
Female Figure Study
Pencil on paper 12.5 x 18.5
(irregular)
Purchased 1982

819.2000
(C524)
Female Figure Study
Pencil on paper 21 x 13.5
Purchased 1982

820.2000
(C525)
Woman Asleep in an Armchair
(squared)
Verso, **Male Figure Study**
Pencil on paper 18 x 12.5
Purchased 1982

821.2000
(C526)
Female Figure Study
Verso, **Landscape with Cottage**
Pencil on paper 18 x 12.5
Purchased 1982

822.2000
(C527)
Female Figure Study, 18 March '01
Pencil on paper 12 x 16
Purchased 1982

823.2000
(C528)
Female Figure Study
Pencil on paper 21 x 13.5
Purchased 1982

824.2000
(C529)
Female Figure Study, 28 Feb.
Verso, **Female Figure Study**
Pencil on paper 17 x 12
Purchased 1982

825.2000
(C530)
Female Figure Study
Pencil on paper 20.5 x 14.5 (squared)
Purchased 1982

826.2000
(C531)
Female Figure Study
Verso, **Male and Female Head Studies**
Pencil on paper 21 x 14
Purchased 1982

827.2000
(C532)
Female Figure Study, 19 May
Verso, **Female Figure Study, May
1918 (?)**
Pencil on paper 12.5 x 18.5
Purchased 1982

828.2000
(C533)
Custom House Steps, 13 June '09
Verso, **Male Head Studies**
Pencil on paper 17 x 12.5
Purchased 1982

829.2000
(C534)
Shawlies
Verso, **Shawlie; Male Figure Study, 26
Dec. '09**
Pencil on paper 12 x 18
Purchased 1982

830.2000
(C535)
Three Shawlies, 6 May '10
Verso, **Shawlie; Male Figure Studies**
Pencil, crayon on paper 14 x 22
Purchased 1982

831.2000
(C536)
Four Shawlies, 30 May '10
Verso, **Male Figure Studies**
Pencil on paper 12.5 x 18.5
Purchased 1982

832.2000
(C537)
**Two Shawlies; Female Figure Sketch,
1 June '10**
Verso, **Male Figure Sketches**
Pencil, crayon on paper 14 x 22
Purchased 1982

833.2000
(C538)
Two Shawlies (squared)
Verso, **Male Figure Sketch**
Pencil on paper 15.5 x 20.5
Purchased 1982

834.2000
(C539)
Shawlie; Male Figure Study
Verso, **Shawlie**
Pencil, watercolour on paper 14 x 22
Purchased 1982

835.2000
(C540)
Shawlie; Female Figure Study
Pencil, crayon on paper 12.5 x 18.5
Purchased 1982

836.2000
(C541)
Shawlie; Female Head Study
Verso, **Two Shawlie Head Studies**
Pencil on paper 20.5 x 13.5
Purchased 1982

837.2000
(C542)
**Figure Study of Woman and Young
Boy**
Verso, **Two Shawlies**
Pencil, crayon on paper 15 x 22
Purchased 1982

838.2000
(C543)
Two Shawlies, 3 May '10
Verso, **Two Shawlies**
Pencil on paper 14 x 21.5
Purchased 1982

839.2000
(C544)
Shawlie
Verso, **Male Figure Studies, 26 Dec.
'09**
Pencil, crayon on paper 18.5 x 12
Purchased 1982

840.2000
(C545)
**Two Shawlies; Male Figure Study, 27
Dec.**
Verso, **Male Figure Study**
Pencil on paper 11.5 x 18.5
Purchased 1982

841.2000
(C546)
Three Shawlies
Pencil, crayon on paper 14 x 21
Purchased 1982

842.2000
(C547)
Shawlie
Pencil, crayon on paper 20 x 13
Purchased 1982

843.2000
(C548)
Shawlie
Pencil on paper 18 x 12 (squared)
Purchased 1982

844.2000
(C549)
Four Shawlies, 23 April '10
Pencil on paper 12.5 x 18 (squared)
Purchased 1982

845.2000
(C550)
Shawlie
Pencil, crayon on paper 19 x 8
(squared)
Purchased 1982

846.2000
(C551)
Three Shawlies
Pencil, crayon on paper 10.5 x 18
(squared)
Signed

Purchased 1982

847.2000
(C552)
Shawlie
Verso, **Sketch of Window**
Pencil on paper 12.5 x 18
Purchased 1982

848.2000
(C553)
Shawlie; Two Female Figure Studies
Verso, **Shawlie; Two Female Figure
Studies** (squared)
Pencil, crayon on paper 14 x 21.5
Purchased 1982

849.2000
(C554)
Shawlie
Verso, **Banister**
Pencil on paper 22.5 x 13
Purchased 1982

850.2000
(C555)
Shawlie
Pencil on paper 21.5 x 14
Purchased 1982

851.2000
(C556)
Shawlie
Pencil on paper 20 x 14 (squared)
Purchased 1982

852.2000
(C557)
Getting Ice Cream, 26 Dec.
Pencil on paper 18.5 x 12 (squared)
Purchased 1982

853.2000
(C558)
Shawlie
Pencil, crayon on paper 18 x 12.5
(squared)
Purchased 1982

854.2000
(C559)
Shawlie
Pencil on paper 19.5 x 13 (squared)
Purchased 1982

855.2000
(C560)
Woman in a Ball Gown
Verso, **Male Figure Study, 31 Jan. '09**
Ink on paper (pencil on verso) 18 x
12
Purchased 1982

856.2000
(C561)
Male and Female Figure Studies
Verso, **Female Figure Study**
Pencil on paper 21.5 x 14
Purchased 1982

857.2000
(C562)
Female Figure Studies
Verso, **Male and Female Figure
Studies**
Pencil on paper 13.5 x 21
Purchased 1982

858.2000
(C563)
Female Figure Study
Verso, **Female Figure Studies**
Pencil on paper 20.5 x 13.5
Purchased 1982

859.2000
(C564)
Female Figure Study (squared)
Verso, **Female Figure Study**
Pencil on paper 21.5 x 13.5
Purchased 1982

860.2000
(C565)
Female Figure Study
Verso, **Male and Female Figure
Studies**
Pencil on paper 22 x 14
Purchased 1982

861.2000
(C566)
Female Figure Study (squared)
Verso, **Male Figure Study**
Pencil on paper 22 x 13.5
Purchased 1982

862.2000
Female Figure Study

(C567)   Pencil on paper 13 x 20 (squared)
               Purchased 1982

863.2000   **Female Figure Studies**
(C568)   Verso, **Female Figure Study, 14 Feb.**
               Pencil on paper 13 x 21
               Purchased 1982

864.2000   **Female Figure Study**
(C569)   Pencil on paper 18 x 12
               Purchased 1982

865.2000   **Female Figure Studies**
(C570)   Verso, **Female Figure Studies; Sketch
               of Horse and Cart**
               Pencil on paper 18 x 13
               Purchased 1982

866.2000   **Female Figure Studies**
(C571)   Verso, **Study of Hand and Arm**
               Pencil on paper 21 x 13
               Purchased 1982

867.2000   **Female Figure Study; Hand Study, 20
(C572)   Feb. '18**
               Verso, **Female Figure Study**
               Pencil on paper 13 x 20.5
               Purchased 1982

868.2000   **Female Figure Study** (squared)
(C573)   Verso, **Female Figure Studies**
               Pencil on paper 13 x 9
               Purchased 1982

869.2000   **Female Figure Studies, Bangor;
(C574)   Sketches, 10 Bangor 15**
               Verso, **Female Figure Studies**
               Pencil on paper 12.5 x 18.5
               Purchased 1982

870.2000   **Female Figure Studies**
(C575)   Pencil on paper 13.5 x 19 (squared)
               Purchased 1982

871.2000   **Female Figure Study**
(C576)   Pencil on paper 17.5 x 12.5
               Purchased 1982

872.2000   **Female Figure Study, 20 March '10**
(C577)   Verso, **Female Figure Study**
               Pencil on paper 12 x 16
               Purchased 1982

873.2000   **Female Figure Study, Sept. 28**
(C578)   (squared)
               Verso, **Male Figure Study**
               Pencil on paper 21.5 x 13.5
               Purchased 1982

874.2000   **Female Figure Study, July '07**
(C579)   Pencil on paper 21 x 13.5
               Purchased 1982

875.2000   **Female Figure Study, Aug. '07**
(C580)   Pencil on paper 21.5 x 13.5
               Purchased 1982

876.2000   **Female Figure Study, Oct. '07**
(C581)   Verso, **Two Head Studies**
               Pencil on paper 21 x 13.5
               Purchased 1982

877.2000   **Two Female Head Studies, 12 Nov.
(C582)   '07**
               Pencil on paper 21 x 14 (squared)
               Signed
               Purchased 1982

878.2000   **Old Lady Reading, 17 Nov. '07**
(C583)   Pencil on paper 22 x 14
               Signed
               Purchased 1982

879.2000   **Female Figure Study, 21 Feb. '08**
(C584)   Signed
               Verso, **Nude Leg Study**
               Pencil on paper 21 x 13.5
               Purchased 1982

880.2000   **Female Figure Study, 21 Feb. '08**
(C585)   Signed
               Verso, **Female Head Study**
               Pencil on paper 19 x 14
               Purchased 1982

881.2000   **Female Figure Study, 13 March '08**
(C586)   Pencil on paper 21 x 13.5 (squared)
               Signed
               Purchased 1982

882.2000   **Female Figure Study, 8 '08**
(C587)   Verso, **Male and Female Figure
               Studies**
               Pencil on paper 21.5 x 14
               Purchased 1982

883.2000   **Female Figure Study, 21 Aug. '08**
(C588)   (squared)
               Signed
               Verso, **Male and Female Figure
               Studies**
               Pencil on paper 21 x 13.5
               Purchased 1982

884.2000   **Female Figure Study, 29 Nov. '08**
(C589)   Pencil on paper 17.5 x 12
               Purchased 1982

885.2000   **Woman Asleep in a Chair, 3 Jan. '09**
(C590)   Verso, **Female Figure Study, 5 Jan. '09**
               Pencil on paper 20.5 x 14
               Purchased 1982

886.2000   **Female Figure Study, 9 Feb. '09**
(C591)   Verso, **Two Male Head Studies**
               Pencil on paper 14 x 22
               Purchased 1982

887.2000   **Female Figure Studies, 1 April '09**
(C592)   Verso, **Female Figure Studies; Male
               Head Study, 1 April '09**
               Pencil on paper 21 x 13.5
               Purchased 1982

888.2000   **Female Figure Studies, 21 April '09**
(C593)   Pencil on paper 14 x 21
               Purchased 1982

889.2000   **Female Figure Studies, April '09**
(C594)   Verso, **Female Figure Studies**
               Pencil on paper 13.5 x 21
               Purchased 1982

890.2000   **Girl Standing, View from Window,
(C595)   Landscape, June '09**
               Signed
               Verso, **Female Figure Studies,
               Woodvale Park**
               Pencil on paper 20 x 13.5
               Purchased 1982

891.2000   **Female Figure Studies, 14 June '09**
(C596)   Verso, **Female Figure Studies, 14 June
               '09**
               Pencil on paper 13.5 x 20

               Purchased 1982

892.2000   **Female Figure Studies, Garden Party,
(C597)   14 June '09**
               Verso, **Two Female and Two Child
               Figure Studies**
               Pencil on paper 20.5 x 13.5
               Purchased 1982

893.2000   **Female Figure Studies, 14 June '09**
(C598)   Verso, **Female Figure Studies**
               Pencil on paper 13.5 x 20.5
               Purchased 1982

894.2000   **Female Figure Studies, July '09**
(C599)   Verso, **Female Figure Studies**
               Pencil on paper 13.5 x 20.5
               Purchased 1982

895.2000   **Female Figure Studies, 14 July '09**
(C600)   Verso, **Female Figure Study**
               Pencil on paper 20.5 x 13.5
               Purchased 1982

896.2000   **Female Figure Studies, 4 July '09**
(C601)   Verso, **Male Head Studies**
               Pencil on paper 13.5 x 20.5
               Purchased 1982

897.2000   **Female Figure Studies, 12 July '09**
(C602)   Verso, **Female Figure Studies, 12 July
               '09**
               Pencil on paper 13.5 x 21
               Purchased 1982

898.2000   **Female Figure Study, 8 Aug. '09**
(C603)   Verso, **Female Figure Studies, 8 Aug.
               '09**
               Pencil on paper 13 x 14
               Purchased 1982

899.2000   **Female Figure Studies, 10 Nov. '09**
(C604)   Verso, **Female Figure Studies**
               Pencil on paper 12 x 17.5
               Purchased 1982

900.2000   **Female Figure Study, 6 Jan. '10**
(C605)   Pencil on paper 18.5 x 12.5
               Purchased 1982

901.2000   **Male and Female Figure Studies, Feb.
(C606)   '10** (squared)
               Verso, **Female Figure Studies, Edie, 20
               Feb. '10**
               Pencil on paper 12.5 x 18
               Purchased 1982

902.2000   **Figure Costume Studies, 27 Feb. '10**
(C607)   Verso, **Female Figure Studies**
               Pencil on paper 12.5 x 18
               Purchased 1982

903.2000   **Female Figure Study, 7 March '10**
(C608)   Verso, **Female Figure Study**
               Pencil on paper 12.5 x 18
               Purchased 1982

904.2000   **Female Figure Study, 7 March '10**
(C609)   (squared)
               Verso, **Embracing Couple**
               Pencil, crayon on paper (pencil only
               on recto) 12.5 x 18
               Purchased 1982

905.2000   **Female Figure Study, 7 March**
(C610)   (squared)
               Verso, **Female Figure Study**

Pencil on paper 18 x 12.5
Purchased 1982

906.2000 **Female Figure Study, 10 March '10**
(C611)   Verso, **Female Head Study**
Pencil on paper 18 x 12.5
Purchased 1982

907.2000 **Female Figure Study, 25 March '10**
(C612)   Pencil on paper 18 x 12.5
Purchased 1982

908.2000 **Female Figure Studies** (squared)
(C613)   Verso, **Sketches at St. George's
Market, 25 March**
Pencil on paper 12.5 x 18
Purchased 1982

909.2000 **St. George's Market, 25 March '10**
(C614)   Verso, **Male and Female Figure
Studies**
Pencil on paper 12.5 x 18
Purchased 1982

910.2000 **Female Figure Study, 11 April '10**
(C615)   Pencil on paper 18 x 12.5 (squared)
Purchased 1982

911.2000 **Female Figure Studies, 18 April '10**
(C616)   Pencil on paper 18 x 12.5 (squared)
Purchased 1982

912.2000 **Female Figure Studies, 2 May '10**
(C617)   Pencil, crayon on paper 12.5 x 18
Purchased 1982

913.2000 **Female Figure Study, 2 May '10**
(C618)   Verso, **Female Figure Study**
Pencil, crayon on paper 18 x 12.5
Purchased 1982

914.2000 **Female Figure Study, 6 May '10**
(C619)   Verso, **Female Figure Study**
Pencil on paper 18 x 12.5
Purchased 1982

915.2000 **Female Figure Study**
(C620)   Pencil, crayon on paper 18 x 12.5
Purchased 1982

916.2000 **Female Figure Study, 9 May '10**
(C621)   Verso, **Female Head Study**
Pencil on paper 18 x 12.5
Purchased 1982

917.2000 **Female Figure Study, 9 May '10**
(C622)   (squared)
Verso, **Female Figure Study**
Pencil on paper 18 x 12.5
Purchased 1982

918.2000 **Female Figure Study, 9 May '10**
(C623)   Pencil, crayon on paper 12.5 x 18
Purchased 1982

919.2000 **Female Figure Study, 19 May '10**
(C624)   Verso, **Female Figure Study, May '10**
Pencil on paper 12.5 x 18 (squared)
Purchased 1982

920.2000 **Female Figure Studies, 2 June '10**
(C625)   Verso, **Female Figure Studies**
Pencil, crayon on paper 12.5 x 18
Purchased 1982

921.2000 **Female Figure Study, Market, 10 June
(C626)   '10**
Verso, **Female Figure Studies**

Pencil on paper 12.5 x 18
Purchased 1982

922.2000 **Woman at Sewing Machine, 25 July
(C627)   '10** (squared)
Verso, **Woman at Sewing Machine, 25
July '10**
Pencil, crayon on paper 12.5 x 18
Purchased 1982

923.2000 **Female Figure Studies, 8 Nov. '10**
(C628)   Pencil on paper 12.5 x 18
Purchased 1982

924.2000 **Female Figure Study with Upraised
(C629)   Arm, 25 Aug. '15** (squared)
Verso, **Female Figure Study with
Upraised Arm, 25 Aug. '15**
Pencil on paper 18 x 12.5
Purchased 1982

925.2000 **Female Head and Leg Studies, 12
(C630)   May '15**
Verso, **Female Figure Studies**
Pencil on paper 12.5 x 18
Purchased 1982

926.2000 **Munitions' Worker at Mackie's, 1916**
(C631)   Pencil on paper 20.5 x 13.5
Signed
Purchased 1982

927.2000 **Female Figure Study, 17 March '17**
(C632)   Pencil on paper 12.5 x 18
Purchased 1982

928.2000 **Female Figure Study with Upraised
(C633)   Arm, 25 April '18**
Pencil on paper 18 x 12.5
Purchased 1982

929.2000 **Woman at Sewing Machine, 18 April
(C634)   '10** (squared)
Pencil on paper 12.5 x 18
Purchased 1982

930.2000 **Market Scene, Friday, 10 June '10**
(C635)   (squared)
Verso, **Female Figure Study**
Pencil, crayon on paper 18 x 12.5
Purchased 1982

931.2000 **Female Figure Study, 29 April '10**
(C636)   Pencil on paper 12.5 x 18
Purchased 1982

932.2000 **Male Figure Studies, 29 April '10**
(C637)   Verso, **Male Figure Studies**
Pencil on paper (pencil, crayon on
verso) 14 x 22
Purchased 1982

933.2000 **Child Figure Studies, Portadown, 28
(C638)   March '10**
Verso, **Three Female Figure Studies**
Pencil on paper 12.5 x 18
Purchased 1982

934.2000 **Three Female Figure Studies; Male
(C639)   Figure Study, Portadown, 28 March
'10**
Verso, **Child Figure Study; 'You're a
Quare Toff'; 'I say, I Can See your
Laundry'**
Pencil on paper 12.5 x 18
Purchased 1982

935.2000 **Male Figure and Head Studies,
(C640)   Portadown, 28 March '10**
Pencil on paper 12.5 x 18 (squared)
Purchased 1982

936.2000 **Two Men with a Cart, 26 Dec. '09**
(C641)   Pencil on paper 18 x 12.5 (squared)
Purchased 1982

937.2000 **Man beside a Trestle Table**
(C642)   Pencil, crayon on paper 18 x 12.5
(squared)
Purchased 1982

938.2000 **Three Female Figure Studies; Child
(C643)   Figure Study, 26 Dec. '09**
Verso, **Child Figure Study**
Pencil on paper 12.5 x 18
Purchased 1982

939.2000 **Two Female Figures in Fancy Dress;
(C644)   Female Head Study of Gipsy with
Tambourine, 29 Jan. 1909**
Pencil on paper 14 x 21
Purchased 1982

940.2000 **Figure Study of Coachman, 29 Jan.
(C645)   '07** (squared)
Verso, **Study of Horse**
Pencil on paper 21.5 x 14
Purchased 1982

941.2000 **Figure Study of Boy Seated Reading a
(C646)   Book, 14 Jan. '07**
Verso, **Figure Study of Reclining Man**
(squared)
Pencil on paper 20.5 x 13.5
Purchased 1982

942.2000 **Figure Study of Man Seated Reading
(C647)   a Book, Sept. '07**
Pencil on paper 20.5 x 13.5
Signed
Purchased 1982

943.2000 **Figure Study of Seated Man Reading,
(C648)   Sept. '07**
Pencil on paper 19 x 13.5 (squared)
Purchased 1982

944.2000 **Figure Study of Seated Man Reading,
(C649)   Oct. '07**
Pencil on paper 21 x 13.5
Signed
Purchased 1982

945.2000 **Figure Study of Seated Man, Oct. '07**
(C650)   Verso, **Two Studies**
Pencil on paper 21.5 x 13.5
Purchased 1982

946.2000 **Two Self-Portrait Studies; Study of a
(C651)   Child's Head, Oct. '07**
Pencil on paper 21 x 13.5
Purchased 1982

947.2000 **Figure Study of Seated Man Reading
(C652)   a Paper, Oct. '07**
Pencil on paper 21.5 x 13.5
Purchased 1982

948.2000 **Two Male Figure Studies, Nov. '07**
(C653)   Verso, **Male Figure Study, Nov. '07**
Pencil on paper 22 x 15
Purchased 1982

949.2000 **Figure Study of Seated Man Reading,**

(C654) Nov. '07
Pencil on paper 21.5 x 13.5
Signed
Purchased 1982

950.2000 Three Male Head Studies, 12 Dec.
(C655) 1907
Signed
Verso, Male Head Studies
Pencil on paper 21 x 14
Purchased 1982

951.2000 Reclining Male Figure Study, 12 Dec.
(C656) '07 (squared)
Verso, Study of Trousered Legs
(Male)
Pencil on paper 14 x 21.5
Purchased 1982

952.2000 Two-part Male Figure Study, 13 Dec.
(C657) '07
Pencil on paper 14 x 21.5
Purchased 1982

953.2000 Male Figure Study, 14 Dec. '07
(C658) Pencil on paper 21.5 x 14
Purchased 1982

954.2000 Male Figure Study, 28 Dec. '07
(C659) Verso, Male Figure Study, 28 Dec. '07
Pencil on paper 21.5 x 14
Purchased 1982

955.2000 Male Figure Study, 9 Jan. '08
(C660) Signed
Verso, Male Figure Study; Male Head
Study
Pencil on paper 21.5 x 14
Purchased 1982

956.2000 Male Figure Study, 9 Jan. '08
(C661) Pencil on paper 21.5 x 14
Signed
Purchased 1982

957.2000 Seated Male Figure Study, 9 Jan. '08
(C662) Signed
Verso, Seated Male Figure Study
Pencil on paper 21.5 x 14
Purchased 1982

958.2000 Figure Study of Coachman, 29 Jan.
(C663) '08
Pencil on paper 21.5 x 14
Signed
Purchased 1982

959.2000 Figure Study of Reclining Man, 20
(C664) Feb. '08
Pencil on paper 13.5 x 22 (squared)
Purchased 1982

960.2000 Figure Study of Man Reclining on a
(C665) Couch, 27 Feb. '08 (squared)
Verso, Two Male Head Studies
Pencil on paper 14 x 21.5
Purchased 1982

961.2000 Five Male Figure Studies, April '08
(C666) Pencil on paper 21.5 x 14
Purchased 1982

962.2000 Seated Male Figure Study, 19 April
(C667) '08
Verso, Reclining Male Figure Study
Pencil on paper 21.5 x 14
Purchased 1982

963.2000 Reclining Male Figure Study
(C668) Verso, Male Figure and Head Study,
13 July '08
Pencil on paper 13.5 x 21
Purchased 1982

964.2000 Two Seated Male Figure Studies; Dog
(C669) Study, Aug. '08
Verso, Two Male Head Studies
Pencil on paper 13.5 x 21
Purchased 1982

965.2000 Three Male Figure Studies, Aug. '08
(C670) Verso, Two Male Figure Studies
Pencil on paper 14 x 22
Purchased 1982

966.2000 Four Male Figure Studies; Head
(C671) Study, Aug. '08
Verso, Four Male Figure Studies
Pencil on paper 14 x 22
Purchased 1982

967.2000 Four Male Figure Studies, Aug. '08
(C672) Pencil, crayon on paper 13.5 x 21
Purchased 1982

968.2000 Five Male Figure Studies, Aug. '08
(C673) (David Allen's Drawing Office?)
Verso, Two Male Figure Studies; Two
Male Leg Studies
Pencil on paper 14 x 22
Purchased 1982

969.2000 Two Reclining Male Figure Studies, 2
(C674) Aug. '08
Verso, Female Figure Study
Pencil on paper 21 x 13.5
Purchased 1982

970.2000 Male Figure Study Smoking a Pipe;
(C675) Male Head Study, 2 Aug. '08
Verso, Male Figure Study
Pencil on paper 21 x 13.5
Purchased 1982

971.2000 Five Male Figure Studies, 8 Aug. '08
(C676) Verso, Four Male Figure Studies
Pencil on paper 21.5 x 13.5
Purchased 1982

972.2000 Six Male Figure Studies, 8 Aug. '08
(C677) Verso, Male Figure Study; Male Head
Study; Study of a Canon, 8 Aug. '08
(Carrickfergus Castle?)
Pencil on paper 21.5 x 13.5
Purchased 1982

973.2000 Three Male Figure Studies, 8 Aug. '08
(C678) Verso, Seven Male Head Studies, Aug.
'08
Pencil on paper 21.5 x 13.5
Purchased 1982

974.2000 Two Male Figure Studies, 26 Aug. '08
(C679) Verso, Reclining Male Figure Study
Pencil on paper 13.5 x 21
Purchased 1982

975.2000 Male Figure Study, 27 Aug. '08
(C680) Verso, Two Male Figure Studies
Pencil on paper 20 x 8
Purchased 1982

976.2000 Two Male Figure Studies; Male Head
(C681) Study, 26 Sept. '08 (squared)
Verso, Male Figure Study; Four Male

Head Studies, Sept. '08
Pencil on paper 20.5 x 13
Purchased 1982

977.2000 Seated Male Figure Study, 7 Oct. '08
(C682) Pencil on paper 20.5 x 13
Signed
Purchased 1982

978.2000 Two Seated Male Figure Studies, 22
(C683) Oct. '08
Verso, Male Figure Study
Pencil on paper 14 x 21
Purchased 1982

979.2000 Two Male Head Studies, 1 Nov. '08
(C684) Verso, Seated Male Figure Study;
Male Head Study
Pencil on paper 21 x 13.5
Purchased 1982

980.2000 Two Male Head Studies, 30 Nov. '08
(C685) Verso, Seated Male Figure Study
Pencil on paper 13.5 x 21
Purchased 1982

981.2000 Seated Male Figure Study Reading a
(C686) Book, 1 Dec. '08 (One of Conor's
Brothers)
Signed
Verso, Study of Male Legs (for recto)
Pencil on paper 17.5 x 12
Purchased 1982

982.2000 Reclining Male Figure Study, 5 Dec.
(C687) '08
Verso, Reclining Male Figure Study, 5
Dec. '08
Pencil on paper 13.5 x 21.5
Purchased 1982

983.2000 Reclining Male Figure Study; Male
(C688) Head Study, 6 Dec. '08
Verso, Seated Male Figure Study
Reading; Male Leg Study
Pencil on paper 21 x 13.5
Purchased 1982

984.2000 Two Seated Male Figure Studies, 13
(C689) Dec. 1908
Verso, Seated Male Figure Study
Pencil on paper 13.5 x 21
Purchased 1982

985.2000 Seated Male Figure Study, 27 Feb. '09
(C690) Pencil on paper 18 x 12
Purchased 1982

986.2000 Seated Male Figure Study, 11 March
(C691) '09 (One of Conor's Brothers?)
Pencil on paper 21.5 x 13.5
Purchased 1982

987.2000 Sleeping Male Figure Study, 19
(C692) March '09 (One of Conor's
Brothers?)
Pencil on paper 12 x 17.5
Purchased 1982

988.2000 Two Seated Male Figure Studies, 28
(C693) March '09 (squared)
Verso, Two Male Figure Studies
Pencil on paper 14 x 20.5
Purchased 1982

989.2000 Sketch of Artist at an Easel; Head
(C694) and Hat Study, 12 June '09; Billy

Corr Sketching
Pencil on paper 20.5 x 13.5
Purchased 1982

990.2000
(C695)
Sketch of Artist at an Easel, June '09
Verso, Male Figure Study; Four Male Head Studies
Pencil on paper 20.5 x 13.5
Purchased 1982

991.2000
(C696)
Three Male Figure Studies, Custom House Steps, 13 June '09
Verso, Study for Ice-cream Cart; Female Figure Study; Ice-cream Cart, 13 June '09
Pencil on paper 17.5 x 12
Purchased 1982

992.2000
(C697)
Study of Seated Man Sleeping beside a Kitchen Table, 8 July '09
Verso, Study of Seated Man
Pencil on paper 13.5 x 20.5
Purchased 1982

993.2000
(C698)
Study of Man Sleeping on a Couch, 1 Aug. '09
Verso, Male Figure Study; Male Head Study
Pencil on paper 12 x 17.5
Purchased 1982

994.2000
(C699)
Two Male Head Studies, 17 Nov., 19 Nov. '09
Verso, Male Figure Study
Pencil on paper 14 x 22
Purchased 1982

995.2000
(C700)
Two Male Head Studies, 18 Dec. '09 (Old Man with Bowler Hat)
Pencil on paper 10.5 x 16
Purchased 1982

996.2000
(C701)
Study of Man Holding a Rifle; Shooting Range, 24 Dec. '09
Verso, Two Male Figure Studies; Male Head Study; Female Head Study
Pencil on paper 12 x 18
Purchased 1982

997.2000
(C702)
Throwing Balls, Chapel Fields, 25 Dec. '09
Verso, Sketch of House or Tent
Pencil on paper 19 x 11.5
Purchased 1982

998.2000
(C703)
Two Male Figure Studies of Upper Torso and Head, 25 Dec. '09
Verso, Seated Male Figure Study; Male Head Study; Hat Study
Pencil on paper 11.5 x 19
Purchased 1982

999.2000
(C704)
Study of Man and Cart; Man Selling Beads; Orange Cart, 25 Dec. '09
Pencil on paper 18.5 x 12 (squared)
Purchased 1982

1000.2000
(C705)
Male Figure Study; Study of Male Legs, 13 Jan. '10
Verso, Two Male Figure Studies; Male Head Study
Pencil on paper (pencil, crayon on verso) 14 x 21.5
Purchased 1982

1001.2000
(C706)
Three Male Figure Studies; Three Studies of Male Arms, 14 Jan. '10

Verso, Four Male Figure Studies
Pencil on paper 14 x 21.5
Purchased 1982

1002.2000
(C707)
Three Male Figure Studies, 20 Feb. '00
Verso, Four Male Figure Studies
Pencil on paper 22 x 14.5
Purchased 1982

1003.2000
(C708)
Two Studies for Seated Male Figures, 26 Feb. '10
Verso, Three Studies for Seated Male Figures
Pencil on paper 13 x 19
Purchased 1982

1004.2000
(C709)
Study for Seated Male Figure; Male Head Study, 26 Feb. '10
Verso, Hand Study; Study of Boat
Pencil on paper 13 x 19
Purchased 1982

1005.2000
(C710)
Three Male Figure Studies, April '10
Verso, Twelve Male Hand and Arm Studies
Pencil on paper 14 x 22
Purchased 1982

1006.2000
(C711)
Sketches for 'Boy Playing Accordion, Ballyhaft Races', 2 April '10
Verso, Two Male Figure Studies; Study of a Bookie
Pencil, crayon on paper 12.5 x 18
Purchased 1982

1007.2000
(C712)
Two Male Figure Studies, Killinchy Yacht Races, 9 April '10
Verso, Three Figure Studies at the Races
Pencil on paper 12 x 17.5
Purchased 1982

1008.2000
(C713)
Three Male Figure Studies, 12 April '10 (squared)
Verso, Two Male Figure Studies; Male Head Study; Three Male Head Studies
Pencil, crayon on paper 14 x 22
Purchased 1982

1009.2000
(C714)
Three Male Figure Studies, 9 June '10
Verso, Five Male Figure Studies
Pencil on paper 14 x 22
Purchased 1982

1010.2000
(C715)
Four Male Figure Studies; Railway Carriage Going to Portadown, 10 July 1917 (squared)
Verso, Male Figure Studies in a Railway Carriage
Pencil on paper 12.5 x 18.5
Purchased 1982

1011.2000
(C716)
Three Male Figure Studies; Male Head Study, 25 July '10
Verso, Six Male Figure Studies
Pencil on paper 14.5 x 22
Purchased 1982

1012.2000
(C717)
Three Male Figure Studies, 28 June '10
Verso, Four Figure Studies of Men Digging
Pencil on paper 18.5 x 12.5

Purchased 1982

1013.2000
(C718)
Ten Studies of Male Heads, Hats, Arms and Upper Torsos, 7 July '10
Verso, Six Studies of Male Heads, Arms and Upper Torsos
Pencil on paper 13.5 x 22
Purchased 1982

1014.2000
(C719)
Four Male Figure Studies, 15 Aug '10
Verso, Three Male Figure Studies
Pencil on paper 14 x 22
Purchased 1982

1015.2000
(C720)
Five Male Figure Studies, 24 Aug. '10
Verso, Three Male Figure Studies (at David Allen's?)
Pencil on paper 14 x 22
Purchased 1982

1016.2000
(C721)
Two Male Figure Studies at a Desk; Male Head Study, 25 Aug. '10 (at David Allen's?)
Verso, Three Studies of Male Legs
Pencil on paper 14 x 22
Purchased 1982

1017.2000
(C722)
Male Figure Study, 3 Oct. '10
Verso, Male and Female Figure Studies Sitting on a Park Bench, 28 Aug. '10
Pencil on paper 18 x 12
Purchased 1982

1018.2000
(C723)
Four Male Figure Studies, 29 Aug. '10
Verso, Two Male Figure Studies; Male Head and Leg Study
Pencil on paper 14 x 22
Purchased 1982

1019.2000
(C724)
Three Male Figure Studies, 21 Oct. '10
Verso, Two Male Figure Studies; Three Head Studies; Arm and Hand Study
Pencil on paper 14.5 x 21.5
Purchased 1982

1020.2000
(C725)
Roadworks or Building Site, 10 Feb. '11
Verso, Three Male Figure Studies
Pencil on paper 12 x 18
Purchased 1982

1021.2000
(C726)
Studies of Workmen, 16 Feb. '11
Verso, Two Male Figure Studies
Pencil on paper 13.5 x 21
Purchased 1982

1022.2000
(C727)
Roadworks, 10 Feb. '11
Verso, Four Male Figure Studies
Pencil on paper 12 x 18
Purchased 1982

1023.2000
(C728)
Studies of Printing Workers and Road Workers, 20 July 1917
Verso, Five Male Figure Studies; Male Head Study
Pencil on paper 14 x 21.5
Purchased 1982

1024.2000
(C729)
Male Figure Study, 5 Dec. '04
Verso, Three Horse Studies
Pencil on paper 21 x 13.5
Purchased 1982

1025.2000 **Study of Man with a Barrel Organ,**
(C730)   **'10**
Verso, **Study of Horse in Harness**
Pencil on paper 21 x 13.5
Purchased 1982

1026.2000 **Male Figure Study, Jan. 2**
(C731)   Verso, **Male Figure Study; Male Head**
Study, Jan. 2
Pencil on paper 21 x 13.5
Purchased 1982

1027.2000 **Study of Policeman with a Cape**
(C732)   Verso, **Study of Soldier with a Kilt**
Pencil on paper 21.5 x 14
Purchased 1982

1028.2000 **Three Studies of Policeman with a**
(C733)   **Cape**
Verso, **Study of Policeman**
Pencil on paper 21.5 x 14
Purchased 1982

1029.2000 **Three Male Figure Studies**
(C734)   Verso, **Three Male Figure Studies**
Pencil on paper 11.5 x 18.5
Purchased 1982

1030.2000 **Three Studies of Policemen's Capes**
(C735)   Verso, **Two Male Figure Studies**
Pencil on paper 21 x 13.5
Purchased 1982

1031.2000 **Three Figure Studies of Policemen**
(C736)   Verso, **Four Male Figure Studies**
Pencil on paper 21 x 13.5
Purchased 1982

1032.2000 **Two Male Figure Studies**
(C737)   Verso, **Male Figure Study; Child's**
Head Study
Pencil on paper 14 x 22.5
Purchased 1982

1033.2000 **Two Male Figure Studies; Male Head**
(C738)   **Study; Associated Sketches**
Verso, **Male Figure Study in**
Theatrical Costume; Study of
Bagpipes
Pencil on paper 14 x 22
Purchased 1982

1034.2000 **Four Male Figure Studies** (squared)
(C739)   Verso, **Figure Study of Soldier in**
Dress Uniform; Study of Banister
Post
Pencil on paper 14 x 22
Purchased 1982

1035.2000 **Male Figure Study; Three Studies of**
(C740)   **Male Legs**
Verso, **Three Male Figure Studies**
Pencil, crayon on paper 14.5 x 22
Purchased 1982

1036.2000 **Three Male Head Studies; Two Male**
(C741)   **Figure Studies; Male Leg Study**
Verso, **Four Male Figure Studies**
Pencil on paper 14.5 x 12.5
Purchased 1982

1037.2000 **Three Studies of Workmen in**
(C742)   **Overalls**
Verso, **Three Male Figure Studies**
Pencil on paper 14 x 23
Purchased 1982

1038.2000 **Study of Workmen in Overalls**
(C743)   Verso, **Three Male Figure Studies**
Pencil on paper 18.5 x 12.5
Purchased 1982

1039.2000 **Figure Study of Workman on**
(C744)   **Wooden Scaffolding**
Verso, **Three Male Figure Studies on**
Work Site
Pencil on paper 18.5 x 12.5
Purchased 1982

1040.2000 **Roadworks**
(C745)   Verso, **Study of Two Workmen, One**
with a Wheelbarrow
Pencil on paper 12.5 x 18.5
Purchased 1982

1041.2000 **Five Figure Studies of Workmen**
(C746)   Verso, **Three Figure Studies of**
Workmen
Pencil on paper 13.5 x 21
Purchased 1982

1042.2000 **The Flute Band**
(C111)   Crayon on paper 48 x 60 (sight)
Signed
Acquired 1961

1043.2000 **The Farmers' Race (1932)**
(C1256)   (Lisnalinchy, Co. Down)
Crayon on paper 48.1 x 58 (sight)
Signed
Acquired 1961

1044.2000 **The Hillsborough Hunt (1950)**
(C129)   Oil on board 48 x 58.3 (sight)
Signed
Acquired 1961

1045.2000 **Out for a Dander (1907)** (Donegal)
(C130)   Ink, watercolour on paper 20.1 x 22.7
(sight)
Signed, dated
Acquired 1961

1046.2000 **The Ice-cream Cart (1908)** (York
(C131)   Street, Belfast)
Ink, watercolour on paper 16.7 x 12
(sight)
Signed
Acquired 1961

1047.2000 **Eleanor - the Black Frock**
(C133)   Oil on canvas 90.5 x 70.8 (sight)
Signed
Purchased 1982

1048.2000 **Gathering Potatoes (1945)** (near
(C134)   Strangford, Co. Down)
Crayon on paper 38 x 46.5 (sight)
Signed
Acquired 1961

1049.2000 **Strangford Lough (1934)**
(C112)   Oil on canvas 63.5 x 76
Signed, dated
Acquired 1961

1053.2000 **Two Male Figure Studies, One of a**
(C747)   **Runner; Study of Male Legs**
Verso, **Study of Male Runner; Two**
Head Studies
Pencil on paper 14 x 22.5
Purchased 1982

1054.2000 **Two Male Figure Studies** (one

(C748)   squared)
Verso, **Two Male Figure Studies in**
Plus Fours
Pencil on paper 14 x 21.5
Purchased 1982

1055.2000 **Study of Man with a Washtub on a**
(C749)   **Chair**
Verso, **Study of Reclining Man**
Pencil on paper 21 x 13.5
Purchased 1982

1056.2000 **Study of Three Seated Men Wearing**
(C750)   **Caps**
Verso, **Landscape**
Pencil on paper 12 x 18
Purchased 1982

1057.2000 **Study of Man Standing on a Ship's**
(C751)   **Deck**
Pencil on paper 19 x 12
Purchased 1982

1058.2000 **Study of Preacher** (squared)
(C752)   Pencil on paper 21.5 x 14
Purchased 1982

1059.2000 **Man with a Barrel Organ in the**
(C753)   **Street**
Pencil, crayon on paper 21 x 13.5
Purchased 1982

1060.2000 **Cowboy**
(C754)   Pencil, watercolour on paper 21 x 13
Purchased 1982

1061.2000 **Portraits of Men Watching Races?**
(C755)   Pencil on paper 13.5 x 21
Purchased 1982

1062.2000 **Kicking the Ball, Ballyhaft Races**
(C756)   Verso, **Male Figure Sketch; Sketches**
of Marquees
Pencil on paper 18.5 x 12
Purchased 1982

1063.2000 **Study of Four Men at the Bookies**
(C757)   Pencil on paper 15.5 x 20.5
Purchased 1982

1064.2000 **Study of Man Leaning on a Counter**
(C758)   (David Allen's Drawing Office?)
Pencil on paper 22.5 x 14
Purchased 1982

1065.2000 **Three Male Figure Studies**
(C759)   Verso, **Six Male Figure Studies**
Pencil on paper 13.5 x 22
Purchased 1982

1066.2000 **Study of Three Men at Desks** (at
(C760)   David Allen's?)
Verso, **Four Male Figure Studies**
Pencil on paper 15 x 13
Purchased 1982

1067.2000 **Six Male Figure Studies** (at David
(C761)   Allen's?)
Verso, **Male Figure Study; Male Leg**
Studies
Pencil on paper 14 x 22.5
Purchased 1982

1068.2000 **Study of Seated Man Writing at a**
(C762)   **Table**
Verso, **Female Head Study**
Pencil on paper 21.5 x 13.5

Purchased 1982

1069.2000 **Two Figure Studies of Man Reading a**
(C763) **Newspaper**
Verso, **Study of Seated Man**
Pencil on paper 23.5 x 13.5
Purchased 1982

1070.2000 **Study of Man Seated at a Table**
(C764) Verso, **Sketch of Man**
Pencil on paper 22 x 14.5
Purchased 1982

1071.2000 **Figure Study of Man Seated on a**
(C765) **Bench**
Verso, **Male Figure Studies**
Pencil on paper 14.5 x 22
Purchased 1982

1072.2000 **Three Male Figure Studies**
(C766) Verso, **Study of Man in an Apron;**
Five Male Figure Studies
Pencil on paper 22 x 15
Purchased 1982

1073.2000 **Four Male Figure Studies**
(C767) Verso, **Study of Man Seated on a**
Stool
Pencil on paper 14 x 22
Purchased 1982

1074.2000 **Two Male Figure Sketches**
(C768) Verso, **Three Male Figure Sketches**
Pencil on paper 22 x 14
Purchased 1982

1075.2000 **Three Male Figure Studies, Two at**
(C769) **Draughtsmen's Tables** (at David
Allen's?)
Verso, **Two Male Figure Studies; Two**
Male Hand Studies
Pencil, crayon on paper 14 x 22
Purchased 1982

1076.2000 **Study of Man in a Deck Chair; Study**
(C770) **of Reclining Man**
Verso, **Three Male Figure Studies**
Pencil, crayon on paper 21 x 13.5
Purchased 1982

1077.2000 **Male Figure Studies**
(C771) Verso, **Male Figure Studies**
Pencil on paper 15 x 11
Purchased 1982

1078.2000 **Five Figure Studies of Men Bending**
(C772) **forward**
Pencil on paper 21 x 13.5
Purchased 1982

1079.2000 **Study of Man Seated on a Stool; Four**
(C773) **Male Studies**
Verso, **Five Male Figure Studies**
Pencil on paper 14.5 x 22
Purchased 1982

1080.2000 **Study of Male Torso** (in Uniform?)
(C774) Verso, **Three Male Studies**
Pencil on paper 21 x 14
Purchased 1982

1081.2000 **Male Figure Study**
(C775) Verso, **Four Studies of Men in**
Football or Rugby Kit
Pencil on paper 13.5 x 21
Purchased 1982

1082.2000 **Five Male Figure Studies**
(C776) Verso, **Five Male Figure Studies;**
Figure Study of a Child
Pencil on paper 13.5 x 21
Purchased 1982

1083.2000 **Five Male Figure Studies**
(C777) Verso, **Six Male Leg Studies; Study of**
Man Leaning on Elbows
Pencil on paper 14 x 22
Purchased 1982

1084.2000 **Male Figure Study**
(C778) Verso, **Male Figure Study**
Pencil on paper 22 x 13.5
Purchased 1982

1085.2000 **Male Figure Studies**
(C779) Verso, **Male Figure Studies, One**
Seated
Pencil on paper 14 x 22
Purchased 1982

1086.2000 **Two Seated Male Figure Studies**
(C780) Verso, **Reclining Male Figure Study**
Pencil on paper 13.5 x 21.5
Purchased 1982

1087.2000 **Figure Study of Man Lying on his**
(C781) **Front**
Verso, **Figure Study of Man Seated on**
a Stool
Pencil on paper 14 x 22
Purchased 1982

1088.2000 **Male Figure Study**
(C782) Verso, **Male Figure Study**
Pencil on paper 14 x 22
Purchased 1982

1089.2000 **Three Male Figure Studies; Male**
(C783) **Head Study** (at David Allen's?)
Verso, **Male Leg Studies**
Pencil on paper 14.5 x 22
Purchased 1982

1090.2000 **Figure Sketch of Man Sitting on a**
(C784) **Chair; Male Head Study**
Verso, **Two Male Head Studies**
Pencil on paper 14 x 22
Purchased 1982

1091.2000 **Male Figure Study**
(C785) Pencil on paper 13.5 x 21
Purchased 1982

1092.2000 **Two Male Figure Studies**
(C786) Verso, **Study of Crossed Male Legs**
Pencil on paper 21 x 13.5
Purchased 1982

1093.2000 **Figure Study of Seated Man with**
(C787) **Crossed Legs**
Verso, **Two Male Head Studies; Male**
Arm Study
Pencil on paper 21 x 13.5
Purchased 1982

1094.2000 **Figure Study of Seated Man**
(C788) Pencil on paper 20 x 13
Purchased 1982

1095.2000 **Two Male Figure Studies; Sketch of**
(C789) **Boat**
Pencil on paper 21.5 x 14
Purchased 1982

1096.2000 **Two Male Figure Studies; Two Male**
(C790) **Leg Studies**
Verso, **Thirteen Male Head Studies**
Pencil on paper 14 x 22
Purchased 1982

1097.2000 **Figure Study of Sleeping Man**
(C791) Pencil on paper 13.5 x 21.5
Signed
Purchased 1982

1098.2000 **Six Male Figure Studies**
(C792) Verso, **Sixteen Studies of Male Heads**
and Headgear
Pencil on paper 14.5 x 22
Purchased 1982

1099.2000 **Three Male Figure Studies; Two Male**
(C793) **Leg Studies**
Verso, **Six Male Figure Studies; Male**
Leg Study
Pencil on paper 14.5 x 22
Purchased 1982

1100.2000 **Male Figure Study; Male Head Study;**
(C794) **Male Leg Study**
Verso, **Male Figure Study; Two Face**
Studies in Profile
Pencil on paper 21 x 14
Purchased 1982

1101.2000 **Study of Male Torso in Jacket**
(C795) Verso, **Male Head and Shoulder**
Study
Pencil on paper 22 x 14
Purchased 1982

1102.2000 **Male Leg Study; Study of Male Torso**
(C796) **in Jacket**
Verso, **Two Male Leg Studies**
Pencil on paper 22 x 14
Purchased 1982

1103.2000 **Two Male Figure Studies** (at David
(C797) Allen's?)
Verso, **Seven Male Figure Studies**
Pencil on paper 22 x 14
Purchased 1982

1104.2000 **Seven Male Figure Studies**
(C798) Verso, **Eight Male Figure Studies**
Pencil on paper 14 x 22
Purchased 1982

1105.2000 **Six Male Figure Studies**
(C799) Verso, **Seven Male Figure Studies**
Pencil on paper 14 x 22
Purchased 1982

1106.2000 **Two Male Figure Sketches; Male Leg**
(C800) **Study**
Verso, **Male Figure Study**
Pencil on paper 14 x 22
Purchased 1982

1107.2000 **Two Male Figure Studies; Male Torso**
(C801) **Study**
Verso, **Sketch of Cart**
Pencil on paper 21 x 14
Purchased 1982

1108.2000 **Two Male Figure Studies; Male Torso**
(C802) **Study**
Verso, **Sketch of Cart**
Pencil on paper 14.5 x 22
Purchased 1982

1109.2000
(C803)
Two Male Figure Studies; Male Torso Study; Male Head Study
Verso, Five Male Figure Studies
Pencil on paper 14 x 22
Purchased 1982

1110.2000
(C804)
Figure Study of Seated Man; Male Head Study; Dog Head Study
Verso, Hand Study
Pencil on paper 21 x 14
Purchased 1982

1111.2000
(C805)
Figure Study of Seated Man
Verso, Two Male Figure Studies
Pencil on paper 14 x 21
Purchased 1982

1112.2000
(C806)
Male Figure Studies
Verso, Three Male Figure Studies
Pencil on paper 14 x 22
Purchased 1982

1113.2000
(C807)
Two Male Figure Studies; Figure Study of Seated Man
Verso, Three Male Figure Studies
Pencil on paper 14.5 x 22
Purchased 1982

1114.2000
(C808)
Three Male Figure Studies
Verso, Male Figure Study; Study of Man's Boots
Pencil on paper 14.5 x 23
Purchased 1982

1115.2000
(C809)
Three Male Figure Studies
Verso, Two Male Figure Studies
Pencil on paper 21 x 14
Purchased 1982

1116.2000
(C810)
Five Male Figure Studies
Verso, Male Figure Study; Three Male Head Studies; Three Male Leg and Boot Studies
Pencil on paper 14 x 22
Purchased 1982

1117.2000
(C811)
Study of Sleeping Man
Pencil on paper 12.5 x 17.5
Purchased 1982

1118.2000
(C812)
Study of Male Head and Shoulders
Pencil on paper 22 x 15
Purchased 1982

1119.2000
(C813)
Male Figure Study
Verso, Unidentifiable Line Drawings
Pencil on paper 20 x 13
Purchased 1982

1120.2000
(C814)
Two Figure Studies of Men Seated on Stools; Two Male Figure Studies
Verso, Three Studies of Male Legs
Pencil on paper 22 x 15
Purchased 1982

1121.2000
(C815)
Four Male Figure Studies
Verso, Three Male Figure Studies
Pencil on paper 14 x 22
Purchased 1982

1122.2000
(C816)
Male Figure Studies
Verso, Male Figure Studies
Pencil on paper 14.5 x 21.5
Purchased 1982

1123.2000
(C817)
Two Male Figure Studies; Male Figure Study

Verso, Two Male Figure Studies; Sketch of Lamp-post
Pencil on paper 21.5 x 14
Purchased 1982

1124.2000
(C818)
Five Male Figure Studies; Hand Study
Verso, Two Male Figure Studies; Sketch of Cap; Sketch of Lion and Elephant
Pencil on paper 14 x 22
Purchased 1982

1125.2000
(C819)
Four Male Figure Studies
Pencil on paper 24 x 15
Purchased 1982

1126.2000
(C820)
Four Male Figure Studies
Verso, Two Male Figure Studies
Pencil on paper 14.5 x 22
Purchased 1982

1127.2000
(C821)
Two Sketches of Men's Plus Fours
Verso, Male Figure Study
Pencil on paper 21 x 14
Purchased 1982

1128.2000
(C822)
Figure Study of Man Sitting on a Stool; Five Male Leg Studies
Verso, Male Figure Study; Associated Studies
Pencil on paper 14.5 x 22
Purchased 1982

1129.2000
(C823)
Study of Arm and Hand of Melodeon Player
Pencil on paper 21 x 14
Purchased 1982

1130.2000
(C824)
Figure Study of Seated Man
Verso, Figure Study of Two Men Working; Two Male Head Studies
Pencil on paper 21 x 13.5
Purchased 1982

1131.2000
(C825)
Five Male Head Studies
Verso, Male Figure Study; Associated Sketch
Pencil on paper 22 x 14
Purchased 1982

1132.2000
(C826)
Male Figure Study; Male Head Study; Arm Study
Verso, Eight Studies of Men's Heads Wearing Trilbys; Study of Boots
Pencil on paper 22 x 14
Purchased 1982

1133.2000
(C827)
Four Studies of Men's Coats
Verso, Four Leg Studies; Male Head Study
Pencil on paper 14 x 22
Purchased 1982

1134.2000
(C828)
Five Studies of Male Heads Wearing Various Headgear; Three Associated Upper Torso Male Studies
Verso, Study of Photographer
Pencil on paper 14 x 22
Purchased 1982

1135.2000
(C829)
Two Male Figure Studies
Verso, Three Studies of Men's Jackets; Two Male Head Studies
Pencil on paper 14 x 22
Purchased 1982

1136.2000
(C830)
Two Male Head Studies
Verso, Male Figure Studies
Pencil on paper 21 x 13
Purchased 1982

1137.2000
(C831)
Four Male Figure Studies
Verso, One Male Head Study
Pencil on paper 15 x 23
Purchased 1982

1138.2000
(C832)
Three Male Head Studies; Study of Man Sitting on a Chair; Male Leg Study
Verso, Three Male Head Studies
Pencil on paper 12 x 17.5
Purchased 1982

1139.2000
(C833)
Study of Man in a Top Hat and Dress Suit; Three Male Figure Studies
Verso, Three Male Figure Studies; Male Head Study
Pencil on paper 14 x 22
Purchased 1982

1140.2000
(C834)
Male Figure Study
Verso, Male Figure Study
Pencil on paper 22 x 15
Purchased 1982

1141.2000
(C835)
Male Figure Study; Three Male Leg Studies
Verso, Four Male Leg Studies; Two Male Figure Studies
Pencil on paper 14 x 22
Purchased 1982

1142.2000
(C836)
Two Male Figure Sketches; Two Male Head Studies
Verso, Two Figure Studies of Men Seated on High Stools; Two Male Leg Studies
Pencil on paper 14 x 22
Purchased 1982

1143.2000
(C837)
Two Male Figure Studies; Two Male Leg Studies
Verso, Eleven Male Facial Studies; Two Hand Studies
Pencil on paper 14 x 22
Purchased 1982

1144.2000
(C838)
Two Male Head Studies; Head Study
Verso, Various Male Figure Studies
Pencil on paper 22 x 14
Purchased 1982

1145.2000
(C839)
Five Male Figure Studies
Verso, Two Male Facial Studies; Arm Studies
Pencil on paper 14 x 22
Purchased 1982

1146.2000
(C840)
Figure Study of Seated Man
Verso, Male Figure Study; Three Male Head Studies
Pencil on paper 14 x 22
Purchased 1982

1147.2000
(C841)
Figure Study of Man Smoking a Pipe
Verso, Figure Study of Reclining Man
Pencil on paper 14 x 22
Purchased 1982

1148.2000
(C842)
Male Facial Study; Sketch of Coat; Sketch of Male Leg
Verso, Four Male Figure Studies

Pencil on paper 14 x 22
Purchased 1982

1149.2000 Six Male Figure Studies
(C843) Verso, Six Male Facial Studies; Sketch
of Jacket
Pencil on paper 14 x 22
Purchased 1982

1150.2000 Two Male Figure Studies; Sketch of
(C844) Ship
Verso, Four Facial Studies of Men in
Caps
Pencil on paper 13.5 x 21
Purchased 1982

1151.2000 Facial Study of Sleeping Man
(C845) Pencil on paper 12.5 x 19
Purchased 1982

1152.2000 Two Male Figure Studies
(C846) Verso, Male Figure and Facial Studies
Pencil on paper 14 x 22
Purchased 1982

1153.2000 Two Male Figure Studies
(C847) Verso, Two Male Figure Studies
Pencil on paper 21 x 13
Purchased 1982

1154.2000 Three Male Figure Studies
(C848) Verso, Two Male Figure Studies
Pencil on paper 21 x 13.5
Purchased 1982

1155.2000 Four Male Figure Studies
(C849) Verso, Male Figure Studies
Pencil on paper 15 x 23
Purchased 1982

1156.2000 Male Figure Sketch; Male Leg Sketch
(C850) Verso, Male Figure Sketch from Back,
Upper Torso only
Pencil on paper 22 x 15
Purchased 1982

1157.2000 Two Male Figure Sketches;
(C851) Associated Male Limb Sketches
Verso, Male Figure Sketches;
Associated Male Limb Sketches
Pencil on paper 15 x 22
Purchased 1982

1158.2000 Three Male Figure Sketches
(C852) Verso, Figure Sketch of Horse and
Jockey; Sketch of Bricklayer's Hod
Pencil on paper 21 x 14
Purchased 1982

1159.2000 Male Figure Sketch; Male Facial
(C853) Studies; Two Studies of Men's Jackets
Verso, Six Studies of Male Legs
Pencil on paper 14 x 22
Purchased 1982

1160.2000 Two Male Figure Studies; Three Male
(C854) Facial Studies; Sketch of Man's Jacket
Verso, Two Male Figure Studies;
Associated Studies
Pencil on paper 14 x 22
Purchased 1982

1161.2000 Male Figure Study and Other
(C855) Sketches
Verso, Male Figure Study; Head
Study and Other Sketches
Pencil on paper 14 x 22

Purchased 1982

1162.2000 Two Male Figure Studies; Two Male
(C856) Leg Studies
Verso, Two Male Figure Studies; Male
Leg Study
Pencil on paper 14.5 x 22.5
Purchased 1982

1163.2000 Figure Study of Man in an Apron
(C857) Verso, Male Figure Study; Associated
Sketches
Pencil on paper 21.5 x 15
Purchased 1982

1164.2000 Three Male Figure Studies;
(C858) Associated Sketches
Verso, Twelve Torso Sketches of Men
Wearing Braces
Pencil on paper 14 x 22
Purchased 1982

1165.2000 Male Figure Sketch; Three Associated
(C859) Sketches
Verso, Male Figure Sketch; Associated
Sketches
Pencil on paper 14 x 22
Purchased 1982

1166.2000 Figure Study of Soldier in an
(C860) Overcoat, with Rifle over Shoulder
Verso, Figure Study of Seated Man;
Two Male Torso Studies
Pencil on paper 14 x 22
Purchased 1982

1167.2000 Figure Study of Man Seated on a
(C861) Stool; Associated Studies
Verso, Five Male Figure Studies
Pencil on paper 14 x 22.5
Purchased 1982

1168.2000 Three Male Figure Studies
(C862) Verso, Male Figure Study; Associated
Studies
Pencil on paper 14 x 22
Purchased 1982

1169.2000 Two Male Figure Studies; Three Male
(C863) Leg Studies
Verso, Figure Study of Man Seated at
a Drawing Board; Four Torso Studies;
Male Leg Study
Pencil on paper 14.5 x 22
Purchased 1982

1170.2000 Two Male Figure Studies; Associated
(C864) Sketches
Verso, Male Figure Studies; Male Leg
Study
Pencil on paper 14.5 x 22
Purchased 1982

1171.2000 Two Male Figure Studies (at David
(C865) Allen's?)
Verso, Figure Study of Man Seated at
a High Workbench; Two Associated
Leg Studies
Pencil on paper 14.5 x 22
Purchased 1982

1172.2000 Associated Male Leg, Head, Torso
(C866) and Hand Studies, 2 March '10
Verso, Male Figure Study; Torso
Study; Three Male Head Studies
Pencil on paper 14.5 x 22

Purchased 1982

1173.2000 Figure Study of Man Seated at a High
(C867) Workbench
Verso, Male Figure Study; Associated
Sketch
Pencil on paper 22 x 14
Purchased 1982

1174.2000 Figure Study of Man Bending over
(C868) Pencil on paper 22 x 13.5
Purchased 1982

1175.2000 Two Male Figure Studies; Associated
(C869) Sketches
Verso, Male Figure and Head Studies
Pencil on paper 14.5 x 22.5
Purchased 1982

1176.2000 Male Figure Study; Male Torso Study
(C870) Pencil on paper 13.5 x 21
Purchased 1982

1177.2000 Figure Study of Back of Man Seated
(C871) on a Garden Bench
Verso, Figure Study of Man in a Hat,
Digging
Pencil on paper 18 x 12.5
Purchased 1982

1178.2000 Figure Study of Man in a Suit and
(C872) Hat
Verso, Study of Coat Hanging from
Coat Hook
Pencil on paper 22.5 x 14
Purchased 1982

1179.2000 Two Male Figure Studies; Associated
(C873) Sketches
Verso, Male Figure Studies; Three
Cap Studies
Pencil on paper 14 x 22
Purchased 1982

1180.2000 Study of Man in a Cap
(C874) Verso, Three Male Figure Studies
Pencil on paper 21 x 13.5
Purchased 1982

1181.2000 Three Male Figure Studies; Male Leg
(C875) Study; Male Head Study
Verso, Male Figure Studies
Pencil on paper (pencil, crayon on
verso) 14 x 22.5
Purchased 1982

1182.2000 Three Male Figure Studies
(C876) Verso, Sketches of Man's Raincoat
Pencil on paper 12.5 x 18
Purchased 1982

1183.2000 Figure Sketch of Man Wearing a Cap
(C877) Pencil on paper 19 x 11
Purchased 1982

1184.2000 Study of Man's Legs
(C878) Pencil on paper 13 x 14 (squared)
Purchased 1982

1185.2000 Study of Male Torso in a Jacket
(C879) Verso, Study of Men's Feet in Shoes
Pencil on paper 22 x 15
Purchased 1982

1186.2000 Study of Man Leaning on a Counter;
(C880) Six Associated Studies
Verso, Six Male Figure Studies

Pencil on paper 14.5 x 22
Purchased 1982

1187.2000 Two Male Figure Studies; Head
(C881) Study of Man Wearing a Cap
 Verso, Two Figure Studies of Seated
 Man
 Pencil on paper 22 x 13.5
 Purchased 1982

1188.2000 Male Figure Study
(C882) Verso, Male Leg Study
 Pencil on paper 22 x 14.5
 Purchased 1982

1189.2000 Figure Study of Seated Man, 6 Oct.
(C883) Verso, Figure Study of Seated Man;
 Associated Sketch
 Pencil on paper 21.5 x 13.5
 Purchased 1982

1190.2000 Figure Study of Seated Man; Male
(C884) Leg Study
 Verso, Figure Study of Seated Man;
 Male Leg Study
 Pencil on paper 22 x 14
 Purchased 1982

1191.2000 Study of Man Wearing a Cap Leaning
(C885) forwards; Sketch of Cap
 Verso, Male Figure Study
 Pencil on paper 22 x 14
 Purchased 1982

1192.2000 Study of Seated Man Reading a Book
(C886) Verso, Figure Study of Seated Man
 Pencil on paper 21 x 13.5
 Purchased 1982

1193.2000 Male Figure Study
(C887) Verso, Figure Study of Seated Man;
 Associated Arm Sketch
 Pencil on paper 22 x 15
 Purchased 1982

1194.2000 Three Male Figure Studies; Two
(C888) Associated Sketches
 Pencil on paper 14.5 x 22
 Purchased 1982

1195.2000 Three Male Figure Studies
(C889) Verso, Male Figure Studies
 Pencil on paper 14.5 x 22
 Purchased 1982

1196.2000 Male Figure Study; Six Associated
(C890) Leg Studies of Men in Breeches
 Verso, Figure Study of Man Seated on
 a Park Bench; Associated Male Hand
 and Head Studies, April
 Pencil on paper 14.5 x 22
 Purchased 1982

1197.2000 Nine Male Leg Studies; Male Figure
(C891) Study; Two Male Torso Studies
 Verso, Four Male Figure Studies;
 Three Male Leg Studies
 Pencil on paper 22 x 29
 Purchased 1982

1198.2000 Four Male Figure Studies of Men in
(C892) Suits
 Verso, Study of Photographer with a
 Camera; Sketch of Camera; Male
 Figure Study; Male Head Study
 Pencil on paper 14.5 x 22
 Purchased 1982

1199.2000 Two Male Figure Studies; Male Head
(C893) Study
 Verso, Study of Man's Feet; 'Pitfall'
 Pencil on paper 14.5 x 22
 Purchased 1982

1200.2000 Figure Study of Seated Man; Two
(C894) Male Leg Studies
 Verso, Five Male Figure Studies
 Pencil on paper 14.5 x 22
 Purchased 1982

1201.2000 Four Male Figure Studies
(C895) Verso, Three Male Figure Studies;
 Male Leg Study
 Pencil on paper 14.5 x 22
 Purchased 1982

1202.2000 Figure Study of Man Seated in an
(C896) Armchair
 Verso, Figure Study of Man Washing
 in a Basin; Figure Study of Man
 Seated on a Wooden Kitchen Chair
 Pencil on paper 21.1 x 13.5
 Purchased 1982

1203.2000 Figure of Reclining Man Wearing a
(C897) Sun-hat and Reading a Book;
 Associated Studies
 Pencil on paper 21.5 x 14
 Purchased 1982

1204.2000 Two Male Figure Studies
(C898) Pencil on paper 13.5 x 21.5
 Signed
 Purchased 1982

1205.2000 Figure Study of Man Seated at a
(C899) Table, Wearing a Suit and Bowler Hat
 (squared)
 Verso, Male Figure Study; Male Arm
 Study
 Pencil on paper 22 x 14
 Purchased 1982

1206.2000 Male Figure Study; Associated
(C900) Sketches; Gas Fittings?
 Verso, Figure Study of Man Sitting on
 the Ground; Three Male Leg Studies
 and other Sketches
 Pencil on paper 14 x 22
 Purchased 1982

1207.2000 Figure Study of Seated Man; Study of
(C901) Eyes
 Verso, Figure Study Wearing a Toga
 Pencil on paper 21 x 14
 Purchased 1982

1208.2000 Two Male Figure Studies
(C902) Pencil on paper 14 x 22
 Purchased 1982

1209.2000 Four Male Figure Studies
(C903) Verso, Five Male Figure Studies
 Pencil on paper 14 x 22
 Purchased 1982

1210.2000 Four Workmen, 16 Feb. '11
(C904) Verso, Figure Study of Man at a
 Washbasin; Sketch of a Towel?
 Pencil on paper 12 x 19
 Purchased 1982

1211.2000 Figure Study of Man in a Bowler Hat
(C905) Pencil on paper 10 x 14.5 (squared)
 Purchased 1982

1212.2000 Two Male Figure Studies
(C906) Verso, Two Male Figure Studies
 Pencil on paper 12 x 17.5
 Purchased 1982

1213.2000 Figure Study of Man Seated on a
(C907) Wooden Stool; Male Leg Study
 Verso, Male Leg Study
 Pencil on paper 16 x 22
 Purchased 1982

1214.2000 Figure Study of Man Seated on a
(C908) High Stool
 Pencil on paper 22 x 14
 Purchased 1982

1215.2000 Figure Study of Man Seated on a
(C909) High Stool
 Verso, Male Figure Study
 Pencil on paper 22 x 14
 Purchased 1982

1216.2000 Figure Study of Man Seated on a
(C910) High Stool
 Pencil on paper 22 x 14
 Purchased 1982

1217.2000 Three Male Figure Studies
(C911) Pencil on paper 14.5 x 22
 Purchased 1982

1218.2000 Three Male Figure Studies
(C912) Pencil on paper 14 x 21.5
 Purchased 1982

1219.2000 Two Male Figure Studies; Male Leg
(C913) Study
 Verso, Figure Study of Man Seated on
 a Wooden Chair; Male Figure Study
 Pencil on paper (pencil, crayon on
 verso) 14 x 21.5
 Purchased 1982

1220.2000 Two Male Figure Studies; Male Head
(C914) Study
 Verso, Figure Study of Seated Man
 Reading a Book; Male Head Study
 Pencil on paper 13 x 18.5
 Purchased 1982

1221.2000 Male Figure Study
(C915) Verso, Figure Study of Male Torso
 Pencil on paper 18 x 12
 Purchased 1982

1222.2000 Figure Study of Man with
(C916) Outstretched Arms
 Pencil on paper 16 x 12
 Purchased 1982

1223.2000 Figure Study of Sleeping Man Sitting
(C917) on the Ground, with Arms Folded
 Verso, Male Figure Study
 Pencil on paper 13.5 x 21.5
 Purchased 1982

1224.2000 Figure Study of Man in a Coat and
(C918) Bowler Hat Using a Salt Shaker?
 Verso, Figure Study of Man in a Coat
 and Hat with Tumbler of Hot Drink
 Pencil on paper 21 x 14.5
 Purchased 1982

1225.2000 Two Male Figure Studies; Sketch of
(C919) Wooden Wheelbarrow
 Verso, Figure Study of Man Sitting on
 a Wooden Chair

Pencil on paper 14 x 21.5
Purchased 1982

1226.2000 **Figure Study of Man Sitting on a**
(C920) **Wooden Chair** (squared)
Verso, **Outline of Male Figure Study**
Pencil on paper 21 x 14
Purchased 1982

1227.2000 **Two Male Figure Studies; Associated**
(C921) **Sketches**
Verso, **Sketches Associated with Male
Figure Studies**
Pencil on paper 14 x 22
Purchased 1982

1228.2000 **Five Male Figure Studies**
(C922) Verso, **Four Studies of Male Legs;
Male Figure Study**
Pencil on paper 14 x 22
Purchased 1982

1229.2000 **Two Male Figure Studies; Male Leg**
(C923) **Study; Three Male Torso Studies**
Verso, **Four Male Leg Studies; Two
Male Torso Studies**
Pencil on paper 14 x 22
Purchased 1982

1230.2000 **Three Male Figure Studies**
(C924) Verso, **Figure Study of Man Seated on
a Stool; Four Associated Sketches**
Pencil, crayon on paper 14.5 x 22
Purchased 1982

1231.2000 **Three Male Leg Sketches; Two**
(C925) **Sketches of Men's Jackets**
Verso, **Figure Study of Reclining Man;
Four Sketches of Men's Jackets**
Pencil on paper 14.5 x 22
Purchased 1982

1232.2000 **Five Male Figure Studies**
(C926) Verso, **Male Figure Study; Five
Associated Sketches**
Pencil on paper 14.5 x 22
Purchased 1982

1233.2000 **Two Male Figure Studies**
(C927) Verso, **Figure Study of Man in a
Workman's Apron; Figure Study of
Man Wearing a Cap, with Hand over
Mouth; Four Associated Sketches**
Pencil on paper 14 x 22
Purchased 1982

1234.2000 **Figure Study of Man with Hands in**
(C928) **Pockets**
Verso, **Figure Study of Seated Man
Wearing a Bowler Hat**
Pencil on paper 22 x 14
Purchased 1982

1235.2000 **Figure Study of Man with Raised**
(C929) **Arm**
Verso, **Male Head Study; Associated
Sketch**
Pencil on paper 22 x 14
Purchased 1982

1236.2000 **Figure Study of Seated Man**
(C930) Verso, **Three Male Figure Studies;
Four Head Studies of Men Wearing
Caps**
Pencil on paper 22 x 14
Purchased 1982

1237.2000 **Two Male Figure Studies; Associated**
(C931) **Leg Study**
Verso, **Male Figure Study; Sketch of
Man's Jacket**
Pencil on paper 20 x 13.5
Purchased 1982

1238.2000 **Figure Study of Man Reading a**
(C932) **Newspaper**
Pencil on paper 21 x 13
Purchased 1982

1239.2000 **Three Male Figure Studies;**
(C933) **Associated Sketches**
Verso, **Interior of Room through
Doorway and Window, with Two
Figures inside**
Pencil on paper 13 x 20
Purchased 1982

1240.2000 **Male Figure Study**
(C934) Verso, **Male Leg Study; Sketch of
Coat**
Pencil on paper 22 x 14
Purchased 1982

1241.2000 **Three Male Figure Studies; Two**
(C935) **Associated Leg Studies**
Verso, **Male Head Study; Male Torso
Study; Two Male Leg and Arm
Studies**
Pencil on paper 15 x 22
Purchased 1982

1242.2000 **Figure Study of Seated Man**
(C936) Verso, **Male Head Study**
Pencil on paper 21.5 x 14
Purchased 1982

1243.2000 **Figure Study of Man Seated in a**
(C937) **Chair**
Pencil on paper 14.5 x 22
Purchased 1982

1244.2000 **Figure Study of Man Seated on a**
(C938) **Wooden Chair**
Pencil on paper 19.5 x 13
Purchased 1982

1245.2000 **Male Figure Study**
(C939) Verso, **Male Figure Study**
Pencil on paper 22 x 14.5
Purchased 1982

1246.2000 **Two Male Figure Studies; Associated**
(C940) **Sketches**
Verso, **Two Male Figure Studies;
Three Male Leg Studies; Torso Study**
Pencil on paper (pencil, crayon on
verso) 22 x 14
Purchased 1982

1247.2000 **Three Male Figure Studies; Male Leg**
(C941) **Study; Male Head Study**
Verso, **Two Male Figure Studies; Four
Head Studies of Men Wearing Hats**
Pencil on paper 14 x 22
Purchased 1982

1248.2000 **Figure Study of Seated Man; Outline**
(C942) **of Male Figure Study**
Pencil on paper 13 x 20 (squared)
Purchased 1982

1249.2000 **Figure Study of Seated Man**
(C943) Verso, **Two Male Figure Studies**
Pencil on paper 22 x 14.5

Purchased 1982

1250.2000 **Figure Study of Seated Man**
(C944) Verso, **Hand Study**
Pencil on paper 22 x 14.5
Purchased 1982

1251.2000 **Male Figure Study; Outline of Male**
(C945) **Arm and Torso**
Verso, **Figure Study of Man Wearing a
Bowler Hat**
Pencil on paper 22 x 14.5
Purchased 1982

1252.2000 **Figure Study of Man Seated on a**
(C946) **Wooden Chair**
Verso, **Male Leg Study**
Pencil on paper 22 x 14.5
Purchased 1982

1253.2000 **Three Studies of Seated Man**
(C947) **Reading**
Verso, **Male Figure Study; Male Head
Study**
Pencil on paper 22 x 14.5
Purchased 1982

1254.2000 **Figure Study of Man in a Workman's**
(C948) **Apron**
Verso, **Figure Study of Man Wearing a
Hat**
Pencil on paper 22 x 14.5
Purchased 1982

1255.2000 **Two Figure Studies of Seated Men,**
(C949) **One Smoking a Pipe** (squared)
Verso, **Male Figure Study; Two Male
Head Studies**
Pencil on paper 21 x 13
Purchased 1982

1256.2000 **Figure Study of Sleeping Man**
(C950) (squared)
Verso, **Figure Study of Seated Man
Wearing a Cap; Figure Study of Man
in a Dress Suit; Associated Sketches**
Pencil on paper 14 x 21
Purchased 1982

1257.2000 **Figure Study of Seated Man Smoking**
(C951) **a Pipe**
Verso, **Figure Study of Seated Man;
Two Male Head Studies**
Pencil on paper 21 x 14
Purchased 1982

1258.2000 **Male Figure Study; Three Associated**
(C952) **Sketches**
Verso, **Figure Study of Man in a
Workman's Apron; Figure Study of
Man in Breeches; Male Leg Study**
Pencil on paper 14 x 22
Purchased 1982

1259.2000 **Three Male Figure Studies; Two Male**
(C953) **Head Studies**
Verso, **Five Associated Studies of Man
Wearing a Workman's Apron**
Pencil on paper 14 x 22
Purchased 1982

1260.2000 **Figure Study of Man Sleeping in a**
(C954) **Chair; Four Associated Head Studies**
Pencil on paper 14.5 x 22
Purchased 1982

1261.2000 **Male Leg Studies, Feb. 11**
(C955)   Verso, **Figure Study of Man with
          Hands on Head**
          Pencil on paper 12 x 10
          Purchased 1982

1262.2000 **Three Male Figure Studies, Feb. 11**
(C956)   Verso, **Four Associated Male Figure
          Studies**
          Pencil on paper 12 x 18
          Purchased 1982

1263.2000 **Study of Man Playing a Piano**
(C957)   Verso, **Two Male Figure Studies; Male
          Head Study**
          Pencil on paper 21 x 13.5
          Purchased 1982

1264.2000 **Figure Study of Man Leaning over a
(C958)   Table** (at David Allen's?)
          Verso, **Male Figure Study of Clown?**
          Pencil on paper 21 x 13.5
          Purchased 1982

1265.2000 **Figure Study of Seated Man**
(C959)   Pencil on paper 21.5 x 13
          Signed
          Purchased 1982

1266.2000 **John with Toothache, 17 Oct. '07**
(C960)   Verso, **Figure Study of Seated Man,
          18 Oct.**
          Pencil on paper 21.5 x 13
          Signed both sides
          Purchased 1982

1267.2000 **Horse and Dog Studies**
(C961)   Verso, **Human and Animal Studies**
          Pencil on paper 19.5 x 11.5
          Purchased 1982

1268.2000 **Study of Ladies' Feet Wearing Shoes**
(C962)   Pencil on paper 20 x 10.5
          Purchased 1982

1269.2000 **Studies from the Antique**
(C963)   Verso, **Studies of Bones**
          Pencil on paper 11 x 19
          Purchased 1982

1270.2000 **Human and Animal Anatomical
(C964)   Studies**
          Verso, **Human Detail Studies**
          Pencil on paper 11 x 19
          Purchased 1982

1271.2000 **Human Anatomical Studies**
(C965)   Pencil on paper 17.5 x 11
          Purchased 1982

1272.2000 **Male and Female Figure Studies**
(C966)   Verso, **Human Detail Studies**
          Pencil on paper 17 x 11
          Purchased 1982

1273.2000 **Human Anatomical Studies**
(C967)   Verso, **Human Anatomical Studies;
          Sketch of Back of Car or Carriage**
          Pencil on paper 20.5 x 11.5
          Purchased 1982

1274.2000 **Human Detail Studies**
(C968)   Verso, **Animal Anatomical Studies**
          Pencil on paper 12 x 19
          Purchased 1982

1275.2000 **Human and Animal Detail Studies**

(C969)   Verso, **Human Detail Studies**
          Pencil on paper 20 x 11.5
          Purchased 1982

1276.2000 **Human Anatomical Studies**
(C970)   Verso, **Human and Animal
          Anatomical Studies**
          Pencil on paper 20.5 x 11.5
          Purchased 1982

1277.2000 **Human Anatomical Studies**
(C971)   Verso, **Human and Animal
          Anatomical Studies**
          Pencil on paper 20.5 x 11.5
          Purchased 1982

1278.2000 **Human and Animal Anatomical
(C972)   Studies**
          Verso, **Human and Animal
          Anatomical Studies**
          Pencil on paper 20.5 x 11.5
          Purchased 1982

1279.2000 **Human Anatomical Studies**
(C973)   Verso, **Human and Animal
          Anatomical Studies**
          Pencil on paper 20.5 x 11.5
          Purchased 1982

1280.2000 **Human and Animal Anatomical
(C974)   Studies**
          Pencil on paper 20.5 x 11.5
          Purchased 1982

1281.2000 **Anatomical Face Studies**
(C975)   Verso, **Human Anatomical Studies**
          Pencil on paper 15 x 11
          Purchased 1982

1282.2000 **Human Anatomical Studies**
(C976)   Verso, **Human Anatomical Studies**
          Pencil on paper 16.5 x 11.5
          Purchased 1982

1283.2000 **Human Anatomical Studies**
(C977)   Verso, **Human Anatomical Studies**
          Pencil on paper 20 x 12
          Purchased 1982

1284.2000 **Human and Animal Studies**
(C978)   Verso, **Human Detail Studies**
          Pencil on paper 16.5 x 11.5
          Purchased 1982

1285.2000 **Human Detail Studies**
(C979)   Verso, **Human Detail Studies**
          Pencil on paper 16.5 x 11.5
          Purchased 1982

1286.2000 **Human Anatomical Studies from the
(C980)   Antique**
          Verso, **Human and Animal
          Anatomical Studies**
          Pencil on paper 15 x 11
          Purchased 1982

1287.2000 **Human Detail Studies**
(C981)   Verso, **Human and Animal Studies**
          Pencil on paper 17.5 x 11
          Purchased 1982

1288.2000 **Human and Animal Studies**
(C982)   Verso, **Human and Animal
          Anatomical Studies**
          Pencil on paper 16.5 x 11.5
          Purchased 1982

1289.2000 **Human Detail Studies**
(C983)   Verso, **Human Detail Studies**
          Pencil on paper 17.5 x 11
          Purchased 1982

1290.2000 **Human and Animal Anatomical
(C984)   Studies**
          Verso, **Human and Animal
          Anatomical Studies**
          Pencil on paper 16.5 x 11.5
          Purchased 1982

1291.2000 **Human Anatomical Studies; Heads**
(C985)   Pencil on paper 15 x 9
          Purchased 1982

1292.2000 **Studies from the Antique**
(C986)   Pencil, watercolour on paper 15 x 11
          Purchased 1982

1293.2000 **Study of Hand Holding on to a Bar**
(C987)   Pencil on paper 18.5 x 12.5
          Purchased 1982

1294.2000 **Human Studies and Studies of Coats**
(C988)   Verso, **Human Anatomical Studies**
          Pencil on paper 17.5 x 11
          Purchased 1982

1295.2000 **Human Anatomical Studies; Studies
(C989)   of Clothes**
          Verso, **Human Anatomical Studies**
          Pencil on paper 19 x 12
          Purchased 1982

1296.2000 **Study of Hands**
(C990)   Pencil on paper 21 x 13
          Purchased 1982

1297.2000 **Studies of Legs**
(C991)   Verso, **Human and Animal
          Anatomical Studies**
          Pencil on paper 20 x 11.5
          Purchased 1982

1298.2000 **Human Anatomical Studies**
(C992)   Verso, **Human Anatomical Studies**
          Pencil on paper 20 x 11.5
          Purchased 1982

1299.2000 **Human Anatomical Studies**
(C993)   Verso, **Human Anatomical Studies**
          Pencil on paper 20 x 11.5
          Purchased 1982

1300.2000 **Human Detail Studies**
(C994)   Verso, **Human Detail Studies**
          Pencil on paper 20 x 11.5
          Purchased 1982

1301.2000 **Human and Animal Anatomical
(C995)   Studies**
          Verso, **Human Anatomical Studies**
          Pencil on paper 20.5 x 12
          Purchased 1982

1302.2000 **Human Anatomical Studies; Studies
(C996)   of Coats**
          Verso, **Human Anatomical Studies**
          Pencil on paper 20.5 x 12
          Purchased 1982

1303.2000 **Human Detail Studies**
(C997)   Verso, **Human Detail Studies**
          Pencil on paper 15 x 12
          Purchased 1982

1304.2000 **Studies of Drapery**

(C998) Verso, **Studies of Drapery; Mill Scene**
Pencil on paper (pencil, watercolour on verso) 17 x 10.5
Purchased 1982

1305.2000 **Study of Rifle and Waterbottle**
(C999) Pencil on paper 22 x 13.5
Purchased 1982

1306.2000 **Two Figure Studies of Soldiers**
(C1000) Verso, **Figure Study of Soldier; Two Head Studies of Soldiers**
Pencil on paper 22 x 13.5
Purchased 1982

1307.2000 **Figure Study of Soldier**
(C1001) Pencil on paper 22 x 13.5
Purchased 1982

1308.2000 **Two Figure Studies of Soldiers**
(C1002) Verso, **Figure Study of Soldier; Male Figure Study; Male Leg Study; Two Studies of Soldiers' Heads**
Pencil on paper 22 x 13.5
Purchased 1982

1309.2000 **Figure Study of Soldier**
(C1003) Pencil on paper 22 x 13.5
Purchased 1982

1310.2000 **Study of Soldier's Head**
(C1004) Pencil on paper 22 x 13.5
Purchased 1982

1311.2000 **Male Head Study** (probably a
(C1005) Soldier)
Pencil on paper 22 x 14.5
Purchased 1982

1312.2000 **Figure Study of Soldier**
(C1006) Pencil on paper 22 x 14.5
Purchased 1982

1313.2000 **On the March** (Figure Study of
(C1007) Soldier)
Pencil on paper 22 x 14.5
Purchased 1982

1314.2000 **Figure Study of Soldier**
(C1008) Pencil on paper 22 x 14.5
Purchased 1982

1315.2000 **Figure Study of Soldier**
(C1009) Verso, **Outline Figure Study of Soldier**
Pencil on paper 22 x 14.5
Purchased 1982

1316.2000 **Figure Study of Soldier Sitting in a**
(C1010) **Chair**
Verso, **Male Head Study**
Pencil on paper 22 x 14.5
Purchased 1982

1317.2000 **Captain Simpson (1916)**
(C1011) Pencil on paper 22 x 14.5
Signed, dated
Purchased 1982

1318.2000 **Figure Study of Soldier; Male Figure**
(C1012) **Study**
Verso, **Two Studies of Soldiers' Torsos**
Pencil on paper 22 x 14.5
Purchased 1982

1319.2000 **Sketch of Rifle; Male Head Study**
(C1013) Verso, **Sketch of Hand Holding a Piece of Paper**

Pencil on paper 22 x 11.5
Purchased 1982

1320.2000 **Study of Chair; Study of Rifle**
(C1014) Pencil on paper 22 x 11.5
Purchased 1982

1321.2000 **Figure Study of Soldier; Associated**
(C1015) **Sketch**
Verso, **Study of Rifle**
Pencil on paper 22 x 11.5
Purchased 1982

1322.2000 **Figure Study of Soldier Sitting on a**
(C1016) **Park Bench**
Pencil on paper 22 x 11.5
Purchased 1982

1323.2000 **Figure Study of Soldier**
(C1017) Verso, **Sketch of a Painting of a Soldier**
Pencil on paper 22 x 11.5
Purchased 1982

1324.2000 **Figure Study of Soldier Playing the**
(C1018) **Bagpipes**
Verso, **Study of Soldier's Legs**
Pencil on paper 22 x 11.5
Purchased 1982

1325.2000 **Sketches of Bagpipes and Chanter**
(C1019) Pencil on paper 22 x 11.5
Purchased 1982

1326.2000 **Figure Study of Soldier**
(C1020) Verso, **Back View of Above, at Holywood, May 10**
Pencil, crayon on paper 18 x 12.5
Purchased 1982

1327.2000 **Figure Study of Soldier**
(C1021) Pencil on paper 22.5 x 14
Purchased 1982

1328.2000 **Figure Study of Soldier**
(C1022) Pencil on paper 22.5 x 14
Signed
Purchased 1982

1329.2000 **Men Reading, 20th RIR** (Figure
(C1023) Studies of Soldiers Sitting on a Bench, Reading)
Verso, **Outline Study of Seated Man**
Pencil on paper 22.5 x 14
Purchased 1982

1330.2000 **Sketch of Open window; Sketch of**
(C1024) **Rifle Hanging from Coat Hook**
Pencil on paper 22.5 x 14
Purchased 1982

1331.2000 **Figure Study of Soldier; Figure Study**
(C1025) **of Man in a Workman's Apron; Female Head Study**
Verso, **Figure Study of Seated Soldier; Male Head Study**
Pencil on paper 22.5 x 14
Purchased 1982

1332.2000 **Figure Study of Soldier; Sketch of**
(C1026) **Soldier's Haversack; Sketch of Door**
Verso, **Sketch of Wooden Door with Soldiers' Barracks in Background**
Pencil on paper 22.5 x 14
Purchased 1982

1502.2000 **Men of Iron, 1922** *(Illus.p.387)*
(C1265) Oil on canvas 106 x 70 (sight)

Signed
Provenance unknown

1503.2000 **The Opening of the First Northern**
(C1266) **Ireland Parliament, 22 June 1921**
Watercolour, crayon on paper 95 x 127 (squared)
Provenance unknown

1504.2000 **The Opening of the First Northern**
(C1267) **Ireland Parliament, 22 June 1921**
Charcoal on paper 95 x 125 (fragmentary)
Provenance unknown

1505.2000 **Scene at Cenotaph**
(C1268) Charcoal on paper 137 x 82
Provenance unknown

CRAIG, James Humbert 1877-1944 (Irish)

351.1978 **Donegal Scene** *(Illus.p.387)*
Oil on board 36 x 25.5
Signed
Donated by Mrs. A. Erskine, 1978

CURRAN, Adrian 20th century (Irish?)

1402.2000 **Painful State 1**
Sculpture, stone, ht. 26
Provenance unknown

D

DAVIES, G. 19th century (Irish?)

1403.2000 **The Giant's Causeway (1872)**
Oil on canvas 114 x 160
Signed
Provenance unknown

DIXON, Charles 20th century (Irish?)

1404.2000 **'Titanic' Fitting Out at Queen's**
Island, Belfast, 1912
Watercolour, gouache on paper 20.5 x 38.5 (sight)
Signed
Provenance unknown

1405.2000 **White Star Liner 'Britannic', 1914**
(Illus.p.387)
Oil on canvas 100 x 152 (sight)
Signed
Provenance unknown

DIXON, Donald 20th century (Irish?)

79.2000 **Tom Herron Winning the 1978**
Senior TT Race, Isle of Man (1979)
Gouache on paper 35 x 55.5 (sight)
Dated
Donated by Winifred Poole, 2000

E

EVANS, David b.1934 (Irish)

752.1995 **House in the Mournes** (Baird's Farm)
Watercolour on paper 43 x 63 (sight)
Signed
Donated by the Ulster Folklore Society, 1995

F

FLANAGAN, Philip b.1960 (Irish)

1406.2000 **The Railway Builders (1993)**
Sculpture, bronze 242 x 121 x 2.8
Signed, dated
Purchased 1993

FLANAGAN, Terence Philip b.1929 (Irish)

1407.2000 **Stone Pier, Weir's Bridge, Enniskillen**
Watercolour on paper 75 x 60
Purchased 1993

FOSTER, Myles Birket 1825-99 (English)

1408.2000 **Bridge over a River**
Watercolour, gouache on paper 7 x
9.5 (sight)
Signed
Provenance unknown

FRAZER, Hugh fl.1813-61 (Irish)

660.1974 **View of the Lagan at the Third Lock (1864)** (Newforge)
Oil on panel 31 x 49
Donated by Mrs. Parker, 1974

1409.2000 **Molly Ward's Cottage on the River Lagan (1864)**
Oil on panel 31 x 49
Provenance unknown

1410.2000 **View of the Lagan at the Second Lock (1864)** (Mickey Taylor's)
Oil on panel 31 x 49
Provenance unknown

FRENNAIS, T. P. 19th century (French?)

1411.2000 **Portrait of a Horse (1852)** (Ridden by Hugh Montgomery of Ballydrain in the Charge of the Light Brigade at Balaclava, 25 October 1854)
Oil on canvas 35.5 x 46
Signed, dated
Provenance unknown

FRIERS, Rowel Boyd 1920-98 (Irish)

1412.2000 **Portrait of the Artist** (Caricature of William Conor)
Ink, watercolour on paper 24 x 18 (sight)
Signed
Provenance unknown

1413.2000 **News, Gilroy Gives Up Titles (1963)** (Cartoon Sketch)
Ink on card 22.5 x 32
Signed, dated
Provenance unknown

1414.2000 **Police Entering a Bank on August Bank Holiday** (Cartoon Sketch)
Ink on card 24 x 32
Signed
Provenance unknown

1415.2000 **Anti-Smoking Clinic (1964)** (Cartoon Sketch)
Ink on paper 27.5 x 38.5
Signed, dated
Provenance unknown

1416.2000 **A Crowd of Smokers (1964)** (Cartoon Sketch)
Ink on card 22 x 38
Signed, dated
Provenance unknown

1417.2000 **Two Men in a Car Passing a Bus Queue** (Cartoon Sketch)
Ink on card 24 x 31
Signed
Provenance unknown

1418.2000 **An Old Man Taunting Disgruntled Schoolchildren** (Cartoon Sketch)
Ink on card 21.5 x 27
Signed
Provenance unknown

1495.2000 **Brilliant Innings, Sir!**
Ink, gouache on paper 31 x 21.5
Signed
Purchased 1982

G

G., J. C. [J. C. G.] 19th century (Irish?)

1419.2000 **Coastal Scene**
Oil on canvas 35 x 56
Signed
Provenance unknown

GLENN, A. 20th century (Irish?)

1496.2000 **William Conor with 'Ulster Past and Present' Mural**
Ink on paper 23 x 13 5
Signed
Purchased 1982

H

HANAN, G. R. 20th century (Irish?)

1420.2000 **'Alice'** (Red Tank Locomotive)
Oil on board 50 x 74.5 (sight)
Provenance unknown

HEARD, Joseph 1799-1859 (English)

1421.2000 **Wooden Paddle Steamer 'Falcon'**
(Illus.p.387)
Oil on canvas 69 x 90 (sight)
Signed
Provenance unknown

HOLLYWOOD, William b.1923 (English, worked in Ireland)

227.1995 **Royal Navy Plane and Submarine (1953)**
Oil on canvas 75 x 62
Signed, dated
Donated by Mr. B. Coulter, 1995

I

INGLIS, Archie fl.1919-25 (Irish)

1497.2000 **Caricature of William Conor with a Palette (1924)**

Ink on paper 18 x 10.5
Signed, dated
Purchased 1982

J

JANSEN, G. 20th century (?) (British?)

274.1984 **SS 'Kathleen'**
Oil on canvas 50 x 75 (sight)
Signed
Donated by W. A. McFadden, 1984

JANSEN, H. J. 20th century (Belgian?)

1422.2000 **SS 'Orlock Head' (1927)**
Oil on canvas 35 x 55 (sight)
Signed, dated
Provenance unknown

JARVIS, W. Howard 20th century (Irish?)

1423.2000 **Short Sunderland Flying Boats**
Oil on canvas 69 x 88
Signed
Provenance unknown

1424.2000 **Harbour Scene** (Belfast?)
Oil on canvas on board 87 x 155
Signed
Provenance unknown

JONES, Sir Thomas Alfred c.1823-93 (Irish)

1425.2000 **Mountain Scene** (Mournes?)
Watercolour on paper 11.5 x 16.5 (sight)
Provenance unknown

JOHNSTON, J. 20th century (Irish)

294.1977 **'Duke of Albany', Fleetwood (1908)**
Oil on canvas 61.2 x 46
Signed, dated
Donated by Thompson Steele, 1977

445.1977 **British Barque 'Lord Templemore', Belfast (1911)**
Oil on canvas 67 x 98 (sight)
Signed, dated
Donated by J. McGlaughlin, 1977

10.1981 **Four-masted Barque 'Dundonald' (1922)**
Oil on paper 43 x 72 (sight)
Signed, dated
Donated by J. C. Stanley, 1981

1426.2000 **Ship 'Formosa'**
Oil on paper 54 x 77 (sight)
Signed
Provenance unknown

1427.2000 **Four-masted Barque 'Lord Wolseley' (1916)**
Oil on canvas 60 x 85 (sight)
Signed, dated
Provenance unknown

K

KENDRICK, Matthew c.1797-1874 (Irish)

1428.2000 **SS 'Great Britain' Stranded in Dundrum Bay, Co. Down** *(Illus.p.387)*
Oil on panel 36.5 x 75.5 (sight)
Signed
Purchased 1998

KING, Brian b.1942 (Irish)

1051.2000 **Reflection: 2 (1977)**
Sculpture, steel 365 x 183 x 23
Commissioned by the Northern Ireland Public Service Alliance for NIPSA Headquarters. Donated by NIPSA; year unknown

1052.2000 **Reflection: 2 (1977)** (Maquette)
Sculpture, steel 33.3 x 17 x 4.5
Donated by the Northern Ireland Public Service Alliance; year unknown

KYLE, Georgina Moutray 1865-1950 (Irish)

481.1980 **Study for 'Girls and Gulls at Ardglass'**
Oil on canvas 17.9 x 23.7
Signed
Bequeathed by Miss Elizabeth Hicks, 1980

483.1980 **The Boats at Volendam, Holland**
Oil on canvas 38 x 30
Bequeathed by Miss Elizabeth Hicks, 1980

484.1980 **Fishing Boats in a Harbour**
Oil on canvas 35 x 24
Bequeathed by Miss Elizabeth Hicks, 1980

485.1980 **The Pink Sails at Honfleur**
Oil on canvas 34 x 24
Signed
Bequeathed by Miss Elizabeth Hicks, 1980

486.1980 **Corner of Mother's Drawing Room at Richmond**
Pastel on paper 29 x 33
Bequeathed by Miss Elizabeth Hicks, 1980

1429.2000 **Fruit and Vegetable Markets, Belfast** *(Illus.p.387)*
Oil on canvas 54 x 45 (sight)
Provenance unknown

L

LECKEY, James 20th century (Irish)

1060.1989 **The 'Titanic' Men Go Home (1988)**
Oil on board 40 x 45.5
Signed, dated
Donated by the artist, 1989

LOCKART, Robert 19th-20th century (Irish?)

234.1977 **SS 'Belfast' of Belfast (1910)**
Oil on canvas 44 x 65 (sight)
Signed, dated
Donated by Angus McDonald, 1977

LOCKWOOD, F. W. fl.1886-1910 (Irish)

1430.2000 **Sweat House, Ballyshannon (1910)**

Watercolour on paper 17 x 22 (sight)
Signed, dated
Provenance unknown

LOSCOMBE, Maria and **Louisa** 19th century (Irish)

1431.2000 **Album of Sixty-one Sketches of Irish Figure, Landscape and Townscape Studies, Executed in Waterford (c.1824)**
Watercolour on paper 9.5 x 15.5 (page size)
Donated by Mr. and Mrs. V. Littauer, 1984

1. Two Shepherds with a Dog
2. Horse and Cart
3. Woman on a Horse with Panniers
4. Man with a Horse and Cart Carrying Turf
5. Man and Woman on Donkeys
6. Man and Woman with Three Donkeys
7. Two Men Sawing Wood
8. Man and Woman Carrying Milk Pails
9. Three Women in cloaks
10. Woman with a Turf Basket; Woman Selling Fish
11. Woman Carrying a Basket of Vegetables; Beggar Woman with Two Children
12. Three Market Women
13. Woman Selling a Lobster to a Well-dressed Gentleman
14. Two Market Women
15. Bianconi Car (?)
16. Man Leading a Horse and Cart
17. Woman Smoking a Pipe, together with a Man
18. Market Scene with Two Men, a Woman and a Horse
19. Three Women Selling Poultry
20. Passengers Boarding a Small Sailing Boat
21. Two Men Digging
22. Woman and Girl Selling Apples
23. Women Laundering in a Stream
24. Woman with a Horse and Cart
25. Fishmonger with Two Female Customers
26. Woman Selling Milk to Two Women and a Boy
27. Cobbler with a Male Customer
28. Two Women Weighing Flour
29. Women Selling Bread
30. Provision Car
31. Three Women, One Carrying Geese
32. Woman Carrying a Butchered Pig; Woman Carrying Two Salmon
33. Four Women Gutting Fish
34. Horse and Cart Carrying Three Well-dressed Children
35. Woman Selling Carrots and Parsnips; Women Selling Bread
36. Two Men Fording a Stream
37. A Fishwife and an Eccentric Character
38. Two Women with a Donkey

39. Three Men with a Donkey, Unloading Fish from a Boat
40. Cobbler with a Male Customer; Woman Selling Apples
41. Four Women Drawing Water from a Pump
42. A Group of Five Women and a Man
43. A Basket Weaver
44. A Couple Dancing to Uillean Pipes
45. Three Marines and Two Sailors
46. Four Men in Cloaks
47. Three Market Women in Cloaks
48. Three Beggars
49. Three Men with Turf Spades
50. Two Market Women Carrying Large Baskets
51. Man Selling Straw; Man Selling Newspapers
52. Waterford Castle (Reginald's Tower)
53. Two Panoramic Views of a Harbour (Double-spread Pages)
54. Panoramic View with a Ruined Abbey (Double-spread Pages)
55. Panoramic View with a Ruined Church (Double-spread Pages)
56. Panoramic View with a Formal Garden (Double-spread Pages)
57. Bridge over River
58. A Distant View of the Same Bridge
59. Another View of the Same Bridge
60. Mr. Hobbes at Newrath House, One Mile from Waterford, 1824
61. Two Studies of a Church and an Obelisk

LYNAS, Dante Langtry 20th century (Irish)

781.1975 **Three-masted Topsail Schooner 'Result'**
Oil on panel 38.5 x 88 (sight)
Signed
Donated by the artist, 1975

M

'MAC' 20th century (Irish)

1432.2000 **Caricature of William Conor at his Easel (1926)**
Ink, gouache on paper 22.5 x 17
Signed, dated
Purchased 1982

McAULEY, Charles J. 1910-99 (Irish)

1433.2000 **Cushendall about 1947**
Oil on board 38 x 50
Donated by John Hewitt, 1965

McBRIDE, John 20th century (Irish)

1499.2000 **Profile of William Conor 1881-1968 (1937)**
Pencil on paper 15 x 9 (Envelope)
Signed
Purchased 1982

MacCABE, Gladys b.1918 (Irish)

1498.2000 **William Conor 1881-1968**

Oil on canvas 73 x 82 (sight)
Signed
Purchased 1982

McCRACKEN, Morton 19th century (Irish?)

295.1976　**Schooner 'Alpha'**
Chalk on paper 48 x 65 (sight)
Signed
Donated by Dr. G. Gillespie, 1976

McILVENNY, William 19th century (Irish)

1434.2000　**Sailing Ship 'George B. Balfour' (1884)**
Oil on canvas 53 x 81 (sight)
Signed, dated
Provenance unknown

McKELVEY, Frank 1895-1974 (Irish)

1043.1978　**Lisburn, 1847**
Watercolour on paper 77 x 47
Purchased 1978

1435.2000　**Richard Hayward 1892-1964, as Mrs. McIlhagga of Belfast**
Charcoal on paper 46.5 x 35 (sight)
Signed
Provenance unknown

McLEOD, Neil 19th century (Irish?)

1436.2000　**Portrait of E. J. Cotton, 1895**
Oil on canvas 126 x 100
Signed
Donated by the Ulster Transport Authority, 1963

McNEILL, D. 20th century (Irish)

1437.2000　**Threshing Corn in Glenarm about 1918 (1971)**
Oil on canvas 46 x 61
Signed, dated
Provenance unknown

MORRISON, George W. 20th century (Irish)

503.1977　**Fair Head**
Watercolour on paper 48 x 32
Donated by Mr. Anderson, 1977

MULHALL, D. B. 20th century (Irish?)

1438.2000　**'Mary Joseph' N55 (1976)** (Small Coastal Steam Engine)
Oil on canvas 50.5 x 76
Signed, dated
Provenance unknown

P

PHELPS, Rev. Robert 19th century (Irish?)

1050.2000　**A View of the Deerpark, Glenarm (1842)**
Watercolour on paper 34.2 x 48.2 (sight)
Provenance unknown

PIPER, John b.1903 (English)

623.1975　**The Auction**

Oil on board 39 x 61
Donated by John Hewitt, 1975

PIPER, Raymond b.1923 (English, works in Ireland)

1389.1993　**Limited Mail, Pulled by Engine 'Theseus' No. 114, Leaving Amiens Street, Dublin for Belfast**
Pencil on paper 36 x 54 (sight)
Signed
Donated by Mrs. Chris Lyons, 1993

387.1999　**Portrait of Richard Hayward 1892-1964 (1961-63)**
Oil on canvas 76 x 61
Signed
Donated by Mrs. Richard Hayward, 1999

PRAEGER, Sophia Rosamond 1867-1954 (Irish)

125.1987　**Bust of a Girl**
Sculpture, bronze, ht. 49
Donated by Miss F. F. McCormick, 1965

1439.2000　**Taking Shelter**
Ink on paper 16 x 17.5
Signed
Donated by Mrs. Murdoch, 1928

1440.2000　**On the Sea Wall** (Three Children)
Sculpture, plaster, ht. 14
Signed
Provenance unknown

1441.2000　**Fionnuala and the Children of Lir**
Sculpture, plaster; measurements unknown
Provenance unknown

PURVIS, T. G. 20th century (Irish?)

142.1984　**Four-masted Barque 'Marion Lightbody'**
Oil on canvas 40 x 60 (sight)
Signed
Donated by Mrs. Sally Kane, 1984

R

RAINEY, D. 20th century (Irish)

1442.2000　**'Divis' (1977)** (Small Coaster)
Oil on canvas 40.5 x 61
Signed, dated
Provenance unknown

REEVE, Alan 20th century (Irish?)

1500.2000　**Full-length Caricature of William Conor 1881-1968 (1939)**
Ink on paper 28 x 16.5
Signed, dated
Purchased 1982

REID, Nano 1910-81 (Irish)

313.1984　**Portrait of Carl Hardebeck (c.1936)** (Illus.p.387)
Oil on canvas 60.9 x 50.8
Signed
Purchased 1984

ROBIE, Kenneth A. 20th century (Irish?)

1834.1993　**RMS 'Titanic' Departs Belfast Lough, 2 April 1912 (1993)**
Oil on canvas 50 x 102
Signed, dated
Donated by the Ulster Titanic Society, 1993

ROMNEY, Ruth 20th century (Irish)

1443.2000　**William Dargan 1799-1867**
Sculpture, bronze bust, ht. 42
Purchased 1993

ROSS, Bob 20th century (Irish)

1444.2000　**Cultra Manor** (Ulster Folk and Transport Museum)
Ink on paper 25 x 33 (sight)
Signed
Provenance unknown

1445.2000　**Coalisland Spade Mill** (Ulster Folk and Transport Museum)
Ink on paper 25 x 33 (sight)
Signed
Provenance unknown

1446.2000　**Coshkib Hill Farm** (Ulster Folk and Transport Museum)
Ink on paper 25 x 33 (sight)
Signed
Provenance unknown

1447.2000　**Wellbrook Beetling Mill** (Ulster Folk and Transport Museum)
Ink on paper 25 x 33 (sight)
Signed
Provenance unknown

S

SELLAR, Robert G. b.1920 (Scottish, lives in Ireland)

1448.2000　**Turf Shelter near Limavady**
Watercolour on paper 24 x 30.5 (sight)
Signed
Provenance unknown

1450.2000　**Orange Arch, Scott Street off Sandy Row, Belfast (1946)**
Watercolour on paper 24 x 34 (sight)
Signed, dated
Provenance unknown

SHANKS, Maurice fl.1925-62 (Irish)

1501.2000　**'Our Conor Has a Second Choice when Pictures Fail - his Golden Voice' (1960)** (Christmas Card)
Pencil, watercolour on card 15 x 10
Signed, dated
Purchased 1982

SOUTHWOLD, W. S. 20th century (British?)

74.1976　**Full-rigged Ship 'Star of Russia'**
Oil on canvas 53 x 83
Signed
Purchased 1976

SPROAT, Rimmer 20th century (British?)

1451.2000 **Cross-channel Steamer 'Graphic' (1913)**
Watercolour on paper 37 x 52 (sight)
Signed, dated
Provenance unknown

STEVENSON, Mrs. F. 19th century (British?)

1452.2000 **Sailing Ships Aground on a Beach**
Wash on paper 10 x 15 (sight)
Donated by the artist, 1962

1453.2000 **Castle on a Hill**
Wash on paper 10 x 15 (sight)
Donated by the artist, 1962

STEVENSON, Patric 1909-83 (Irish)

317.1977 **Albert Basin, Newry, July 1952 (1952)**
Gouache, ink on paper 30.5 x 48
Signed, dated
Donated by the artist, 1977

T

THOMSON, Hugh 1860-1920 (Irish)

38.1975 **Rathlin Island from near Dunseverick Castle** (Illustration for Stephen Gwynn's *Highways and Byways in Donegal and Antrim*)
Pencil, ink on paper 17 x 22 (sight)
Purchased 1975

39.1975 **Coming down Slieve League** (Illustration for Stephen Gwynn's *Highways and Byways in Donegal and Antrim*)
Ink on paper 17 x 22 (sight)
Signed
Purchased 1975

U

UNKNOWN, 18th century

1051.1965 **A Stable**
Oil on canvas 44.5 x 58
Bequeathed by Florence Irwin, 1965

1052.1965 **An Inn Yard**
Watercolour on paper 44 x 56 (sight)
Bequeathed by Florence Irwin, 1965

1409.1970 **John Kennedy of Cultra 1746-1801**
Oil on canvas 75 x 62 (sight)
Donated by heirs of the Kennedy estate (per Mrs. R. Philips), 1970

1410.1970 **Hugh Kennedy of Cultra 1711-63**
Oil on canvas 75 x 67 (sight)
Donated by heirs of the Kennedy estate (per Mrs. R. Philips), 1970

1418.1970 **Mrs. John Kennedy 1755-1828**
Oil on canvas 74 x 62 (sight)
Donated by heirs of the Kennedy estate (per Mrs. R. Philips), 1970

1055.2000 **Dutch Scene with Windmills**
Watercolour on paper 20 x 34 (sight)
Provenance unknown

1454.2000 **Ann Sitlington b.1726**
Oil on canvas 76 x 63.5
Donated by the Misses Duffin, 1963

UNKNOWN, late 18th-early 19th century

1057.2000 **White Mansion by a Lakeside**
Watercolour on paper 16.5 x 24 (sight)
Provenance unknown

UNKNOWN, 19th century

2437.1943 **Profile of State Coach, with an Earl's Coronet and Coat of Arms**
Gouache, gum on paper 13.5 x 27 (sight)
Provenance unknown

1408.1970 **Charles Pratt Kennedy 1789-1875**
Oil on canvas 81 x 54 (sight)
Donated by heirs of the Kennedy estate (per Mrs. R. Philips), 1970

1411.1970 **Grace Dorothea Kennedy 1783-1819**
Oil on panel 65 x 57 (sight) (oval)
Donated by heirs of the Kennedy estate (per Mrs. R. Philips), 1970

425.1973 **Full-rigged British Ship in Heavy Seas**
Oil on canvas 52 x 90 (sight)
Donated by William Milner, 1973

830.1975 **Full-rigged Ship 'Star of Persia'**
Oil on canvas 64 x 87 (sight)
Donated by Thomas Ross, 1975

275.1984 **SS 'Kathleen'**
Oil on canvas 45 x 67 (sight)
Donated by W. A. McFadden, 1984

203.1985 **Portrait of a Bearded Young Man**
Oil on board 57 x 46
Donated by Samuel Sinclair, 1985

97.1997 **Dr. Moore**
Oil on canvas 92 x 60
Donated by Mrs. Dorothy Reid, 1997

1056.2000 **Highland Cattle in a Glen**
Oil on canvas 30.5 x 40.5
Provenance unknown

1458.2000 **Portrait of a Woman (c.1880)**
Oil on paper (?) 55 x 44.6 (sight)
Provenance unknown

1459.2000 **Portrait of a Young Woman (c.1880)**
Oil on canvas 60 x 44 (sight)
Provenance unknown

1460.2000 **Portrait of a Gentleman (c.1890)**
Oil on canvas 92 x 71
Provenance unknown

1461.2000 **Portrait of a Lady (c.1890)**
Oil on canvas 76 x 54
Provenance unknown

1462.2000 **Langford Kennedy 1787-1850**
Oil on canvas 31 x 25.5
Donated by heirs of the Kennedy estate (per Mrs. R. Philips), 1970

1464.2000 **Charles Pratt Kennedy 1789-1875**
Chalk, pastel on paper 48 x 37.5 (sight) (oval)
Provenance unknown

1465.2000 **Vue de Dordrecht**
Oil on canvas 35 x 55 (sight)
Provenance unknown

1466.2000 **Rev. Samuel Hanna, Minister of Rosemary Street Presbyterian Church 1799-1840**
Oil on canvas 76 x 63.5
Provenance unknown

1467.2000 **Rev. John McNaughten**
Oil on canvas 127 x 103
Donated by members of Rosemary Street Presbyterian Church; year unknown

1468.2000 **Portrait of a Gentleman**
Oil on canvas 74 x 62
Provenance unknown

1469.2000 **Glenarm, Barbican Tower, Church, Village, Garron Point in the Distance**
Pencil, watercolour on paper 31 x 48 (sight) (oval)
Provenance unknown

1471.2000 **Portrait of a Man Wearing Gaelic Dress**
Oil on canvas 102 x 81
Provenance unknown

1472.2000 **Portrait of a Gentleman (c.1840)** (possibly a Clergyman)
Oil on canvas 74 x 62
Provenance unknown

1473.2000 **Pat Byrne Playing 'Patrick's Day' on 17 March 1772** (a Fiddler)
Oil on canvas 48.5 x 35.5
Donated by Mrs. Joseph O'Malley, 1969

1474.2000 **Portrait of Mrs. Frances Dobson Osborne of Altmover, Co. Londonderry**
Oil on canvas 61 x 46
Donated by Miss Stewart, 1984

1475.2000 **Old Woman at a Spinning Wheel**
Oil on canvas 111 x 85
Provenance unknown

1476.2000 **Portrait of an Old Gentleman (c.1870)**
Oil on canvas 90 x 70
Provenance unknown

1477.2000 **Portrait of a Young Gentleman**
Oil on canvas 100 x 70
Provenance unknown

1478.2000 **Portrait of a Young Gentleman (c.1850)**
Oil on panel 33.5 x 28 (oval)
Provenance unknown

1480.2000 **Cavehill from Molly Ward's** (Style of Hugh Frazer fl.1813-61)
Oil on canvas 44.5 x 62
Provenance unknown

UNKNOWN, 20th century

408.1983 **'Torr Head'** (Headline Steamship)

Oil on board 30 x 35.5
Donated by Lissack and Roscoe
(Solicitors), 1983

**1309.1988 Old Linen Bleaching Works, Known
as Low Park Green, near
Cullybackey, Co. Antrim**
Watercolour on paper 15 x 25 (sight)
Donated by Thomas Carlton, 1988

**837.1995 Sail-Steamship, Castle Lines, South
African Service**
Watercolour on paper 21 x 27
Donated by Samuel Murray, 1995

491.1999 Portrait of Rev. William Park d.1925
Oil on canvas 130 x 95
Donated by Rosemary Street
Presbyterian Church, 1999

1483.2000 Steam Coaster 'Bellavale' (1912-14)
Oil on canvas 45 x 75 (sight)
Provenance unknown

1481.2000 Harry Ferguson 1884-1960
Oil on canvas 61 x 51
Provenance unknown

V

VARLEY, Cornelius 1781-1873 (English)

1484.2000 Irish Car
Ink, wash on paper 17.5 x 18.5 (sight)
Signed
Provenance unknown

1485.2000 Irish Car
Ink, wash on paper 21 x 26 (sight)
Signed
Provenance unknown

W

WALKER, David Bond 1891-1977 (Irish)

**386.1998 Portrait of Richard Hayward 1892-
1964 as a Young Man**
Chalk on paper 53.5 x 40 (sight)
Signed
Donated by Mrs. Richard Hayward,
1998

WEYTS, P. 19th century (Belgian)

**1486.2000 'Amelia' of Dundee, Robert Law,
Master, 1840 (Ship Portrait)**
Crystoleum on glass 52 x 69
Signed
Provenance unknown

**1487.2000 'Lady Sale' of Dundee, Robert Law,
Master, Passing Flushing, 1847 (Ship
Portrait)**
Crystoleum on glass 54 x 71
Signed
Provenance unknown

WHITLA, Norman 20th century (Irish)

**1.1992 Great Northern Railway Locomotive
No. 90 in Adelaide Shed, Belfast
(1991)**
Oil on canvas 40.5 x 61
Signed, dated
Donated by Tom Gallagher Art
Gallery, Belfast, 1992

WILKS, Maurice C. 1910-84 (Irish)

1488.2000 Holywood from Cultra, 1760 (1939)
(from a Print Published by Marcus
Ward, c.1836)
Watercolour on paper 25.5 x 26.5
(sight)
Signed
Provenance unknown

WILLMOTT, F. M. 20th century (British?)

1489.2000 Mountain Scene (Mournes?)
Watercolour on paper 18 x 27 (sight)
Signed
Provenance unknown

1490.2000 Desert Scene with Cactus
Watercolour on paper 23.5 x 17
(sight)
Signed
Provenance unknown

WRIGHT, Michael 20th century (Irish?)

85.1998 1929 Ards TT Race
Watercolour on paper 25 x 30 (sight)
Signed
Provenance unknown

drawings paintings & sculptures

the ulster museum fine art collection

John White Abbott 1763-1851
Near Rydal Hall (1791)
U734

John White Abbott 1763-1851
Peamore Park, near Exeter (1793)
U735

John Absolon 1815-95
Landscape with Distant River
U975

Joseph Denovan Adam 1841-96
Still Life (1888)
U3

John Clayton Adams 1840-1906
The Cherry Orchard
U2

Herbert Alexander 1874-1946
The Ruined Castle of Grimaud
U976

Robert Weir Allan 1851-1942
Waiting for the Tide
U1

Helen Allingham 1848-1926
Feeding the Chickens (1878)
U977

Thomas Allom 1804-72
Stirling Bridge
U2113

218

Cristofano Allori 1577-1621
St. Francis in Prayer
U26

Henry C. Allport fl. 1808-23
Temple of the Sybil, Tivoli (1809)
U978

William Anderson 1757-1837
Wapping
U979

Lady Mabel Annesley 1881-1959
Tully Cross
U981

Lady Mabel Annesley 1881-1959
Table at a Window
U1263

Karel Christian Appel b.1921
Portrait of César (1956)
U515

Edward Ardizzone 1900-79
Arrival of American Troops in Northern Ireland - Troops just Landed
U982

Kenneth Armitage b.1916
Two Standing Women (1955)
U961

Arthur Charlton Armstrong b.1924
Bedroom at Ballylough (c.1956)
U231

Romek Árpád 1883-1960
Brass and Glass
U232

William Ashford 1746-1824
Landscape with Carriage and Horses (c.1781)
U2295

John Astley 1724-87
**The Molyneux Family of Castledillon,
Co. Armagh (1758)**
U702

James Atkins 1799-1833
Young Girl in a White Dress
U547

James Atkins 1799-1833
**George Hamilton, 3rd Marquess of
Donegall 1797-1883 (1824)**
U2570

Samuel Atkins fl.1787-1808
Sailing Ships
U736

Samuel Austin 1796-1834
Church of St. Ouen, Rouen
U1636

Gillian Ayres b.1930
Untitled (1963)
U434

Alfred Rawlings Baker 1865-1939
Hay Harvest (1918)
U1922

Robert Ballagh b.1943
Inside No. 3 (1979)
U2534

Robert Ballagh b.1943
Portrait of Dr. Liam McCormick 1916-96
U4935

Brian Ballard b.1943
Light Strips (Purple) (1972)
U1681

John Banting 1902-72
Two Models (1935)
U1843

Joseph Barber 1757-1811
Landscape with Cottage
U985

Rupert Barber fl.1736-72
Mrs. Anne Donnellan (1752)
U1889

Thomas Barker of Bath 1769-1847
The Tinkers (c.1780-90)
U795

John James Barralet c.1747-1815
View in Glenarm Deer Park
U2598

John James Barralet c.1747-1815
Glenarm River and Bridge, Looking towards the Sea
U2600

John James Barralet c.1747-1815
**Marchioness of Antrim's Cottage,
Glenarm Deer Park**
U2602

John James Barralet c.1747-1815 or Pupil
North East View of Garron Point (1794)
U2603

Barralet Pupil
View in Home Park, Glenarm (1796)
U2601

Barralet Pupil
Presbyterian Meeting House, Glenarm
U2604

Barralet Pupil
Glenarm Church (1796)
U2605

William James Barre 1830-67
Design for Albert Memorial Clock, Belfast
U2705

George Barret, Jnr. 1767-1842
Westminster from Vauxhall
U987

George Barret, Snr. 1728/32-84
The Waterfall at Powerscourt
U2418

William H. Barribal fl.1919-38
A 1920s Lady at a Party
U2553

James Barry 1741-1806
Venus Anadyomene (c.1772)
U14

William Henry Bartlett 1858-1932
**The End of the Fair, Back to the Island
(1910)**
U4810

Rose Barton 1856-1929
St. Patrick's Close, Dublin (1881)
U1570

Pompeo Batoni 1708-87
**James Stewart of Killymoon, Co. Tyrone
1741-1821 (1767)**
U5047

Rev. Narcissus George Batt 1824-98
Rievaulx
U3995

Edward Bawden 1903-89
**Private Gul Sahir Khan, Royal Indian
Army Service Corps**
U1182

Leslie Baxter, 20th century
Mount Charles (1952)
U4761

Walter Bayes 1869-1956
A French Hotel
U990

Keith Stuart Baynes 1887-1977
**The Garden, Villa des Bois de St. Joseph
(c.1932)**
U677

Sir William Beechey 1753-1839
Portrait of a Woman (c.1785-95)
U696

Vanessa Bell 1879-1961
Flowers in a Ginger Jar (1931)
U440

Berenger Benger 1868-1935
Steyning, Sussex
U991

William Mineard Bennett c.1778-1858
Portrait of a Young Lady (1810)
U1183

Charles Bentley 1805/6-54
Fishing Boats Entering Port
U1434

Nicolaes Claesz Berchem 1620-83
Landscape with Figures and Animals
U7

Horia Bernea b.1938
Steeple (1997)
U4819

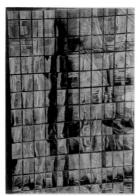

Edward Bernstein, 20th century
Codrington Library (1979)
U2654

Robert Bevan 1865-1925
The Yard Gate, Mydlow (c.1907)
U691

Robert Bevan 1865-1925
Tapster Water
U739

Jan van Bijlert 1597/98-1671
St. Matthew (c.late 1620s)
U229

Max Bill 1908-94
Condensation towards Yellow (1965)
U517

Frances Bindon c.1690-1765 (attribt.)
George Macartney 1671-1757 (c.1750)
U105

Cyril Walter Bion 1889-1976
Himalayan Snowfield (c.1925)
U252

Samuel John Lamorna Birch 1869-1955
Tweed's Fair River, Melrose
U437

George William Bissill 1896-1973
Avoca Bridge, Co. Wicklow (c.1932-33)
U1927

Basil Blackshaw b.1923
The Field (1953)
U238

Basil Blackshaw b.1923
A Road
U1185

Basil Blackshaw b.1923
Conversation in a Field (1952-53)
U4766

Basil Blackshaw b.1923
The Barn (Blue II) (1991-92)
U4942

Doris Violet Blair fl.1940s-'80s
Shattered Dwellings
U1682

Doris Violet Blair fl.1940s-'80s
The Arrival (1936)
U3597

John Humphrey Bland 1828-1919
At Montreux (c.1906-7)
U15

David Bomberg 1890-1957
Self-Portrait with Palette (1931)
U4709

Sir Muirhead Bone 1876-1953
Alfriston, Sussex
U741

Samuel Bough 1822-78
The Tower of Said: Desert Landscape with Figures
U993

Michael J. Bourke (Micheál J. de Burca)1913-85
The Heckler (c.1935)
U1226

Gretta Bowen 1880-1981
Library (c. 1953)
U4767

Boyd and Evans, 20th century
Horizon (1982)
U2657

Arthur Boyd b.1920
Landscape with Moose (1980)
U4739

Elizabeth Frances Boyd fl.1896-1935
Venice, Rio della Croce
U608

Alicia Boyle 1908-97
Potato Washers, Connemara (1949)
U242

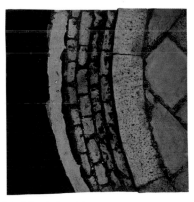

Mark Boyle b.1934
**Street Corner Study: London Series
(1967-69)**
U683

Thomas Shotter Boys 1803-74
The King's Palace, Brussels
U742

Hercules Brabazon Brabazon 1821-1906
View of Sousse, Tunisia
U743

Hercules Brabazon Brabazon 1821-1906
Grand Canal, Venice
U744

Charles Brady 1926-97
Sweet Bag and Egg Box
U2510

Charles Braithwaite 1875-1941
The Village Street
U630

Jacques-Émile-Edouard Brandon 1831-97
**Drawing for Fresco in the Church of S.
Brigida in Piazza Farnese, Rome (1878)**
U1576

Sir Frank William Brangwyn 1867-1956
The Drinkers (1912)
U435

Xavier Bricard, 19th-20th century
Sous les Lauriers (1911)
U5

Kathleen Bridle 1897-1989
Lough Erne from Rossfad (1945)
U994

Henry Bright 1810-73
Orford Beach
U4675

Gerald Leslie Brockhurst 1890-1978
Portrait of a Man (late 1920s)
U2584

William Henry Brooke 1772-1860
**Wellington Bridge over the Scar and
Seven Castles of Clonmines (1833)**
U2328

Deborah Brown b.1927
The Fair Day (c.1951)
U243

Deborah Brown b.1927
Glass Fibre Form (1974)
U2298

Deborah Brown b.1927
Lucy Brown (1952)
U4769

Jan Brueghel I ('Velvet') 1568-1625 (after)
Landscape with Windmills
U17

Pieter Brueghel II 1564-1638 (after)
Spring (1633)
U12

Pieter Brueghel II 1564-1638 (after)
Winter
U13

School of Bruges, early 16th century
Madonna and Child (The Carrickfergus Madonna)
U1180

Adam Buck 1759-1833
Annie Charlotte Hill Aged about Ten (1832)
U1179

Edgar Bundy 1862-1922
The Last Ingredient: Three Huntsmen Sitting around a Punchbowl
U4687

James Howard Burgess c.1810-90
The Giant's Causeway
U998

James Howard Burgess c.1810-90
Vale of Aber, near Bangor, North Wales (1871)
U999

James Howard Burgess c.1810-90
Cahan Abbey, with the O'Cahan Tomb, Dungiven, Co. Londonderry
U1001

Rodney Joseph Burn 1899-1985
Sketch of an Imaginative Subject
U2679

Edward Burra 1905-76
Dublin Street Scene No. 1 (1947-48)
U745

Mildred Anne Butler 1858-1941
A Sheltered Corner
U1209

Mildred Anne Butler 1858-1941
A Sunshine Holiday (1897)
U1635

Werner Buttner b.1954
Self-Portrait with Nun Dolls (1986)
U4809

Randolph Caldecott 1846-86
An Awkward Predicament
U746

William Callow 1812-1908
A Scene on the Rhine (1839)
U1003

Sergio de Camargo 1930-90
Relief No. 141 (1967)
U532

Sir David Young Cameron 1865-1945
Hills of Angus
U747

Arthur M. Campbell d.1994
Red Mill, Whitehouse (1948)
U1004

Cecilia Margaret Campbell 1791-1857
The Giant's Causeway
U748

Christopher Campbell 1908-72
Self-Portrait: The Artist and his Sister (c.1930)
U2425

Christopher Campbell 1908-72
Study for 'Self-Portrait: The Artist and his Sister' (1930)
U2426

Christopher Campbell 1908-72
Ploughman (1930s)
U5006

George Campbell 1917-79
Claddagh Duff, Connemara (c.1950-51)
U272

George Campbell 1917-79
Slack Day, Smithfield (c.1941-42)
U274

George Campbell 1917-79
Near Alicante, Andalusia (c.1951-52)
U1005

George Campbell 1917-79
Hot Day, Alicante Way (c.1951)
U4771

John Henry Campbell 1757-1828
Lake of Killarney, Co. Kerry (1815)
U752

John Henry Campbell 1757-1828
Sugar Loaf Mountain, Co. Wicklow
U2101

Lawrence Campbell 1911-68
Head of Jack B. Yeats 1871-1957 (1944)
U4846

John Carey 1861-1943
Surprised (1890)
U1006

Joseph William Carey 1859-1937
Dundrum, Co. Down (1924)
U1007

Joseph William Carey 1859-1937
Rothesay (1890)
U1008

Joseph William Carey 1859-1937
View in Scotland (1886)
U1188

Joseph William Carey 1859-1937
Old Houses, Howth (1887)
U1189

Sir Anthony Caro b.1924
Rainy Day (1971)
U1430

Tom Carr 1909-99
Twilight, Moyadd (1952)
U263

Tom Carr 1909-99
Ormond Quay, Dublin (c.1939)
U2084

Tom Carr 1909-99
Self-Portrait with Vermeer Jug (c.1980)
U4746

Alexander Carse fl.1797-1838 (attribt.)
View of Edinburgh from Leith Mills
(c.1820)
U2674

Richard Carver d.1754
Landscape with Figures
U132

Patrick Caulfield b.1936
Girl in a Doorway (1969)
U964

Giacomo Ceruti 1698-1767
Boy with Vegetables
U19

Giacomo Ceruti 1698-1767
Boy with a Dog
U20

César b.1921
Une Place au Soleil (1960)
U969

Alfred Edward Chalon 1780-1860
A Reception
U1406

James Charles 1851-1906
The Goat Girl
U562

James Charles 1851-1906
The Haystacks
U587

Charles Sidney Cheston 1882-1960
River Barges
U1396

Herbert Chipp fl.1877-98
River Scene with Trees and Woman on Towpath (1878)
U1687

Gerard Chowne 1875-1917
A Park with a Pond
U1011

Giovanni Battista Cipriani 1727-85
Seated Classical Female Figure
U2110

Carey Clarke, 20th century
Forestry Plantation, Winter
U258

Cyril Clarke, 20th century
Smithfield Market
U571

David Clarke, 20th century
Sevillana I (1949)
U278

Harry Clarke 1889-1931
Cartoon for St. Hubert
U2644

Margaret Clarke 1888-1961
Robin Redbreast
U5008

Rosemary Clarke-Smith, 20th century
**Dorothea Slate Quarry, Nantlle, North
Wales (c.1968-69)**
U709

Sir George Clausen 1852-1944
Sunrise on the Road
U443

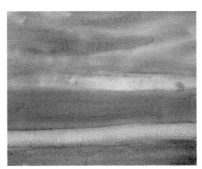

Sir George Clausen 1852-1944
Twilight
U755

Luke Clennell 1781-1840
Greenwich Park
U756

Maurice Cockrill b.1936
Lawrence of Arabia's Brother (1979)
U2652

Bernard Cohen b.1933
Knot (1962)
U527

Simon Coleman b.1916
Interior with a Man at Breakfast Table (1944)
U2078

George Joseph Collie 1904-75
Blighted Hopes (c.1933)
U279

Thomas Collier 1840-91
The Path over the Moors
U1014

Cecil Collins 1908-89
Figure Seated in a Chair (1942)
U757

Patrick Collins 1910-94
Travelling Women (1957)
U267

Charles Edward Conder 1868-1909
In the Shadow of Pan (1905)
U758

William H. Conn 1895-1973
Illustration to 'Willy Gilliland'
U1577

William H. Conn 1895-1973
Illustration to 'The Burial of King Cormac'
U1578

William Conor 1881-1968
The Jaunting Car (c.1933)
U254

William Conor 1881-1968
Coortin' (c.1922)
U256

William Conor 1881-1968
The City Hall under Snow (c.1920s)
U269

William Conor 1881-1968
Off: The Ulster Division (1915)
U1229

William Conor 1881-1968
Men of the Home Front
U1239

William Conor 1881-1968
Weaving
U2322

Jane Bennett Constable b.1865
The Last Sheaves: October Harvest Sketch
U2685

James Conway 1891-1968
Sez You (1934)
U277

Patric Coogan b.1935
6.10 p.m.
U4724

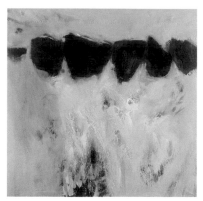

Barrie Cooke b.1931
Current (1962-63)
U253

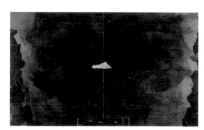

Barrie Cooke b.1931
Big Tench Lake (1972)
U2287

Thomas Cooley 1795-1872
Couple at a Games Table (1816)
U1871

Winifred Cooper fl.1905-29
Girl Using Pirn Winder or Swift (1918)
U1588

Edward Bainbridge Copnall 1903-73
Mother and Child (1930)
U1857

Daniel Corkery 1878-1964
Frankfield, Cork
U760

Emily D. Corry 1873-1942
Elderberries
U275

John Sell Cotman 1782-1842
Harlech Castle (c.1803-4)
U761

Laurence Coulter b.1937
**Professor Anne Crookshank b.1927
(1994)**
U4976

David Cox 1783-1859
The Snowstorm
U762

David Cox 1783-1859
Near Bettws-y-Coed
U763

John Robert Cozens 1752-97
Capo di Bove
U767

Jack Crabtree b.1938
Portrait of Brian Friel b.1929 (1986-87)
U4707

Jack Crabtree b.1938
Patterson's Spade Mill, Templepatrick
U4969

James Humbert Craig 1877-1944
The Kerry Coast (c.1928)
U271

Walter Crane 1845-1915
A Pastoral (1872)
U1274

Ebenezer Crawford 1830-74
**Sketch for 'An Incident of the Great
Plague of London, 1665' (1872)**
U1275

Martin Cregan 1788-1870
**Francis Johnston 1760-1829, his Wife and
Two Nephews (c.1827)**
U731

Donato Creti 1671-1749
Pastoral Landscape with Figures
U24

Joshua Cristall 1767-1847
A Stick Gatherer near Hastings (1807)
U1019

David Crone b.1937
By Railings (1991)
U4890

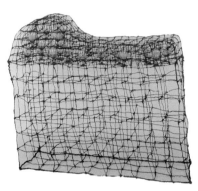

Dorothy Cross b.1956
Passion Bed (1990)
U5002

Nicholas Joseph Crowley 1819-57
John Ward 1777-1836 (c.1836)
U643

William Crozier b.1930
Still Life
U749

William Cruickshank fl.1866-79
Still Life with Dead Hare and Grouse
U4510

William Cruickshank fl.1866-79
Bird's Nest and Lilac
U4511

Michael Cullen b.1946
Mexican Video Banditti and the Prosciutto Hunters
U4979

Willam A. Cuthbertson fl.1920-46
On the Beach
U2681

Francis Danby 1793-1861
The Folly, Blaise Castle, near Bristol
U769

Francis Danby 1793-1861
Ringsend from Beggar's Bush, Co. Dublin
U2095

Francis Danby 1793-1861
Mill near Beggar's Bush, Co. Dublin
U2096

Francis Danby 1793-1861
Castle Archdale on Lough Erne, Co. Fermanagh
U2097

Francis Danby 1793-1861
Dunleary from the South
U2098

George Dance 1741-1825
William Dickson 1745-1804, Bishop of Down and Connor (1794)
U2460

Charles Davidson 1824-1902
Newcastle, Co. Down
U770

Lilian Lucy Davidson 1879-1954
Low Tide, Wicklow (c.1934)
U609

Alan Davie b.1920
Imp of Clubs (1957)
U535

Anthony Davies b.1947
Old Couple at Home (1990)
U4815

John Davies b.1946
Man with Ring (1975)
U2413

Edward Dayes 1763-1804
Dunfermline Abbey, Fife, Scotland
U1020

Rose de Crespigny fl.1891-1929
Charing Cross Bridge, London
U1022

Peter de Francia b.1921
Figure Drawing (1962)
U4776

William Delamotte 1775-1863
Ghent (1818)
U771

Edward Delaney b.1932
Cathedral No. 1 (1965)
U1758

Dirck van Delen 1605-71
Interior of a Renaissance Church (1652)
U32

Anthony Devis 1729-1816
Olivares and La Brisca
U772

Arthur Devis 1711-87
Richard Boyle, 2nd Earl of Shannon 1727-1807 (1748)
U2312

Peter de Wint 1784-1849
Landscape with Cottage
U773

Peter de Wint 1784-1849
An Upland Village
U774

E. M. O'Rorke Dickey 1894-1977
San Vito Romano (1923)
U282

E. M. O'Rorke Dickey 1894-1977
Budleigh Salterton from Jubilee Park (1925-26)
U4902

Robert Dighton 1752-1814
Mr. William Irwin (1798)
U2530

Gerard Dillon 1916-71
Yellow Bungalow (1954)
U283

Gerard Dillon 1916-71
Medical Students (c.1949)
U287

Gerard Dillon 1916-71
The Yellow Field
U288

Gerard Dillon 1916-71
Self-contained Flat
U4974

James Dixon 1887-1970
**British Minesweepers at Work between
Tory Island and the Mainland (1965)**
U284

John Dixon d.1970
Tory Island
U733

Samuel Dixon fl.1748-69
The Red-legged Partridge from Barbary
U2329

Samuel Dixon fl.1748-69
The Peacock Pheasant from China
U2330

Jiri Georg Dokoupil b.1954
Untitled (1982)
U4694

Goyo Dominguez b.1960
Bodegon Bellini (1996)
U5043

Rita Donagh b.1939
'. . . morning workers pass . . .'
U2509

Adam Tannochie Donald 1911-91
Small Farm, Donegal
U4842

Antony Donaldson b.1939
Iris (1968)
U958

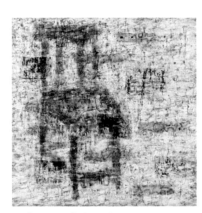

Micky Donnelly b.1952
Connolly's Chair (1992)
U4945

Harry R. Douglas 1862-1934
Isaac W. Ward 1834-1916
('Belfastiensis')(c.1895-1905)
U33

Jessie Douglas fl.1893-1928
Cherry Ripe
U1023

Richard Doyle 1824-83
Girl Reading
U1024

Richard Doyle 1824-83 or Charles
Altimont Doyle 1832-93
Fairy Ploughing
U1025

Malcolm Drummond 1880-1945
Landscape with Trees (c.1925)
U2077

Susanna Drury fl.1733-70
East Prospect of the Giant's Causeway (c.1739)
U1652

Susanna Drury fl.1733-70
West Prospect of the Giant's Causeway (c.1739)
U1653

Jean Dubuffet 1901-85
Femme et Bébé (1956)
U524

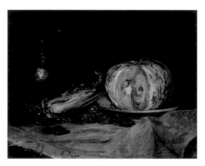

Edouard-Jacques Dufeu 1840-1900
Still Life
U657

Rita Duffy b.1959
Nuptial Grooming (1994)
U4984

George du Maurier 1834-96
'Valour in the Field'
U1595

Edward Duncan 1803-82
Two Studies of a Peasant Woman
U1509

Ronald Ossory Dunlop 1894-1973
Buildings at Walberswick
U446

Barthélémy du Pan 1712-63
Augusta of Saxe-Gotha, Princess of Wales 1719-72 (c.1745)
U129

Barthélémy du Pan 1712-63
Frederick, Prince of Wales 1707-51 (c.1745)
U130

Henry Edridge 1769-1821
Paris: Notre Dame and Ille de la Cité
U1558

Handel Edwards b.1923
The Miner's Kitchen (1973)
U2522

Mary Ellen Edwards 1839-c.1908
Young Girl with Kitten
U1035

Peter Edwards b.1955
Portrait of Michael Longley b.1939 (1989-90)
U4825

Felim Egan b.1952
Line Composition - Blue (1979)
U2523

Paul Egestorff d.1995
Fusion (1948)
U4818

Jane Erin Emmet 1873-1957
The Sierra Nevadas, Granada (c.1921)
U307

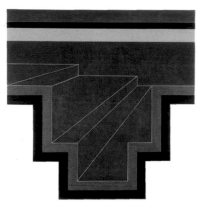

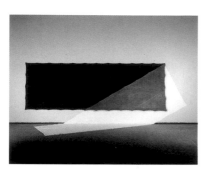

Koji Enokura b.1942
Untitled (1979)
U4682

Sir Jacob Epstein 1880-1959
Crouching Nude
U948

Sir Jacob Epstein 1880-1959
Ahmed (1932)
U966

Chung Eun-Mo b.1946
Villa Amnissos Projection - Red (1990)
U4936

Richard E. Eurich 1903-92
Boats at Lyme Regis (1937)
U596

David Evans b.1934
Interior of Art Galleries, Ulster Museum (1992)
U4957

Clara Ewald d.c.1949
Mrs. Glen Hamilton (1946)
U297

Henri Fantin-Latour 1836-1904
The Wedding Feast at Cana (1867)(after Veronese)
U128

David Farquharson 1839-1907
Spring in the Trossachs (1890-91)
U601

Micheal Farrell 1940-2000
Study Monochrome (1967)
U521

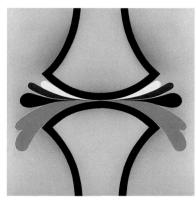

Micheal Farrell 1940-2000
Pressé Series with Cream (1970)
U723

A. Romilly Fedden 1875-1939
The Fun of the Fair (1908)
U2575

Luis Feito b.1929
Cuadro No. 281 (1961)
U290

Shaun Ferguson b.1963
Shepherd's Farm 3
U4840

John Duncan Fergusson 1874-1961
The Liberty Men (1916)
U451

Brian Ferran b.1940
Conchobor (1971)
U2333

Anthony Vandyke Copley Fielding 1787-1855
Bay Scene - Sunset (1819)
U775

Anthony Vandyke Copley Fielding 1787-1855
Seascape, Storm off Dover (?)
U776

Jonathan Fisher d.1809
View of the Ferry and Castle of Narrow Water (c.1771)
U659

William Mark Fisher 1841-1923
Landscape with Sheep (c.1881-87)
U453

William Mark Fisher 1841-1923
Corner of the Lake
U778

Barry Flanagan b.1941
New Metal Piece (1978)
U2555

Terence Philip Flanagan b.1929
Gortahork (2) (1967)
U549

Terence Philip Flanagan b.1929
Weir on the Blackwater River, Co. Cork (1993)
U5041

John Flaxman 1755-1826
Swedenborgian Subject (?)
U779

Sir William Russell Flint 1880-1969
A Neglected Domain
U781

Thomas Flintoff c.1809-91
Gordon Augustus Thomson 1799-1886 (1885)
U1941

James Forrester 1730-76 (attribt.)
The Falls of Powerscourt
U1037

Jean-Antoine-Siméon Fort 1793-1861
Swiss Scene (1829)
U1038

Myles Birket Foster 1825-99
Bringing Daddy's Dinner
U782

Myles Birket Foster 1825-99
Lyme Regis from the Charmouth Road
U783

Myles Birket Foster 1825-99
A Pedlar
U1191

Myles Birket Foster 1825-99
The Haymakers
U1560

Myles Birket Foster 1825-99
Going to Market
U1639

Myles Birket Foster 1825-99
Cattle Crossing a Bridge
U4513

Myles Birket Foster 1825-99
Oranges and Lemons - Mediterranean
U4514

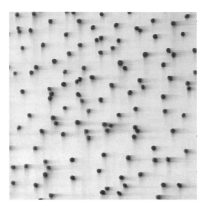

Mark Francis b.1962
Negative (4) (1994)
U5036

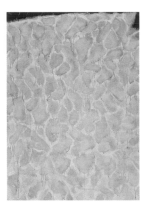

Sam Francis 1923-94
Grey Space (1950-51)
U553

Helen Frankenthaler b.1928
Sands (1964)
U534

Percy French 1854-1920
Landscape near Falcarragh, Co. Donegal
U1192

Rowel Boyd Friers 1920-98
The Poachers (1946)
U292

George Arthur Fripp 1813-96
Raby Castle, Co. Durham
U1040

William Powell Frith 1819-1909
Sterne and the French Innkeeper's Daughter
U631

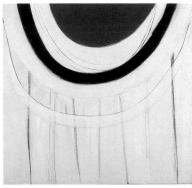

Sir Terry Frost b.1915
Mars Orange and Black (1961)
U520

Roger Eliot Fry 1866-1934
Valley of the Rhone (1930)
U452

William Arthur Fry 1865-1936
Howd's Hole, Ardglass
U1252

David Fulton 1848-1930
An Autumn Morning
U37

John Henry Fuseli 1741-1825
Pylades and Orestes Escaping from Tauris with Iphigenia (c.1810-20)
U785

John Henry Fuseli 1741-1825
Two Courtesans at a Window (1790)
U786

John Henry Fuseli 1741-1825
Studies of Three Courtesans with Extravagant Hairstyles (1807)
U787

John Henry Fuseli 1741-1825
Woman at a Dressing Table (1792)
U788

John Henry Fuseli 1741-1825
Seated Woman with Finger on Mouth (c.1796-99)
U789

John Henry Fuseli 1741-1825
Mrs. Fuseli in a Large Hat (c.1792-95)
U790

John Henry Fuseli 1741-1825
Two Women with Fans Walking in a Garden (1795)
U792

John Henry Fuseli 1741-1825
Milton when a Boy, Instructed by his Mother (c.1796-98)
U793

John Henry Fuseli 1741-1825
Study after a Roman Portrait Bust of a Lady (1810)
U794

G. L. Gabriel b.1958
S-Bahnhof Friedrichstrasse (1991)
U4896

Thomas Gainsborough 1727-88
Miss Theodosia Magill 1744-1817, afterwards Countess of Clanwilliam (1765)
U5067

Frederick O'Neill Gallagher, 19th –20th century
A View on the Seine (1915)
U2574

Léon Gambier, 20th century
Port de Dieppe (1948)
U458

Norman Garstin 1847-1926
Arabs, Tangier (1885)
U2587

Norman Garstin 1847-1926
At the Fair
U2588

Norman Garstin 1847-1926
Roundabout, Diest
U2589

Edmund Garvey d.1808
A View of Kilkenny
U1181

Henry Gastineau 1791-1876
Voreppe - on the Road to the Grande Chartreuse
U1042

Henry Gastineau 1791-1876
Glenarm, Co. Antrim (1859)
U1822

Henri Gaudier-Brzeska 1891-1915
Masque Ornementale (1912)
U974

Wilhelmina Geddes 1888-1955
Portrait of Rosamond Praeger 1867-1954
U1397

Sir Ernest George 1839-1922
Rotterdam (1879)
U1043

Mark Gertler 1892-1939
Sleeping Nude (1928)
U456

Sir John Gilbert 1817-97
Don Quixote and Rosinante
U1640

Stephen Gilbert b.1910
Untitled (1950)
U4751

255

Arthur Gilmer 1882-1929
Peat Stacks
U1341

Sawrey Gilpin 1733-1807
Landscape with Cattle, Donkeys and Horses (1799)
U1641

Rev. William Gilpin 1724-1804
Mountain Landscape with Bridge
U1642

Charles Ginner 1878-1952
Clarendon Dock, Belfast (1921)
U455

Charles Ginner 1878-1952
Storm over Clearbury Ring
U798

Lady Beatrice Glenavy 1883-1968
Enigma (c.1930s)
U2529

Isobel Lilian Gloag 1865-1917
One of London's Citizens
U1044

Albert Goodwin 1845-1932
Lincoln Cathedral
U799

Edward Goodwin fl.1801-15
Kenilworth Castle (1814)
U1643

W. R. Gordon 1872-1955
Clady Bridge, Glendun
U1046

Spencer Frederick Gore 1878-1914
Applehayes (c.1909-10)
U459

Richard Gorman b.1946
Lifetenant (1989-90)
U4807

David Gould 1872-1952
Sketch near Lisburn (c.1915)
U39

Carol Graham b.1951
Light Falls Within (1978)
U2506

Carol Graham b.1951
Portrait of James Galway b.1939 (1988)
U4749

Duncan Grant 1885-1978
Interior (1918)
U454

Hugh Grant b.c.1865/67-d.c.1947
**Lavery's at the Back of the Wood,
Soldierstown (1903)**
U1586

Anthony Green b.1939
**Mr. and Mrs. Stanley Joscelyne: The
Second Marriage (1972)**
U1842

Benjamin Richard Green 1808-76
Tintern Abbey
U1049

Christine Gregory 1880-1962
The Circle of Spring (1921)
U1789

Charles Grey 1808-92
**Captain Alexander Chesney 1755-1843
(1841)**
U30

Moses Griffith 1747-1819
Kenilworth Castle
U4800

Samuel Hieronymus Grimm 1733-94
**St. Paul's Cathedral from St. George's
Fields (1770)**
U1644

Francis Grose 1731-91
Rochester Castle (1768)
U949

Anthony Gross 1905-84
Red Cock and Black Hen
U801

John Percival Gülich 1864-98
On the Quay, Belfast (1889)
U1873

Sir Herbert James Gunn 1893-1964
**Field-Marshal The Viscount Montgomery
of Alamein and Hindhead, GCB, DSO
1887-1976 (1944)**
U2225

Carl Haag 1820-1915
Ruins of the Palace of Diocletian, Split (1855)
U1050

Carl Haag 1820-1915
Rocks on a Hill Overhanging the Rhine (1852)
U1398

Johan van Haensbergen 1642-1705
Portrait of a Gentleman (c.1690)
U53

Willem van der Hagen fl.1700-40
Landing of King William of Glorious Memory at Carrickfergus, 1690 (c.1728)
U43

Louis Haghe 1806-85
A Church Interior (1868)
U1210

Friedemann Hahn b.1949
Kopf mit Hut und welken Blumen (1989)
U4895

Clifford Hall 1904-73
Place du Tertre, Paris (1934)
U463

Kenneth Hall 1913-46
Trafalgar Square IV - October 8th 1937
U4977

Eva Henrietta Hamilton 1880-1959
Tobar Pádraig, Co. Mayo (1925)
U315

Hugh Douglas Hamilton 1739-1808
**James Moore O'Donnell 1770-1806
(c.1795-96)**
U48

Hugh Douglas Hamilton 1739-1808
Lord Edward Fitzgerald 1763-98 (c.1798)
U4975

Letitia Marion Hamilton 1880-1964
Donkeys (c.1930-32)
U586

Richard Hamilton b.1922
Bronze by Gold (1948)
U2571

Rev. Jack Paul Hanlon 1913-68
The Grey Hat
U306

Rev. Jack Paul Hanlon 1913-68
The Flowershop
U1223

Rev. Jack Paul Hanlon 1913-68
Chimney Sweep (1965)
U1225

James Duffield Harding 1797-1863
An Eastern Landscape (1834)
U1051

Philip Hardwick 1792-1870
A London Street
U1053

James Hardy, Jnr. 1832-89
The Ballad (1861)
U41

Thomas Bush Hardy 1842-97
Boulogne (1877)
U4673

Fairlie Harmar, Viscountess Harberton
1876-1945
L'Aveyron (c.1932)
U462

Colin Harrison b.1939
A and the Dog (1974)
U2294

Sarah Cecilia Harrison 1863-1941
Henry Joy McCracken 1767-98 (1926)
U49

Henry Albert Hartland 1840-93
A Country Lane
U802

Henry Albert Hartland 1840-93
Carriganass Castle, Co. Cork
U2479

John Hassall 1868-1948
'The Whole Town's Talking'
U1294

Benjamin Haughton 1865-1924
Winter in a Devon Valley
U310

Wilfred J. Haughton 1921-99
First Snow in Norfolk (1960-61)
U303

Samuel Hawksett 1801-59
Robert Langtry d.1859 (c.1843)
U585

Claude Hayes 1852-1922
A Windmill in Sussex
U1561

Edwin Hayes 1819-1904
Morning after the Storm off Yarmouth
U634

John Haynes-Williams 1836-1908
**Sir Robert Lloyd Patterson, JP, DL, FLS
1836-1906 (1897)**
U1953

Thomas Hearne 1744-1817
Caister Castle, Norfolk
U803

Hendrik Heerschop 1620-72
The Alchemist's Shop
U11

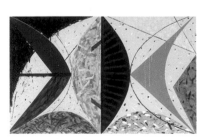

Brian Henderson b.1950
Brilliant Crack NYC (1987)
U4756

Thomas Hennell 1903-45
Loading into Barn, Kilpeck, Herefordshire
U1054

Patrick Hennessy 1915-81
The Old Tree (c.1970-71)
U4973

William John Hennessy 1839-1917
Fête Day in a Cider Orchard, Normandy (1878)
U4708

Robert Henri 1863-1929
Achill Island, Co. Mayo (1913)
U4889

Emily Grace Henry 1868-1953
Paul Henry 1876-1958 (c.1898-1900)
U294

Emily Grace Henry 1868-1953
Professor Robert Mitchell Henry 1873-1950
U295

Olive Henry 1902-89
Road Block, Belfast (1940)
U1056

Paul Henry 1876-1958
Dawn, Killary Harbour (1921)
U301

Paul Henry 1876-1958
Leenane (1913)
U311

Paul Henry 1876-1958
My Friend Michael Mangan (1910-12)
U2081

Paul Henry 1876-1958
Water Meadows (1907)
U2086

Paul Henry 1876-1958
Arthur O'Gorman Lalor (1916)
U4960

Paul Henry 1876-1958
The Potato Digger (1912-15)
U4972

Paul Henry 1876-1958
The Blacksmith (1910-13)
U4999

Sir Hubert von Herkomer 1849-1914
An Old Bavarian Peasant Woman
U1057

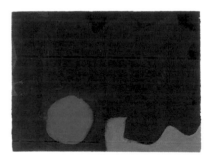

Patrick Heron 1920-99
Ceruleum and Scarlet in Ultramarine with Emerald and Violet Edges, 1970
U2369

John Frederick Herring, Snr. 1795-1865
(attribt.)
Farmyard Scene
U567

Patrick Hickey b.1927
Landscape, Ireland (1950s)
U305

George Elgar Hicks 1824-1914
The Hon. Winifred Sturt (1882)
U1718

George Elgar Hicks 1824-1914
Study for 'The Last Shilling' (1852)
U1732

George Elgar Hicks 1824-1914
Flower Seller (1852)
U1733

George Elgar Hicks 1824-1914
Female Nude Kneeling
U1748

Joseph Highmore 1692-1780 (attribt.)
Portrait of a Boy (c.1740)
U50

Derek Hill 1916-2000
Tory Island from Tor More (1958-59)
U299

James John Hill 1811-82
The Gleaners
U42

Robert Hills 1769-1844
Deer in a Highland Glen
U1058

Roger Hilton 1911-75
January 1962 (1962)
U545

Sydney Ivon Hitchens 1893-1979
Spring in Autumn (1967)
U551

William Hoare of Bath 1707-92 (after)
Alexander Pope 1688-1744
U1865

William Hodson fl.1885-89
Town and Castle of Carrickfergus (1886)
U1059

James Holland 1800-70
A Venetian Canal
U804

William Hollywood b.1923
MacArt's Fort (1951)
U5046

Robert Home 1752-1834
Captain Waddell Cunningham 1730-97 (c.1786)
U23

Evie Hone 1894-1955
Ruin at Ardmore (c.1946)
U308

Evie Hone 1894-1955
Composition (prob.c.1920-33)
U805

Horace Hone 1756-1825
Portrait of Major Holt Waring c.1722-1806 (1796)
U1885

Nathaniel Hone 1718-84
A Boy Deliberating on his Drawing (c.1769)
U228

Nathaniel Hone 1831-1917
Landscape with Cattle
U565

Nathaniel Hone 1831-1917
On the Nile
U887

Richard Hooke 1820-1908
George Benn 1801-82
U2341

Albert Houthuesen 1903-79
Wheels, Maes Gwyn Farm (1934)
U2585

Ken Howard b.1932
Ulster Crucifixion (1978)
U5005

John Hoyland b.1934
3:8:68 (1968)
U720

Eric Hesketh Hubbard 1892-1957
Dunluce Castle
U579

Jean-Baptiste-Louis Hubert 1801-after
1865
Cattle by a Stream
U1065

Jean-Baptiste-Louis Hubert 1801-after
1865
Trees and a Water Spout (1829)
U1068

John Hughes 1865-1941
Thérèse (1896)
U2415

Frederick W. Hull 1867-1953
Winter above Ligoniel
U313

Frederick W. Hull 1867-1953
The White Rocks, Portrush (c.1913-14)
U578

Cecil Arthur Hunt 1873-1965
Evening at Valoscura, San Rafael, California
U1069

Cecil Arthur Hunt 1873-1965
Gibraltar
U1211

George Leslie Hunter 1877-1931
Fishing Village
U4777

George Leslie Hunter 1877-1931
Ceres, Fife: Church and Village
U4778

John Frederick Hunter 1893-1951
Still Life and Figures
U309

Mercy Hunter 1910-89
Friar's Bush Graveyard, Belfast (1953)
U1683

Robert Hunter fl.1752-1803
**Simon Harcourt, 1st Earl Harcourt 1714-
77 (1772-75)**
U47

Fabio Hurtado, 20th century
Three Seated Women and a Dog
U728

Paul Huxley b.1938
Spanish Cubism (1978)
U2676

Julius Caesar Ibbetson 1759-1817
View of Beeston Castle, Cheshire
U38

Joseph Murray Ince 1806-59
Off Calshot Castle (1848)
U1070

Filippo Indoni fl.1883-89
Italian Girl Spinning with Distaff
U1071

James Dixon Innes 1887-1914
Olives at Collioure (1911)
U464

Hans Iten 1874-1930
Small Holding in Switzerland
U317

Hans Iten 1874-1930
Les Capucines
U318

Hans Iten 1874-1930
Surge of the Sea, Ardglass
U319

Hans Iten 1874-1930
Her Little Holding
U548

Hans Iten 1874-1930
Spring Flowers
U588

Hans Iten 1874-1930
Autumn
U632

Hans Iten 1874-1930
Still Life with Oysters
U635

Robert Kirkland Jamieson 1881-1950
The Pool
U466

Willem Georg Frederik Jansen 1871-1949
Cattle Entering the Stall
U563

Georges Jeannin 1841-1925
Roses
U600

James Hunter Jeffrey 1874-after 1932
Brown's Bay, Islandmagee (1932)
U1073

Mainie Jellet 1897-1944
Seated Female Nude (1921-22)
U2293

Mainie Jellet 1897-1944
Abstract (1922)
U2296

Mainie Jellet 1897-1944
Seated Nude (1914-15)
U2384

Paul Jenkins b.1923
Phenomena Borne by Red (1963)
U528

Janeric Johansson, 20th century
Struggle for Power (1981)
U2653

Augustus John 1878-1961
Vivien (c.1929)
U323

Augustus John 1878-1961
The Red Feather (c.1911)
U327

Gwen John 1876-1939
Cat
U2075

Nevill Johnson 1911-99
Summer Solstice (1978)
U2476

Allen Jones b.1937
Automatic Shift (1969)
U554

David Jones 1895-1974
Seascape: Caldy Island (1927)
U807

Kent Jones b. 1949
Cheetah (1981)
U2646

Basil Jonzen b.1916
West African Still Life (1943)
U1212

George McDowell Kane 1889-1954
Portrait of Hans Iten 1874-1930 (1913)
U1567

George McDowell Kane 1889-1954
Portrait of Forrest Reid 1875-1947 (1915)
U2220

Maxim Kantor b.1957
Two Versions of History (1993)
U4983

Joseph Malachy Kavanagh 1856-1918
Gipsy Encampment on the Curragh
U2381

John Keane b.1954
The Other Cheek? (1989)
U5068

Séan Keating 1889-1977
Slan Leat a Athair/Goodbye, Father (1935)
U589

Harry Kernoff 1900-74
Boon Companions (1934)
U1074

Harry Kernoff 1900-74
**Bend in the Road near Richmond, Surrey
(1947)**
U4811

Richard Kidd b.1952
Northumber (1980)
U2579

Richard Kidd b.1952
Polar Cathedral (1991)
U4939

Brian King b.1942
Zig (1969)
U954

Cecil King 1921-86
Easter (1974)
U2297

Phillip King b.1934
Through (1965)
U952

Phillip King b.1934
Ascona (1972)
U2359

Yeend King 1855-1924
Stick Gatherers
U656

Sir Godfrey Kneller 1646/49-1723
(attribt.)
William III 1650-1702
U583

Sir Godfrey Kneller 1646/49-1723
(attribt.)
Mary II 1662-94
U584

John Prescott Knight 1803-81
William Sharman Crawford, MP 1781-1861 (c.1843)
U4501

Marek Komza, 20th century
House (1977)
U184

Pauline Evelyn Konody fl.1926-36
Summer Mist
U1075

Georgina Moutray Kyle 1865-1950
La Marché dans la Rue, Concarneau (c.1925)
U337

Georgina Moutray Kyle 1865-1950
The Incoming Tide (c.1937)
U338

Georgina Moutray Kyle 1865-1950
The Lifting of the Fog at the Gasworks, Belfast (c.1926)
U342

Charles Lamb 1893-1964
A Lough Neagh Fisherman (1920)
U345

Charles Lamb 1893-1964
Leenane
U5018

Henry Lamb 1883-1960
Men on a Park Bench (1903)
U1537

Gene Lambert b.1952
Still Life No. 4 (1991)
U4898

Biagio dalle Lame d. after 1575 (attribt.)
Marriage of the Virgin
U753

Elish Lamont 1816-70
Miss O'Hara of Ballymena
U1891

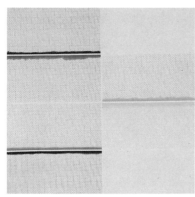

Mark Lancaster b.1938
Cambridge Standard (1969)
U1174

Giovanni Lanfranco 1582-1647 (after)
Glorification of the Virgin
U197

Peter Lanyon 1918-64
Rosewall (1960)
U2355

Philip Alexius de Laszlo 1869-1937
Priscilla, Countess Annesley d.1941 (1915)
U639

James Latham 1696-1747
**Captain Charles Janvre de la Bouchetière
d.c.1743 (c.1730-35)**
U2513

John Latham b.1921
Observer 4 (1959)
U538

Filippo Lauri 1623-94
Pan and Diana
U85

Sir John Lavery 1856-1941
The Bridge at Grès (1901)
U60

Sir John Lavery 1856-1941
**His Eminence Cardinal Logue 1840-1924
(1920)**
U64

Sir John Lavery 1856-1941
The Red Hammock (1936)
U66

Sir John Lavery 1856-1941
The Green Coat (1926)
U68

Sir John Lavery 1856-1941
**Daylight Raid from my Studio Window, 7
July 1917**
U71

Sir John Lavery 1856-1941
The Mother (1909)
U72

Sir John Lavery 1856-1941
The Twelfth of July in Portadown (1928)
U77

Sir John Lavery 1856-1941
The Walls of Marakesh (1920)
U78

Sir John Lavery 1856-1941
The Weighing Room, Hurst Park (1924)
U82

Sir John Lavery 1856-1941
Second Study for the King, the Queen, the Prince of Wales, the Princess Mary, Buckingham Palace (1913)
U615

Sir John Lavery 1856-1941
Tangier Bay - Sunshine (1920)
U620

Sir John Lavery 1856-1941
The Greyhound (Sir Reginald Lister and Eileen Lavery. The Last British Minister, the Drawing Room, British Legation, Tangier)(1910) U624

Sir Thomas Lawrence 1769-1830
Harriet Anne, Countess of Belfast 1799-1860 (c.1822-23)
U83

Sir Thomas Lawrence 1769-1830
Amelia Anne, Dowager Marchioness of Londonderry d.1829 (c.1825)
U4964

Benjamin Williams Leader 1831-1923
Evening on a Surrey Common (1911)
U119

Edward Lear 1812-88
**Corfu: The Citadel from near the Village
of Ascension (1856)**
U808

Edward Lear 1812-88
Malta (1866)
U809

Louis le Brocquy b.1916
Girl in White (1941)
U234

Louis le Brocquy b.1916
Variety Rehearsal at the Olympia (1942)
U239

Louis le Brocquy b.1916
Tired Child (1954)
U241

Louis le Brocquy b.1916
Recumbent Nude (1958)
U246

Louis le Brocquy b.1916
**Study towards an Image of W. B. Yeats
(1975)**
U2386

John Leech 1817-64
Head of a Girl
U1319

William John Leech 1881-1968
Railway Embankment
U344

William John Leech 1881-1968
Sunflowers
U892

William John Leech 1881-1968
Aloes (c.1920s)
U2709

William Lee-Hankey 1869-1952
The Confession
U1213

Alphonse Legros 1837-1911
Head of a Monk
U1568

William Leighton Leitch 1804-83
Baptistery, S. Marco, Venice
U1076

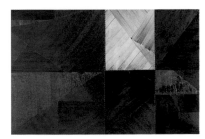

Ciarán Lennon b.1947
Scotoma II/H (1992-93)
U4959

Lë Phö b.1907
Maternity
U4733

Henri Eugène Augustin le Sidaner 1862-1939
Le Gouter au Jardin (1903)
U164

Thérèse Lessore 1884-1945
Sleeping Girl
U893

Michael Leventis b.1944
**Critic in Artist's Studio (David Sylvester)
(1988)**
U4745

John Lewis fl.1740-69
Portrait of an Unknown Man (1748)
U4752

Percy Wyndham Lewis 1882-1957
Seated Woman (1922)
U814

André Lhote 1885-1962
Femme dans sa Cuisine (1935-40)
U1903

John Linnell 1792-1882
**Captain Holland Lecky 1794-1854 (1838-
45)**
U88

John Linnell 1792-1882
Portrait of a Gentleman
U815

John Linnell 1792-1882
Landscape with Sheep (1861)
U816

Lorenzo Lippi 1606-65
An Allegory of Fortune
U36

Lewis Logan fl.1950s
The Cornfield (1955-56)
U817

Alfred Lombard, 19th-20th century
Le Village de Clans
U592

Luca Longhi 1507-80 (attribt.)
The Holy Family with Saints (c.1530)
U2286

Samuel Lover 1797-1868
Master Henry Lover
U1079

Laurence Stephen Lowry 1887-1976
Street Scene (1947)
U355

Strickland Lowry 1737-c.85
Portrait of a Lurgan Volunteer (1780)
U84

Strickland Lowry 1737-c.85
Portrait of a Lady (c.1780)
U712

Strickland Lowry 1737-c.85 (attribt.)
The Family of Thomas Bateson, Esq. 1705-91 (1762)
U1664

Lucebert b.1924
Die Verschwörer (1962)
U518

Frans Joseph Luckx 1802-49
Two Figures at a Window (1847)
U87

John Luke 1906-75
Dr. Alexander Irvine 1863-1941 (1938)
U348

John Luke 1906-75
The Fox (1937)
U352

John Luke 1906-75
Sketch for Mural in Belfast City Hall (1951)
U1907

John Luke 1906-75
The Rehearsal (1950)
U1918

John Luke 1906-75
The Three Dancers (1945)
U1919

John Luke 1906-75
Head of a Woman in Profile (c.1939-40)
U2119

John Luke 1906-75
Seated Nude
U2524

John Luke 1906-75
The Tipster (1928)
U2525

John Luke 1906-75
Self-Portrait
U2526

John Luke 1906-75
The Harbour
U2527

John Luke 1906-75
The Road to the West (1944)
U4781

Gustaf Lundberg 1695-1786
George, 1st Earl Macartney 1737-1806
U86

Edward Lutterell fl.c.1673 d. after 1723
Jan Lutma (1703) (after Rembrandt)
U1432

John Langtry Lynas 1879-1956
Wellington Place from the City Hall Grounds
U350

John Langtry Lynas 1879-1956
My Son Rodin (1925)
U351

John Langtry Lynas 1879-1956
Dante Rossetti Lynas (1924)
U1542

John Langtry Lynas 1879-1956
Self-Portrait (1924)
U1630

William Henry Lynn 1829-1915
Britannia Tubular Bridge over Menai Straits
U1082

William Henry Lynn 1829-1915
Design for St. Andrew's Church, Dublin (1860)
U1864

William Henry Lynn 1829-1915
Design for Unitarian Church, St. Stephen's Green, Dublin (1862)
U2370

Violet McAdoo 1896-1961
Tiled Roofs, Spain (1933)
U1566

James McAldowie fl.1885-1913
'When Autumn Blasts the River Banks Lay Bare'
U1090

Clement McAleer b.1949
Day (1979)
U2700

Clement McAleer b.1949
Night (1979)
U2701

John Alphonsus McAllister 1896-1925
Waterfoot Harbour, Co. Antrim (1924)
U1092

John Alphonsus McAllister 1896-1925
The Brickfield
U1098

John Alphonsus McAllister 1896-1925
**Looking from Ardsbeg, Co. Donegal
(1921)**
U1253

Charles J. McAuley 1910-99
Mid-day on the Moss
U374

Denis McBride b.1939
Variation on a Snowdrop IV (c.1967)
U367

William McBride 1858-1913
The Faggot Gatherers
U604

John McBurney 1877-1917
Waterworks, Antrim Road (1912)
U101

John McBurney 1877-1917
Couple on a Bench in a Garden (1916)
U1540

Samuel McCloy 1831-1904
Two Old friends
U93

Samuel McCloy 1831-1904
**Where the White Foam Kissed my Feet
(c.1898)**
U102

Samuel McCloy 1831-1904
Caught in the Act (c.1885)
U625

Samuel McCloy 1831-1904
Espalier Apple Blossom
U1440

Samuel McCloy 1831-1904
Pieces of Armour on a Bench
U1448

Samuel McCloy 1831-1904
Felled Timber with Burdock
U1450

Samuel McCloy 1831-1904
Stack-building
U1453

Samuel McCloy 1831-1904
Little Girl with Open Book (1892)
U1457

Samuel McCloy 1831-1904
Christmas Carol - O Listen to our Simple Song
U1461

W. J. McClughin 1900-71
Cavehill (1966)
U4784

Dugald Sutherland MacColl 1859-1948
Pont de la Tournelle, Paris
U818

Leonard McComb b.1930
Portrait of Jenny Scott (1987)
U4812

Maurice MacDonagh b.1962
Axis (1993)
U4971

Lawrence MacDonald 1799-1878
Unknown Lady (1851)
U1799

Hector McDonnell b.1947
Bewley's Restaurant II (1980)
U2662

Patrick MacDowell 1799-1870
**Frederick Richard Chichester, Earl of
Belfast 1827-53 (1855)**
U2569

Ambrose McEvoy 1878-1927
Miss Mary Clare (c.1915-20)
U370

Ambrose McEvoy 1878-1927
Portrait of a Lady
U822

Ambrose McEvoy 1878-1927
Standing Nude (c.1920-25)
U823

Archibald A. McGlashan b.1888
Still Life (1925)
U373

Archibald A. McGlashan b.1888
Head of a Child (c.1930)
U377

Maurice MacGonigal 1900-79
'The Olympia', Dublin (c.1935-36)
U369

Bingham McGuiness 1849-1928
Lisieux, Normandy
U2682

Norah McGuiness1901-80
Village by the Sea (1953)
U371

Norah McGuiness 1901-80
The Four Courts, Dublin (1940)
U1254

Norah McGuiness1901-80
**Pattern on the Feather Bed Mountain
(1975)**
U2365

Edward McGuire 1932-86
Portrait of Seamus Heaney b.1939 (1974)
U2107

Edward McGuire 1932-86
Francis Stuart 1902-2000 (1974)
U2278

Frank McKelvey 1895-1974
Evening, Ballycastle (c.1924)
U328

Frank McKelvey 1895-1974
**Study of the Head of an Old Woman
(1916)**
U1099

Stephen McKenna b.1939
Maritime Still Life (1988)
U4753

William Gibbes Mackenzie 1857-1924
My New Shoes! (c.1893)
U89

William Gibbes Mackenzie 1857-1924
River Lagan, near Belfast
U540

William Gibbes Mackenzie 1857-1924
Sunshine, Lagan Woods (1913)
U561

Sine MacKinnon b.1901
Spanish Town (1933)
U4664

Daniel Maclise 1806-70
William Bullen of Kinsale (?) (1829)
U1409

Daniel Maclise 1806-70
Illustration to a Poem
U2265

F. E. McWilliam 1909-92
Head of William Scott 1913-89 (1956)
U968

F. E. McWilliam 1909-92
Woman in Bomb Blast 1974/1 (1974)
U2438

F. E. McWilliam 1909-92
Study for 'Woman in Bomb Blast' (1974)
U2461

F. E. McWilliam 1909-92
Collage (1946)
U4689

F. E. McWilliam 1909-92
Study for 'The Unknown Political Prisoner'
(c.1950-51)
U5024

Joseph McWilliams b.1938
The Governors of Anguilla, Gibraltar, the
Caymen Islands and the Last Governor of
Northern Ireland (1989)
U4805

Simon McWilliams b.1970
Church
U2034

Heinz Mack b.1931
Pyramid of Light (1964)
U525

Thomas Eyre Macklin 1867-1943
City Hall, Belfast, by Floodlight (1935)
U574

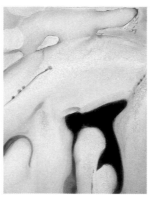

Anne Madden b.1932
Slievecarran (1963)
U356

Conroy Maddox b.1912
Tableau Vivant (1959)
U1431

Nicolaes Maes 1634-93
Portrait of a Woman (1670s)
U208

Marcel Maeyer b.1920
Fair Tent II (1976)
U2451

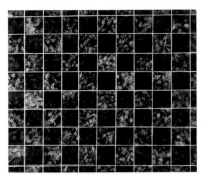

Elizabeth Magill b.1959
Fly Painting (1989)
U4803

James Mahoney 1847-79
Illustration for Charles Dickens' *Our*
Mutual Friend
U2564

Roy de Maistre 1894-1968
Anne, Lady Butler (1954)
U444

José Maldonado b.1962
Eclipse (1991)
U4948

Orazio de Manara b.1804
Frederick Richard Chichester, Earl of
Belfast 1827-53 (1853)
U2366

Harrington Mann 1864-1937
The Bird Cage (1907)
U366

James Bolivar Manson 1879-1945
A Freshening Breeze, St. Briac (c.1907)
U472

Michele Marieschi 1710-43 (circle of)
Capriccio with Classical Ruins and a Harbour
U705

Paul Marny 1829-1914
Gateway
U1088

John Martin 1789-1854
Landscape with Dancing Figures (1820)
U820

Kenneth Martin 1905-84
Chance and Order 12: Black (1973)
U2281

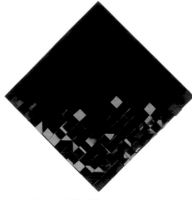

Mary Martin 1907-69
Dispersal: On Black (1967)
U1753

Ferenc Martyn 1899-1986
Abstract Composition
U1762

Master of the Female Half-Lengths
fl.1520-40
Head of a Saint: possibly a Fragment of a Nativity
U1757

Master of the Legend of St. Catherine
fl.1475-1500
Christ Disputing with the Doctors
U972

Assumpcio Mateu b.1952
Tres Fenestres (1992)
U4947

Brigitte Matschinsky-Denninghoff b.1923
Horus II (1960)
U959

Paul Lucien Maze 1887-1979
Boulogne (1925-26)
U470

Ivan Mestrovic 1883-1962
Sir John Lavery, RUA, RHA, RSA 1856-1941 (c.1925-26)
U1760

Paul Ayshford Methuen, 4th Baron
Methuen 1886-1974
Hampton Court (1942)
U824

Colin Middleton 1910-83
Give Me to Drink (1949)
U358

Colin Middleton 1910-83
September Evening, Ballymote (1951)
U360

Colin Middleton 1910-83
Christ Androgyne (1943)
U365

Colin Middleton 1910-83
Lagan: Annadale, October (1941)
U598

Colin Middleton 1910-83
Swan River, Sunset II (1972)
U1882

Colin Middleton 1910-83
Dream of the Moth (1976-77)
U2452

Colin Middleton 1910-83
Head (1938)
U4790

Stanislaus Mikula, 20th century
Defence of Warsaw, September 1939 (1942)
U1602

William Miller d.1779
Rev. George Whitefield 1714-70, Preaching in the Timber Yard at Lurgan, 12 July 1751
U1267

Dhruva Mistry b.1957
Creature (1983)
U4692

Joan Mitchell 1926-92
Painting (1958)
U529

Thomas Mitchell 1735-90
A View of the River Boyne (1757)
U4813

Joseph Molloy 1798-1877
Portrait of a Young Man (c.1820)
U94

Joseph Molloy 1798-1877
Tilbury Fort, River Thames
U104

Alfonso Monreal b.1952
Tiananmen Woman
U4821

Dr. Thomas Monro 1759-1833
Landscape and Trees
U1646

E. Monsclct, 19th-20th century
Landscape with Sheep
U95

Pierre Eugène Montézin 1874-1946
Hans Iten 1874-1930
U57

Jeremy Moon 1934-73
Crusader (1968)
U693

Martin Mooney b.1960
Arch
U4841

Christopher Moore 1790-1863
Sir Richard Griffith 1784-1878 (1859)
U4966

Henry Moore 1898-1986
Working Model for 'Oval with Points'
(1968-69)
U962

Henry Moore 1898-1986
Working Model for 'Three Piece Reclining
Figure: Draped' (1975)
U2404

James Moore, MD 1819-83
**Old Bridge and Entrance Gate to Glenarm
Castle (1844)**
U2893

James Moore, MD 1819-83
Rue de la Fontaine, Havre (1845)
U2899

James Moore, MD 1819-83
Cottage, Cavehill (1845)
U2909

James Moore, MD 1819-83
Near Dunmurry (1845)
U2910

James Moore, MD 1819-83
**Overflow on the Lagan about the Second
Lock (1845)**
U2911

James Moore, MD 1819-83
**Slieve Bernagh from the Trassey Bog,
Mourne Mountains**
U2971

James Moore, MD 1819-83
The Sham Fight at Scarva
U2977

James Moore, MD 1819-83
The First Lock on the Lagan
U4757

Garrett Morphey fl.1680-1716 (attribt.)
**Portrait of an Unknown Man, possibly
Arthur Chichester, 3rd Earl of Donegall
1666-1706**
U1654

Sir Cedric Morris 1889-1982
Birds (1928)
U2289

Edwin A Morrow 1877-1952
A Cold Day, Lincoln
U5048

George Morrow 1870-1955
An African Fable: The Hare and the Lion
U1582

George Morrow 1870-1955
The Fall of Eutychus (1904)
U1584

Norman Morrow 1879-1917
Man and Woman
U1202

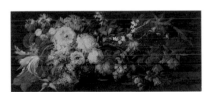

Mary Moser (Mrs. Hugh Lloyd) 1744-1819
Flowerpiece (1769)
U98

Rodrigo Moynihan 1910-90
Apples and Plums (1943?)
U471

Henry Muhrman 1854-1916
Snow-covered Roofs
U1874

Carolyn Mulholland b.1944
Humming Head
U4930

Rosa Müller fl.1845-60
Rome from the Pincian Hill
U2279

William James Müller 1812-45
Xanthus from the Theatre
U827

William Mulready 1786-1863
Giving a Bite
U829

William Mulready 1786-1863 (attribt.)
Young Girl with a Basket of Eggs
U92

Iza Munce fl.1915-25
The Old Lacemaker (1914)
U1920

Paul Sandby Munn 1773-1845
**Hugh Lloyd's Bridge, near Ffestiniog
(1834)**
U830

Denis Brownell Murphy fl.1763 d.1842
**John Bridge 1755-1834, of
Piddletrenthyde, Dorset (1813?)**
U1892

Noel Murphy b.1970
**Searching shortsightedly for W. B. Y.
(1995)**
U5016

Sir David Murray 1849-1933
Peace at Eve (1894)
U106

Mrs. Eileen Murray 1885-1962
This or Emigration (c.1926)
U648

Daniele Nalin b.1947
**Il Custode dei Cinque Punti Sapienti
(1992)**
U4949

John Northcote Nash 1893-1977
The Garden under Snow (c.1924-30)
U474

John Northcote Nash 1893-1977
View of the Plain
U831

John Northcote Nash 1893-1977
Farm at Kimble
U832

Paul Nash 1889-1946
St. Pancras Lilies (1927)
U477

H. Echlin Neill 1888-1981
Glenariff
U1102

Christopher Richard Wynne Nevinson
1889-1946
A Mountain Landscape in Wales
U473

Andrew Nicholl 1804-86
**The Old Tree in the Glen - June (c.1843-
44)**
U91

Andrew Nicholl 1804-86
**McArt's Fort from the Mountain to
between the Fort and the Caves (c.1828)**
U250

Andrew Nicholl 1804-86
**A Bank of Flowers, with a View of Bray
and the Valley of the Dargle, Co. Wicklow**
U916

Andrew Nicholl 1804-86
Galle Harbour, Ceylon
U919

Andrew Nicholl 1804-86
Doonpoint, Island of Rathlin (c.1828)
U963

Andrew Nicholl 1804-86
Dunluce Castle
U1255

Andrew Nicholl 1804-86
The Giant's Causeway from the West
U1256

Andrew Nicholl 1804-86
Rostrevor (c.1828)
U1427

Andrew Nicholl 1804-86
The Old Mill, Holywood (1834)
U1563

Andrew Nicholl 1804-86
Belfast from Newtownbreda Churchyard
U1692

Andrew Nicholl 1804-86
The Long Bridge, Belfast
U1696

Andrew Nicholl 1804-86
Pigeon Cave and Dunree Fort, Lough Swilly
U1699

Andrew Nicholl 1804-86
Fingal's Cave, Staffa
U2383

William Nicholl 1794-1840
Landscape with Trees
U627

William Nicholl 1794-1840
Knock, near Belfast
U922

William Nicholl 1794-1840
View from Strandtown with Ballymacarret Church and Cavehill in the Distance
U1109

Bertram Nicholls 1883-1952
Ebb Tide, Padstow (1947)
U476

Ben Nicholson 1894-1982
Painting (1935)
U519

Margaret Dorothy Nicholson fl.1920-40
The Model (1928)
U559

Sir William Nicholson 1872-1949
Cinerarias (c.1928)
U475

Erskine Nicol 1825-1904
Rejected (1865)
U603

Erskine Nicol 1825-1904
Paddy at Versailles (1856)
U1111

Erskine Nicol 1825-1904
'The Merican Difficulty' (1862)
U2453

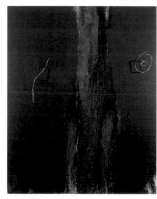

Josep Alvarez Niebla b.1945
Temps de Separacio (1991)
U4946

Paul Nietsche 1885-1950
James Humbert Craig 1878-1944 (1940)
U380

Paul Nietsche 1885-1950
Green Apples (1949)
U381

Paul Nietsche 1885-1950
Portrait of F. L. Green 1902-53 (1946)
U2673

Paul Nietsche 1885-1950
Portrait of Zoltan Lewinter-Frankl 1894-1961 (1943)
U4980

Noel Laura Nisbet 1887-1956
The Dance, or The Followers of Pan (1)
U1875

John Nixon c.1750-1818
Magilligan Mountain (1791)
U2562

John Nixon c.1750-1818
Rostrevor (1791)
U2563

John Nixon c.1750-1818
Giant's Chair at the Causeway, Co. Antrim (1790)
U2582

Kenneth Noland b.1924
Newlight (1963)
U522

Kenneth Noland b.1924
Crystal (1959)
U715

Frank Nortcliffe fl.1930s
Ferragudo, Algarve
U478

John William North 1842-1924
Near Lough Awe
U1112

Charles Oakley b.1925
Tanker Interior (2)
U2291

James George Oben fl.1779-1819
Rock of Fennor on the River Boyne
U833

Dermod O'Brien 1865-1945
The Estuary of the Shannon (1935)
U629

Dermod O'Brien 1865-1945
The Fine Art Academy, Antwerp (1890)
U2643

James Arthur O'Connor 1792-1841
Castle Arras, near Alf, on the Moselle
(c.1833)
U655

John O'Connor 1830-89
The Market Place, Vincenza (1881)
U112

Roderic O'Conor 1860-1940
Field of Corn, Pont Aven (1892)
U389

Roderic O'Conor 1860-1940
Un Bouquet
U2323

Roderic O'Conor 1860-1940
Reclining Nude (c.1906)
U2565

Roderic O'Conor 1860-1940
La Colline Noir
U2566

Roderic O'Conor 1860-1940
View of Pont Aven (1899)
U2675

Roderic O'Conor 1860-1940
Self-Portrait (c.1923-26)
U5037

Helen O'Hara 1846-1920
Evening
U1320

Aloysius O'Kelly 1850-1929
Huckleberry Finn (1885)
U5035

Power O'Malley 1870-1946
Aran Woman
U4820

Tony O'Malley b.1913
Bird in Window (1974)
U2430

Tony O'Malley b.1913
Still Life (1975)
U2431

Tony O'Malley b.1913
Still Life with Onions on a Table (1962)
U2469

Frank O'Meara 1853-88
Autumnal Sorrows (1878)
U2556

Art O'Murnaghan 1872-1954
Nature Rhythm - Dawn (Sunrise Meditation) (1930)
U1113

Art O'Murnaghan 1872-1954
Nature Rhythm - Flames in a Bush (1933)
U1114

Daniel O'Neill 1920-74
The Blue Skirt (1949)
U384

Daniel O'Neill 1920-74
Knockalla Hills, Donegal (1951)
U386

Daniel O'Neill 1920-74
Three Friends (1969-70)
U714

Daniel O'Neill 1920-74
Girl with Fan (1969-70)
U716

Daniel O'Neill 1920-74
Place du Tertre (1949)
U2069

Henry O'Neill 1798-1880
Cashel (1875)
U1257

Jacob van Oost 1601-71
The Holy Family with St. John and St. Elizabeth (1643)
U1867

John Opie 1761-1807
**Sir John Borlase Warren 1753-1822
(1794)**
U115

Sir William Quiller Orchardson 1832-1910
Portrait of Emma Joseph (1904)
U1634

Sir William Orpen 1878-1931
Resting (1905)
U114

Sir William Orpen 1878-1931
Summer Time
U480

Sir William Orpen 1878-1931
Self-Portrait (c.1905-10)
U481

Sir William Orpen 1878-1931
Male Nude Studies
U1217

Walter Frederick Osborne 1859-1903
Cherry Ripe (1889)
U116

Walter Frederick Osborne 1859-1903
Estuary at Walberswick (c.1884-85)
U2382

Séan O'Sullivan 1906-64
Neach (1928)
U388

Séan O'Sullivan 1906-64
George Russell ('AE') 1867-1935 on his Death-bed (1935)
U1869

Henry Marriot Paget 1856-1936
W. B. Yeats 1865-1939 (1889)
U613

James Lynwood Palmer 1867-1941
Trigo (1929)
U610

Samuel Palmer 1805-81
The Piping Shepherd
U835

Giovanni Paolo Panini 1691-1765 (and studio)
Roman Ruins and Figures
U117

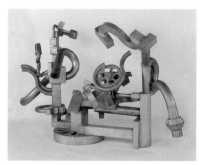

Sir Eduardo Paolozzi b.1924
Crash (1964)
U951

Brynhild Parker fl.1930-38
Quayside, Appledore (c.1930-33)
U484

Richard Dunscombe Parker 1805-81
Grouse, Male and Female
U2388

Richard Dunscombe Parker 1805-81
Snipe, Male and Female
U3490

Richard Dunscombe Parker 1805-81
Gannets, in Two Stages of Plumage, Adult and Immature, 1st Year
U3519

Sir Bernard Partridge 1861-1945
An Interval for Reflection (1924)
U1399

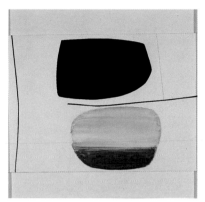

Victor Pasmore 1908-98
Abstract in Black, White and Indigo (Floating World) (1960-61)
U523

Victor Pasmore 1908-98
Still Life with Flowers (c.1939)
U697

Emily Murray Paterson 1855-1934
The Gulls, Polperro
U486

Emily Murray Paterson 1855-1934
Wet Evening on the Riva, Venice
U836

Joseph Paul (of Norwich and London) d.1887
Mill Scene
U619

William Payne fl.1776-1830
View of the Tamar, Cornwall, Moonlight
U1117

William Payne fl.1776-1830
Derwent Lake
U1981

Joseph Peacock 1783-1837
The Patron, or the Festival of St. Kevin at the Seven Churches, Glendalough (1813)
U120

William Pearson fl.1772-1849
Landscape Composition
U838

Aaron Edwin Penley 1807-70
Loch Long, Argyle (1868)
U1118

Newton Penpraze 1888-1978
The Mystic (c.1930s-'40s)
U2672

Samuel John Peploe 1871-1935
Roses
U483

Rev. Matthew William Peters 1741-1814
Portrait of a Lady with a Large Pointed Hat (c.1786-93)
U717

George Petrie 1790-1866
Eagle's Nest, Killarney
U1119

James J. Phillips 1843-1936
L'Hotel de Colombey, Caen (1891)
U2628

Tom Phillips b.1937
Portrait of Barry Douglas b.1960 (1990)
U4826

James George Philp 1816-85
View Looking towards Falmouth (1855)
U1120

Glyn Warren Philpot 1884-1937
Portrait of a Young Man (c.1920)
U390

Otto Piene b.1928
Purgatory Flower (1963-64)
U530

Sir William Pilkington Bt., c.1775-1850
View on the Palatine Hill, Rome
U2109

George John Pinwell 1842-75
The Last Load (1869)
U1121

John Piper 1903-92
Bladon (1945)
U4686

Raymond Piper b.1923
William Conor 1881-1968 (1962)
U1218

Lucien Pissarro 1863-1944
The Allotments (1917)
U124

Lucien Pissarro 1863-1944
Trippleton Farm (1932)
U485

Roland Vivian Pitchforth 1895-1982
Londonderry Base (1944)
U1122

Roland Vivian Pitchforth 1895-1982
Frigate at Pollock Dock, Belfast (1944)
U1219

George Place c.1750-1805
William Ware (c.1790)
U1902

Nicholas Pocock 1740-1821
**Attack of the French Squadron upon the
Coast of Ireland (1799)**
U122

Nicholas Pocock 1740-1821
Stormy Scene on Rocky Coast (1792)
U2302

Polidoro da Caravaggio 1492-1543 (after)
Two Putti
U2114

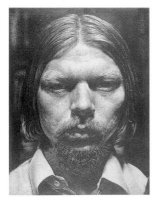

Miervaldis Polis b.1948
Self-Portrait (1975)
U2520

Thomas Pope-Stevens fl.1765-80
**John Reilly of Scarva, Co. Down, MP
1745-1804 (1775)**
U5010

Frederick James Porter 1883-1944
A View from the Artist's Studio (1931)
U482

Sophia Rosamond Praeger 1867-1954
The Philosopher (c.1920)
U1177

Sophia Rosamond Praeger 1867-1954
The Fairy Fountain (c.1900-1)
U1767

William Pratt b.1855 fl.1880-1936
Burning the Shaws
U564

John Skinner Prout 1806-76
Kenilworth Castle
U1123

Samuel Prout 1783-1852
Chapel in the Château d'Amboise
U841

Sarah Henrietta Purser 1848-1943
An Irish Idyll
U121

Sarah Henrietta Purser 1848-1943
John Kells Ingram 1823-1907 (1890)
U1258

Sarah Henrietta Purser 1848-1943
John Butler Yeats 1839-1922 (c.1901)
U4963

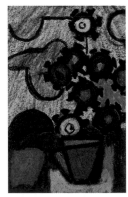

Patrick Pye b.1929
Still Life Study with Flowers
U1759

Jan Symonsz Pynas 1583/84-1631
Adoration of the Golden Calf
U721

Royden Rabinowitch b.1943
Barrel Construction (1964)
U2694

Clifford Rainey b.1948
Portrait of William Scott 1913-89 (1976)
U2410

Clifford Rainey b.1948
**Portrait of F. E. McWilliam 1909-92
(1976)**
U2411

Basil Rakoczi 1908-79
Chez les Sinclair (c.1956)
U4892

Basil Rakoczi 1908-79
Nature Morte au Téléphone (1958)
U4893

Peter Randall-Page b.1954
Dark Fruit (1989)
U4938

William Bruce Ellis Rankin 1881-1941
Sketch for 'The Winning Eight' (1921)
U1600

Margaret Rayner fl.1866-95
Haddon Hall Chapel
U2683

Samuel Rayner fl.1821-72 d.1874
West Porch, Lichfield Cathedral
U1124

Samuel Read 1815-83
The Grey Man, July 28 (1874)
U2490

Russell Sidney Reeve 1895-1970
Riverside, Norwich (1923)
U1125

Nano Reid 1910-81
The Lilter (1933)
U400

Nano Reid 1910-81
Galway Peasant (1929)
U401

Alfred William Rich 1856-1921
Distant View of Lincoln
U1126

W. Richard, 19th century
Italian Farm and Stream
U1487

Ceri Richards 1903-71
**La Cathédrale Engloutie (Dialogue du
Vent et de la Mer) (1962)**
U516

Jennifer Richardson b.1944
In the Fields (1974)
U2292

Charles de Sousy Ricketts 1866-1931
Costume for 'The Mikado' (1926)
U842

Bridget Riley b.1931
Cataract IV (1967)
U533

Elizabeth Rivers 1903-64
Cat and Egg
U495

David Roberts 1796-1864
Church of San Iago, Jerez, Spain (c.1833)
U1323

David Roberts 1796-1864 (attribt.)
Roman Remains at Nijmegen
U140

Hilda Roberts 1901-82
Portrait of George Russell ('AE') 1867-1935 (1929)
U392

Hilda Roberts 1901-82
John Lyle Donaghy 1902-47 (1928)
U1866

William Patrick Roberts 1895-1980
Les Routiers (c.1931)
U492

William Patrick Roberts 1895-1980
Sawing Wood (c.1930)
U496

William Patrick Roberts 1895-1980
Watching a Raid
U1324

Anne Marjorie Robinson 1858-1924
Cavehill from Belfast Harbour
U1127

Anne Marjorie Robinson 1858-1924
Reverie (1914)
U4517

Anne Marjorie Robinson 1858-1924
An Early Victorian
U4530

Anne Marjorie Robinson 1858-1924
The Baptism of St. Brigit by Angels; It was Brigit Wove the First Cloth in Ireland (1918)
U5004

Markey Robinson 1918-99
Woman in White
U4798

Markey Robinson 1918-99
Flower Market near the Madeleine
U5051

Thomas Robinson d.1810
Portrait of a Young Man, possibly a United Irishman (1798)
U136

Thomas Robinson d.1810
Colonel William Sharman 1731-1803 (1798)
U141

Thomas Robinson d.1810
William Ritchie 1756-1834 (c.1802)
U144

William Heath Robinson 1872-1944
A Missionary Being Boiled by Cannibals
U1400

George Fennel Robson 1788-1833
Farmstead with Figures and Trees
U1128

Sampson Towgood Roch(e) 1757/59-1847
Rustics Dancing outside an Inn
U2516

Patsy Dan Rodgers, 20th century
Tory in a Storm (c.1977)
U2445

Alfredo Roldan, 20th century
Antes de la Ducha (1997)
U650

Adriaen Rombouts fl.1660-67
Pancake Night (1667)
U138

Michael 'Angelo' Rooker 1743-1801
View in Hyde Park
U1647

Toma Rosandic 1878-1958
Ecce Homo (1915)
U1811

Dante Gabriel Rossetti 1828-82
**Study of Elizabeth Siddal 1834-62, for
'The Return of Tibullus to Delia'**
U843

Dante Gabriel Rossetti 1828-82
**Study of Elizabeth Siddal 1834-62, for
'The Return of Tibullus to Delia' (1851)**
U3598

Sir William Rothenstein 1872-1945
Oakridge Farm, Late Summer (c.1925)
U494

Sir William Rothenstein 1872-1945
**John Rothenstein as a Child, Feeding
Hens (1904)**
U1750

**Robert Patterson, FRS, MRIA 1802-72
(1889)**
U157

Richard Rothwell 1800-68
Stella in Rome (c.1831-34)
U152

Richard Rothwell 1800-68
Marcus Ward 1806-47
U153

Richard Rothwell 1800-68
**Frederic William Macaulay 1801-39
(c.1826)**
U685

Richard Rothwell 1800-68
**Anna Macaulay, née Hyndman 1801-91
(c.1826)**
U686

Richard Rothwell 1800-68
Portrait of a Boy
U2277

Thomas Leeson Rowbotham, Jnr. 1823-75
**Mountainous Landscape with Bridge
(1868)**
U2561

Thomas Rowlandson 1756-1827
A Tour in Flanders (1792)
U844

Thomas Rowlandson 1756-1827
Study of a Man in Riding Dress
U1201

George William Russell ('AE') 1867-1935
The Watcher
U394

George William Russell ('AE') 1867-1935
The Skipping Rope
U396

George William Russell ('AE') 1867-1935
River in the Sand (1924)
U399

Russian Icon, Crimean School, late 16th-
early 17th century
**St. Demetrius Plunging King John into an
Abyss**
U2231

Russian Icon, Russian School, 17th-18th
century
St. Nicholas
U2232

Russian Icon, Russian School, 18th century
Dormition of the Virgin
U2234

Albert Rutherston 1881-1953
The Maypole in Dorset (1920)
U1754

Adrian Ryan b.1920
Mousehole (1946)
U493

William Sadler II 1782-1839
The Eagle's Nest, Killarney
U227

Kikuo Saito b.1939
Windy Paw (1979)
U2577

Paul Sandby 1731-1809
Caernarvon Castle (1794)
U846

Paul Sandby 1731-1809
**St. George's Chapel, Windsor, from inside
Henry VIII Gate**
U847

Paul Sandby 1731-1809
Edwinsford, Carmarthenshire
U850

Paul Sandby 1731-1809
**View near the Woodyard, Windsor Great
Park**
U851

` Thomas Sandby 1721-98 (after)
The South Terrace, Windsor Castle
U800

Frederick Sandys 1829-1904
Cassandra
U168

Frederick Sandys 1829-1904
Study of a Head (1890)
U852

Robert Scanlan b.1908
Northern Ireland Coast (1941)
U1259

Carl Schmid (?), 19th century
**General Francis Rawdon Chesney 1789-
1872 (1853)**
U618

Ben Schonzeit b.1942
Hot House, Black and White (1979)
U2578

Benno Schotz 1891-1984
Anna May Wong 1907-61 (1933)
U1812

Patrick Scott b.1921
Bog Reflection (1960-61)
U410

William Scott 1913-89
Brown Still Life (1958)
U404

William Scott 1913-89
Still Life (1949)
U2475

William Scott 1913-89
Whites (1964)
U2663

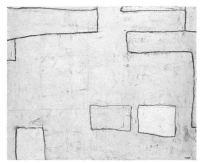

William Scott 1913-89
White with Red Lines (1962)
U2664

William Scott 1913-89
Shapes and Shadows (1962)
U2665

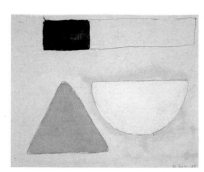

William Scott 1913-89
1st Aegean Suite No. 1 Jan 1969 (1968)
U2669

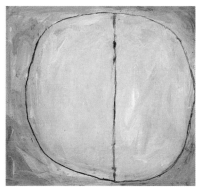

William Scott 1913-89
Grey Circle (1961)
U2670

William Scott fl.1880-1907
Old Town, Bordighera
U2610

Sean Scully b.1945
Fourth Layer (1973)
U2079

Elliott Seabrooke 1886-1950
Fruit (1928)
U502

Wilfred Arthur Seaby 1910-91
Tom King's Cottage, Tolloeragh (1970)
U1881

Ronald Searle b.1920
The Shoe Cleaner, Belgrade (1948)
U1410

Franz van Severdonck 1809-89
Goats (1859)
U180

William Shackleton 1872-1933
Study (1903)
U1601

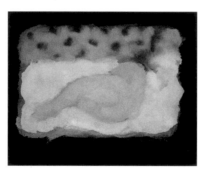

Neil Shawcross b.1940
Nude II (1974)
U2094

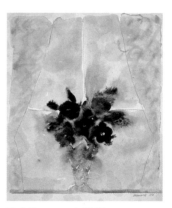

Neil Shawcross b.1940
Flowers (1976)
U2448

Neil Shawcross b.1940
Portrait of Francis Stuart 1902-2000
U2474

Neil Shawcross b.1940
Portrait of Paul Muldoon b.1951 (1978)
U2511

John Sherrin 1819-96
Bird's Nest and Hawthorn (1869)
U1133

Mark Shields b.1963
Self-Portrait: The Troubled Look (1995)
U5015

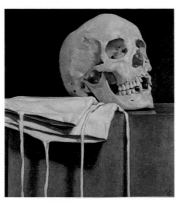

Mark Shields b.1963
Skull - Bianco e Vermiglio (1994)
U5019

Kenneth Denton Shoesmith 1890-1939
Cranes, Baker Street
U2285

Kenneth Denton Shoesmith 1890-1939
Shanghai River
U2356

Kenneth Denton Shoesmith 1890-1939
Tangier - the Flower Seller
U2358

Kenneth Denton Shoesmith 1890-1939
New Orleans. Camouflaged Merchant Ship (1918)
U3622

Kenneth Denton Shoesmith 1890-1939
The Harbour of Piraeus, Athens
U3707

Kenneth Denton Shoesmith 1890-1939
The 'Conway', Liverpool
U3748

Walter Richard Sickert 1860-1942
Suspense (c.1916)
U490

Walter Richard Sickert 1860-1942
Easter (c.1928)
U500

Walter Richard Sickert 1860-1942
Study for 'Suspense'
U854

Henry Singleton 1766-1839
Allegory of the Napoleonic Wars
U1325

Robert Sivell 1888-1958
Sisters (1927)
U497

John Skeaping 1901-80
Bullfight (1934)
U1221

Adam (Frank) Slade b.1875
Cliff End, Sussex
U607

John Joseph Slattery d.1859
Abraham and Isaac (?)
U1626

John Joseph Slattery d.1859
Abraham Sacrificing Isaac
U1628

Stephen Slaughter 1697-1765 (attribt.)
Portrait of a Gentleman (c.1745)
U147

James Sinton Sleator 1885-1950
Portrait of Forrest Reid 1875-1947 (1924)
U163

James Sinton Sleator 1885-1950
Still Life (1923)
U407

James Sinton Sleator 1885-1950
White Marguerites in a Vase
U5069

John 'Warwick' Smith 1749-1831
Naples from the Arinelli
U950

Sir Matthew Smith 1879-1959
Daisies and Pears (c.1920-29)
U499

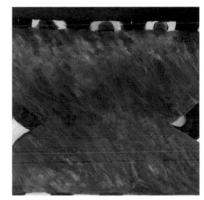

Richard Smith b.1931
Penny (1960)
U537

Sidney Smith 1912-82
From the Flies (1943-44)
U415

Sidney Smith 1912-82
Demolition Squad, North Street
U1546

Sidney Smith 1912-82
Portrait of W. R. Rodgers 1909-69 (1941)
U2590

Sidney Smith 1912-82
Outside Fiesole, Florence (1965)
U2648

Sidney Smith 1912-82
Castlewellan, Co. Down (1940s)
U2649

Sidney Smith 1912-82
Self-Portrait (1946)
U2650

Edward and John Smyth 1749-1812;
c.1773-1840
Francis Johnston 1760-1829
U1164

Edward and John Smyth 1749-1812;
c.1773-1840
**Mrs. Francis Johnston, née Anne Barnes
1769-1841**
U1165

J. B. Smyth, 19th century
Landscape with Church (1874)
U1326

Francesco Solimena 1657-1747
Study for Circe
U158

Estella F. Solomons 1882-1968
**Portrait of Alice Milligan 1866-1953
(1918)**
U405

Estella F. Solomons 1882-1968
**Portrait of Joseph Campbell 1879-1944
(1919)**
U416

Edith Oenone Somerville 1858-1949
Stage Design for 'A Horse! A Horse!':
Castle by Moonlight (c.1930)
U2088

Camille Souter b.1929
The Last of the Radicio (1964)
U704

Gilbert Spencer 1892-1979
Little Milton near Garsington (1926)
U491

Gilbert Spencer 1892-1979
Farm Cart (1929)
U855

Sir Stanley Spencer 1891-1959
Scene from the Marriage at Cana in
Galilee (1935)
U488

Sir Stanley Spencer 1891-1959
Portrait of Daphne Spencer b.1932 (1951)
U489

John Humphrey Spender b.1910
Ruined Square (1948)
U1131

Clarkson Stanfield 1793-1867
The Stack Rock, Co. Antrim (1861)
U167

Clarkson Stanfield 1793-1867
Shakespeare's Cliff, Dover (1849)
U857

Anthony Carey Stannus 1830-1919
Dinant
U560

Anthony Carey Stannus 1830-1919
An Irish Interior
U858

Anthony Carey Stannus 1830-1919
Beating into Port
U859

Anthony Carey Stannus 1830-1919
The Haymakers, Warkworth Castle, Northumberland
U1401

Sir Robert Ponsonby Staples, Bt. 1853-1943
Liner on Stocks (1904-24)
U159

Sir Robert Ponsonby Staples, Bt. 1853-1943
Bangor Boat (1904-24)
U573

Sir Robert Ponsonby Staples, Bt. 1853-1943
Turbine Makers (1904-24)
U597

Sir Robert Ponsonby Staples, Bt. 1853-1943
Flax Pullers (c.1908)
U694

Sir Robert Ponsonby Staples, Bt. 1853-1943
Percy French 1854-1920
U1825

Sir Robert Ponsonby Staples, Bt. 1853-
1943
Self-Portrait (1916)
U1832

Sir Robert Ponsonby Staples, Bt. 1853-
1943
**The Most Rev. William Alexander 1824-
1911, Archbishop of Armagh and Primate
of All Ireland (1899)**
U1835

Hendrik van Steenwyck the Younger
c.1580-1649
Church Interior
U161

Philip Wilson Steer 1860-1942
Yachts on the Solent (1920)
U498

Philip Wilson Steer 1860-1942
The Teme at Ludlow (1900)
U501

Philip Wilson Steer 1860-1942
Haweswater (1904)
U860

Patric Stevenson 1909-83
Breakers, Achill (1953)
U1437

Stella Steyn 1907-87
Woman Seated at a Table (1951)
U5020

Abraham Storck c.1635-c.1710
River Scene
U160

Thomas Stothard 1755-1834
Mother's Present
U1435

James (Seamus) Stoupe 1872-1949
After Milking Time
U418

James (Seamus) Stoupe 1872-1949
Ballylesson
U2352

Johannes Antonie Balthasar Stroebel 1825-1905
Dutch Interior
U165

Ian Stuart b.1926
Grey Box (1967)
U957

William Stuart fl.1850-67
George I Arriving at the Nore in 1714
U29

A. H. Stuart-Hill fl.c.1920-50
Santa Margherita, Italy (c.1927-28)
U460

Ralph R. Stubbs, 19th century
The Nab, Scarborough, South Side (1858)
U171

Edmund Joseph Sullivan 1869-1933
The Art Class
U1268

Thomas Sunderland 1744-1823
Ullswater
U1134

Mary Swanzy 1882-1978
**Reading the 'Employment Offers' Column
(1972)**
U2087

Mary Swanzy 1882-1978
Flowerpiece (c. 1913)
U2324

Mary Swanzy 1882-1978
**Woman in a Green Dress and Cameo
(1920-40)**
U2558

Patrick Swift 1927-83
Positano
U5003

Mark Lancelot Symons 1887-1935
Family Breakfasting (1934)
U1402

Grzegorz Sztabinski, 20th century
Permutations I
U2517

Jacob Taanman 1836-1923
Mother and Child (1867)
U190

Antoni Tapies b.1923
Peinture Verte (1954)
U513

Agostino Tassi 1565-1644
Landscape with Figures
U186

J. Frederick Tayler 1802-89
The Homestead (1853)
U1136

Ernest E. Taylor 1863-1907
John Vinycomb, MRIA 1833-1928 (1892)
U2014

Francis Taylor b.1899
The Windows of Kensington, London (1927)
U1135

Thomas Clement Thompson c.1780-1857
Francis Johnston 1760-1829 (early 1820s)
U729

Hugh Thomson 1860-1920
'Bringing Him to the Point' (1898)
U1140

Hugh Thomson 1860-1920
Illustration for Robert Browning's 'The Pied Piper of Hamelin' (1894)
U1141

Hugh Thomson 1860-1920
'Laying the Cloth' (1899)
U1142

Hugh Thomson 1860-1920
'The Shanachie' (1906)
U1144

Hugh Thomson 1860-1920
Caricature of Harry Lauder 1870-1950
U1585

Geoffrey Tibble 1909-52
Pietà (1950)
U504

Henry Tonks 1862-1937
Girl in a Green Dress
U863

Romeo Charles Toogood 1902-66
Dan Nancy's, Cushendun (1933)
U575

Romeo Charles Toogood 1902-66
Barge at Edenderry (1936)
U653

Francis William Topham 1808-77
**Cottage Interior, Claddagh, Galway
(1845)**
U1413

Francis Towne 1739-1816
Trees and Rocks, Ambleside
U864

Helen Mabel Trevor 1831-1900
The Young Eve (1882)
U189

George Trobridge 1856-1909
**Looking East towards the Castlereagh
Hills from Malone, Arthur James Ward's
Cottage in Foreground**
U1146

George Trobridge 1856-1909
Riverside Meadows, Belvoir Park
U1147

Wolfgang Troschke b.1947
Ohne Titel (1993)
U5021

John Turner b.1916
The Family (1945)
U408

John Turner b.1916
Death of the First Born (1948)
U2554

Joseph Mallord William Turner 1775-1851
Beeston Castle, Cheshire
U865

Joseph Mallord William Turner 1775-1851
Beachy Head Looking towards Newhaven
U866

William Turner (of Oxford) 1789-1862
**View of Magdalen College Tower and
Bridge, Oxford**
U1148

Lucas van Uden 1595-c.1672
Landscape with Figures
U230

Unknown, 16th century (British)
**Robert Devereux, 2nd Earl of Essex 1566-
1601**
U642

Unknown, 16th century (British)
**Walter Devereux, 1st Earl of Essex 1539-76
(1572)**
U4755

Unknown, 17th century (British)
'Le Chandelier'
U195

Unknown, 19th century (British)
Woody Landscape
U873

Unknown, 19th century (British)
Borthwick Castle, Midlothian
U1363

Unknown, 19th century (British)
Portrait of a Man
U4498

Unknown, 19th century (English)
Seated Girl
U759

Unknown, 19th century (English)
River Gorge
U768

Unknown, 19th century (English)
Rome
U936

Unknown, 19th century (English)
Riverside Scene in London
U940

Unknown, 19th century (English)
La Ferté
U946

Unknown, 16th century (Flemish)
St. Jerome in his Study
U669

Unknown, 19th century (French or
English)
Arch of Septimus Severus, Rome
U945

Unknown, 17th century (Irish)
**Captain William Jackson d.1688 (late
1660s)**
U2515

Unknown, 18th century (Irish)
**John Echlin of Thomastown 1723-89
(c.1787)**
U213

Unknown, 18th century (Irish)
A View of Glenarm Castle (c.1768-1812)
U2255

Unknown, 19th century (Irish)
**Elizabeth McTear, née Crawford 1765-
1836 (c.1830)**
U108

Unknown, 19th century (Irish)
**Burning the Effigy of Lundy in Derry
(c.1830)**
U203

Unknown, 19th century (Irish)
**The Blind Harper, Patrick Quinn c.1745-
1812 (c.1800)**
U1571

Unknown, 19th century (Irish)
The Curran, Larne
U2105

Unknown, 19th century (Irish)
William Tennent 1760-1832 (c.1810)
U2270

Unknown, 19th century (Irish)
John Russell of Newforge
U2412

Unknown, 17th century (Italian)
Ecce Homo
U211

Unknown, 17th century (Italian)
Ecce Homo
U2115

Unknown, 19th century (Italian)
Piazza San Marco, Venice
U125

Unknown, 18th century (Unknown
School)
Rev. Samuel Barber
U1898

Unknown, 19th century (Unknown
School)
The Link Boy
U806

Unknown, 19th century (Unknown
School)
Hugh Ritchie
U1897

Wallerand Vaillant 1623-77.
Portrait of a Woman (c.1660-70)
U193

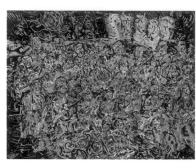

Dara Vallely b.1946
Chicago Pipers' Club
U4934

John B. Vallely b.1941
Trio (1973)
U1870

Doreen Vanston 1903-88
A Dying Animal (c.1943)
U4879

Cornelius Varley 1781-1873
Lixnaw Castle, Co. Kerry (1842)
U1648

John Varley 1778-1842
Waborne Hall, Norfolk
U867

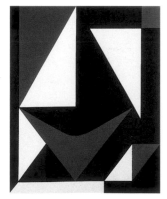

Victor Vasarely 1908-97
Geta (c.1960-63)
U514

Alfred Vickers 1786-1868
In the Vale of Amersham
U732

Jan Christian Vollaert 1709-69
River View
U181

Cornelis de Vos 1584-1651
The Raising of Lazarus
U31

Edward Wadsworth 1889-1949
Gastropoda (1927)
U510

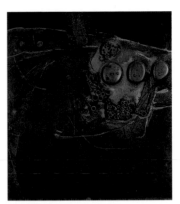

Jaap Wagemaker 1906-72
Image in Relief (1961)
U531

Tom Waghorn 1900-59
Downpatrick (1943)
U4667

William Frederick Wakeman 1822-1900
**Cromlech in the Townland of
Tawnatruffaun, Co. Sligo (1891)**
U2375

Dame Ethel Walker 1861-1951
Summer Afternoon
U507

John Walker b.1939
Touch (1970)
U1886

John Crampton Walker 1890-1942
Geums (c.1930-31)
U595

Patricia Wallace (Mrs. Patricia Griffith)
1913-73
The Haggard
U1150

Alfred Wallis 1855-1942
'Consols Mine Raswall Hill and the Road
Zennor to Farms. The White you See is
Granite' (c.1936)
U690

Thomas Walmsley 1763-1806
Mouth of the Suir, Ireland
U2303

Elijah Walton 1833-80
Abu Simbel, Nubia (1876)
U1151

Leslie Moffat Ward b.1888
A Medway Boat Building Yard
U1260

Barbara Warren b.1925
Child among Rocks (1965-66)
U426

George Waters 1863-1947
April, Colin Glen, Belfast
U4668

Bartholomew Colles Watkins 1833-91
**Ecclesiastical Ruins on Inniscaltra, or Holy
Island, Lough Derg, Co. Galway (c.1863)**
U172

Jan Baptist Weenix 1621-c.1660/61
**Shepherds and Flocks among Classical
Ruins**
U194

William Wells fl.1893-1923
Field Workers
U2038

Franziskus Wendels b.1960
Shaftesbury Square, Belfast (1992)
U4951

Richard Westall 1765-1836
The Three Marys at the Sepulchre
U1178

Francis Wheatley 1747-1801
John, 1st Viscount O'Neill of Shane's Castle 1740-98 (c.1780)
U146

Francis Wheatley 1747-1801
The Belfrey Tower, Furness Abbey, Lancashire (1798)
U2439

Leo Whelan 1892-1956
Interior of a Kitchen (c.1934)
U508

Ethelbert White 1891-1972
Sun through the Wood (c.1932)
U425

Ethelbert White 1891-1972
Below the Mournes
U870

Ethelbert White 1891-1972
Cold Kitchen Farm (1915)
U871

Ethelbert White 1891-1972
The Mourne Mountains
U4801

Francis Wiles 1889-1956
The Dawn of Womanhood (1914)
U1816

Hugh William 'Grecian' Williams 1773-1829
Lake of Avernus (1816)
U1649

Terrick John Williams 1860-1936
A Rain Squall, Concarneau
U511

David Wilson 1873-1934
Telscombe, Sussex
U1261

David Wilson 1873-1934
A Sussex Barn
U1262

David Wilson 1873-1934
General Sir George White 1835-1912
U1593

David Wilson 1873-1934
General Booth 1829-1912 Looks for New Worlds to Conquer (1912)
U1594

David Wilson 1873-1934
View in Hyde Park, London
U4836

David Wilson 1873-1934
White Roses in a Glass (1927)
U5031

David Wilson 1873-1934
Sweet Peas
U5032

James Glen Wilson 1827-63
Emigrant Ship Leaving Belfast (1852)
U178

James Glen Wilson 1827-63
Belfast Quay (1851)
U572

James Glen Wilson 1827-63
The First Lock at Stranmillis (1850)
U4970

Joseph Wilson fl.c.1766-93, d.1793
William Dawson 1759-1834 (c.1780)
U176

Joseph Wilson fl.c.1766-93, d.1793
Miss Maxwell (c.1782)
U183

Joseph Wilson fl.c.1766-93, d.1793
John Magee 1752-1809 (c.1782)
U185

Joseph Wilson fl.c.1766-93, d.1793
William Magee 1750-1827 (c.1782)
U695

Joseph Wilson fl.c.1766-93, d.1793
Lieutenant Hugh Hyndman (c.1782)
U2254

Richard Wilson 1713/14-82
Landscape with Banditti (c.1755-58)
U6

Ross Wilson b.1958
Portrait of Anthony C. West b.1910 (1982)
U2661

Ross Wilson b.1958
Portrait of Brian Moore 1921-99 (1985)
U4688

Edmund Morison Wimperis 1835-1900
A Sunny Vale (1884)
U1156

Edmund Morison Wimperis 1835-1900
The Riverside Pasture (1898)
U1650

Edmund Morison Wimperis 1835-1900
Landscape (1888)
U2062

Theodore Blake Wirgman 1848-1925
**Henry Jones McCance, DL 1829-1900
(1896)**
U2471

Edward Wolfe 1897-1983
The Doorway (c.1929-30)
U506

Christopher Wood 1901-30
Village in Italy (1925)
U509

346

Christopher Wood 1901-30
Street Scene with Trees
U512

Shakspere Wood 1827-86
Alexander Mitchell 1780-1868
U1821

Alfred Joseph Woolmer 1805-92
Scene in Chelsea Park
U606

John Michael Wright the Elder 1617-94
Gentleman in Armour, possibly a Member of the King Family (1680)
U179

John Michael Wright the Elder 1617-94
Robert King, 2nd Baron Kingston 1657-93 (c. 1676)
U216

Joseph Wright of Derby 1734-97
Virgil's Tomb: Sun Breaking through a Cloud (1785)
U2368

Jan Wyck c.1640-1702
A Cavalry Skirmish
U173

Jan Wyck c.1640-1702 (attribt.)
William III 1650-1702
U698

Guy Richard Charles Wyndham 1896-1948
Summer Landscape
U505

William Frederick Yeames 1835-1918
Choir Boys (1891)
U191

Anne Yeats b.1919
One Room (c.1954)
U432

Jack Butler Yeats 1871-1957
On Through the Silent Lands (1951)
U430

Jack Butler Yeats 1871-1957
Grafton Street/Conversation Piece (1923)
U433

Jack Butler Yeats 1871-1957
A Soft Day (1908)
U874

Jack Butler Yeats 1871-1957
The End of the World (1909)
U1329

Jack Butler Yeats 1871-1957
Untitled
U2436

Jack Butler Yeats 1871-1957
Darrynane (in the Sun) (1927)
U4888

John Butler Yeats 1839-1922
Portrait of Acheson T. Henderson, QC
1812-1909 (1891)
U192

drawings paintings & sculptures

the ulster museum botany and zoology collections

Winifred Austen 1876-1964
Helter-skelter Coots
N36

Antoine-Louis Barye 1795-1875
Greyhound and Hare
S18

Antoine-Louis Barye 1795-1875
Stag and Young
S20

Miss Battersby, 19th century
Pompadore Chatterer, Cayenne (1806)
N501 (3)

Miss Battersby, 19th century
Green Woodpecker, England. A Young Bird
N501 (5)

Miss Battersby, 19th century
Blue-tailed Thrush (1806)
N501 (11)

Miss Battersby, 19th century
China Mallow, Belfast
N502 (5)

Miss Battersby, 19th century
Ixia Bicolor
N502 (9)

J. M. Benington, 20th century
Great Spotted Woodpecker
N94

J. M. Benington, 20th century
Redwing on Nest in Iceland (1955)
N96

J. M. Benington, 20th century
Golden Eagle (1955)
N98

L. G. Jackson Booth, 20th century
The Unfortunate Oiled Guillemot
N14

Raymond Booth, 20th century
Stoat in Winter (1974)
N319

Heather Byers, 20th century
Perch (1972)
N383

Heather Byers, 20th century
Rainbow Trout (1971)
N400

Heather Byers, 20th century
Charr (1972)
N401

Con Campbell, 20th century
Arkle and Pat Taaffe
N315

Neville Henry Pennington Cayley
1853-1903
Kookaburra
N78

George Edward Collins 1880-1968
Jay
N43

George Edward Collins 1880-1968
Kingfishers
N286

Dr. Charles John F. Coombes b.1908
Magpie (1966)
N68

Noel William Cusa 1909-91
Roseate Terns (1964)
N13

Noel William Cusa 1909-91
Guillemots (1965)
N32

Edward Julius Detvold 1883-1957
Eagle (1900)
N288

Basil Ede b.1931
Cock Capercaillie in Display
N47

Eric Arnold R. Ennion 1900-81
Widgeon Resting
N17

Trevor Faulkner, 20th century
Lady Amherst Pheasant (1970)
S22

Robert A. F. Gillmor b.1936
Grebe Family
N187

Robert A. F. Gillmor b.1936
Oystercatcher
N255

Mary Grierson, 20th century
Neottia nidus-avis (Bird's Nest Orchid)
(1970)
N396

Morris Harding 1874-1964
Lion (1919)
N155.A9

Morris Harding 1874-1964
Jaguar Resting (1924)
N155.A13

Morris Harding 1874-1964
Leopard in a Tree
N155.A14

John Cyril Harrison 1898-1985
Heron and Widgeon
N302

John Cyril Harrison 1898-1985
Golden Pheasant
N306

Robin Hill b.1932
Jabiru Storks (1964)
N45

Robin Hill b.1932
Cuckoo and Chiffchaffs (1964)
N301

Robert Hills 1769-1844
Stags in a Park
N233

William Hollywood b.1923
Guillemots on Muck Island (1969)
N273

Edward Hurst 1912-72
Longhi Lily
N365

Captain Richard Barrett Talbot Kelly
1896-1971
Heron Sunning Itself
N44

Jonathan Kenworthy, 20th century
Cheetah and Female Impala (1965)
S14

John Gerrard Keulemans 1842-1912
Goldfinches and Great Grey Shrike
N231

John Gerrard Keulemans 1842-1912
Kingfishers
N232

J. Fenwick Landsdowne b.1937
Cuckoo (1963)
N37

R. M. Laws, 20th century
Spur-winged Plover (1963)
N22

Peter John Levi, 20th century
Magpie
N51

George Edward Lodge 1860-1954
Gyrfalcon
N19

George Edward Lodge 1860-1954
Golden Eagle Soaring
N20

John McMillan, 20th century
Robin (1972)
N313

Margaret Mee b. 1909
Aechmea mertensii
N391

Robert W. Milliken b.1920
Rathlin Revisited
N11

Robert W. Milliken b.1920
Teal in the Downpatrick Marshes
N151

Kenneth Newman b.1924
African Fish Eagle (1972)
N309

Joy Parsons b.1913
Toco Toucans
N184

Hubert J. Pepper, 20th century
Common Seals in a Bay (1970)
N280

Roger Tory Peterson, 20th century
King Vultures
N46

David Reid-Henry 1919-77
Gyrfalcon
N9

David Reid-Henry 1919-77
Greenland Falcon
N27

David Reid-Henry 1919-77
Peregrine Falcon
N71

Philip Charles Rickman 1891-1982
Brown Leaves - Blue Tit and Great Tit (1969)
N275

Philip Charles Rickman 1891-1982
Bittern
N356

David Rook, 20th century
Otter in a Stormy Sky
N10

Sir Peter Scott 1909-89
King Eiders (1965)
N76

Allen W. Seaby 1867-1953
Pomarine Skua
N6

Keith Shackleton b.1923
Roseate Tern (1965)
N242

Keith Shackleton b.1923
Horses Drinking (1969)
N311

David Shepherd b.1931
Elephants (1966)
N93

Eileen Alice Soper 1905-90
Badger Twins
N185

Ralph Thompson, 20th century
Lar Gibbon (1965)
N26

Ralph Thompson, 20th century
Porcupine
N34

Ralph Thompson, 20th century
Cacomistle
N35

Archibald Thorburn 1860-1935
Woodcock (1897)
N21

Archibald Thorburn 1860-1935
Cock Blackbird in Distress (1876)
N77

William T. Timyn b.1912
Orang Study Sheet (1971)
N305

Anna Maire Trechslin, 20th century
Phalaenopsis
N366

Charles Frederick Tunnicliffe 1901-79
Young Wings
N3

Charles Frederick Tunnicliffe 1901-79
Whoopers Alighting
N238

Charles Frederick Tunnicliffe 1901-79
Hooded Lanner Falcon
N300

Charles Frederick Tunnicliffe 1901-79
Black-tails Alighting
N307

Arthur Wardle 1864-1949
Bengal Tiger
N320

John C. Wardle, 20th century
Lynx
N183

Donald Watson b.1918
Osprey on a May Morning (1966)
N53

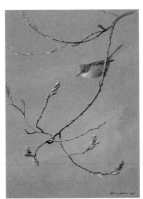

Donald Watson b.1918
Whitethroat (1966)
N54

Donald Watson b.1918
Adder (1966)
N55

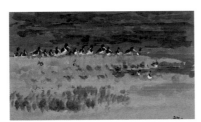

Donald Watson b.1918
Oystercatchers in March
N248

Raymond Cyril Watson b.1935
Tern on the Shore
N49

Raymond Cyril Watson b.1935
Magpies on a Birch Tree
N156

Raymond Cyril Watson b.1935
Puffin over the Water
N182

Raymond Cyril Watson b.1935
Avocets in Flight
N269

Raymond Cyril Watson b.1935
Red-breasted Geese
N370

Maurice Wilson b.1914
Red Deer and Fawns (1972)
N361

Maurice Wilson b.1914
Kingfisher
N364

Joseph Wolf 1820-99
Pallid Harriers
N74

Joseph Wolf 1820-99
Arctic Summer (1877)
N181

drawings paintings & sculptures

the ulster museum

history collection

William James Barre 1830-67
Interior of Ulster Hall, Belfast:
Architectural Perspective (1862)
P80.1984

Doris Violet Blair fl.1940s-'80s
The Erection of a Stirling
P14.1984

Doris Violet Blair fl.1940s-'80s
The Paint Sprayer
P28.1984

Doris Violet Blair fl.1940s-'80s
The Record Breaker
P30.1984

Doris Violet Blair fl.1940s-'80s
Air Sea Rescue - the Search
P40.1984

Philip Brannon, 19th century
Commercial Buildings, etc., Belfast (1841)
P498.1922

Herbert (Hubert?) E. Broderick fl.1951-71
Donegal House, Belfast
P408.1951

Herbert (Hubert?) E. Broderick fl.1951-71
Mistletoe Café, Belfast
P409.1951

Robert J. Bunting fl.c.1914-27
Unitarian Church, 1836, Carrickfergus
(1917)
P86.1973

Robert J. Bunting fl.c.1914-27
**Shipyard, Belfast Road, Carrickfergus,
Year 1880 (1925)**
P96.1973

Robert J. Bunting fl.c.1914-27
**St. Nicholas' Church, Carrickfergus, Year
1918: North View (1922)**
P99.1973

Robert J. Bunting fl.c.1914-27
**St. Nicholas' Church, Carrickfergus: East
View (1922)**
P100.1973

Robert J. Bunting fl.c.1914-27
**Hamilton's Row, Woodburn Road, near
Carrickfergus (1921)**
P114.1973

Robert J. Bunting fl.c.1914-27
**Fairview, near Hamilton's Row, Woodburn
Road (1921)**
P115.1973

Robert J. Bunting fl.c.1914-27
Presbyterian Church, Ballynure (1927)
P158.1973

James Howard Burgess c.1810-90
**River Lagan, Showing Molly Ward's
Cottage (1885)**
P178.1909

James Howard Burgess c.1810-90
Belfast Harbour
P59.1951

James Howard Burgess c.1810-90
Bryansford, Co. Down (1842)
P359.1952

James Howard Burgess c.1810-90
Newcastle, Co. Down
P14.1981

Arthur M. Campbell d.1994
College Place North
P357.1952

John Carey 1861-1943
The Belfast Boat Club
P32.1973

Joseph William Carey 1859-1937
White Linen Hall, Belfast (1900)
P628.1932

Joseph William Carey 1859-1937
Belfast Home Defence Corps (1915)
P37.1980

George A. Carruthers, 19th century
The 'Great Britain', Dundrum Bay, 20 July 1847
P84.1984

Rose Carruthers, 19th century
Parish Church of Knock-Breda at the Newtown-Breda, Co. Down (1860)
P163.1921

Rose Carruthers, 19th century
Old Houses, High Street, Belfast
P358.1927

Herbert Chipp fl.1877-98
The Salmon House, Portrush
P52.1973

M. Crawford, 19th century
Antrim Round Tower (1885)
P113.1977

R. Curzon, 19th century
**Holywood Old Church and Graveyard
(1885)**
P91.1984

Hugh Frazer fl.1813-61
View of Jennymount Mill, Belfast
P35.1980

Hugh Frazer fl.1813-61
Waringstown, Co. Down (1849)
P5.1981

Hugh Frazer fl.1813-61
**A Roadside Inn: View on the
Carrickfergus Road**
P1.1989

Hugh Frazer fl.1813-61
**View of Belvoir House from the South,
with the River Lagan in the Foreground**
P2.1990

William Arthur Fry 1865-1936
'Macedon', Whitehouse, Co. Antrim
P231.1910

William Arthur Fry 1865-1936
**Side View of the Royal Hotel, Belfast
(1920)**
P242.1920

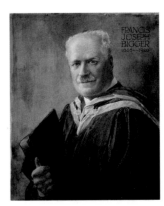

William Arthur Fry 1865-1936
Francis Joseph Bigger 1863-1926
P307.1927

Colin Gibson b.1948
Belfast Rooftops (1969)
P35.1973

W. R. Gordon 1872-1955
Saul, Co. Down
P125.1955

W. R. Gordon 1872-1955
Martin's Farmyard, Upper Malone
P126.1955

Theo. J. Gracey 1895-1959
Castle Market, Belfast (1916)
P576.1916

Theo. J. Gracey 1895-1959
White Linen Hall, Belfast: View of Front
P107.1917

Theo. J. Gracey 1895-1959
Ormeau
P116.1917

Theo. J. Gracey 1895-1959
Malone Toll House about 1820
P164.1917

Theo. J. Gracey 1895-1959
A Bit of Old Ballymacarrett about 1900
P937.1918

Theo. J. Gracey 1895-1959
Hercules Place and Hercules Street
P939.1918

Ernest Hanford fl.1886-99
Old Bangor (1890)
P915.1896

Ernest Hanford fl.1886-99
Pottinger's Entry: View towards High Street (1892)
P136.1951

Ernest Hanford fl.1886-99
Sugarhouse Entry: View towards High Street, Showing Arch at Duffy's Public House (1892)
P140.1951

Ken Howard b.1932
Checking the Wheelbarrow - Army Technical Officer, Belfast City Centre (1978)
P47.1978

Miss Lawson, 19th century
View of Bangor Bay from the Harbour Beach
P12.1980

F. G. Lodge, 20th century
Ulster Club, Castle Place, Belfast (1933)
P376.1935

William Henry Lynn 1829-1915
Proposed Albert Memorial Clock Tower, Belfast (c.1869)
P216.1916

William Henry Lynn 1829-1915
Old Glass House, Ballycastle
P39.1976

William Henry Lynn 1829-1915 (attribt.)
County Antrim Courthouse, Crumlin Road, Belfast
P6.1956

Andrew Lytle fl.1886-1911
Albert Bridge, Belfast (1886)
P386.1921

William McDade fl.1891-1921, d.1946
Old Belfast Water Cart (1921)
P167.1921

William McDade fl.1891-1921, d.1946
**Old Manual Fire Engine Passing the
House of Correction, Belfast (1921)**
P168.1921

James MacIntyre b.1926
Belfast Tramcar (1954?)
P469.1954

Frank McKelvey 1895-1974
**Lower Peter's Hill, Looking towards
North Street, c.1895 (1920)**
P329.1920

Frank McKelvey 1895-1974
Millfield, Belfast, c.1895 (1920)
P347.1920

Frank McKelvey 1895-1974
**Bedeque House, Crumlin Road, Belfast
(1920)**
P437.1920

Frank McKelvey 1895-1974
**Smithfield Market, 1923; View from the
Centre towards One of the Winetavern
Street Entrances (1923)**
P245.1923

Frank McKelvey 1895-1974
Queen's Quay, Belfast, c.1880
P529.1924

Frank McKelvey 1895-1974
The 'Gin Palace', Belfast, 1914 (1924)
P244.1925

Frank McKelvey 1895-1974
**Henry Shaw Ferguson, MD, FRCSE
1815-90**
P119.1928

Frank McKelvey 1895-1974
Murray's Terrace, Belfast
P259.1935

Frank McKelvey 1895-1974
Newtownbreda Village (1921)
P149.1938

Frank McKelvey 1895-1974
**The Rt. Hon. Robert Young 1822-1917
(1920)**
P116.1944

Joseph Molloy 1798-1877
**Lismoyne - Seat of Robert Callwell, Esq.
(1830)**
P821k.1893

Joseph Molloy 1798-1877
**Jennymount - Seat of Robert Thompson,
Esq. (1830)**
P821l.1893

Joseph Molloy 1798-1877
**Ligoniel - Seat of Alexander Stewart, Esq.
(1831)**
P821t.1893

Andrew Nicholl 1804-86
**Waterloo Bridge, Clifden, Connemara
(1836)**
P129.1960

Andrew Nicholl 1804-86
Red Bay, Co. Antrim
P10.1973

John Nixon c.1750-1818
**Mr. Stewart's Ballroom near Lisburn
(1785)**
P2.1980

John Nixon c.1750-1818
Down Hill, the Seat of the Earl of Bristol
P3.1980

John Nixon c.1750-1818
Colrain (1785) (Coleraine)
P13. 1980

John Nixon c.1750-1818
Belfast Poor House (c.1785-90)
P1.1983

J. P. or T. P., 19th century
Newry, Ireland (1812)
P4.1983

Thomas G. Pinkerton fl.1894-1927
Cavehill Bridge, Belfast (1927)
P188.1928

Raymond Piper b.1923
College Place North, Belfast (1951)
P247.1953

Raymond Piper b.1923
**The Wilson House, Dergalt, Strabane
(1965)**
P25.1980

Raymond Piper b.1923
Gray's Printing Shop, Strabane; Kevin the 'Buroo-man' (1965)
P26.1980

Thomas Semple, 19th century
The Late William Dougherty's Fowl Stores (1869)
P3.1985

Harold Speed 1872-1957
Sir Frederick Moneypenny, CVO, CBE, 1859-1932 (c.1929)
P33.1999

A. G. Stafford, 19th century
View on River Lagan (1892)
P45.1978

Anthony Carey Stannus 1830-1919
Belfast High Street, Looking East (c.1851)
P20.1907

Anthony Carey Stannus 1830-1919
Bawn at Bellahill, near Carrickfergus
P7.1974

John Sumner fl.1884-96
The Old Bridge, Newcastle, Co. Down (1890)
P81.1984

M. E. Thompson, 19th century
Garron Tower (1853)
P46.1978

Hugh Thomson 1860-1920
Ormeau Road, Belfast, Looking towards the City from South of the Ormeau Bridge (c.1880)
P785.1937

George Trobridge 1856-1909
**Cooney's Court, Ann Street, Belfast
(1880)**
P111.1908

Unknown, 19th century
Belfast from Lagan Village, 1767
P255.1932

Unknown, 19th century
Oldpark Print Works and Village (c.1860)
P383.1961

Unknown, 19th century
Bessbrook Mill (c.1860)
P21.1973

Unknown, 19th century
**The Drawing Room at Tyrella: Mrs.
Montgomery Reading by the Fire (1831-43)**
P24.1999

Unknown, 19th century (?)
**View of Farmhouse, Corner of Malone
and Stranmillis Roads**
P146.1973

Unknown, 20th century
Old Holywood Road, Belfast (1935)
P124.1973

John Knox Vinycomb 1833-1928
**Old Ormeau Bridge from near Stranmillis
(1860)**
P118.1910

James Glen Wilson 1827-63
**View of the Cathedral and Mall,
Downpatrick (1850)**
P1.1988

drawings paintings & sculptures

the armagh county museum

J. D. B., 19th century
Miss Dorothy Gervais (1895)
50.1960

R. D. Beattie, 20th century
Market Street, Armagh in 1910 (1982)
81.1982

Geoffrey Bevington, 19th century
Portrush (1870)
6.1945

James Black d.1829
City of Armagh (1810)
156.1958

Muriel Brandt 1909-81
Macha's Height (1964)
113.1967

Mary Brown, 20th century
Hollyhocks
8.1982

Mary Brown, 20th century
Moneypenny's Lock on the Newry Canal near Portadown around the Turn of the Century
58.1981

Adam Buck 1759-1833 (attribt.)
Archbishop the Hon. William Stuart of Armagh 1755-1822
77.1996

Christopher Campbell 1908-72 (attribt.)
Jonathan Seaver, FGS, FRCS 1853-1927
149.1957

Tom Carr 1909-99
Oil Lamp and Stuffed Canary (1971)
79.1987

Tom Carr 1909-99
McAuley's Lake (1971)
80.1987

K. A. Caulfeild, 19th-20th century
Drumcairne Formal Garden (1914)
2.1984

Simon Coleman b.1916
The Pond, Stephen's Green, Dublin
1.1957

Helen Colvill 1856-1953
The Mall, Armagh
5.1995

William Conor 1881-1968
Belfast Children (1918)
13.1972

Diana Cowdy b.1918
Interior (1968)
45.1971

Diana Cowdy b.1918
The Black Bank in Armagh (1973)
5.1991

James Humbert Craig 1877-1944
In County Galway
140.1957

Martin Cregan 1788-1870
**Leonard Dobbin, MP for the Borough of
Armagh 1833-38**
157.1958

Thomas Creswick 1811-69
**Charlemont Fort, Co. Armagh, from the
River**
14.1982

T. C. Crookshank, 19th century
Castlecaulfield (1846)
42.1968

George Cuckson, 20th century
The White Walk, Armagh
86.1980

Micheál J. de Burca 1913-85
Summer Evening, Achill
100.1960

Lydia de Burgh b.1923
South Armagh near Forkhill (1983)
35.1993

Robert Donnelly, 19th century
Moyallon House
119.1963

Rev. James Hall Flack, 20th century
Mountain Farmstead near Slieve Gullion
3.1984

Terence Philip Flanagan b.1929
Blue Shore
81.1987

Percy French 1854-1920
To E. R.
3.1943 (7)

Lady Beatrice Glenavy 1883-1968
From the Sea
99.1966

J. D. Gordon, 20th century
'Light and Blight': Houses in High Street, Lurgan
69.1966

W. R. Gordon 1872-1955
Knocknacarry, near Cushendun
5.1945

W. R. Gordon 1872-1955
Cushendun Bridge, Co. Antrim
65.1957

William Greenlees, 19th century
Market Street, Armagh (1838)
73.1979

David G. Hankey, 20th century
Moira Parish Church
69.1975

Dr. Douglas L. Hemmingway 1894-1968
Cottages at Glen Mona, Isle of Man (1938)
84.1976

John Frederick Hunter 1893-1951
Street in Dungannon
27.1987

Joseph Hynes, 20th century
Nasturtiums (c.1988)
42.1989

Clara Irwin 1853-1921
Scotch Street, Armagh (c.1910)
3.1953

Clara Irwin 1853-1921
Market Street, Armagh (c.1920)
4.1953

Clara Irwin 1853-1921
College Street, Armagh (1920)
4.1959

Hans Iten 1874-1930
Belvoir Park
59.1960

Mainie Jellett 1897-1944
Coast Scene (1935)
66.1973

Séan Keating 1889-1977
Life Class
98.1966

Harriet Kirkwood 1880-1953
Tea in the Studio
2.1946

Georgina Moutray Kyle 1865-1950
The End of the Dyke, Volendam
1.1946

Charles Lamb 1893-1964
Taking in the Lobster Pots
134.1947

Charles Lamb 1893-1964
A Connemara Lake
9.1990

Sir John Leslie, Bt. fl.1865-80
Tynan Hunt (1880)
1.1966

James Loder fl.1820-57
Mare, Castledillon Stables (1831)
154.1958

John Luke 1906-75
The Old Callan Bridge (1945)
2.1945

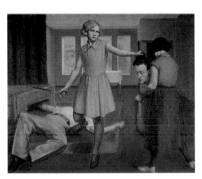

John Luke 1906-75
Judith and Holofernes
42.1980

Maurice MacGonigal 1900-79
Fishing Boats, Clogher Head, Co. Louth
4.1945

Cecil Maguire b.1930
**Long Walk from Claddagh Quay, Galway
(1987)**
16.1992

John Miller, 19th century
**A View of the Principal Front of Gosford
Castle, Armagh**
1.1990

379

Michael Morrow fl.1949-54
Chloe
2.1957

Andrew Nicholl 1804-86 (attribt.)
Narrow Water Castle
100.1975

Thomas Nicholson, 20th century
The Broken Link, Brackagh Lock
51.1969

John Nixon c.1750-1818
Narrow Water, near Newry (1787)
96.1980

John Nixon c.1750-1818
Rostrevor, Seven Miles from Newry
97.1980

John Nixon c.1750-1818
Fathom, near Newry
98.1980

John Nixon c.1750-1818
The Collector's House and Canal near Newry
99.1980

Bea Orpen 1913-80
Harbour Master's House, Aberdeen (1950)
3.1957

Lady Daphne Pitt-Taylor 1889-1945
The Island Cross, Tynan
3.1954

Lady Daphne Pitt-Taylor 1889-1945
Linenhall Street, Armagh (c.1935)
137.1959

G. Power, 19th century
The Moy
14.1997

William Bruce Ellis Ranken 1881-1941
The Yellow Tree
6.1946

Henrietta Roberta Reid 1875-1957
Armagh from the Golf Links (1918)
26.1981

Eugène Riboulet 1883-1972
June in the Cevennes
71.1957

Thomas Robinson d.1810
Thomas Romney Robinson 1792-1882
1.1979

George William Russell ('AE') 1867-1935
Sketch in Oils
39.1940

George William Russell ('AE') 1867-1935
Sunset
52.1940

George William Russell ('AE') 1867-1935
The Traveller
5.1946

George William Russell ('AE') 1867-1935
The Potato Gatherers
1.1949

George William Russell ('AE') 1867-1935
Women on Hillside
2.1950

George William Russell ('AE') 1867-1935
Self-Portrait (1903)
14.1954

George William Russell ('AE') 1867-1935
On the Beach
110.1963

George William Russell ('AE') 1867-1935
Cuchulan at the Ford
111.1965

Stephen Slaughter 1697-1765
John Hoadly 1678-1746, Archbishop of Armagh and Primate of All Ireland (1744)
30.1987

James Sinton Sleator 1885-1950
Self-Portrait
101.1960

James Sinton Sleator 1885-1950
Mrs. MacNamara
60.1966

Patric Stevenson 1909-83
Knockchree and the Mournes from Greencastle, Co. Down (1968)
77.1987

D. Stewart fl.c.1810
Isle of Devenish, Co. Fermanagh
81.1975

Harold Storey, 20th century
Greer's Cottage, Lurgan
20.1976

Unknown, 17th century
The Jacobean Child
103.1990

Unknown, 18th century
Portrait of a Clergyman
31.1954

Unknown, 18th century
Mina Molyneux
151.1958

Unknown, 18th century
Gentleman in a Red Coat
18.1961

Unknown, 18th century
**Rev. William Lodge, DD 1742-1813
(c.1758)**
2.1963

Unknown, 19th century
Charlemont Fort, Co. Armagh
18.1951

Unknown, 19th century
**Lieutenant Jonathan P. Seaver 1790-1822,
15th Foot**
153.1957

Unknown, 19th century
**Sir George K. A. Molyneux, Bt., on
'Pantaloon'**
148.1958

Unknown ,19th century
**Lieutenant-General Sir Thomas
Molyneux, Bt., on 'Masterpiece'**
149.1958

Unknown, 19th century
Sir George K. A. Molyneux, Bt. (1826)
155.1958

Unknown, 19th century
John Francis Gervais 1818-82
96.1960

Unknown, 19th century
Captain Richard Maunsell, 7th Fusiliers
99.1960

Unknown, 19th century
The Paymaster
130.1962

Unknown, 19th century
Killeavy Castle
34.1978

Unknown, 19th century
Armagh Courthouse (1810)
1.1983

Maurice C. Wilks 1910-84
Winter, Cushendun
136.1959

drawings paintings & sculptures

the ulster folk
and transport
museum

Doris Violet Blair fl.1940s-'80s
Lock on the Lagan Canal
271.1982

Reuben Chappell 1870-1940
Steam Coaster 'Glencregagh' (1920-27)
1401.2000

William Conor 1881-1968
The Twelfth (1918)
123.2000 (C20)

William Conor 1881-1968
Having a Haircut
161.2000 (C58)

William Conor 1881-1968
Music in the Park (1947)
180.2000 (C77)

William Conor 1881-1968
The Hurley Players (1948)
202.2000 (C99)

William Conor 1881-1968
Self-Portrait in an MA Gown (1957)
203.2000 (C100)

William Conor 1881-1968
The Studio Dance
209.2000 (C106)

William Conor 1881-1968
Picture House Queue (1930-34)
213.2000 (C110)

William Conor 1881-1968
Trees on the Lagan (1935)
222.2000 (C119)

William Conor 1881-1968
Lamp-post Swinging (1957)
225.2000 (C122)

William Conor 1881-1968
Men of Iron (1922)
1502.2000 (C1265)

James Humbert Craig 1877-1944
Donegal Scene
351.1978

Charles Dixon 20th century
White Star Liner 'Britannic', 1914
1405.2000

Joseph Heard 1799-1859
Wooden Paddle Steamer 'Falcon'
1421.2000

Matthew Kendrick c.1797-1874
SS 'Great Britain' Stranded in Dundrum Bay, Co. Down
1428.2000

Georgina Moutray Kyle 1865-1950
Fruit and Vegetable Markets, Belfast
1429.2000

Nano Reid 1910-81
Portrait of Carl Hardebeck (c.1936)
313.1984

drawings paintings & sculptures

the

acknowledgements

The publisher wishes to thank the following for permission to reproduce work in copyright:

Herbert Alexander, U976 (Fine Art), © Mrs C Alexander; Karel Appel, U515 (Fine Art), © DACS 2000; Kenneth Armitage, U961 (Fine Art), © Kenneth Armitage; Arthur Armstrong, U231 (Fine Art), © Howard Greenaway; Winifred Austen, N36 (Bot & Zoo), © Tony Austen; Gillian Ayres, U434 (Fine Art), © Ms Gillian Ayres; Francis Bacon, U436 (Fine Art), © Estate of Francis Bacon/ARS, NY and DACS, London 2000; Robert Ballagh, U2534, U4935 (Fine Art), © Robert Ballagh; Brian Ballard, U1681 (Fine Art), © Brian Ballard; John Banting, U1843 (Fine Art), © Estate of John Banting; R D Beattie, 81.1982 (Armagh), © R D Beattie (Clonmel); Vanessa Bell, U440 (Fine Art), © 1961 Estate of Vanessa Bell; Horia Bernea, U4819 (Fine Art), © Horia Bernea; Edward Bernstein, U2654 (Fine Art), © Edward Bernstein; Max Bill, U517 (Fine Art), © DACS 2000; Basil Blackshaw, U238, U1185, U4766, U4942 (Fine Art), © Basil Blackshaw; Doris Blair, U1682, U3597 (Fine Art), P14.1984, P28.1984, P30.1984, P40.1984 (History), 271.1982 (UFTM), © Mme Doris Bourguignon; David Bomberg, U4709 (Fine Art), © The Artist's Family; Sir Muirhead Bone, U741 (Fine Art), © Estate of Sir Muirhead Bone; Michael J Bourke (Micheál J de Burca), U1226 (Fine Art), 100.1960 (Armagh), © Aodh Bourke; Gretta Bowen, U4767 (Fine Art), © Mrs Margaret Campbell; Boyd and Evans, U2657 (Fine Art), © Ms Fionnuala Boyd and Leslie Evans; Arthur Boyd, U4739 (Fine Art), © Reproduced with the permission of Bundanon Trust; Alicia Boyle, U242 (Fine Art), © Estate of Alicia Boyle; Mark Boyle, U683 (Fine Art), © Boyle Family for Mark Boyle; Charles Brady, U2510 (Fine Art), © Charles Brady Estate; Kathleen Bridle, U994 (Fine Art), © Dr Carole Durix; Gerald Leslie Brockhurst, U2584 (Fine Art), © Richard Woodward; Deborah Brown, U243, U2298, U4769 (Fine Art), © Ms Deborah Brown; Edward Burra, U745 (Fine Art), Care of Alex Reid and Lefevre, London; Mildred Ann Butler, U1209, U1635 (Fine Art), © Trustees of D A Houblon; Sergio de Camargo, U532 (Fine Art), © Sergio de Camargo; Sir David Young Cameron, U747 (Fine Art), © Estate of Sir David Young Cameron; Arthur M Campbell, U1004 (Fine Art), P357.1952 (History), © Mrs Margaret Campbell; George Campbell, U272, U1005, U4771 (Fine Art), © Mrs Margaret Campbell; John Carey, U1006 (Fine Art), P32.1973 (History), © Alan Carey; Joseph William Carey, U1007, U1008, U1188, U1189 (Fine Art), P628.1932, P37.1980 (History), © Alan Carey; Sir Anthony Caro, U1430 (Fine Art), © Sir Anthony Caro; Tom Carr, U263, U2084, U4746 (Fine Art), 79.1987, 80.1987 (Armagh), © Estate of Tom Carr; Patrick Caulfield, U964 (Fine Art), © Patrick Caulfield 2000. All rights reserved, DACS; César, U969 (Fine Art), © ADAGP, Paris and DACS, London 2000; Carey Clarke, U258 (Fine Art), © Carey Clarke; David Clarke, U278 (Fine Art), © David Clarke; Harry Clarke, U2644 (Fine Art), © David Clarke; Margaret Clarke, U5008 (Fine Art), © David Clarke; Sir George Clausen, U443, U755 (Fine Art), © Clausen Estate; Maurice Cockrill, U2652 (Fine Art), © Maurice Cockrill; Bernard Cohen, U527 (Fine Art), © Bernard Cohen; Cecil Collins, U757 (Fine Art), © Estate of Elizabeth Collins; Patrick Collins, U267 (Fine Art), © Mrs Patricia Collins; William Conor, U254, U256, U269, U1229, U1239, U2322 (Fine Art), 13.1972 (Armagh), (C20) 123.2000, (C58) 161.2000, (C77) 180.2000, (C9) 202.2000, (C106) 209.2000, (C110) 213.2000, (C119) 222.2000, (C122) 225.2000, (C1265) 1502.2000 (UFTM), © By permission of Mrs Patricia Kay Dalzell; Patric Coogan, U4724 (Fine Art), © Patric Coogan; Barrie Cooke, U253, U2287 (Fine Art), © Barrie Cooke; Laurence Coulter, U4976 (Fine Art), © Laurence Coulter; Jack Crabtree, U4707, U4969 (Fine Art), © Jack Crabtree; James Humbert Craig, U271 (Fine Art), 140.1957 (Armagh), 351.1978 (UFTM), © Mrs Marie Broughton Mills; David Crone, U4890 (Fine Art), © David Crone; Dorothy Cross, U5002 (Fine Art), © Care of Kerlin Gallery, Dublin; William Crozier, U749 (Fine Art), © William Crozier; George Cuckson, 86.1980 (Armagh), © Mrs Edna Cuckson; Michael Cullen, U4979 (Fine Art), © Michael Cullen; Noel William Cusa, N13, N32 (Bot & Zoo), © Estate of Noel William Cusa; Alan Davie, U535 (Fine Art), © Alan Davie; John Davies, U2413 (Fine Art), © John Davies; Lydia de Burgh, 35.1993 (Armagh), © Ms Lydia de Burgh HRUA, HUWS; Peter de Francia, U4776 (Fine Art), © Professor Peter de Francia; Edward Montgomery O'Rorke Dickey, U282, U4902 (Fine Art), © Mrs Mary C G Dickey; Gerard Dillon, U283, U287, U288, U4974 (Fine Art), © Gerard Dillon; Jiri Georg Dokoupil, U4694 (Fine Art), © DACS 2000; Goyo Dominguez, U5043 (Fine Art), © Goyo Dominguez; Rita Donagh, U2509 (Fine Art), © Ms Rita Donagh; Micky Donnelly, U4945 (Fine Art), © Micky Donnelly; Harry R Douglas, U33 (Fine Art), © Mrs Sheelagh Bell; Malcolm Drummond, U2077 (Fine Art), © James Drummond; Jean Dubuffet, U524 (Fine Art), © ADAGP, Paris and DACS, London 2000; Rita Duffy, U4984 (Fine Art), © Ms Rita Duffy; Basil Ede, N47 (Bot & Zoo), © Basil Ede; Handel Edwards, U2522 (Fine Art), © Handel Edwards; Peter Edwards, U4825 (Fine Art), © Peter Edwards; Felim Egan, U2523, U2606 (Fine Art), © Felim Egan; Eric Arnold R Ennion, N17 (Bot & Zoo), © Hugh Ennion; Sir Jacob Epstein, U948, U966 (Fine Art), © Tate, London 2000; Chung Eun-Mo, U4936 (Fine Art), © Chung Eun-Mo; Richard E Eurich, U596 (Fine Art), © Courtesy of the Artist's Estate/Bridgeman Art Library; David Evans, U4957 (Fine Art), © Alan Bowness, Hepworth Estate; Micheal Farrell, U521, U723 (Fine Art), © Ms Margaret Early; Trevor Faulkner, S22 (Bot & Zoo), © Trevor Faulkner; A Romilly Fedden, U2575 (Fine Art), © Ms Frances Fedden; Luis Feito, U290 (Fine Art), © DACS 2000; John Duncan Fergusson, U451 (Fine Art), © The Fergusson Gallery, Perth and Kinross Council, Scotland; Brian Ferran, U2333 (Fine Art), © Brian Ferran; Barry Flanagan, U2555 (Fine Art), © Barry Flanagan; T P Flanagan, U549, U5041 (Fine Art), 81.1987 (Armagh) © T P Flanagan; Sir William Russell Flint, U781 (Fine Art), © Mrs S M Russell Flint; Mark Francis, U5036 (Fine Art), © Mark Francis; Sam Francis, U553 (Fine Art), © ARS, NY and DACS, London 2000; Rowel Friers, U292 (Fine Art), © The Rowel Boyd Friers' Estate; Sir Terry Frost, U520 (Fine Art), © Sir Terry Frost; Roger Fry, U452 (Fine Art), © Mrs C A Cole; G L Gabriel, U4896 (Fine Art), © DACS 2000; Wilhelmina Geddes, U1397 (Fine Art), © Mrs Elizabeth M F Geddes; Mark Gertler, U456 (Fine Art), © Luke Gertler; Robert A F Gillmor, N187, N255 (Bot & Zoo), © Robert Gillmor; Lady Beatrice Glenavy U2529 (Fine Art), © Executors of the Estate of Lady Glenavy; Richard Gorman, U4807 (Fine Art), © Richard Gorman; Theo J Gracey, P576.1916, P107.1917, P116.1917, P164.1917, P937.1918, P939.1918 (History) © Permission c/o www.theojgracey.com; Carol Graham, U2506, U4749 (Fine Art), © Ms Carol Graham; Duncan Grant, U454 (Fine Art), © Ms Henrietta Garnett; Anthony Green, U1842 (Fine Art), © Anthony Green; Mary Grierson, N396 (Bot & Zoo), © Ms Mary Grierson; Anthony Gross, U801 (Fine Art), © Anthony Gross Estate; Sir Herbert James Gunn, U2225 (Fine Art), © Paul Gunn and Mrs Chloe Blackburn; Friedemann Hahn, U4895 (Fine Art), © Professor Friedemann Hahn; Eva Henrietta Hamilton, U315 (Fine Art), © Major C R F Hamilton; Letitia Marion Hamilton, U586 (Fine Art), © Major C R F Hamilton; Richard Hamilton, U2571 (Fine Art), © Richard Hamilton; Colin Harrison, U2294 (Fine Art), © Colin Harrison; Wilfred J Haughton, U303 (Fine Art), © Mrs Priscilla Haughton; Brian Henderson, U4756 (Fine Art), © Brian Henderson; Dame Barbara Hepworth, U965 (Fine Art), © Alan Bowness, Hepworth Estate; Patrick Heron, U2369 (Fine Art), © Estate of Patrick Heron 2000. All rights reserved, DACS; Patrick Hickey, U305 (Fine Art), © Twink Hickey; Derek Hill, U299 (Fine Art), © Estate of Derek Hill; Roger Hilton, U545 (Fine Art), © Estate of Roger Hilton 2000. All rights reserved, DACS; Sydney Ivon Hitchens, U551 (Fine Art), © John Hitchens; Albert Houthuesen, U2585 (Fine Art), © Kind permission of the Albert Houthuesen Trust; Ken Howard, U5005 (Fine Art), P47.1978 (History), © Ken Howard; John Hoyland, U720 (Fine Art), © Courtesy of the Artist's Estate/Bridgeman Art Library; George Leslie Hunter, U4777, U4778 (Fine Art), © By permission of the Hunter Family; John Frederick Hunter, U309 (Fine Art), 27.1987 (Armagh), © Estate of John Frederick Hunter; Mercy Hunter, U1683 (Fine Art), © Ms Mercy Little; Fabio Hurtado, U728 (Fine Art), © Care of Philip Solomon on behalf of Fabio Hurtado; Paul Huxley, U2676 (Fine Art), © Paul Huxley; Mainie Jellett, U2293, U2296, U2384 (Fine Art), 66.1973 (Armagh), © Care of Dr Michael Purser, representative of the Heirs and Successors of Mainie Jellett; Paul Jenkins, U528 (Fine Art), © Paul Jenkins; Augustus John, U323, U327 (Fine Art), © Courtesy of the Artist's Estate/Bridgeman Art Library; Gwen John, U2075 (Fine Art), © Estate of Gwen John 2000. All rights reserved, DACS; Nevill Johnson, U2476 (Fine Art), © Mrs M Johnson; Allen Jones, U554 (Fine Art), © Allen Jones; David Jones, U807 (Fine Art), © Trustees, David Jones' Estate; Kent Jones, U2646 (Fine Art), © Kent Jones; John Keane, U5068 (Fine Art), © John Keane; Séan Keating, U589 (Fine Art), 98.1966 (Armagh), © Estate of Séan Keating; Captain Richard Barrett Talbot Kelly, N44 (Bot & Zoo), © Ms C E Talbot Kelly; Jonathan Kenworthy, S14 (Bot & Zoo), © Jonathan Kenworthy; Harry Kernoff, U1074, U4811 (Fine Art), © Ms Catriona Kernoff; Brian King, U954 (Fine Art), © Brian King; Cecil King, U2297 (Fine Art), © Estate of Cecil King; Phillip King, U952, U2359 (Fine Art), © Professor Phillip King; Marek Komza, U184 (Fine Art), © Marek Komza; Georgina Moutray Kyle, U337, U338, U342 (Fine Art), 1.1946 (Armagh), 1429.2000 (UFTM), © Miss Norma Bennett; Charles Lamb, U345, U5018 (Fine Art), 134.1947, 9.1990 (Armagh), © Ms Lailli Lamb de Buitlear; Henry Lamb, U1537 (Fine Art), © Estate of Henry Lamb; Gene Lambert, U4898 (Fine Art), © Gene Lambert; Peter Lanyon, U2355 (Fine Art), © Ms Sheila Lanyon; Philip Alexius de Laszlo, U639 (Fine Art), © By permission of the de Laszlo Foundation; John Latham, U538 (Fine Art), © John Latham; Sir John Lavery, U60, U64, U66, U67, U68, U71, U72, U77, U78, U82, U615, U620, U624 (Fine Art), © Estate of Sir John Lavery/Felix Rosenstiel's Widow & Son Limited; Louis le Brocquy, U234, U239, U241, U246, U2386, U2528 (Fine Art), © Louis Le Brocquy; William John Leech, U344, U892, U2709 (Fine Art), © Ms Barbara V Mitchell; Ciarán Lennon, U4959 (Fine Art), © Ciarán Lennon; Lë Phö, U4733 (Fine Art), © ADAGP, Paris and DACS, London 2000; Henri Eugène Augustin le Sidaner, U164 (Fine Art), © ADAGP, Paris and DACS, London 2000; Peter John Levi, N51 (Bot & Zoo), © Peter John Levi; Percy Wyndham Lewis, U814 (Fine Art), © Estate of Mrs G A Wyndham Lewis; André Lhote, U1903 (Fine Art), © ADAGP, Paris and DACS, London 2000; Morris Louis, U526 (Fine Art), © Morris Louis 1958, Care of Ms Ann M Garfinkle, Attorney for the Estate; Laurence Stephen Lowry, U355 (Fine Art), © By kind permission Miss Carol A Lowry; John Luke, U348, U352, U1907, U1918, U1919, U2119, U2524, U2525, U2526, U2527, U4781 (Fine Art), 2.1945, 42.1980 (Armagh), © Mrs Sarah McKee; Clement McAleer, U2700, U2701 (Fine Art), © Clement McAleer; Charles McAuley,

ACKNOWLEDGEMENTS

U374 (Fine Art), © Estate of Charles McAuley; **Denis McBride**, U367 (Fine Art), © Denis McBride; **Leonard McComb**, U4812 (Fine Art), © Leonard McComb RA; **Hector McDonnell**, U2662 (Fine Art), © Hector McDonnell; **Norah McGuinness**, U371, U1254, U2365 (Fine Art), © Miss Rhoda McGuinness; **Edward McGuire**, U2278 (Fine Art), © Mrs Sally McGuire; **Frank McKelvey**, U328, U1099 (Fine Art), P329.1920, P347.1920, P437.1920 P245.1923, P529.1924, P244.1925, P119.1928, P259.1935, P149.1938, P116.1944 (History), © Robert McKelvey; **Stephen McKenna**, U4753 (Fine Art), © Stephen McKenna; **F E McWilliam**, U967, U968, U2438, U2461, U4689, U5024 (Fine Art), © Estate of F E McWilliam; **Joseph McWilliams**, U4805 (Fine Art), © Joseph McWilliams; **Simon McWilliams**, U2034 (Fine Art), © Simon McWilliams; **Heinz Mack**, U525 (Fine Art), © DACS 2000; **Anne Madden**, U356 (Fine Art), © Ms Anne Madden; **Conroy Maddox**, U1431 (Fine Art), © Conroy Maddox; **Marcel Maeyer**, U2451 (Fine Art), © Marcel Maeyer; **Elizabeth Magill**, U4803 (Fine Art), © Care of Kerlin Gallery, Dublin; **Cecil Maguire**, 16.1992 (Armagh), © Cecil Maguire; **José Maldonado**, U4948 (Fine Art), © José Maldonado, Courtesy Galeria Helga de Alvear, Madrid; **Harrington Mann**, U366 (Fine Art), © The Estate of Harrington Mann; **Kenneth Martin**, U2281 (Fine Art), © The Estate of Kenneth Martin; **Mary Martin**, U1753 (Fine Art), © The Estate of Mary Martin; **Ferenc Martyn**, U1762 (Fine Art), © Mme Margaret Martyn; **Margaret Mee**, N391 (Bot & Zoo), © Greville Mee; **Lord Methuen (Paul Ayshford, 4th Baron Methuen)**, U824 (Fine Art), © James Methuen-Campbell; **Colin Middleton**, U358, U360, U365, U598, U1882, U2452, U4790 (Fine Art), © Ms Jane Middleton Giddens; **Robert W Milliken**, N11, N151 (Bot & Zoo), © Robert W Milliken; **Dhruva Mistry**, U4692 (Fine Art), © Dhruva Mistry; **Alfonso Monreal**, U4821 (Fine Art), © Alfonso Monreal; **Pierre Eugène Montézin**, U57 (Fine Art), © ADAGP, Paris and DACS, London 2000; **Martin Mooney**, U4841 (Fine Art), © Martin Mooney; **Henry Moore**, U962, U2404 (Fine Art), © The works illustrated are reproduced by permission of The Henry Moore Foundation; **Sir Cedric Morris**, U2289 (Fine Art), © Michael and Ms Val Chase; **Rodrigo Moynihan**, U471 (Fine Art), © Fountain Trust; **Carolyn Mulholland**, U4930 (Fine Art), © Ms Carolyn Mulholland; **Noel Murphy**, U5016 (Fine Art), © Noel Murphy; **Daniel Nalin**, U4949 (Fine Art), © Daniel Nalin; **John Northcote Nash**, U474, U831, U832 (Fine Art), © Estate of John Northcote Nash, care of New Grafton Gallery, London; **Paul Nash**, U477 (Fine Art), © Tate, London 2000; **Kenneth Newman**, N309 (Bot & Zoo), © Kenneth Newman; **Ben Nicholson**, U519 (Fine Art), © Angela Varren-Taunt 2000. All rights reserved, DACS; **Sir William Nicholson**, U475 (Fine Art), © Mrs Elizabeth Banks; **Josep Alvarez Niebla**, U4946 (Fine Art), © DACS 2000; **Paul Nietsche**, U380, U2673, U4980 (Fine Art), © George Nitsche; **Isamu Noguchi**, U980 (Fine Art), © The Isamu Noguchi Foundation Inc.; **Kenneth Noland**, U522, U715 (Fine Art), © Kenneth Noland/VAGA, New York/DACS, London 2000; **Dermod O'Brien**, U629, U2643 (Fine Art), © Anthony O'Brien; **Roderic O'Conor**, U389, U2323, U2565, U2566, U2675, U5037 (Fine Art), © Sister Theophane Dwyer; **Tony O'Malley**, U2430, U2431, U2469 (Fine Art), © Tony O'Malley; **Daniel O'Neill**, U384, U386, U714, U716, U2069 (Fine Art), © Mrs Patricia Forster; **Bea Orpen**, 3.1957 (Armagh), © By kind permission C E F Trench; **Sir William Orpen**, U114, U480, U481, U1217 (Fine Art), Ms C Casey; **Séan O'Sullivan**, U388, U1869, (Fine Art), © Miss J O'Sullivan; **Sir Eduardo Paolozzi**, U951 (Fine Art), © Eduardo Paolozzi 2000. All rights reserved, DACS; **Joy Parsons**, N184 (Bot & Zoo), © Ms Joy Parsons FRSA,SWLA; **Sir Bernard Partridge**, U1399 (Fine Art), © Reproduced by permission of Punch Ltd; **Victor Pasmore**, U523, U697 (Fine Art), © Victor Pasmore Estate; **Newton Penpraze**, U2672 (Fine Art), © R N Penpraze; **Samuel John Peploe**, U483 (Fine Art), © Reproduced by permission of the Artist's Estate; **Tom Phillips**, U4826 (Fine Art), © Tom Phillips 2000. All rights reserved, DACS; **Otto Piene**, U530 (Fine Art), © Otto Piene; **John Piper**, U4686 (Fine Art), © The Piper Estate; **Raymond Piper**, U1218 (Fine Art), P247.1953, P25.1980, P26.1980 (History), © Raymond Piper; **Roland Vivian Pitchforth**, U1122, U1219 (Fine Art), © Gerald S Pitchforth; **Miervaldis Polis**, U2520 (Fine Art), © Miervaldis Polis; **Sophia Rosamond Praeger**, U1177, U1767 (Fine Art), © The National Trust, Northern Ireland Region/USPCA/NSPCC in Northern Ireland; **Sarah Henrietta Purser**, U121, U1258, U4963 (Fine Art), © Estate of Sarah Henrietta Purser; **Patrick Pye**, U1759 (Fine Art), © Patrick Pye; **Clifford Rainey**, U2410, U2411 (Fine Art) © Professor Clifford Rainey; **Basil Rakoczi**, U4892, U4893 (Fine Art), © Mme Jacqueline Robinson; **Peter Randall-Page**, U4938 (Fine Art), © Peter Randall-Page; **Henrietta Roberta Reid**, 26.1981 (Armagh), © By kind permission of Miss Lois Reid; **Nano Reid**, U400, U401 (Fine Art), 313.1984 (UFTM), © Estate of Nano Reid; **David Reid-Henry**, N9, N27, N71 (Bot & Zoo), © Bruce Henry; **Ceri Richards**, U516 (Fine Art), © The Estate of Ceri Richards; **Charles de Sousy Ricketts**, U842 (Fine Art), © The Artist's Estate; **Bridget Riley**, U533 (Fine Art), © Ms Bridget Riley; **Hilda Roberts**, U392, U1866 (Fine Art), © Ms Eithne Clarke; **William Patrick Roberts**, U492, U496, U1324 (Fine Art), © Estate of John Roberts, care of Mishcon de Reya Solicitors, London; **Markey Robinson**, U4798, U5051 (Fine Art), © Estate of Markey Robinson; **William Heath Robinson**, U1400 (Fine Art), © Laurence Pollinger Limited and the Estate of Mrs J C Robinson; **Patsy Dan Rodgers**, U2445 (Fine Art), © Patsy Dan Rogers; **Sir William Rothenstein**, U494, U1750 (Fine Art), © Mrs Diana Rosenstein; **George William Russell ('ÆE')**, U394, U396, U399 (Fine Art), 39.1940, 52.1940, 5.1946, 1.1949, 2.1950, 14.1954, 110.1963, 111.1965 (Armagh), © 2000, reprinted in part by the permission of Russell & Volkening as agents for the Estate of George William Russell; **Albert Rutherston**, U1754 (Fine Art), © Estate of Albert Rutherston; **Adrian Ryan**, U493 (Fine Art), © Estate of Adrian Ryan; **Kikuo Saito**, U2577 (Fine Art), © Kikuo Saito; **Ben Schonzeit**, U2578 (Fine Art), © Ben Schonzeit; **Patrick Scott**, U410 (Fine Art), © Patrick Scott; **Sir Peter Scott**, N76 (Bot & Zoo), © Courtesy Philippa Scott; **William Scott**, U404, U2288, U2475, U2663, U2664, U2665, U2669, U2670 (Fine Art), © William Scott Estate; **Sean Scully**, U2079 (Fine Art), © Sean Scully; **Allen W Seaby**, N6 (Bot & Zoo), © Estate of Allen W Seaby; **Wilfred Arthur Seaby**, U1881 (Fine Art), © David Seaby; **Ronald Searle**, U1410 (Fine Art), © Ronald Searle; **Keith Shackleton**, N242, N311 (Bot & Zoo), © Keith Shackleton; **Neil Shawcross**, U2094, U2448, U2474, U2511 (Fine Art), © Neil Shawcross; **David Shepherd**, N93 (Bot & Zoo), © David Shepherd. David Shepherd has asserted his right to be identified as the author of this work in accordance with the Copyright, Design and Patents Act, 1998; **Mark Shields**, U5015, U5019 (Fine Art), © Mark Shields; **Kenneth Denton Shoesmith**, U2285, U2356, U2358, U3622, U3707, U3748 (Fine Art), © 2000, reproduced with the kind permission of The Furness Group; **Walter Richard Sickert**, U490, U500, U854 (Fine Art), © Estate of Walter R Sickert 2000. All rights reserved, DACS; **John Skeaping**, U1221 (Fine Art), © Estate of John Skeaping; **James Sinton Sleator**, U163, U407, U5069 (Fine Art), © Mrs C M Slator; **Sir Matthew Smith**, U449 (Fine Art), © 2000 by permission of the copyright owner; **Richard Smith**, U537 (Fine Art), © Richard Smith; **Estella F Solomons**, U405, U416 (Fine Art), © Mrs Frances Sommerville; **Edith Oenone Somerville**, U2088 (Fine Art), © Sir Toby Coghill; **Eileen Alice Soper**, N185 (Bot & Zoo), © Chris Beetles Limited, St James's, London; **Camille Souter**, U704 (Fine Art), © Ms Camille Souter; **Gilbert Spencer**, U491, U855 (Fine Art), © Courtesy of the Artist's Estate/Bridgeman Art Library; **Sir Stanley Spencer**, U487, U488, U489 (Fine Art), © Estate of Stanley Spencer 2000. All rights reserved, DACS; **Sir Robert Ponsonby Staples**, U159, U573, U597, U694, U1825, U1832, U1835 (Fine Art), © Ms Hazel Radclyffe-Dolling; **Philip Wilson Steer**, U498, U501, U860 (Fine Art), © Tate, London 2000; **Patric Stevenson**, U1437 (Fine Art), 77.1987 (Armagh), © Mrs Dorothy B Stevenson; **Stella Steyn**, U5020 (Fine Art), © Dr Keith Ross; **James (Seamus) Stoupe**, U418, U2352 (Fine Art), © Alistair F Stoupe; **Graham Sutherland**, U503 (Fine Art), © Successors of Graham Sutherland; **Mary Swanzy**, U2087, U2324, U2558 (Fine Art), © Miss Mary St C S Tullo; **Patrick Swift**, U5003 (Fine Art), © Frank Swift; **Grzegorz Sztabinski**, U2517 (Fine Art), © Grzegorz Sztabinski; **Antoni Tapies**, U513 (Fine Art), © ADAGP, Paris and DACS, London 2000; **Ralph Thompson**, N26, N34, N35 (Bot & Zoo), © Ralph Thompson; **Archibald Thorburn**, N21, N77 (Bot & Zoo), © By courtesy of Felix Rosensteil's Widow & Son Limited; **William T Timym**, N305 (Bot & Zoo), © David R M Oxford; **Henry Tonks**, U863 (Fine Art), © Mrs G Bevis; **Romeo Charles Toogood**, U575, U653 (Fine Art), © Mrs E Toogood; **Wolfgang Troschke**, U5021 (Fine Art), © Wolfgang Troschke; **Charles Frederick Tunnicliffe**, N3, N238, N300, N307 (Bot & Zoo), © The Estate of C F Tunnicliffe; **John Turner**, U408, U2554 (Fine Art), © John Turner; **Dara Vallely**, U4934 (Fine Art), © Dara Vallely; **John B Vallely**, U1870 (Fine Art), © John B Vallely; **Victor Vasarely**, U514 (Fine Art), © Mme Michele Vasarely; **Edward Wadsworth**, U510 (Fine Art), © Estate of Edward Wadsworth; **John Walker**, U1886 (Fine Art), © John Walker; **Barbara Warren**, U426 (Fine Art), Ms Barbara Warren, RHA.; **Donald Watson**, N53, N54, N55, N248 (Bot & Zoo), © Donald Watson; **Franziskus Wendels**, U4951 (Fine Art), © DACS 2000; **Ethelbert White**, U425, U870, U871, U4801 (Fine Art), © Ethelbert White Estate; **Maurice C Wilks**, 136.1959 (Armagh), © Ms Stephanie Wilks; **Terrick John Williams**, U511 (Fine Art), © Estate of John Terrick Williams; **Ross Wilson** U2661, U4688 (Fine Art), © Ross Wilson; **Christopher Wood**, U509, U512 (Fine Art), © H G Dalziel Smith; **Guy Richard Charles Wyndham**, U505 (Fine Art), © Miss Joan Wyndham; **Anne Yeats**, U432 (Fine Art), © Miss Anne Yeats; **Jack Butler Yeats**, U428, U430, U433, U874, U1329, U2436, U4888 (Fine Art), © Miss Anne and Michael Yeats;

Whilst every effort has been made to contact copyright holders, the publisher would nevertheless welcome information on any oversight which may have occurred. The publisher would also like to thank the individuals who provided information regarding artists' estates; also the various organisations and institutions which did likewise. Without such assistance, the clearance of copyright would have been much more onerous.